Sustainable Development and Planning VI

WITPRESS

WIT Press publishes leading books in Science and Technology.
Visit our website for new and current list of titles.
www.witpress.com

WITeLibrary

Home of the Transactions of the Wessex Institute. Papers presented at Sustainable
Development VI are archived in the WIT eLibrary in volume 173 of WIT Transactions on
Ecology and the Environment (ISSN 1743-3541). The WIT eLibrary provides the
international scientific community with immediate and permanent access to individual
papers presented at WIT conferences.
Visit the WIT eLibrary at www.witpress.com.

SIXTH INTERNATIONAL CONFERENCE ON
SUSTAINABLE DEVELOPMENT AND PLANNING

SUSTAINABLE DEVELOPMENT AND PLANNING VI

CONFERENCE CHAIRMEN

C.A. Brebbia
Wessex Institute of Technology, UK

E. Beriatos
University of Thessaly, Greece

INTERNATIONAL SCIENTIFIC ADVISORY COMMITTEE

R. Brandtweiner
R. Brewster
J. Chakwizira
M. Di Gangi
L.B. Dos Santos Argueta
S. Favro
C. Poveda
A. Pratelli
R. Rojas-Caldelas
F. Russo

Organised by
Wessex Institute of Technology, UK

Sponsored by
WIT Transactions on Ecology and the Environment
International Journal of Sustainable Development and Planning

WIT Transactions

Transactions Editor

Carlos Brebbia
Wessex Institute of Technology
Ashurst Lodge, Ashurst
Southampton SO40 7AA, UK

Editorial Board

Sustainable Development and Planning VI

EDITOR

C.A. Brebbia
Wessex Institute of Technology, UK

WITPRESS Southampton, Boston

Editor:

C.A. Brebbia
Wessex Institute of Technology, UK

Published by

WIT Press
Ashurst Lodge, Ashurst, Southampton, SO40 7AA, UK
Tel: 44 (0) 238 029 3223; Fax: 44 (0) 238 029 2853
E-Mail: witpress@witpress.com
http://www.witpress.com

For USA, Canada and Mexico

Computational Mechanics Inc
25 Bridge Street, Billerica, MA 01821, USA
Tel: 978 667 5841; Fax: 978 667 7582
E-Mail: info@compmech.com
http://www.witpress.com

British Library Cataloguing-in-Publication Data

A Catalogue record for this book is available
from the British Library

ISBN: 978-1-84564-714-8
eISBN: 978-1-84564-715-5
ISSN: 1746-448X (print)
ISSN: 1743-3541 (on-line)

The texts of the papers in this volume were set individually by the authors or under their supervision. Only minor corrections to the text may have been carried out by the publisher.

Printed in Great Britain by Lightning Source, UK

PREFACE

This book contains some of the papers presented at the 6th International Conference on Sustainable Development and Planning, held in Kos, Greece. It is the latest meeting in a series that started in 2003 in Skiathos (Greece) and continued in Bologna (2005), the Algarve (2007), Cyprus (2009) and the New Forest, home of the Wessex Institute of Technology in the UK (2011).

Problems related to development and planning affect rural as well as urban areas and are present in all regions of the world. Increasing urbanisation has resulted in the deterioration of the environment and loss of quality of life. Urban development can also aggravate the problems faced by rural areas, such as forests, mountain regions, coastal areas and many others. Taking into consideration the interaction between different regions and developing new methodologies for monitoring, planning and implementation of novel strategies can avoid solutions leading to environmental pollution and non-sustainable use of available resources.

Energy savings use and eco-friendly building approaches have become an important part of modern development, which places special emphasis on resource optimisation. Planning has a key role to play in ensuring that these solutions, as well as new materials and processes are incorporated in the most efficient manner.

The Conference deals with all aspects of development and planning and brings together scientists and other stakeholders from across the globe to discuss the latest advances in the field, as well as to seek and highlight developments in managerial strategies and assessment tools for policy and decision makers.

I am grateful to all authors for their excellent contributions and most especially to the members of the Scientific Advisory Committee, who helped to review the papers included in this Volume.

C.A. Brebbia
Kos, Greece, 2013

Contents

Section 6: Sustainability and the built environment

Section 7: Sustainable tourism

Section 8: Sustainable solutions in emerging countries

Section 9: Environmental economics

Section 10: Energy resources

Section 11: Sustainability assessment and management
(Special session organised by C. A. Poveda)

Section 12: Waste management

Section 13: Improving safety of users in evacuation
(Special session organised by F. Russo)

Section 1
City planning

Assessment of outdoor thermal comfort and its relation to urban geometry

R. Cocci Grifoni[1], G. Passerini[2] & M. Pierantozzi[2]
[1]School of Architecture and Design, Camerino University, Italy
[2]Department of Energetics, Marche Politechnic University, Italy

Abstract

Microclimate conditions in urban open spaces are directly linked to the configuration of street axes and building heights and their attributes. Within street canyons, public places, and open spaces, the local microclimate depends directly on the physical properties of the surrounding surfaces and objects, producing well-known effects that can decrease or increase thermal loads. All of these phenomena can greatly influence the comfort of a city and the thermal comfort of pedestrians. Thermal comfort is an indicator that cannot be easily converted into physical parameters. However, it may be defined more qualitatively as the range of climatic conditions in which most people feel comfortable. One well-recognized thermal comfort index used to measure comfort levels inside a space is the predicted mean vote (PMV). Fanger's PMV index has been widely used in the last ten years. It is based on six factors: air temperature, air speed, humidity, mean radiant temperature, metabolic rate, and clothing levels. The comfort equation establishes relationships among the above-mentioned environmental variables, clothing type, and metabolic rate. The authors present results of PMV simulations using a multi-objective optimization tool (i.e., modeFrontier). ModeFRONTIER is an integration platform used to optimize and arrange PMV algorithms linked to urban geometry parameters (e.g., the height-to-width (H/W) ratio of urban streets). The optimization process employs given constraints, custom procedural algorithms, and genetic algorithms to examine a wide urban space and identify interesting relationships among the variables considered. Urban geometry, meteorological data, and latent influences are examined and negotiated quantitatively to improve outdoor thermal comfort.
Keywords: predicted mean vote, predicted percentage of dissatisfied, outdoor thermal comfort, multi-objective optimization.

WIT Transactions on Ecology and The Environment, Vol 173, © 2013 WIT Press
www.witpress.com, ISSN 1743-3541 (on-line)
doi:10.2495/SDP130011

1 Introduction

Outdoor public spaces have become the heart of civic life in the city where people carry out their activities and leisure. It is well known that improving the quality of life in urban centres does require not only efficient buildings, but also climatically sensitive urban public spaces that can enhance and enrich urban life.

Recent worldwide studies [1] have indicated the influence of densely built urban areas on the formation of urban climate conditions as well as on the determination of the microclimate. The influence of urban geometry on the microclimate and human comfort in urban spaces is a very important aspect to consider when estimating outdoor comfort. In addition, the climate of the outdoor urban space has important effects on the energy consumption of cities, and the processes that create these climates are very complex. Therefore, the most precise way to calculate or assess the impact of changes is to use numerical methods (several models already exist), which are able to deal with the complexity of urban structures and even take into account human thermal comfort.

In this study, the PMV thermal comfort index [2] was used and its diurnal variation assessed by introducing the representative day technique in order to obtain information on correlations between thermal comfort and meteorological parameters.

The Representative Day (RD) [3] is determined by the actual data of the day in the period considered, where the sum of the mean-square differences among its monitored quantities averaged within each hour, and the same quantities for all other days at the same hour, is minimised.

The microclimate analysis of an urban space must consider all meteorological conditions such as solar incidence and radiation exchanges, local wind characteristics, topography, vegetation and the presence of water. Beyond these factors, the urban design, the morphology of the buildings, and the behaviour of individuals are also factors that influence the thermal conditions of the outdoor spaces considered.

The city of Ancona was chosen as case study because it represents a typical example of Mediterranean city located in central Italy (namely Marche region), characterized by long, hot summers and mild winters. The investigations in this study are almost exclusively limited to the summer period (June to September) throughout a meteorological data series (2009-2012) because climatic hot-stress in urban open spaces mainly occurs during this season of the year.

In particular, this paper builds upon recent work in parametric optimization in order to assess the outdoor thermal comfort in urban spaces. Specifically, a new tool has been developed using a powerful environment for symbolic and numerical computing and data visualization (Wolfram Mathematica TM), aiming at linking information computed in a bio-climate model to the representative day technique using a parametric optimization with different algorithms (e.g., Simplex and genetic algorithms).

2 Outdoor thermal comfort

2.1 PMV thermal comfort index

Thermal comfort is defined in the ISO 7730 [4] as "The condition of mind that expresses satisfaction with the thermal environment". It is an indicator that cannot be easily converted into physical parameters. However, thermal comfort can be defined more qualitatively as the range of climatic conditions in which most people feel comfortable. The most widely used thermal comfort index is the predicted mean vote (PMV) index, which was developed by Fanger and Toftum [5]. Fanger states that two conditions must be achieved to maintain thermal comfort. The first is the real resultant of skin temperature and the body's core temperature, which provides a sensation of thermal neutrality. The second is the realization of the body's energy balance, which is based on the conservation of energy:

$$M + W + R + C + E_D + E_{RD} + E_{SW} + S = 0 \tag{1}$$

where M is the metabolic rate (internal energy production), W is the physical work output, R is the net radiation of the body, C is the convective heat flow, ED is the latent heat flow to evaporate water diffusing through the skin, ERD is the sum of heat flows for heating and humidifying the inhaled air, ESW is the heat flow due to evaporation of sweat, S is the storage heat flow for heating or cooling the body mass.

Fanger has derived a comfort equation from the equation for heat balance. It is a function of six parameters that influence thermal comfort. In fact, PMV is a function of two human variables and four environmental variables: clothing insulation, human activity, air temperature, air relative humidity, air velocity and mean radiant temperature. The values of the PMV index have a range from -3 to +3, which corresponds to the occupant's feeling, from cold to hot, while the PMV null value represents a neutral sensation. The thermal stress established by the PMV is based on the steady state of heat transfer between the body and the environment. It is an empirical equation used to evaluate the mean vote on a rating scale of thermal comfort of a large population of people. To develop a curve and get average results, people were exposed to different environments at different spans of time. The term PPD represents the predicted percentage of people dissatisfied at each PMV. The predicted distribution of votes is given in Table 1.

Table 1:   Distribution of individual thermal sensation for different values of mean vote [4].

PMV	PPD	People predicted to vote (%)		
		0	-1, 0 or +1	-2,-1,0,+1 or +2
+2	75	5	25	70
+1	25	30	75	95
+0.5	10	55	90	98
0	5	60	95	100
-0.5	10	55	90	98
-1	25	30	75	95
-2	75	5	25	70

The value of PPD increases whenever PMV absolute value increases i.e. it moves from zero. A curve has been developed to predict the percentage of people dissatisfied as a function of Predicted Mean Vote (Fig. 1).

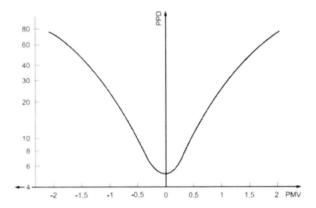

Figure 1:   Predicted Percentage of Dissatisfied (PPD) as a function of Predicted Mean Vote (PMV) [4].

2.2 Urban morphology

Urban geometry determines the ability of natural light to reach building surfaces and the possibility of using natural ventilation within homes; hence, it acts directly on the urban microclimate, influencing the energy consumption of individual buildings and the entire urban organism. In recent years, much research and many applications have looked at the energetic efficiency of buildings and explored the idea of integrating architecture and renewable energy. In contrast, issues related to phenomena in the urban scale have not been studied sufficiently, nor have relationships between the small and large scales. Synergistic relationships between individual buildings and urban spaces have not been sufficiently investigated from a systemic viewpoint, nor has a shared view on the relationships between urban form, energetic efficiency of the city, and quality of life been developed. Today, there is no shared theory that is applicable and usable by planners. What emerges, however, is the need for a close transdisciplinary comparison, since there are many parameters to consider in urban sustainability, and these include in particular, meteorological parameters, building height, urban density and the system of open and green spaces.

The character of a city or a built environment is described in relation to its built form and level of social activities, both of which, therefore, should be included in urban spaces. In addition, the city and its public spaces can only be built in the form of streets, squares, and blocks of familiar dimensions and character [6]. All of these elements should be integrated appropriately to create better urban spaces. Blocks consist of buildings, and streets and squares are defined by blocks. The character of each of these elements affects the perception of the urban space. The width of the street, the height and size of the blocks, etc., are just a few factors that contribute to the urban space. Recent studies around the world have indicated the strong influence of densely built urban areas on the formation of urban climate conditions and particularly on the determination of the microclimate.

The outdoor thermal environment is impacted by the built environment, e.g., building dimensions, street weight, anthropogenic heat, evaporation and evapotranspiration of plants, shading by trees, and so on. In an urban context, building density increases substantially.

Today, more than half of the Earth's inhabitants live in urbanized areas, and this phenomenon is destined to grow. Urbanization forces cities' boundaries to expand, and the urban fabric to become denser. In general, new constructions take the form of tall building structures along relatively narrow streets. As a consequence of the altered heat balance, the air temperatures in densely built urban areas are generally higher than in the surrounding rural hinterland, a phenomenon known as the "Urban Heat Island" (UHI). The heat island is the most obvious climatic manifestation of urbanization [7]. Several causes for the UHI phenomenon were identified by Oke [8], and their relative importance was examined in some studies, [9–11] as an example the reduced convective heat removal due to the reduction of wind speed and the trapping of short- and long-wave radiation between buildings. It is well known that urban areas without high climatic quality use more energy for air conditioning in summer as well as more electricity for lighting. Moreover, discomfort and inconvenience to the urban population due to high temperatures, wind tunnel effects in streets, and unusual wind turbulence due to incorrectly designed high-rise buildings is very common. As consequence, it is very important to improve outdoor comfort and reduce high temperatures in urban areas. Climate measurements from urban and suburban stations, as well as specific measurements performed in urban canyons in Athens, Greece, revealed a doubling of the cooling load of urban buildings and a tripling of the peak electricity load for cooling, while the minimum COP (Coefficient of Performance) value of air conditioners decreased up to 25% because of the higher ambient temperatures [12].

3   Parametric optimization

ModeFRONTIER is a multi-objective and multidisciplinary software that allows for statistical analysis and minimization with various techniques.

The optimization process guided by modeFRONTIER therefore allows climatic and spatial conditions guaranteeing PMV minimization and identification of the related PPD to be determined. While climate variables are easy to understand because they come from the ranking in the calculation of the representative day, spatial variables can be varied to minimize discomfort effectively and therefore optimize comfort.

In general, the optimization can be single-objective or multi-objective. The attempt to optimize a project or system in which a single objective is present usually means applying methods to the gradient in which the algorithms look for the minimum or maximum of a function according to the established objective. One of the methods for managing multi-objective optimization consists in summing all of the objectives (adequately weighted) into a unique function in order to reduce the problem to a single-objective optimization problem. This method, however, has the disadvantage that such weights, which should be furnished a priori by the user, influence the solution. In addition, if the objectives are all different, it could be difficult or even useless to try to formulate a single-objective function.

Multi-objective optimization techniques sidestep these problems by keeping the objectives separated within the optimization process. The role of the optimization algorithm consists in identifying solutions that are found on the trade-off curve, better known as the Pareto frontier. A common characteristic of such solutions is the fact that by improving one objective, at least one of the other objectives worsens.

Figures 2 and 3 show scatter plots related to the PMV and PPD generated in

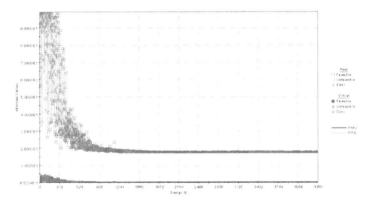

Figure 2:   Simultaneous trends of the PMV and PPD.

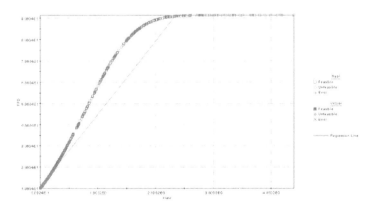

Figure 3:   Pareto frontier of optimal solutions in PMV-PPD analysis.

the optimization process made by modeFRONTIER. Such graphs associate pairs of objectives that the optimization process aims to minimize.

Each point on the graph represents a solution analyzed during the optimization process; the solutions are situated on the Pareto frontier of optimal solutions, which emerges from the scatter plot. The simultaneous convergence to the minimum value can be seen from their asymptotic behaviour.

3.1 Factor analysis

Factor analysis is a statistical technique that allows a decrease in the complexity of the number of variables that explain a phenomenon to be obtained.

The effect is just to show the importance of the variation of a certain property (or product of them) with respect to the PMV or PPD. It may be negative whenever it leads to an inverse or positive if there is a direct proportion between the factor considered and the output variable. The input variables taken into account are: temperature, street width, building height, mean radiant temperature, wind speed and relative humidity.

The output variables are PMV and PPD. The coefficients of the best-fitting polynomial are clearly displayed in the factor analysis chart parameters table (Fig. 4).

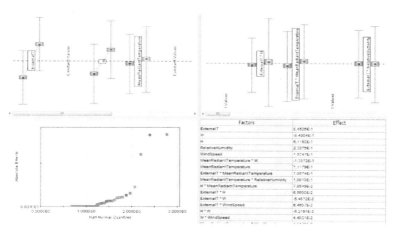

Factors	Effect
ExternalT	8.4626E-1
W	-4.8404E-1
H	4.1190E-1
RelativeHumidity	2.3373E-1
WindSpeed	1.5747E-1
MeanRadiantTemperature * W	-1.3372E-1
MeanRadiantTemperature	1.1176E-1
ExternalT * MeanRadiantTemperature	1.9574E-1
MeanRadiantTemperature * RelativeHumidity	1.0010E-1
H * MeanRadiantTemperature	7.8849E-2
ExternalT * H	6.5800E-2
ExternalT * W	5.4872E-2
ExternalT * WindSpeed	5.480E-2
H * W	4.5219E-2
W * WindSpeed	4.4021E-2

Figure 4:   Factor analysis chart showing the coefficients of the best-fitting polynomial.

In Figure 4 starting from the left upper and rotating clockwise, we have:

- the effect of the individual variables,
- the effect of the product of the different variables (thus their combination),
- the quantitative effect of the factors,
- the effect of various factors from a graphical point of view.

The results obtained show that temperature, building height, and street width are related to the best direct relationship (namely temperature and building height) or inverse relationship (street width).

To analyse the PPD behaviour, a program written in Wolfram Mathematica was used. The choice was determined by the fact that this software is a general-purpose language suitable for our need to link the PPD evaluation with the geometrical H/W ratio.

The rPPD (representative Predicted Percentage Dissatisfied) algorithm takes weather data for a specific region as input and calculates the PMV and the PPD for the RD.

The advantage of this instrument is its user-friendliness. In addition, it not only individually calculates all the meteorological parameters for an RD, the thermal comfort indices as well as the PMV and PPD, but it also links them to the geometrical factor (H/W ratio), highlighting their interdependence. Moreover, the interdependence of these quantities can be simulated in relation to different variables using a parametric optimization tool (e.g., ModeFRONTIER).

4 The case study

Analysis was carried out for the city of Ancona in the Marche Region in central Italy (Figure 5). Ancona is the largest city in the Marche Region, and in the past it has been intermittently destroyed by earthquakes and wars, forcing city districts to take new shapes without delay. "Modern" Ancona is laid out in a grid pattern of wide streets fronted by modern commercial buildings that are interspersed with ancient buildings and monuments. As mentioned before, urban density is the distribution of urban elements on the ground such as houses, urban alignments, empty plots, vegetation, etc. In addition, the space between buildings

Figure 5:   Map of the Marche Region, Italy.

(including streets) and the average height of buildings also contribute to the urban density, which affects the local climate and the thermal comfort of the inhabitants.

Ancona's climate can be categorised as Mediterranean. It is mild, with summers that are warm but refreshed by a generous sea breeze and winters with regular seasonal rains. In mountainous areas, the summers are fresh and the winters are cold with ample snow possible.

The study area is generally occupied by medium- to low-scale buildings. The average building height is about 2–3 floors. There are few buildings that rise to 5–6 floors. Most of the buildings are rather old; a few modern buildings are being built. The urban density is not considered very high and the H/W ratio can be estimated at about 2. The H/W ratio affects shading patterns and solar radiation. Therefore, this H/W ratio creates both positive and negative effects on the microclimate. In order to evaluate the representative day, monthly summer periods were analysed in the interval considered (2009–2012). During typical summer months (beginning in May and continuing through September), air temperature can become very high and the daily amplitude can be relatively wide. Despite the statistical rarity of a heat wave event, temperature records were set repeatedly in recent years. The meteorological parameters evaluated for the representative day and the metabolic variables considered for the case study are given in Table 2.

Table 2:   Input variables.

Variables	Range
Temperature	24.2–28 °C
Wind speed	2.7–5.0 m/s
Relative humidity	51.0–68.0%
Street width	3.0–8.0 m
Building height	6.5–15 m
Clothing insulation	0.5 clo
Metabolic rate	1.2 met

5   Results and discussion

The first simulation was carried out using the case study parameters (Table 2) and the Simplex algorithm to minimize the PMV. The results obtained are shown in Figure 6 and summarized in Table 3.

Table 3:   Results of the simulation performed using the Simplex algorithm.

H	W	T	Metabolic rate	Relative humidity	Wind speed	Clothing insulation	PMV
6.514 m	7.87 m	24.3 °C	1.2 met	51.01 %	2.78 m/s	0.5 clo	0.9

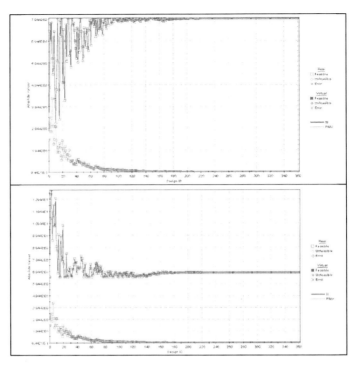

Figure 6: Street width (W) behaviour (up) and building height (H) behaviour (down) for the PMV minimization using the Simplex algorithm.

In this simulation, we have assumed metabolic rate and clothing insulation to be constant. The minimum value for PMV (0.9) is reached for small height (6.5 m) and large street width (7.9 m). As consequence, an important factor influencing outdoor comfort is urban geometry, which refers to the dimensions and spacing of buildings within a city. In fact, urban geometry influences wind flow, energy absorption, and a given surface's ability to emit long wave radiation back into space.

We decided to use a multi-objective optimization using an evolutionary algorithm and consider a larger range of building heights (6.5–15 m) and street widths (3–15 m) in order to evaluate the relationship between comfort parameters (e.g., PPD and PMV) and the geometrical H/W ratio. The results are summarized in Figure 7 and Table 4. It is clear from Table 4 how minimum

Table 4: Results of the simulation performed using an evolutionary algorithm.

H	W	T	Metabolic rate	Relative humidity	Wind speed	Clothing insulation	PMV	PPD
7.14 m	14.88 m	24.4°C	1.2 met	55.3 %	3.2 m/s	0.5 clo	4.39E-05	5.00

values for the PPD and PMV (high thermal comfort) are obtained for a large street width (14.88 m) and moderate building height (7.1 m). The H/W ratio can be considered an important parameter in determining the comfort level of open spaces.

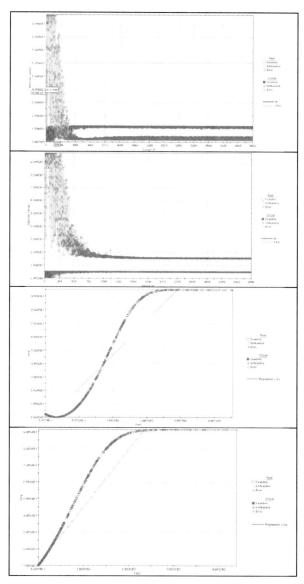

Figure 7:   Simultaneous trends of the PMV and PPD, and their Pareto Frontiers.

6 Conclusions

The primary goal in climate-conscious urban design is to achieve outdoor comfort. It is well known that urbanization tends to aggravate the negative effects of climate during summer seasons due to the increased thermal capacity, lack of water for evapotranspiration, and the "canyon effect". This generally causes thermal discomfort in Mediterranean cities during summer periods. Therefore, urban designers should prevent heat build up in the in cities and promote convective cooling at night. In this paper, we have considered how urban design can improve the thermal comfort of cities through urban form or urban geometry (e.g., street layout, building density, building morphology, height-to-width ratio). The building geometry was modified in terms of H/W ratio and interesting results have been obtained. This can only be considered a first step because the design of thermally comfortable urban spaces deals with a collection of various issues. Therefore future research will include the effect of wind patterns on thermal comfort in urban environments, the materials used in buildings and their effect on outdoor thermal comfort, green spaces, viability, and so on.

References

[1]   RUROS. Rediscovering the Urban Realm and Green Spaces, CRES, Building Department, 2004.
[2]   Fanger, P.O. *Thermal comfort*, McGraw-Hill, New York, 1972.
[3]   R. Cocci Grifoni, M. Pierantozzi, S. Tascini, G. Passerini, Assessing the representativeness of thermal comfort in outdoor spaces, *Sustainable City 2012, Ecology and the Environment*, pp. 835–846 2012.
[4]   ISO 7730 Moderate thermal environments – determination of the PMV and PPD indices and specification of the conditions for thermal comfort, International Standards Organization, Geneva, 1994.
[5]   Fanger P. and Toftum, J. Extension of the PMV model to non-air-conditioned buildings in warm climates. *Energy and Buildings*, **34** pp. 533–536, 2002.
[6]   Krier, R. *Urban Space*, Academy Editions London, 1979.
[7]   Landsberg, H.E., *The Urban Climate*. Academic Press Inc., New York, US, 1981.
[8]   Oke, T.R., The energetic basis of the urban heat island, *Quarterly Journal of the Royal Meteorological Society* **108(455)** pp. 1–24, 1982.
[9]   Oke, T.R. The energetic basis of the urban heat island. Quarterly Journal of the Royal Meteorological Society, **108** pp. 1–24, 1982.
[10] Peterson, T.C. and Owen, T.W. Urban heat island assessment: metadata are important. Journal of climate, **18(14)** pp. 2637–2646, 2005.
[11] Kim, Y.H. and Baik, J.J. Maximum urban heat island intensity in Seoul. *Journal of Applied Meteorology*, **41(6)** pp. 651–659, 2002.
[12] Santamouris M., *Energy and climate in the urban built environment*, James & James Ltd, London, UK, 2001.

Tale of two cities: urban planning for the 21st century eco-metropolis

A. Villacampa[1] & N. Hedayati[2]
[1]Wessex Institute of Technology, UK
[2]Politecnico di Milano, Italy

Abstract

During the first decade of the 21st century, urban planners have introduced new concepts and strategies to design sustainable cities. By the end of that decade, the idea of eco-cities has become a reality and a goal that many European capitals have reached or are about to reach. In contrast with classical urban planning methods, town planning has nowadays focused on sustainability, improvement of life quality and social aspects. The planning of the town focuses more on the user and the sense of community. Large-scale strategies are nowadays combined with human scale and adaptability. The improvement of live quality has to deal now with concepts as low air pollution levels, green areas, good public transport networks, bike-friendly cities and outdoors sports among others. Two representative case studies of these new urban planning principles are the cities of London and Copenhagen. On the first case, the largest European city has suffered a huge transformation to adapt itself to the Olympic Games. On the second case, a small capital with rather more than one million inhabitants is on its way to achieve the title of the most sustainable city in Europe. In the two cases, town-planning strategies have been diverse but the core of both remains sustainability. This paper aims to analyse these two cases comparing their different contexts with the concept of eco-city as a common background. Our main goal is to study contemporary urban planning and identify transformation processes of cities nowadays. The influence of the recession environment in which Western countries are currently immerse has conditioned as well many decisions that involve citizens, public administration, real state investors and urban planners on the same level.
Keywords: urban planning, sustainable development, London, Copenhagen, eco-city, town planning.

WIT Transactions on Ecology and The Environment, Vol 173, © 2013 WIT Press
www.witpress.com, ISSN 1743-3541 (on-line)
doi:10.2495/SDP130021

1   Historical perspectives and current context

Efforts to render cities environmentally and socially sustainable are not new. Urban planning and regeneration over the last century have been influenced by attempts to balance the effects of large-scale urbanisation, such as environmental degradation, social differences and urban sprawl. The Garden City, New Town and Techno-City are 19th century examples of city reinvention in the post-industrial era [1]. The term eco-city was introduced in the 1980s when the environmental movement by Richard Register settled the "Urban Ecology initiative" leading to the first international eco-city conference in 1990, a collection of proposals on urban planning, transportation, housing, economics and development with a few practical examples. It was after the 1992 United Nations Earth Summit in Rio de Janeiro and its sustainable development program, Agenda 21, when eco-city concepts started to be translated into practice.

In the early 2000s geographic spread and international globalisation led to policy uptakes and practical implementations of the eco-city phenomenon [1]. These initiatives rapidly increased thanks to policy implementations like, for instance, the European Commission's "Eco-City Project" and the World Economic Forum's "Slim City".

2   Characterization and definition of an eco-metropolis

In 2011, there were 178 sustainable development initiatives that represented a significant mainstreaming of urban sustainability. In addition, assessment procedures for the evaluation of sustainability levels of architecture and urban plans have recently begun to emerge. The definition of eco-city indicators and the establishment of standards became complex as the number of eco-initiatives increased. Concepts like "low-carbon city", "solar city", "smart city" and "sustainable city" have augmented while the current context of urban sustainability is involving international, national and local governmental, non-governmental and private actors operating through public, private and mixed partnerships [2]. The most basic indicators specify in which terms urban sustainability affects to a certain community and its elements and goals are defined from the environmental, economic and social sustainable development in relation to urban settings. These indicators can be used for monitoring and assessing improvements and deteriorations for certain aspects of sustainability. In the case of Copenhagen 2015, an indicator of sustainable life quality can be defined in terms of access to parks that will correspond to the 90% of Copenhageners being able to walk to a park, a beach or a sea swimming pool in less than 15 minutes [3]. In the case of London 2012, an indicator of sustainable social development is the Olympic and Paralympic village consisting of 2018 apartments in 11 plots that will be converted into a residential community, contributing to the regeneration of the Stratford area of London.

The definition of urban sustainability indicators comes from technical analyses, national and local policies and specific urban conditions with variations due to stakeholder involvement [4]. Considering the project for London 2012, local policies had to face the effect of the Global Financial Crisis in 2008, which lead to specific implications for design and procurement [5].

The development and application of urban sustainability indicators should be considered in technical and governance terms being applied in policy-making and as part of a social process. From this perspective, indicators can be understood as strategic instruments to influence policy and taken as tools for social learning. Under governance, indicators are an institutional process to define policy, generate knowledge and apply them in practice [6].

3   Framework for London 2012 and Copenhagen 2015

The methods of measuring urban sustainability vary with the context, with no recognised overarching framework and a lack of standardization. This way, eco-city frameworks and their governances are outlined by: work strategy, performance assessment, and social learning [4]. If we compare the framework of *London's Olympic and Paralympics Games 2012* and *Copenhagen 2015*, their main sustainability indicators can be analyzed as listed in figure 1.

Copenhagen (DK) Eco-metropolis 2015; individual eco-city initiative (retrofit);
Key elements:
- 4 categories (cycling, climate change, leisure, health)
- total of 10 indicators across 4 categories (2015 targets)
- goal of involving citizens and business community
Key functions:
- A: distinctive local definition for competitive advantage
- B: clear performance measurement
- C: social learning through active community involvement
London (UK) Olympic and Paralympic Games 2012; individual eco-city initiatives (infill & new build);
Key elements:
- urban improvements focused on the Strafford area
- improvement of existing green areas and new green belt (park)
- high sustainability requirements for the architecture: temporary buildings, recyclable materials and elements, legacy
Key functions:
- A: sustainable urban improvements & high energy efficient temporary & new architecture
- B: clear performance and assessment by the ODA
- C: social learning through active community involvement in the whole London Greater Area-

A = work strategy; B = performance assessment; C = social learning.

Figure 1:   Sustainability indicators for London 2012 and Copenhagen 2015: from reference [2].

4   Sustainable urban strategy for London 2012 Olympic and Paralympic summer games

London has been the first city to host the Summer Olympic Games for the third time in modern history. The organising committee showed their capability to arrange the event and great commitment with technical innovation, sustainability efficiency and social involvement. High quality architecture was combined with urban planning for the event and the future of the city. The temporality of some buildings of the Olympic Park and Village met the adaptability of other venues in a sustainable system of urban planning, transportation and architecture [7].

The Olympics have traditionally been a catalyst to renovate the infrastructures of hosting cities. Beijing 2008 and Athens 2004 focused on reducing air pollution whereas the Sydney Olympics 2000 were the *Green Games*. In London 2012, the Organizing Committee aimed to make the Games environmentally friendly. Barcelona 1992 and Tokyo 1964 used the Olympics as an asset for urban regeneration: while Tokyo reintroduced the city to the world after the II World War, Barcelona used the Games to develop major infrastructure regeneration bringing to the city international recognition and becoming a model for urban planning thanks to the Games. The city of London and the Organizing Committee took a similar approach by using the 2012 Olympics to improve the eastern boroughs of London Greater Area [7]. As common background for all Olympic cities, a new stadium had to be specially constructed and almost every host city has had to either improve an airport, or build a new one. In the case of London, Heathrow was already an international airport capable of handling the increased load of passengers only building the new Terminal 5 as a requirement [7].

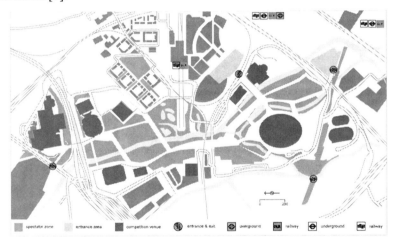

Figure 2:   Olympic games Venues, London 2012 [8].

For the *Olympic and Paralympic Summer Games 2012,* 15 of the 33 competition venues already existed and the large majority of events were held in the Olympic Park, the Central Cluster, and the River Cluster (figure 2). The Olympic Park was the most popular area holding venues for 13 sporting events. The Olympic Village provided beds to over 17,000 persons in 4,200 residential buildings [7].

Previous to the Olympics, the city of London improved a large number of infrastructure, sporting arenas and facilities. For instance, the London

Underground renovated lines to ensure safety and efficiency since 33% of spectators were expected to come from the Greater London into the Inner City. Transportation by road was also improved with the Olympic Route Network (ORN) around London [9].

Greenwich, Hackney, Newham, Tower Hamlets, and Waltham Forest were the boroughs hosting venues for London 2012. The Olympic Delivery Authority (ODA) oversaw the implemented infrastructure in each borough being responsible for venue construction and new roads to support the influx of people during the Games [9]. Many of the boroughs concentrated on the implementation of a residents' employment program in the construction and the running of the Games as a catalyst for poverty-stricken neighbourhood development [7].

5 Sustainable architecture strategy for London 2012

The Olympic Delivery Authority applied a sustainability strategy for the architecture and urban planning of London 2012 in many levels. The built environment comprehended the built-up areas and gardens in the UKBAP. That way, buildings were designed as wildlife habitats with green roofs, living walls and nesting and roosting boxes integrated in the structures [10]. On the same way, parks, squares and amenity spaces were an essential component of the master plan. In order to promote biodiversity in the Olympic Park, planted trees were predominantly native, amenity grasslands were established as species and rich lawns and ornamental planting included wildlife attractive species. A preliminary target for 1.67 ha of habitat was to be created by 2014 with some areas already established by 2012.

To match the strong environmental requirements that ODA fixed for London's 2012 venues the key sustainability criteria of reducing, reusing and recycling were adopted by *Populous Architecture* to create a compact, flexible and light-weight design of the Olympic Stadium to be transformed after the Games from 80,000 capacity venue to a minimum of 25,000 seat venue form.

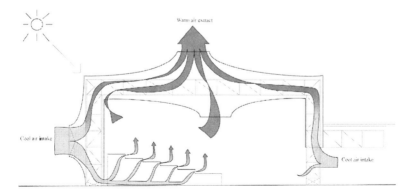

Figure 3:   Cross section of the Shooting Venue. Olympic Games London 2012 [11].

Sustainability was also the key driver in the design of the Basketball Arena by *Wilkinson Eyre,* one of the biggest temporary venues ever created for any Olympic and Paralympic Games [11].

The arena was made out of robust individual components that can be easily dismantled and subdivided for re-use with over two-thirds of the materials and components identified for recycle. In the case of the Velodrome, ODA set a member of challenging sustainability targets for the project by *Hopkins Architects* focusing on the minimization of the energy and water demand and the integration of this into the fabric of the building to reduce reliance on systems and infrastructure as shown on the use of maximum daylight: a much more efficient solution to reduce carbon emissions. Moreover, sustainability was a main feature in *Magma Architecture*'s shooting venue at the Royal Artillery Barracks. All three removable ranges were configured in a crisp, white double curved membrane facade studded with vibrantly coloured openings. All three of the venues were fully mobile and all their components could be easily reassembled. No composite materials or adhesives were used. The need for artificial lighting was reduced thanks to the semi-transparent facades and the ventilation was fully natural (figure 3) [11].

An efficient design solution for the Olympic and Paralympic Village was a challenge for the design team -*Robert Bird Group*- to enable configuration for an immediate use and its subsequent further adaptation into a total of 1350 private and social housing units. The planning approach was based upon the "Maida Vale" model found in parts of North London where the interiors of blocks are given over to gardens shared by residents. The residential apartment buildings consisting of three floors of maisonettes were combined with duplex family maisonette units due to market decisions. As a result, the Olympic Village was the first large-scale residential scheme to be designed to Code for Sustainable Homes Level 4 containing: energy and CO_2 emissions, water, materials, surface water run-off, waste, pollution, health and well-being, management and ecology. In addition, ODA included as a sustainable criteria: 20% of materials (by value) to have recycled content; 25% of aggregates (by weight) to be from recycled or secondary sources; 0% of Prohibited and Referable Materials; Global Warming Potential (GWP) of all insulation to be less than 5 and responsible sourcing of materials [11].

The Biodiversity Action Plan (BAP) designed for London 2012 was a challenge for the Olympic Park, becoming an asset for London and the catalyst for large- scale regeneration of one of the most deprived areas in the UK. The Games were a short-lived event but the area continued to develop thereafter into a significant sporting, social, economic, cultural and environmental hub for local, metropolitan, national and international visitors. The Olympic Park was also part of a wider vision to create an extended network of interconnected green spaces (green infrastructure) [10]. Legacy conditions were considered as part of the London Development Agency's (LDA's) Legacy Masterplan Framework (LMF) study. The Olympic Park BAP required a Biodiversity Action Plan for the Olympic construction, games and legacy transformations. The plan established targets and provided guidance on how to enhance biodiversity through the

Olympics to the Legacy Transformation phase in 2014; underpinning in the construction phase by the Ecological Management Plan to protect existing habitats and species and to improve access to nature. The BAP will bring local people an opportunity to be involved in nature conservation providing guidance to enable the designers, builders and operators of the Olympic Park to maintain and enhance biodiversity [10]. The BAP was one of the documents produced by the ODA that also included the Urban Design and Landscape Framework (UDLF), the *Waterspace Masterplan* and Lightning Strategy. These documents, in combination with the emerging Parklands and Public Realm design, will provide a framework for the whole package. Key stakeholders were consulted as part of the design process to develop and implement the BAP. The range of habitats included reflected the biodiversity of the site before construction began but also the desire to restore the vegetation that had disappeared from the area and the waterways. In view of this, the ODA adopted an overall target to create, by 2014, at least 45 ha of a new habitat which will eventually mature to meet a quality standard of Site of Borough Importance (SBI) Grade 1 or better [10].

6   Copenhagen's ambitious goal

Copenhagen is an important European capital and the largest Scandinavian city. But, while visiting Copenhagen the chaos of a "Capital City" does not surround visitors. Instead, the first things to be noticed are the calmed and relaxed atmosphere, the nearness to forests and sea and the ring of bicycle bells passing by. Perhaps these are the factors that make Copenhageners some of the happiest and healthiest citizens in the world. Even though, the city of Copenhagen will be setting new standard for, the healthy and clean cities of the future.

City officials have decided to make Copenhagen a better place to live by creating the first carbon neutral capital in the world by 2025, and the first step to achieve this goal is to reduce the CO_2 Emissions by 20% between the years 2005 to 2015 [12]. This ambitious goal will make Copenhagen a more pleasant city to live and it will also create new 21st century green jobs introducing Copenhagen as a centre for future sustainable research and development in the international community.

7   Urban strategy

In order to achieve these ambitious goals (e.g. Copenhagen's First Carbon Neutral Capital in the world) an intelligent urban planning to allow the city expand in size and population for a cleaner and a healthier future is required.
Copenhagen has always inspired other cities to create a healthier environment, going from the famous blue bicycle lanes to its energy production or the improvement of recreational areas, pedestrian streets and a more active and vibrant social environment for the citizens.

During the modernist movement of the 1960s, the urban planning was focused on automobiles. Tall residential buildings, with vast empty spaces in between them where constructed in the suburbs of many major cities around the world, being connected to the city centres by large motorways. However, that plan not only demonstrated to be harmful towards the environment and the health of the citizens, but it also established huge flaws in an urban context. The large empty spaces and the distances between the buildings created a lifeless environment.

In 1968 School of Architecture at the Royal Danish Academy of Fine arts, started the research about Public Space, Public Life and Pedestrian Flow in the city of Copenhagen [14], initiating a series of methods and strategies to create a more pedestrian and bicycle friendly environment. This way, Danish urban designers proposed an urban environment to prioritize people needs "making places better for people" [14] (figure 4).

First pedestrian promenade in 1962: 15,800 m

By 1973, the network of pedestrian streets connected the most important locations in the city centre: 49,200 m

The network of car-free streets and squares in 2005: 99,770 m

Figure 4:   Development of Copenhagen's Pedestrian area from 1962 to 2005 [14].

According to Jan Gehl, "people don't change their behaviour when you tell them to, but when the context compels them" [14]. So with the right urban planning and strategies, the city officials can provide an opportunity for the citizens to become involved in improving the living conditions within the community.

On the contrary, more roads do not always translate into less traffic. With a smart planning, the city can provide an active modern neighbourhood with less car traffic because the users can adapt to the new traffic system removing car usage priority [15]. Copenhagen has been providing better and safer atmosphere for pedestrians and cyclists thanks to a human scale design, the increase of urban life, social activities and human interaction integrated into the urban fabric of the city. In order to encourage people to engage in various urban activities, public spaces must provide protection, security, reasonable space, urban furniture and visual quality.

During the 90s, Copenhagen started converting many of its open-air parking lots, into enjoyable public areas. This transition created good business environment a more active life style for Copenhageners and gave rebirth to derelict historical areas. Well-designed urban spaces will encourage more people to walk and more visitors will attract more people; but new public spaces are not the only strategy to help Copenhagen to achieve its goal. The city has initiated an urban scheme called "Green and Blue Capital City" to provide clean parks and beaches for the great majority of Copenhageners, by the year 2015. This fact will attract more visitors and will provide an environment of peace and relaxation as well as a chance for physical activity for the citizens. Today 60% of Copenhageners are living within 15 minutes walking distance of a green or blue area. Moreover, Copenhagen city officials have decided to provide 90% of their citizens with a 15 minutes walking distance to a green or blue area by the year 2015. In the words of Jan Gehl, a city planning should consider "Life, Space, Building – in that order" [15].

8 Transportation

Copenhagen has developed a safe and comfortable well-designed network of bicycle lanes. Today, around 35% of commuters cycle to work or education centres with the aim of a further increase of this number to 50% by the year 2015 [13]. Copenhagen's extensive bicycle lanes have created a more human friendly urban environment, a more liveable city, less traffic congestions, lower noise and air-pollution and a reduction in carbon emissions. In addition, studies have shown that for every kilometre travelled by bicycle instead of a car the society gains 0.16€, and the cyclist's healthcare cost is reduced by 0.77€ [13]. Today the city is improving the cycling conditions for Copenhageners increasing the amount of pedestrian and bicycle bridges across the city. Moreover, once the "Bicycle Super Highways" are constructed, direct bicycle connection to the city centre from the suburbs will be possible.

To achieve the transportation demands of a modern capital city, Copenhagen has been vastly investing in its public transportation system. Statistics show that the improvements in the public transportation system have decreased the number of cars trips in the city centre from 351,000 trips in 1970 to 284,900 car trips in 2010. These improvements include the expansion of the underground network, travel cards for train, metro and bus; real time bus stop information system; online journey planner, smart phones ticket selling applications, a bike-friendly public transportation system, electric cars charging facilities and car-sharing policies.

9 Sustainable energy

Currently 22% of Denmark's electricity is produced by wind energy. To reduce carbon emissions and to create new high skilled green jobs this number is expected to reach 50% by the year 2020 [13].

Moreover, Copenhagen has one of the most efficient waste management systems sending 2% of its waste to landfill (this figure was 40% back in 1988). Properly filtered waste-energy power plants meet the high Danish emission regulations while providing the city heat and electricity. In addition, 98% of household in Copenhagen are connected to the "District Heating System" that produces energy reusing the surplus heat for heating the households avoiding sea ejection.

The city of Copenhagen is planning to meet 75% of its CO_2 reduction goals by the year 2015 through upgrading its energy supply [12]. Moreover, the city is determined to help citizens to save more energy through better education, more public awareness and tougher building codes. All these would mean, less carbon emissions, less dependence on fossil fuel, less energy consumption and a much more stable economy.

10 Copenhagen 2025

The city of the future is no longer about demonstrating economic power through skyscrapers and bigger highways, but it is about creating a better, welcoming and a vibrant urban environment for all with healthier environment policies. Statistics are showing how Copenhagen has been able to reduce its CO_2 emissions by more than 20% from 2005 to 2011 [13]. City's three main strategies for accomplishing its goal are:

- Implementation of smart urban policies to improve pedestrian-friendly environment that will generate better public spaces and healthier outdoor activities for the citizens.
- Development of a more efficient transportation system
- Increase of sustainable energy production with lower energy consumption.

By achieving its goal, Copenhagen will become an important research hub for international green clean-tech companies. With its current district heating system and the existing extensive bicycle lanes, Copenhagen is already a step closer towards its target. Moreover, one of the city's most valuable assets in this case is the extremely environmentally conscious public opinion, a motivating factor for Copenhagen to become the first carbon neutral capital in the world by the year 2025.

11 Conclusion

What this paper has presented are two strategies of sustainable development and town planning improvements in the 21st Century. The first significant difference is the scale of the two case studies: Greater London has a density of population of 5,200/km^2 on an area of 1570 km^2 of which only 2.5 km^2 were part of the development plan whereas Copenhagen's population is over one million people settled on 445 km^2 with a metropolitan area of 3030 km^2. On the first case, the city of London and the Greater Area have taken the Olympic Games as a chance to improve the existing infrastructures mainly focusing on sustainable innovative architecture. On the second case, Copenhagen 2015 consists of a whole urban plan for a city that already has good infrastructures for a sustainable growth. In both cases public awareness and politics conditioned the planning from diverse points of view but at the same time many common policies and urban development practices were applied. In the case of Copenhagen, sustainability is a basic right and a concern for citizens and government instead of an asset for economical development thanks to an international event. These facts condition the strategy and its consequences: the city of Copenhagen required a global urban planning strategy and the city of London developed punctual urban improvements with repercussions for the city itself and the greater area focusing on the efficiency of the new architecture introduced in the urban grid. This way,

Copenhagen's planning was based on self-commitment and London actions had a primary goal with secondary consequences considered as a legacy. In both cases, common goals as low carbon emissions, improvement of public transport, an accessible city, bike and pedestrian-friendly town, accessible green areas and life quality improvement are present.

The improvement process of Copenhagen seems to be a natural evolution of a group of existing factors whereas London had to adjust the specific improvements to the city with further sustainable goals as a legacy of the event. This shows how a city had to adapt itself to a large-scale short-term event instead of having a natural improvement through urban planning. The development of London had to fit in the requirements of the Olympics while Copenhagen's is the consequence of a constant town renovation. Any of the cases included urban sprawl. Furthermore, London integrated new architecture relatively close to the centre of the city to develop derelict areas with industrial backgrounds and social needs. Many of the new buildings were temporary being unassembled after the Games to give those spaces back to the city. Green areas to be enjoyed and reached by everybody were basic on both planning strategies, a constant on European urban planning nowadays.

The scale of each city has set different standards to achieve their sustainable goals. On each case the aims are significant and vital to provide a better standard of living for their citizens, and to improve their international image. London showed how a mega-polis can host a gigantic international event while keeping sustainable planning in mind, whereas Copenhagen wanted to improve the negative outcome of the United Nations Climate Change Conference COP15 by aiming to become the first carbon neutral capital in the world and to make Copenhagen a leader in green and sustainable growth.

From the management point of view, Copenhagen has been commissioned and managed by the city town hall whereas the Olympic Delivery Authority (ODA) commissioned and managed London's urban plan for the Games. This difference conditioned the speed of the improvements and the decisions taken. Copenhagen is implementing policies that imply long-term actions and on-going processes and London had to reach a struggling deadline on a first phase that will be continued through two further phases. These frameworks had effects on the development of the planning and conditioned the adaptation of the citizens to the transformation. In the case of London, the goal was the legacy that the Games could leave to the citizens and for Copenhagen the strategy is based on how to improve a city for its own citizens.

References

[1]   Joss, S. Eco-Cities: a global survey 2009. The Sustainable City VI. Urban Regeneration and Sustainability; pp. 239-250, WIT Press, Southampton (UK) 2010.

[2]   Joss, S; Tomoziu D; Cowley R. Eco-city indicators: Governance challenges. The Sustainable City VII: Urban Regeneration and Sustainability, Vol. 1; pp. 109-120. WIT Press, Southampton (UK) 2012.

[3] Eco-City Project; European Commission, 2008 [On-line] http://www.ecocity-project.eu/

[4] *Eco-metropolis: Our vision for 2015. City of Copenhagen*; Technical and Environmental Administration; Denmark, 2007 [on-line] www.kk.dk/ecometropolis

[5] Raggett, T; *Construction of the London 2012 Olympic and Paralympic Village; Olympic structures for London 2012*; The Structural Engineer; Vol. 90, Issue 6; pp. 39-44; The Institution of Structural Engineers; London; June 2012.

[6] Hezri, A.A. Dovers, S.R. *Sustainability indicators, policy and governance: issues for ecological economics*. Ecological Economics, 60(1), pp. 86-99, 2006.

[7] Creeth, A. Spazzarini, E. Shultz, C. Cordell, Z; *Identifying and Evaluating the Impacts of the 2012 Olympics: London Borough of Hounslow*; Worcester Polytechnic Institute; June 2011.

[8] Olympic Games Venues, London 2012 ©Crown Copyright and database right 2011. Ordnance Survey 10046062.

[9] *The Olympic Delivery Authority.* From 3/29, 2011, http://www.london2012.com/about-us/the-people-delivering-the-games/the-olympic-delivery-authority/index.php

[10] Olympic Delivery Authority; *Olympic Park Biodiversity Action Plan*; PDT submission, October 2008 http://www.london2012.com/documents/general/traveladviceforbusiness-

[11] *London 2012. The Greenest games Ever*; Espazio Magazine Issue num. 2; November 2012; pp. 12-31; Editorial EspaZio, Spain.

[12] Copenhagen Climate Plan. (August 2009). City of Copenhagen. http://www.subsite.kk.dk/sitecore/content/Subsites/CityOfCopenhagen/SubsiteFrontpage/LivingInCopenhagen/ClimateAndEnvironment.aspx

[13] Copenhagen Solution For Sustainable Cities. (October 2012). City of Copenhagen http://www.arup.com/Publications/Copenhagen_Solutions_for_Sustainable_Cities.aspx

[14] These Are Some of The Cities We Have Worked With. (October 2012). Gehl Architects http://issuu.com/gehlarchitects/docs/ga_major_projects_book_single_pages

[15] Gehl, J. *Cities for People*. Island Press, Washington DC, 2010.

Social and environmental indexes to determine the impacts of closed neighbourhoods in Brazil

F. J. M. Pedrazzi & F. T. Conceição
UNESP, Univer. Estadual Paulista, IGCE, Brazil

Abstract

São Paulo State, in Brazil, is getting increasingly crowded, like in other third world countries around the world, so should give great importance to city development. This work considered the phenomenon of closed neighbourhoods (CN) as an important factor to city planning, papers report many impacts of this model of neighbourhoods in other countries, but in Brazil its impacts are not yet well listed in the literature. The aim of this work was to determine indicators to achieve the social and environmental performances and verify their applicability on three different closed neighbourhoods in São Paulo state, Brazil. The indicators were condensed on indexes: water management, waste management, energy and emissions, legal compliance, environment and buildings, risk management, health and education and governance. The preliminary results indicated several social and environmental problems in all indexes.
Keywords: gated villages, closed neighbourhoods, social and environmental performance, indicators and indexes, Brazil.

1 Introduction

Against the past urbanization trend, where downtowns were considered the best living place, a new trend for the dispersion of the outlying neighbourhoods is being verified in a fractal model [1]. In this model, appear several enclaves in the outliers of the cities, many of them with access control, edges with wall or fences and closed gates, restricting the access [2].

Checking this situation, Manzi and Smith-Bowers [3] set out by arguing that a taxonomy of gating and walls in residential areas is better expressed through the term gated residential development (GRD), rather than the more confusing 'gated community' or 'closed neighbourhood'.

WIT Transactions on Ecology and The Environment, Vol 173, © 2013 WIT Press
www.witpress.com, ISSN 1743-3541 (on-line)
doi:10.2495/SDP130031

The same authors say that GRD are places where the public spaces were privatized, like greenbelts and recreational areas, this become a problem if the government does not prepare the city for growth, since entrepreneurs are taking advantage of new spatial scale thinking, besides understanding the local government failures.

It's known that in countries as Europe and North America the concept of "club goods" is the most frequent cause of walling, like the concept of exclusivity. This means the exclusivity of living in a closed neighbourhood with all the privileges are a preponderant factor for the family to choose living in it. In others, like Brazil, Argentina and other third world countries, the main walling causes are the absence of public security and the lack of efficient public services.

Despite all the reasons, closed neighbourhoods may cause several environmental and social impacts. Bockstaller and Girardin [4] proposed the validation of the use of indicators to conduct environmental analysis, since these tools have become prerequisites for the implementation of the concept of sustainable development [5]. These indicators, when tangible stimulate the interest and participation of people [6, 7], discussion of improving the socio-environmental issues at the community level falls.

The decision criteria for the definition of the indicators must follow the principles from Donnelly *et al.* [8], which produced a hall of "strategic indicators of environmental performance". Thus, the aim of this work was to determine 8 indexes, composed with at least 5 indicators each, to assess the social and environmental impacts of closed neighbourhoods.

2 Description of method

The environmental and social performance index is based on a Brazilian standard NBR ISO 14031:2004, Social Carbon methodology [9, 10] and from Donnelly *et al.* [8]. These methodologies are based on application of environmental and social indicators to achieve better management practices.

The application of the indicators was based on the PDCA, an iterative four-step management method used in business for the control and continuous improvement of processes and products (Figure 1). The first stage, "PLAN", consisted in determining the indicators. They are based on the literature, visits to closed neighbourhoods. It was considered also the scientific bibliography, manuals, standards and empirical experiences. Based on these data, where created indicators to represent the management practices. Table 1 presents the scores to each indicator, being the worse and better management practices scored with 1 and 5 points, respectively.

The next step was "DO". All the developers must give permission for this study in the closed neighbourhoods. Application of the proposed method will be conducted using semi-conducted interviews and visits to the manager or the president of the closed neighbourhoods. The questionnaire asked respondents to rate suggested responses on a scale from 1 to 5, allowing respondents to add their own responses.

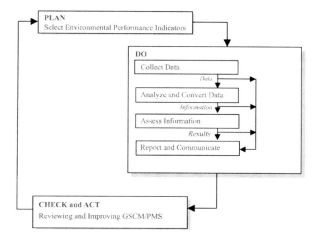

Figure 1:   Plan – Do – Check – Act, modified from NBR ISO 14031:2004.

Table 1:   Possible scores to each indicator.

Scenario / score	1	2	3	4	5
Rating	Bad	Critical	Regular	Satisfactory	Good

The third and fourth steps ("CHECK" and "ACT") consist about the analysis of the indicators. The social and environmental performance is composed by the arithmetic mean of the indexes. Each index is composed by the arithmetic mean of the indicators, being the score below 3 (regular) considered as a bad result.

After this, it will be suggested an action plan, based on OECD model (pressure-state-response) [11], which allowed identifying the social and environmental impacts, assisting to the management strategies.

3   Indexes and indicators

The proposed indicators were chosen inside 9 indexes with at least 5 indicators each. The indexes chosen were: water management, waste management, energy and emissions, legal compliance, environment and buildings, risk management, health and education and governance.

Water management:
- Water resources management plan;
- Type and compliance for subterranean water catchment;
- Targets for water consumption and its reduction in common areas;
- Campaigns for responsible water use;
- Water leaks detection and loss index;

- Sectorization of water consumption;
- Water reuse/recycling;
- Monitoring of superficial and groundwater potability;
- Wastewater discharge;
- Storm water management program.

Waste management:
- Solid waste management plan;
- Frequency and selective collection;
- Waste reduction targets;
- Emissions control in waste collecting;
- Management of construction and demolition waste;
- Management of green waste;
- Intermediate disposal of undifferentiated waste;
- Destination for fluorescent bulbs;
- Batteries and lead-acid batteries scrap management;
- Used tires management and disposal;
- Plaster waste management and disposal.

Energy and emissions:
- Power consumption management plan;
- Lighting of common sites;
- Street lighting technologies;
- Sources of energy for common areas;
- Purchases of efficient appliances and electronics;
- Monitoring electricity usage;
- Emissions management plan;
- Monitoring of greenhouse gases emissions and their reductions;
- Internal transport and logistics.

Legal compliances:
- Plan for recovery of degraded areas;
- Mandatory preservation areas;
- Environmental infractions;
- Extension of green areas in the neighbourhood;
- Permeable batch in the neighbourhood;
- Existence and management practices for contaminated areas;
- Compliance with licensing requirements;
- Licence to management of paint cans, solvents, fuel oil and lubricating oil;
- Granting water use.

Soil use and biodiversity:
- Public roads pavement;

- Quotient between impervious areas (ai) and built area (ac);
- Exposed soil and erosions;
- Vegetable coverage of open areas;
- Stability margins and slopes;
- Common green area per capita;
- Maintenance of green areas methods;
- Urban forestry in sidewalks;
- Environmental enrichment with native species;
- Exotic pets in public areas;
- Diversity forestry and vegetation management;
- Vegetation cover per inhabitant;
- Permeable areas perpetuation of gardening in homes

Risk management:
- Fire fighting system and people training brigade;
- Analysis of social risks;
- Analysis of environmental risks;
- Program risk management;
- Training of staff in emergency situations;
- Security guards qualification.

Environment and buildings:
- Buildings rules standardization;
- Grease trap installation;
- Standardization of sidewalks;
- Control of soil impermeabilization in homes;
- Rainwater use politics;
- Solar heating politics;
- Waste management and control in buildings;
- Supervision of buildings and housing;
- Legal and certified wood use - collective and/or residual buildings;
- Supplier control.

Health and education:
- Program of environmental education;
- Community kitchen- gardens;
- Education program for transit for children and youth;
- Monitoring with aged;
- Program for prevention and control of chronic no communicable diseases;
- Education program for finance and policy for children and youth;
- Nutritional education program;

Governance:
- Quality management program;
- Community relationship;
- Community representation in collegiate;
- Opened accountancy;
- Sustainable buying policies.

4 Case study

To validate the proposed method, 3 closed neighbourhoods in Sorocaba/SP, Brazil were chosen, as listed above:

Closed neighbourhood A (CN A):
Opened in 2006, a medium class, total area of 113,163,04 m², green reserved area of 17,692.82 m² (16%), pavimentation for streets of 28,721.12 m² (25%), area reserved for public goods of 5,871.41 m² (5%), lots of 60,687.32 m² (54%), number of lots 212, average area for each lot = 250 m²;

Closed neighbourhood B (CN B):
Opened in 1973, high class, 100 lots, total area of 922.471,82 m², green reserved area of 0,00 (0%), pavimentation for streets of 129,959.00 m² (14%), area reserved for public goods of 164.616,71 m² (18%), lots of 617.400,00 m² (67%), number of lots of 100, average area for each lot = 5,000 m²;

Closed neighbourhood C (CN C):
Opened in 2010, medium class, total area of 363,000.00 m², green reserved area of 90,919.46 m² (25%), pavimentation for streets of 91,401.21 (25%), area reserved for public goods of 17.678,21 m² (5%), lots of 146,707.21 m² (40%), recreation area of 16,293.19 (4%), number of lots of 414, average area for each lot = 312 m²;

Sorocaba is a Brazilian city located in São Paulo State. It is the fourth most populous in the interior of São Paulo with a population of 594,000 inhabitants. It has an area of 456.0 km², of which 349 km² (76%) area is urban. The region of Sorocaba possesses fourteen municipalities, with more than 1.3 million inhabitants.

In 2010, the population density of Sorocaba was 1,113.92 inhabitants/km², while the average region is 148 inhabitants/km². Sorocaba has a potential annual per capita consumption estimated at USD 1,000 for the urban population and USD, being the 30th Brazilian city with the greatest potential for consumption [12].

It is estimated that in Sorocaba over 100,000 people lives in closed neighbourhoods and dwellings, which are spread by chaotically in the peripheral areas of city. The gated communities are predominantly formed by houses of middle and high classes, with terrain ranging from 250, 300, 700 and 5,000 m². As increases the size of the lots, there is an empirical relationship with the purchasing power of the owners.

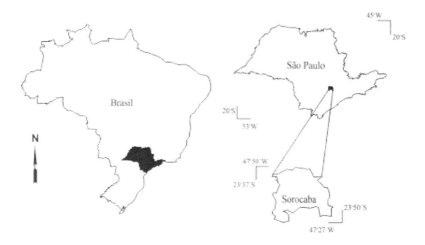

Figure 2:   Location of Sorocaba, SP, Brazil.

Over the last twelve years, the city has undergone several urbanization projects, becoming today one of the top ten best cities or living in São Paulo State. Despite its credits, there is a lot of pressure from commercial developers to create high density and high rise buildings. In many cases, the "sustainable" small scale ideas clash with the business plans of big developers.

Sorocaba won over 3 years state awards from a program called "Green-blue municipality", which aims to environmental management of São Paulo State. Sorocaba has a municipal office to care about environmental programs since 2009. Some modest attitudes are being done; the municipality has seventy miles of bike paths created in the city's main avenues.

5   Preliminary results

The method proposed is being applied in these 3 closed neighbourhoods at Sorocaba. Figure 3 presents some picture illustrating the problems found in these closed neighbourhoods. Preliminary results indicated several social and environmental negative aspects, such as:

Water management: process of siltation caused by the lack of indigenous forests vegetation cover in the areas of permanent preservation and urban drainage without desanding (CN B, Figure 3A);

Waste management: lack of selective waste collection policy causes loss of recyclable materials and unnecessary disposal on landfills or waste dumps (CN A, Figure 3B);

Figure 3:   Some environmental problems, verified on a field survey.

Energy and emissions: lack of control over the use of electricity leads to loss of energy and generation of hazardous waste (lamps, batteries, among others).

Legal compliances: areas of permanent preservation, protected by Brazilian law without indigenous forests coverage (CN B, Figure 3C). Lack of environmental compliance (granting for water use) for river channel modification and margins occupied by non-indigenous species (CN A, Figure 3D); Areas of permanent preservation, protected by Brazilian law (30 m on each margin) occupied by urban use (CN B, Figure 3E).

Soil use and biodiversity: Soil exposure without any management practices (CN C, Figure 3F). Reforestation project without any observation of introduction of species threatened by extinction, according to IUCN (CN A, Figure 3G).

Risk management: there is no survey of social and environmental risks in the 3 closed neighbourhoods studied;

Environment and buildings: Despite the lack of policies for sustainable buildings, some individual actions can be observed, i.e. rainwater collection to reuse in toilets and irrigation in a private house (CN A, Figure 3H).

Health and education: no education practices and health-related activities are applied in the 3 closed neighbourhoods studied;

Governance: quality management program, community relationship, community representation in collegiate, opened accountancy and sustainable buying policies are not documented.

6 Conclusion

The method proposed, using index and indicators, is feasible for an appraisal of the social and environmental management of closed neighbourhood.

At the moment, the preliminary results obtained in 3 closed neighbourhoods at Sorocaba city, located in São Paulo State, indicated various social and environmental problems in all indexes.

At the end of this work, the numerical scores of each index will be achieved, with these results it is going to be possible to list and make action plans to the each problems occurring in these closed neighbourhoods, allowing proposing improvements in social and environmental management practices for their sustainability.

Acknowledgements

We would like to thank João de Araújo Junior for reviewing the manuscript and for the National Council of Scientific and Technological Development (CNPq) for the financial support.

References

[1] Caldeira, T. Cidade de Muros. Crime, segregação e cidadania em São Paulo. São Paulo: Edusp/Editora 34.

[2] Atkinson, R. The politics of gating (A response to Private Security and Public Space by Manzi and Smith-Bowers), European Journal of Spatial Development, Debate Article. Available on: http://www.nordregio.se /Global/EJSD/Debate/debate080506.pdf. 2008.

[3] Manzi, T. and Smith-Bowers, B. Private Security and Public Space: New Approaches to the Theory and Practice of Gated Communities. European Journal of Spatial Development. Debate article. Available on www.nordregio.se/EJSD/refereed22.pdf. 2006.

[4] Bockstaller C, Girardin P. How to validate environmental indicators. Agric Syst. Volume 76, PP-639–653. 2003.

[5] Hansen, J.W. Is agricultural sustainability a useful concept? Agricultural Systems 50, 117–143. 1996.

[6] Fung, A., Wright, E.O. (Eds.). Deepening democracy: institutional innovations in empowered participatory governance. Verso, London. 2003.

[7] Graymore, M.L.M, Sipe, N.G., Rickson, R.E. Sustaining Human Carrying Capacity: a tool for regional sustainability assessment. Ecological Economics, 69, PP. 459-468. 2010.

[8] Donnelly, A., Jones, M., O'Mahony, T., Byrne, G. Selecting environmental indicator for use in strategic environmental assessment. Env. Imp. Assessment review, vol. 27, PP-161-175. 2007.

[9] Rezende D. and Merlin S. Carbono social - Agregando valores ao desenvolvimento sustentável. Editora: PEIROPOLIS. Available on: http://www.socialcarbon.org/uploadDocs/Documents/Social_Carbon_book _pt.pdf. 2003.

[10] Santos C.K.N. 2008. Metodologia do carbono social – manual do multiplicador. Palmas, Instituto Ecológica.

[11] OECD. OECD core set of indicators for environmental performance reviews. Environment monographs, number 83. Paris. 1993.

[12] IPC. Os 500 municípios que mais consomem no Brasil. Available on http://www.ipcbr.com/downpress/Ranking_IPC_2010_2009_500Maiores. pdf. Accessed on 14/02/2012. 2010.

Towards sustainable waterfront transformation: through the Mediterranean to Montenegro

S. R. Jelovac
Department for Environmental Design, University La Sapienza, Italy

Abstract

The milestone of the research study is focusing on the definition of a model for the sustainable transformation of the waterfront in Montenegro in order to integrate and contextualize the Montenegrin coast within the Mediterranean Basin and to refund and detect local identity. Marine, port and fluvial cities can be considered as laboratories for the process of urban renewal in terms of residential areas, transport, public spaces and the quality of the environment. The aim of the research will focus on their formation, transformation and opportunities to regenerate in a sustainable key, from scenarios of transformation and development strategies, to action and design guidelines as a possible model of urban development and environmental transformation. After studying the international scene in this topic, the research will focus on three case studies of actual urban waterfront development in Montenegro, which are currently in the process of transformation. The selection of case studies will be identified at international level, according to the main 'ingredients' for a sustainable cohabitation between ports and cities and for a lasting success in waterfront regeneration processes. Now spread out and developed at a global dimension, involving both big cities but also medium and small-scale cities at all latitudes and in all continents, waterfront regeneration is in many cases the starting point for the regeneration of the city itself and of its relocation in the international context.

Keywords: waterfront, urban regeneration, urban renewal, creative cities, identity, Mediterranean, Montenegro, Brownfield.

WIT Transactions on Ecology and The Environment, Vol 173, © 2013 WIT Press
www.witpress.com, ISSN 1743-3541 (on-line)
doi:10.2495/SDP130041

1 Introduction

In the modern city, the success of the quality of life embodied in public places is increasingly accepted as a guarantee factor for overall success. As such, modern cities have realized the importance of the role of water for a better quality of life. Many cities around the world create ambitious waterfront projects, trying to solve their problems related to water and combining them with improved public spaces. Innovative technologies give us the space as a legacy for significant urban renewal, so the harbour areas become a modern urban design laboratory.

The transformation of the urban waterfront is, without doubt, one of the great chapters of urban renewal in the last 15 years, and we can say with certainty that this will be an extremely important issue in the following decades.

This paper examines some selected examples of cities in Europe and the world (Barcelona, Marseilles, Rotterdam, Bordeaux, Hamburg) with its waterfront projects. It examines the state of the art of the development in the complex Mediterranean context and shows the beginnings of a successful implementation in Montenegro and those who just should establish its urban policy, including water and strategies for creating a space to interact with the water and contribute to changing the quality of urban life of citizens.

Also, the purpose of this paper is to investigate the main factors for the realization of creative waterfront regeneration, and how they stimulate sustainable innovation, in order to achieve economically, socially and environmentally sustainable solutions in the cities on the water, with the ultimate goal to draw some recommendations for development of selected case studies in Montenegro.

2 Modern city and the waterfront transformation

Technical, political, social and economic transformation in modern cities has caused significant changes in the spatial configuration of the city as a whole and especially on their waterfronts. Since the 1970s, the experience of urban rehabilitation, recycling of existing urban structures and their adaptiveness to new uses has provided new ways of doing things in the cities. The possibility of using former industrial areas and ports provides a qualitative and economic development for the city. New uses in these recycled areas are generally labelled as triggers of acceleration and development of the city and public spaces. In a similar manner the complex Porto Montenegro in Montenegro, the territory of the former Arsenal, for a few years made results on an international scale, which will later through this study be further elaborated.

The modern city is constantly transformed through various processes of reconstruction where urban waterfront regeneration receives its full significance, with the intention of becoming a space for interaction of two systems, land and water as a collective heritage, urban fabric and port, the space of constant evolution, specialized transition and dynamic change, thus generating one of the most modern urban phenomena.

3 State of the art in the process of waterfront development

This study was preceded by the analysis of carefully selected international case studies, in accordance with the main components for a sustainable synergy between ports and cities, as well as continued success in the long term regeneration process, where space is interpreted in an innovative way; protecting resources and the cultural and historical heritage, preserving memories and renewing local identity.

The 1980s began with a phase of urban transformation that changed the appearance of many European cities by eliminating the use of industrial areas, port facilities and railways. This process of transformation introduced the cultural zone, residential, commercial or tertiary facilities, focusing both on the need for integration of different procedures in order to facilitate the realization of complex operations. Marshall's [1] criticism made for waterfront developments marking the danger of seeing waterfronts as cure-alls for problematic cities and that a "rubber stamp" waterfront design can deal with the issues is noteworthy. "Busquets [2] defines the state of today's city as fragmented and once again the public space as a strategy that can provide cohesion for the city which consists of parts (each with its independent management and projects). The waterfront would have to act as such a cohesive space.

Today, the construction of the waterfront also reflects the multipurpose and multi-modal thinking that dominates the town planning and designing of the modern era, which, at the same time represents a departure from post-war paradigms. The common principles, mainly related to the mixed-use of pedestrian character were applied within the frames recognizing what makes waterfronts special. Usually, these are their history, nature, challenges /opportunities that are related to their post-industrial state, and their central position in the city. Within the planning of the waterfront, the emphasis is on communication, because the planners' approach is to strive to overcome barriers, and to foster the interaction between water and land, for workers between the port and the urban fabric. It should be noted that waterfront renovation projects, which are currently being established in many European cities are part of the complex creative operations which today increasingly become a new element to city attractions.

Experience of creative cities may be attributed to the promotion of the territory, the competitiveness of which is based on local specifics related to the value of "city symbol." Such areas are becoming a real "creative clusters" (Sepe [3]), and they are the result of economic initiatives and structural innovations implemented in the appropriate local economic development strategies that are based on territorial qualities and special local features.

Major events and their long-term effects have turned several cities on the water into undisputed protagonists of the latest urban events. The cities of Valencia and Saragossa are among the latest ones, i.e. the most recent cities that are playing on the water and use regional marketing as a resource and for their revitalization. The mix of tourism and culture for local development and designing a new urban image at an international level by organizing a big event is a widespread formula that is now established (consolidated) in many successful experiences (Sepe [3]).

Typical examples of renewal of "creative clusters" of coastal zones can be found, in addition to the area Hafencity in the Guggenheim Museum, in Bilbao, Valencia, in the Baltic, in Newcastle, at the Albert Docks, the Tate Gallery, in Liverpool and the museum in Antwerp.

Barcelona, Marseille and Genoa have always been three harbours, each determined by their specificity; especially interesting as samples for the study, and today, each for a key and the precise role they play in relation to the Mediterranean and continental regions, and at the same time, due to a tendency to be increasingly recognized, not only as separate entities, but perhaps in the most interesting way, as single entities.

4 International case studies

4.1 Barcelona

The city of Barcelona has undergone a significant change since 1980. This urban transformation was the result of three interrelated urban processes: the improvement of the transport system and infrastructure, the construction of centrality, and economic reconversion. Holding the 1992 Olympic Games was another impetus of urban transformation; four of twelve Areas of Centrality were the Olympic installation. They have directed property development and stimulated neighbourhood revitalization where they were located (Riera and Keogh [4]).

Barcelona is a pioneer in the use of large-scale events to promote the city and its neighbourhoods. These events have resulted in large development projects, Port Vell, Port Olympic and Forum 2004, all of these events acted as engines of redevelopment of the attractive coastline and promenade, the high-end housing and the shift from industrial production to economic knowledge. Barcelona is also known as a prominent example where the embodiment in public areas is accepted as a factor in the overall success, using its high-quality waterfront urban areas as a part of improving urban policy.

4.2 Marseille: the active port vs. the urban fabric

Consultation, diversification, urban form and architectural form, partnership and sociability are the principles that have been represented in the process of urban regeneration of the Port of Marseilles as part Euroméditerranée project. This process was strategically managed by diversified activities and processes involving the community and evaluating possible scenarios of strategic development, in order to define and implement a joint project that will bridge the gap between the city and the sea. The connection between the port space and public space was created along the waterfront and gap was overcome and enabled "coexistence" between active port and populated city that preserves its historic and cultural resources, and its identity as a port [5].

From this perspective, the problem has become a strategic resource, and many studied examples in the best way show that the worst social problems arise when a public space is not working. Therefore, just the availability of space ready for the modification was the starting point to a local "regeneration". That is why public space in the context of urban renewal becomes a challenge, opportunity, resource, perspective.

4.3 Bordeaux

The waterfront renovation in Bordeaux is an excellent example of cultural regeneration, creative transformation and socio-economic change, whose success in 2007 brought this historic city to the definition by UNESCO as exceptional value and in 2010 it won the award European City of the Year granted by the Academy of Urbanism [6]. During this process, the strategy was not the construction of a mega structure designed by big names in international architecture, as in other cases of the waterfront and the renewal of the waterfront area, including, for example Barcelona, Valencia or Hamburg, but a number of medium-sized urban interventions aimed at linking different cultures and the mainland of both coasts, and improving of the quality of life, encouraging people to bear the costs of restructuring. In this long process of transformation, the population was cooperating in a variety of ways which led to the adoption of common needs, and support of residents and stakeholders (Matteini [7]).

4.4 Hamburg

The Hafencity project in Hamburg is known as one of the largest and most ambitious in Europe. Although it provides only a partial recovery of the port warehouse, this project has the intention to restore the historic part of the city and to give it the identity of a maritime city.

Reconstruction of the coast was divided into several stages. During the first phase attention was focused on the theme of water, which is understood as an element around which the economy of the city was developed. Then it was followed by a phase that, on the one hand, was characterized by the disappearance of the shipyard as the city has concentrated on the opposite side of the harbour, coast and river, while on the other hand, this phase was characterised by expanding to new sectors. In the next phase the growth of tourism had a fundamental role in launching the strategy of redefining the port system. Then the communication phase followed, with the launch of a public debate on the subject of the port and its re-draft that included the participating of citizens through exhibitions, conferences, competitions and publications [8].

The process of regeneration of Hafencity zone in Hamburg is the operation of the largest urban scale requalification in Europe. With its surface of 155h, the project envisages, in the interval of 20 years, the implementation of a new part of the city which would be surrounded by water, and would be intended for living, work and play. The project includes various factors, including historical identity, multiple uses, preservation of public spaces, as well as almost all of the "10 principles of sustainable development of urban waterfronts," which were established during the United Nations Global Conference Urban 21, held in Berlin in 2000 [9].

4.5 Rotterdam: the port in the city

Rotterdam Port makes the city one of the major ports in the world along the way thanks to the great capacity of the "institutional adaptation" and "innovative" planning based on policy coordination, expanded participation in decision-making processes, cooperation between the different agencies and entities; it is hard to distinguish the port from the city. Revitalization of the area of 202 hectares has transformed a very derelict space to an area that in only a few years has attracted businesses, residents and tourists, thanks to the integrated planning and coordination between different work teams (de Greef [10]).

The regeneration program for the port area has become an integrated project at an urban level, strategic for the city and its residents, and it has been developed with a special focus on public interest and social goals.

Each of the above mentioned territories (*Barcelona, Marseilles, Bordeaux, Hamburg, Rotterdam,...*) of waterfront urban renewal is a unique case, and they represent a sufficient acknowledgment of the diversity and local compromise in relation to the developed programmes. Analysis of these cases highlights several important aspects of introducing diversity through each case study: philosophy of urban management; the political concept of urbanization; characteristics of the site; local urban dynamics of city and port, etc.

When we talk about urban waterfront regeneration as a sustainable way of transforming the space and the importance of interdisciplinarity, it is appropriate to also mention several important general guidance points at a European level such as the National Agency for Urban Requalification (ANRU – Agence Nationale pour Renovation Urbaine).

These principles are the common denominator of the successful researched examples of waterfront development, and they include: "consultation: citizen involvement from the initial stages of regeneration projects as a key element for the success of the entire operation; diversification: the prediction of different typologies of accommodation, enhancement of existing functionality, easy cultural and social integration, urban and architectural form: re-modelling of the settlements, rehabilitation of buildings, deconstruction and reconstruction, personalization, to give a new quality of residential habitat; partnership: cooperation among all local stakeholders (government authorities of different levels, the third party sector, entrepreneurs) who are involved in the requalification project is the driving force of the effectiveness and efficiency; sociability: an operation in settlement and architecture is the opportunity to define the project of social development, education and public services, economic development, local employment and the administration of the city" (ANRU [11]).

Researched international case studies as examples of successful urban waterfront regeneration, although separate and distinct from each other, have inspired the creation of the "10 Principles of Sustainable Development of Urban Waterfronts," which were defined during the United Nations Global Conference Urban 21, held in Berlin in 2000 and which was developed in the seminars promoted in collaboration with the International Centre of Cities on Water in Venice [12]. These principles were adopted at the WaterfrontExpo held in Liverpool in 2008 and can be the link to a complex and common process of transformation and the key to a positive impact on an urban and territorial level.

1.   Determine the quality of water and the environment. A prerequisite for the development of the shoreline is the quality of water in systems of streams, rivers, canals, lakes, bays and seas. The city administrations are responsible for the sustainable recovery of deserted coastlines and for remediation and clean up of polluted waters.

2.   Waterfront is an integral part of the existing urban fabric. New waterfront interventions should be an integral part of the existing city and the territory thus contributing to its vitality and local development. Water is part of the urban landscape and should be used in a clearly defined purpose, such as transport, culture and leisure (recreation).

3.   Historical identity gives a character to the place. Use of the combined wealth of events, landscapes, nature, presented by water will give the character and significance to the waterfront. Preserving history and local traditions is an important element of this renewal.

4.   Multi use is a priority. Coastal area should offer a variety of activities of cultural didactic, commercial, housing type that will properly use the presence of water. Residential neighbourhoods should be mixed both functionally and socially.

5.   Public access is a prerequisite. Waterfront must be accessible visually and physically to residents and tourists of all ages and revenues. The construction of public spaces should be at the highest quality level in order to allow their frequent use.

6.   Planning within public-private partnerships speeds up the process. Development of new waterfronts should be presented from the perspective of public-private partnerships. State institutions should coordinate policy in terms of interventions projects and aspects of management, as well as to guarantee the quality of planning and social equilibrium. Private institutions should be involved from the very beginning to be well acquainted with the market and accelerate development.

7.   Public participation is one of the elements of sustainability. The city is supposed to have benefits from sustainable development of the coastal area, not only in ecological and economic, but also in social terms. The population should be well informed and involved in decisions and processes from the very beginning.

8.   Waterfront developments are long-term projects. They need to be gradually used so the entire city can derive benefit from their potential. This is a challenge in the long run that has a need for a variety of disciplines and types of actors. Public administration must give incentives from a political point of view

as well, in order to guarantee the realization of the objectives independently of economic conditions and short-term interests.

9.   Revitalization is a continuous process. All urban instruments should use a detailed analysis of the function and importance of the coast which is the subject of this process. Plans can be flexible, can adapt to the changes and include all disciplines.

10.   Profit of shoreline of international networks. Renewal of the coast is a very complex task, which recruits professionals of various disciplines. The exchange of knowledge within the international network of contacts may include shorelines and provide both individual and global support in major projects, completed and current ones (Giovinazzi [13]).

5   Mediterranean context and identity

Mediterranean complex context is contributed by the need to address current life needs and their satisfaction: immigration, fast mobility, heterogeneity and growing fast numerical, cultural and religious variability of the urban population, uncontrolled progress of mass tourism industry, of which the Mediterranean, and particularly its port towns, are a privileged target, forcing constant adjustments, additions and substitutions in the definition of urban systems. Identity of Mediterranean towns is constantly faced with current rapid transformations, assumed a more complex meaning in prescribing logics that govern them and simultaneously define them, both within themselves, to solve its systemic dynamics, and elsewhere, as a steady and hidden connected and simultaneously differently unique and special. More than in the past, the identity of the port cities of the Mediterranean basin represents a value, an additional determinant, what sets it apart and qualifies it at a local as well as global level.

6   Montenegro's case studies

6.1 Arsenal in Tivat: Porto Montenegro creative regeneration of waterfront

Joint preservation of the industrial and maritime heritage of the Adriatic is of great importance and may have pronounced synergistic effects and its complex and broader geographic consideration multiplies its effects.

All these shipbuilding and ship repair assets are connected by common historical destiny, and even the preservation of the industrial and historic heritage of the Arsenal in Tivat, should be considered in the context of a legacy of the whole geographical territory of the Adriatic Sea and all adjacent countries and, in the near future, the Mediterranean – the Adriatic part of united Europe;

The Arsenal in Tivat, which was built in the late 19th century by the Austro-Hungarian Navy, is one of the first occurrences of industrialization in the area of Boka Kotorska. Also, it represents a significant part of the industrial and maritime, in particular, military-maritime heritage of the entire Adriatic. In its 120 years of existence, it is connected with many historical, professional, political, geo-strategic and other aspects of similar or equivalent institutions, on the shores of the Adriatic.

The initial idea during the valorisation and organisation of the space of 165 hectares was the formation of a coastal place oriented and open to the sea which, during the season and off-season, will function actively, in accordance with the needs of the population, visitors and users of space (fig. 1). This is achieved by planning an exclusive nautical tourism centre and sustainable marina with 850 berths, which will be designed for the reception of mega-yachts, and small boats

THE VILLAGE | MASTERPLAN

	PORTO MONTENEGRO VILLAGE			
1	JETTY 1 - Completed	11	VENICE SQUARE - Completed
2	JETTY 2 - Completed	12	HOTEL DEVELOPMENT - In planning
3	JETTY 3 - Completed	13	LIDO POOL - Open
4	JETTY 4 - Completed	14	VILLAGE SQUARE - In planning
5	HARBOUR MASTER - Operational	15	CAPTAIN'S PARK
6	TEUTA RESIDENCES - Completed	16	NAUTICAL MUSEUM - Completed
7	ZETA RESIDENCES - Completed	17	SPORTS & YACHT CLUB - Completed
8	OZANA RESIDENCES - Completed	18	TENNIS COURTS - Completed
9	MILENA RESIDENCES - Under construction	19	INTERNATIONAL SCHOOL - Open
10	TARA RESIDENCES - Under construction		

Figure 1:   Porto Montenegro, Master plan.

for sport and recreation. These amenities have requested the planning of other activities as well, such as residential business, commercial and service activities, which, depending on the needs and interests, will benefit the users and visitors in different utilization regimes (during the season and low season) [14].

Transport accessibility, creation of new urban matrix, the introduction of exclusive content of nautical tourism, adequate tourist offer, connection of the place with the contents in the surrounding and focus on natural values of the place were all together the prerequisites for this area to experience a transformation and affirmation as a tourist destination of the highest category.

Completion of this complex and its subsequent operation will create a significant revenue generator for the labour force in Montenegro. This exquisite marina will attract very wealthy mega-yacht owners and guests in Montenegro, having a positive impact on all those sectors of the economy serving the market of high paying tourists, such as private banking and real estate agencies.

Transformation of Arsenal in Tivat (Porto Montenegro) is an excellent example of waterfront creative regeneration which has become an integral part of the existing urban fabric and it has contributed to its vitality by preserving industrial past as an integral element of sustainable redevelopment. Porto Montenegro Waterfront has become part of the urban landscape of the city of Tivat and has been used for special functions, such as transport on water, entertainment and culture, housing, leisure ... and its benefits are reflected not only in ecological and economic terms, but also social ones. The proposed complex Porto Montenegro would bring a lot of positive impact on national and global development strategy for Montenegro. The place with intensive traffic and economic development, which once was damaged and inaccessible area of the city, became one of the most valuable areas on the Montenegrin coast which implements its development at the local level and is presented and promoted at an international level.

6.2 Port Milena Waterfront: from disconnected landscape to sustainable port

The project is the product of cooperation of the studies from Venice and Montenegro in response to the program guidelines as defined by the Government of Montenegro for the requalification and rehabilitation of the zones of very sensitive heritage in terms of natural and physical inherited structures.

The locality of Port Milena is positioned in the eastern part of the Municipality of Ulcinj and it is developed around the channel harmoniously at the length of 3.6 km and the area of 120 ha. The channel Port Milena is man-made, in fact it was made on the order of Montenegrin King Nikola at the end of the 19th century, in order to drain the swamp area where the salt works is located today. An interesting aspect of the water flow is that the channel was made with the aim to make fresh water from the hinterland flow into the sea, however, because of the currents, sea water started to flow into the channel going all the way to the swamp area. The area occupied by water is 28 ha, and the width of the channel varies from a minimal 48 meters to a maximum of 94 meters, with the average of 36 m. The widest part is located eastwards, and the channel flows into the sea in the south between the Cape Djeran [15] and Velika Paža (Big Beach); one of the most beautiful sandy beaches of the Adriatic Sea. Big Beach is 12 km long and its potential will be discussed in the next section.

Analysis of urban and architectural reality of this territory has established the social issues, individualism, which stems from widespread illegal construction and lack of control in the territory. Illegal construction is a phenomenon that has developed in recent years, which seems unstoppable, and it produces the risks leading the town of Ulcinj to collapse, preventing any economic development, and above all, the development of tourism.

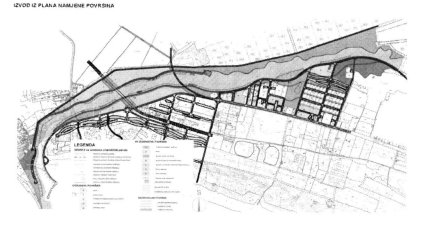

Figure 2:   Master plan – Port Milena Waterfront.

Lack of integration in this area with the town, the alienation of the population, poor tourist attendance, poor water quality, unused extraordinary landscape characteristics and diversity and loss of identity are just some of the critical points that trigger the process of redevelopment and allow different scenarios. To respond to this critical reality, which is present on the entire national territory, not only in Ulcinj, the plan proposes solutions of social sustainability. In the region of the channel, the marina with about 350 berths is planned, which would be integrated with future programs (commercial, recreational and cultural) across the pedestrian promenade that follows the coast channels, while urbanity of new residential areas – housing typology of collective type is seen through a multitude of great public spaces interconnected with aqueous fluids and pedestrian communications and revitalized linear public spaces along the canal (fig. 2).

Plans include also buildings of tourist resorts, dock, lighthouse, works on the main infrastructure, thematic parks, equipped green areas, maintaining the local vegetation, sport and areas for providing hospitality services. Such project selection enables satisfying the wish for development of marine and inland navigation, and that the zone become especially attractive for international investment and tourism.

Proposed interventions would encourage the revival of the channel coast of Porta Milena and its linkage to the coast, with the city, and the articulation of a new promenade along the entire length of 3.5 km canal to allow the beginning of the dynamic process of change in these areas, thus creating the conditions for the creation of the planned secondary centre of this municipality.

These activities should preserve the landscape, cultural and natural heritage, and they should improve economic conditions, public and private ones, and eventually, they should increase the awareness among the population of their own environment [16].

This example of urban waterfront regeneration could become unique in the Mediterranean because of its local features, multicultural diversity, the contrast in scenery, great natural characteristics, rich biodiversity, then the strategic cross-border connections and relations with neighbouring Albania with which the municipality of Ulcinj is bordered. The area of Port Milena is also important for the broader context of the city, the region and the whole of Montenegro, and through its valorisation and future development it can be of great international importance [17].

6.3 Velika plaza (Big Beach), "Velika plaza: challenge of a life time"

Port Milena Waterfront is the gate, the entrance to the next case study, Velika plaza with its hinterland territory exceptionally qualified potential to become an attractive tourist destination, having in mind the fact that in the 80s it was one of the most beautiful beaches in Europe. In accordance with development guidelines provided for in national and local plans, the area is recognized to have potential for tourism development. Its natural and cultural characteristics enable supply of various alternatives of hospitality buildings so that different target groups can be satisfied and demands of the international market can be met [18]. As a commitment of the master plan for tourism development, the regional master plan for tourism development in the Ulcinj region has recommended Velika plaza as a site model for the development of a high quality tourist complex because the space of this beach is unique on the eastern coast of the Adriatic Sea and is largely owned by the state, so it is necessary to deal with the complicated issues of ownership, because in this space not much is built, and this provides an unusual chance in the Mediterranean to achieve a "great and long-lasting tailored unique concept," because the size of the space provides a permanent, yet the rich use to the extent to achieve significant economic effects for the region and Montenegro, because Ulcinj so far remained undeveloped due to its geographical position on the border, but the neighbourhood with Albania allows cross-border cooperation in many tourist areas [19].

Velika Plaza was chosen as a model project in order to avoid unplanned construction and simultaneously define the target frame for the economically interesting and environmentally acceptable gradual reconstruction. The area Velika plaza covers about 1450 ha. Out of this, 400 hectares are tourism groups, and 30 hectares has been earmarked for communications. The arranged recreation area covers about 120 hectares and the zone of beaches and dunes about 280 ha. The remaining 620 ha is planned as a free space – untouched nature (protected area).

The main pedestrian axis is about 10 m wide. This multi-functional boulevard is the most important part of the whole concept. Lengthwise, it connects various modules and offers comfortable access to the recreational facilities in the green belt. The construction on Velika Plaza is concentrated on the western part, and the environmentally sensitive area in the eastern part will be kept free as a natural park and protected from human impacts. The construction will be divided into individual units, called "modules", among which a public free zone will be located. These green belts divide the buildings, preventing the formation of continuous settlement, and serve to residents and tourists as a place for recreation (fig. 3) [20].

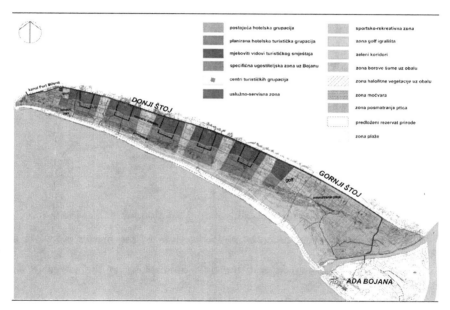

Figure 3:   "Velika Plaza" – general concept.

"Velika Plaza, challenge of a life time" – in organization of the Ministry for Spatial Planning and Environment, sponsored by the Government of Montenegro, the sustainable waterfront community has been implemented as an international master planning competition which has given a vision for the future development of this area.

The vision and positions represented by the state are to develop an exemplar high category sustainable waterfront resort community providing a wide range of uses and community facilities, including workforce housing. Given the scale and linear nature of the site, it is envisaged that a number of distinct "places" or neighbourhoods will be created, each distinctive and attractive in their own right but cohesive within an overarching masterplan and design framework. A leading edge environmental, economic and socio/cultural sustainability ethos will permeate all aspects of the development, from masterplanning through to operation and long term management" [21].

The winning company is Van Den Oever, Zaaijer and Partners, architecten Amsterdam/Stijlgroep Landscape and Urban Design Rotterdamealth.

The winning solution views on development of Velika Plaza as a unique opportunity to develop the landscape in symbiosis with the buildings and to reinforce and repair the landscape structure.

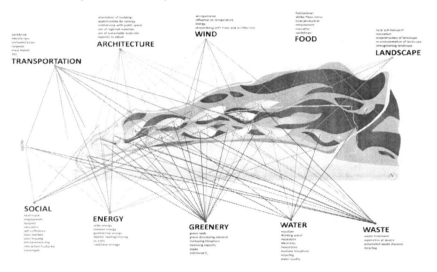

Figure 4:   General concept: winning solution for Velika Plaza.

The basic development potential and objectives of the master plan are, as follows:
- Retain, reinforce and expand authentic atmosphere at the edges of the planning area;
- Velika Plaza is unique in scale and dimensions.

Other projects along the Adriatic coast are small, intimate spots in a hilly landscape, offering a completely different experience of the coast – much more intimate and smaller scale than Velika Plaza. Velika Plaza is unique in its scale, dimensions and possibilities, and for this reason represents a significant addition to the existing development along the cost.

The development of Velika Plaza offers a unique opportunity to develop the landscape in symbiosis with the buildings and to reinforce and repair the landscape structure. In addition, unique functions that reflect the unique qualities of this area can be sought. This is an area for walking, swimming, contemplation, nature experiences, water sport another form of leisure
- Integral design approach: inter-relating plan and landscape.
The landscape and the sea have a direct influence on the direction of the design

decisions. This will create a symbiosis between the sea, the landscape and the urban development plan. Panoramic views will be linked to the built environment. This iconic location combines nature reserves and public spaces in a natural way. The continuity of the landscape and the built environment will be achieved through the introduction of transitional zones, whereby the structures can naturally flow into one another. This organic approach will be reinforced by the layered nature of the landscape and its organic relationship with built environment (fig. 4) [22].

In addition to the above mentioned ANRU principles and analysis of relevant planning documents, the development strategy of the Municipality of Ulcinj, as well as several national strategies and European and directives, the tendency was to allocate and implement the strategy for the future development of the principles of sustainable development of urban waterfronts. These principles can be stated as follows: quality of water and environment must be provided; waterfronts are part of the existing urban fabric; historical identity gives a character; mixed use is a priority, public access is a prerequisite; private-public partnership in the planning accelerates the process; participation of public is an element of sustainability; waterfronts are long-term projects;

7 Conclusion

After analyzing many planning documents for the waterfront development, in addition to confirmatory "10 Principles of Sustainable Development of Urban Waterfronts", many common key criteria are recognized for a successful future of these interventions, and these are: Locally specific-creating of waterfront with specific fetaures which reflect local diversity, values and characteristics. Connected – visual and physical connection reintegrates waterfront with immediate environment, city centre. Public – providing access to the waterfront. Public participation in shaping of vision for waterfront construction.

Multi-use – implementing of various purposes which enable whole day and whole year activity. Multi modal: providing quality infrastructure for all types of transportation. Dynamic waterfront reflects and constantly changes due to economic and cultural changes that occur in the city [23].

In order to support long-term evolution and success, the waterfront should be planned and designed so that it contains elements of flexibility that will enable them to adapt to change.

Transformation of the waterfront relating to the territories which operate as a system that had not been planned for construction earlier refers to strategies that respond to the new dynamics of the market and leads to intervention at various different levels of sensitivity, practical approach and conceptual freedom which is based on location observation and urban process.

Regeneration of the waterfronts represents an extraordinary opportunity for cohesion and "uphold" territory as a whole, the ability to become the engine for sustainable development, and therefore the waterfront developments have become real "laboratories for experimentation" and the central theme of planning [24].

References

[1]   Marshall, R., *Waterfronts in Post-Industrial Cities.* Spon Press. New York, 2001.
[2]   Busquets, J., *Barcelona Revisited: transforming the city within the city. CityEdge. case studies in contemporary urbanism* (ed. Charlesworth, E.) Architectural Press, Oxford, 2005.
[3]   Sepe, M., *Creative Urban Regeneration*, 2009.
[4]   Riera, P. and Keogh, G. Chapter 12: Barcelona, in Berry, J. and McGreal, S. *et al.* European Cities, *Planning Systems and Property Market*, London, E and FN SPON, 1995.
[5]   http://www.euromediterranee.fr
[6]   www.academyofurbanism.org.uk
[7]   Matteini, T., *Complessità, integrazione e diversità nel paesaggio urbano di Bordeaux*, Rivista Ricerche per la progettazione del paesaggio, Università di Firenze, 2008.
[8]   http://www.hafencity.com
[9]   Hafencity Hamburg GmbH, Projects; Insights in the Current Developments, Hamburg, 2008.
[10]   de Greef, P., *Rotterdam Waterstad 2035* (Rotterdam Watercity 2035), Internationale Architectuur Biennale Rotterdam, Episode Publishers, Rotterdam, 2005.
[11]   ANRU, *Observatoire national des zones urbaines sensibles*, Rapport 2009, www.anru.fr
[12]   www.citiesonwater.com; www.waterfront-net.org
[13]   Giovinazzi, M., *Port Cities and Urban Waterfront: Transformations and Opportunities*, 2009.
[14]   Spatial urban plan - Arsenal Tivat, Kotor, Montenegro, 2012.
[15]   Spatial plan of special purpose "Morsko Dobro", Kotor, Montenegro. 2007.
[16]   Spatial urban plan – Rt Djerane – Porta MIlena, 2009.
[17]   National strategy for sustainable development of Montenegro, Government of Montenegro, 2007.
[18]   Environmental assessment of urban development in Ulcinj, 2002.
[19]   Regional master plan for tourism development, Municipality of Ulcinj, 2008.
[20]   "Velika Plaza" – General Concept, Spatial plan of special purpose "Morsko Dobro" Kotor, Montenegro, 2007.
[21]   www.velikaplaza.info
[22]   www.oz-p.nl
[23]   2012 Waterfront plan update, Waterfront planning, best practices, 2012.
[24]   Carta M., *Creative city*, LISt, Barcelona, 2007.

Section 2
Environmental management

The leverage of corporate environmental protection concepts on employee motivation

D. Bartik[1], A. Hoeltl[2] & R. Brandtweiner[3]
[1]University of Applied Sciences BFI Vienna, Austria
[2]Department for Management and Economics,
Danube University Krems, Austria
[3]Institute of Information Management and Control,
Vienna University of Economics and Business, Austria

Abstract

Corporate environmental protection is nowadays no longer just a marketing tool or an annoying necessity for a good reputation, but for many companies an integrated element of the corporate culture and of doing business. In a case study of a company in Austria, this paper investigates a feasible additional advantage for corporate environmental protection in terms of a positive leverage on employee motivation. After giving an overview of the most important theoretical approaches and tools regarding corporate responsibility, incentives, and employee motivation, the influence of the environmental protection concept of Kommunalkredit Austria AG on the job motivation of its employees is analysed on the basis of a questionnaire covering all corporate responsibility related topics. The results show a spill-over effect of a company's increased social responsibility on the behaviour and performance of the employees.

Keywords: corporate environmental management, corporate social responsibility, environmental management system, employee motivation, stakeholder management.

1 Introduction

Today's companies face not only economic but more and more societal compulsion. The formation of the corresponding public opinion is supported by critical media reports and documentations as well as by nonfiction books offering black and white lists concerning the societal performance of companies.

WIT Transactions on Ecology and The Environment, Vol 173, © 2013 WIT Press
www.witpress.com, ISSN 1743-3541 (on-line)
doi:10.2495/SDP130051

Thus environmental and social responsibilities have become important rules of conduct in the business world.

A company's commitment to corporate social responsibility (CSR) means a corporate policy with orientation towards strategic, long-term, and resource friendly value creation, compared to focusing exclusively on short-term profit.

Values, attitudes, and norms regarding environmental protection made public by companies do not only influence the purchase behaviour of consumers but also the motivation of the companies' employees [1]. According to the hypothesis about a better performance of employees caused by different motivation methods, the paper investigates the influence of corporate environmental protection on the employee motivation. Thus the present societal challenges for companies can be used as an opportunity for a sustainable success in business.

The paper gives an overview of the theoretical concepts of CSR, of corporate environmental management systems, and of employee motivation, as well as presenting the results of a corresponding case study of a bank in Austria, using the theoretical concepts in conjunction with interviews of employees and managers [2].

2 Theoretical approaches

Theoretical concepts relevant for analysing a relationship between CSR and employee motivation are presented. On the one hand stakeholder management and CSR as well as concepts of corporate environmental management, while on the other types and theories of motivation and incentives.

2.1 Stakeholder management

Compared to the shareholder value approach focusing predominantly on the owner of the company, stakeholder management is a much broader approach considering all internal and external economic and social interdependences. Meanwhile it's common knowledge that a good rapport with the stakeholders is essentially for a long-term and sustainable business success [3]. Stakeholders can influence actively the behaviour of a company. As different stakeholders have diverging interests, it's difficult for a company to satisfy all of them. First of all it's essential to identify the relevant stakeholders with their interests and strengths, mainly with the stakeholder analysis, in order to implement these aspects in the company's strategy [4]. A thorough involvement of the stakeholders can minimize the corporate risks possible by CSR. Further an open and transparent relationship to the stakeholders, including the employees, confirms responsible economic activity. By combining CSR and the stakeholder approach, not only can unfavorable effects be avoided, but in fact competitive advantages are created.

2.2 Corporate social responsibility

There are several definitions of CSR, but the key point is a societal responsible business going beyond legal requirements. According to Schneider [5] a final definition of CSR is not possible or useful, as CSR is a "moving issue", a dynamic and for each enterprise individual process.

The European Commission published a new definition of CSR [6] as "the responsibility of enterprises for their impacts on society". Thus companies should have in place an appropriate process for "maximising the creation of shared value for their owners/shareholders and for their other stakeholders and society at large, and for identifying, preventing and mitigating their possible adverse impacts".

For the integration of CSR into the company's strategy a first starting point is the analysis of the supply chain. This helps optimising the social image and increasing the competitiveness of the company. Further a detailed analysis of the range of products is recommended. It's important that CSR is not an *additional* task of the company, but is integrated in the corporate strategy. CSR has to be connected closely to the core business and should be integrated directly in the management of the company [7].

CSR is a controversially discussed concept. The advantages are seen as a win-win concept for the society and the company itself [8]. Further it strengthens the relationship with the stakeholders and has a positive influence on human resource management. CSR supports the employee motivation and their satisfaction, which has a positive effect on the working atmosphere and in consequence on productivity. A more intensive communication culture enables the company to cater to the customer's wishes and needs in a better and more efficient way. Additionally CSR can create new business options and markets, and by that promote innovation. Finally CSR activities can help to improve the environmental and social balance sheet of the company. The voluntariness of the CSR approach is seen as an advantage but also as a disadvantage. Due to the lack of formal regulation, the information to stakeholders is not standardized and therefore a comparison of the CSR performance of different companies is difficult. The feasible misuse of CSR as a marketing strategy is a further issue.

Related concepts for societal responsible management are e.g. sustainable development, sustainable management, and corporate citizenship.

2.3 Corporate environmental management

Corporate environmental management includes all aspects of corporate environmental policy. One definition is that environmental protection is considered in all business processes including planning, implementation and controlling [9]. The business objective environmental protection is set in respect to other business objectives. A definition according to EMAS (eco-management and audit scheme) [10] determines that "environmental management system means the part of the overall management system that includes the organisational structure, planning activities, responsibilities, practices, procedures, processes and resources for developing, implementing, achieving, reviewing and maintaining the environmental policy and managing the environmental aspects".

Corporate environmental management is characterized by four attributes: a multidimensional orientation of the goals, a cross-corporate character, a cross-functional character, and a proactive behaviour.

The most important regulations regarding environmental management systems are ISO 14001 [11] and EMAS.

2.3.1 Environmental management system under DIN EN ISO 14001

In 1993 the first efforts for a standardization system related to environmental protection were achieved by ISO (International Organization for Standardization) of the Business Council for Sustainable Development. In 1996 ISO 14001 was launched and republished as a new, improved version in 2004. EN ISO 14001 has become the international benchmark for environmental management systems, which can be used worldwide by all economic branches, and has been implemented in 138 countries.

The requirements to an environmental management system according to ISO 14001 are defined as a continuously improvement process running through the cycle of planning, implementation, controlling, and improvement.

2.3.2 Environmental management system under EMAS

The European Council adopted the Council Regulation (EEC) No 1836/93 [12], called EMAS, which is legally valid in all member states of the European Union. Companies now have the possibility to voluntarily participate in a standardized environmental management system and audit scheme. EMAS is an environmental management system based on legal regulations, while ISO 14001 is the result of private-sector standardization.

The requirements of ISO 14001 are core components of EMAS. Additionally EMAS calls for an "environmental statement" and special efforts regarding the compliance with all applicable legal requirements relating to the environment, the environmental performance, the external communication and relationships, and the employee involvement.

2.4 Employee motivation

Environmental protection and the concept of CSR can have positive effects to the employee motivation. Emotions, thoughts, awareness and unconscious actions, and automatic reactions are components forming the activity of human beings. A definition of motivation means the useful aspect of a bundling of these activities, which refers to the intensity of the behaviour, the quality and the direction [13]. The motivation provides insights into the motives of acting and behaviour of human beings. Motivation is generated by perceived stimulation conditions, which is the pre-requirement for target-oriented behaviour.

Motivation is a hypothetical creation, which means that the intervening variable between personal circumstances and observable behaviour is hardly or not directly measurable. But it is possible to observe input and output of the behaviour of an employee directly, which enables an empirical investigation.

2.4.1 Types of motivation

In general it is distinguished between intrinsic and extrinsic motivation [14]. The latter cannot only be satisfied by the work or its environment, but by the result of the performance on the job. We know monetary motives, security motives and status motives. In the context of management, intrinsic motivation means that the motives of an employee can be satisfied by the work itself. It's differentiated between performance motives, competence motives, and sociality motives.

2.4.2 Theories of motivation

Motivation is an important topic in management and different theoretical approaches have been developed. Each theory concentrates on a different key aspect, distinguishing in content theories and process theories. The latter analyses, how motivation influences the behaviour, while the content theory focuses on the question, what generates motivation? We present the ideas of some of the most important motivation theories.

2.4.2.1 Maslow's hierarchy of needs This is a content theory and one of the oldest and renowned motivation theories worldwide. According to Maslow [15] the needs of human beings can be explained by five basic needs. First the physiological needs as a precondition for survival, like sleep, hunger and thirst. Second the personal safety regarding a secure livelihood and physical threats. Social affiliation is at the next level of Maslow's hierarchy of needs including love, friendship and partnership. These are followed by self-esteem, which means the personal feelings of achievement, and the need for recognition. On the top of the hierarchy we find the self-actualisation, like self-fulfillment and realisation of the own potential.

Under Maslow's hierarchy of needs the higher needs occur only when the respective lower need is satisfied.

2.4.2.2 Herzberg's two-factor-theory This theory is a content theory, as well. Herzberg [16] stated that job dissatisfaction and job satisfaction are not two specifications of one characteristic, but have to be considered as two independent variables. The two variables are the hygiene factors, showing the dissatisfaction, and the motivators, showing the job satisfaction. Hygiene factors can avoid dissatisfaction, but they cannot contribute to satisfaction (e.g. payment, personnel management policy, relationships between colleagues). Employees take these factors for granted, in case they are missing, it's perceived as a deficit. Compared to that, motivators can produce satisfaction. Motivators are related more to the job content than to job conditions (e.g. recognition, performance and success, responsibility, individual development).

By this theory Herzberg shows that on the one hand people look for development and self-actualisation, but on the other hand they try to avoid pain and reluctance. Compared to Maslow's theory, the two-factor-theory is empirically verified.

2.4.2.3 Vroom's expectancy theory Nowadays this theory [17] is the basis for all newer process theories. By means of this theory the dynamic of motivation processes in the organisational context can be demonstrated. People are more motivated acting in a specific manner, the more they expect a result from their individual action to be to their own benefit. Therefore the motivation depends on the characteristics of the personality of the employee, and the factors of the situation.

The theory can explain the most essential aspects of the employee motivation process, depending crucial on the combination of the organisational and individual goals.

2.4.2.4 Adams' equity theory This theory is also a process theory, and is based on balance thinking. Employees expect a fair compensation for their work. Adams [18] defines the inputs of the employee as education, intelligence, talents, loyalty, hard work and the outputs such as job security, esteem, salary, recognition, reputation, or responsibility. The comparison with the colleagues is important. The importance of determining motivation as a relative factor – on the basis of individual perception – is emphasised.

The validation of the equity theory, mainly concerning the salary, shows good results. One finding is the comparison with colleagues. A perceived imbalance can lead to a motivation to create the desired balance.

2.5 Incentives

As soon as a company grants immaterial or material compensations to people who are willing to contribute with time and other resources to the company objective, we talk about incentives [19].

The motivated behaviour of an employee can be activated for a concrete goal. If this goal is achieved, satisfaction arises. But each employee has different needs. Each behaviour or performance of an employee is connected to situational incentives. The incentives have an essential impact on the realisation of his or her motives. But before an employee is willing to make an effort to provide a specific performance, he or she balances up the compensation for his or her effort. We can understand this compensation as the incentive. Each behaviour of an employee is caused by a motive, and employees and their motives are influenced strongly by subjective perceived incentives. Additionally, motives of employees can change over time, e.g. the motive "reputation by hard work" can change to "more time for the family".

2.5.1 Types of incentives
This part gives a brief overview of the different types of incentives.

2.5.1.1 Material and immaterial incentives Material incentives are of monetary nature in the context of the job performance of the employee, like salary, bonuses, commissions, fringe benefits and profit sharing. Immaterial incentives are related to the job content and the work task of the employee, like self-fulfillment, social contacts and status, leadership, responsibility, and personal development.

2.5.1.2 Incentives of the organisational environment These are the incentives of the entire environment of the organisation, perceived by the employee, and their influences on his or her willingness for performance and his or her satisfaction. Examples are the corporate culture, working atmosphere, and corporate concepts for environmental protection. For the latter it's essential that the employees can actually perceive them in their working environment. Corporate environmental protection has to be implemented, theoretical concepts themselves and lip services cannot stimulate incentives. This approach shows the importance of the connection between corporate concepts and corporate culture.

2.5.1.3 Incentive corporate culture The corporate culture reflects the values of the company internally as well as externally. A corporate culture with strong expressions of characteristics, with which employees can identify themselves, is a primarily positive motivation factor.

2.5.2 Incentive corporate environmental protection

According to the theories of incentives, corporate environmental protection can be classified as an incentive for employees, as far as the concept is adequately communicated and perceptible. If a company lives a well-developed corporate culture concerning environmental protection and sustainability, this can work as a motivation for employees.

Higher output through shared values between the company and the employees is one option for the influence of corporate environmental protection on the employee motivation. Due to an overlapping of the values of a corporate environmental protection concept with the values and expectations of the employees, a shared value is created. This can contribute to higher performance or willingness for performance of employees, and consequently increase the output of the company.

Another option is the increase of a company's attractiveness for qualified and motivated new employees, because of the incorporation of corporate environmental protection. Intrinsic motives of jobseekers can be activated.

3 Empirical study

The theoretical basis will now be applied on a practical example. A bank has been selected as a case study object.

3.1 Kommunalkredit Austria AG

Established as a specialist bank in 1958 to provide low-interest, long-term loans for Austrian local authorities, Kommunalkredit Austria AG today operates as its strategic core business in the field of public infrastructure finance and municipal project, focused on local authorities, municipalities, provincial governments and public institutions [20]. The bank's profile of services covers a broad range, from project consulting, budget management and asset management consulting to a wide variety of financing services. Kommunalkredit Austria AG leads projects in social infrastructure, energy, environment and transport to sustainable success. The company has approximately 300 employees.

3.2 Census questionnaire

Beside an intensive secondary analysis of documents concerning existing concepts and procedures, the main instrument of analysis was a survey. The questionnaire comprised twenty standardized (rating scales) and two open questions. The questionnaire covered all CSR related topics in order to find out, whether the activities of the company somehow influence the job motivation of the employees of the Kommunalkredit Austria AG or not.

3.3 Findings

The case study has shown that the company supports the environment with several entrepreneurial concepts. Hereinafter we will show if and to what extent this environmental and CSR related concepts, have an influence on the employees and their motivation.

3.3.1 Corporate CSR policy and the consideration of sustainability in managerial processes

As a public sector company, the Kommunalkredit Austria AG has a role model function regarding social and environmental values. The sustainability policy of the company includes important environmental protection principles for achieving and holding long term success and healthy economic growth. As the survey has shown this attitude was transferred to the employees and became part of the corporate culture and is certainly reflected in the corporate mission statement with the following wording:

> "Our actions determine the holistic mental activity, i.e. the considerate and ecological aspects, the environmental compatibility and ethical criteria."

As long ago as 1997, EMAS (Environmental Management and Audit Scheme), an environmental management system had been introduced into the company. Based on this system a comprehensive sustainability management concept has been established. Since 2004 the company has published annual sustainability reports. For the bank and its employees this sustainability management system is not only an advertising tool but an embodiment for the whole organisational structure. Everybody, i.e. every employee is part of the system. This means, that sustainability in operations and a general corporate behaviour that adheres high corporate social responsibility standards are accepted at all levels of the company. According to the results of the survey employees live these CSR related values throughout their individual actions and take personal responsibility to achieve the goals.

3.3.2 Energy and climate protection

Renewable energies accounted about 65% of overall energy consumption in 2010. Kommunalkredit Austria AG uses "green" electricity since 2003. "Green" electricity means, that the electricity is powered by "Naturstrom Plus" of Alpen Adria Energy AG. Naturstrom Plus is certified with the Austrian ecolabel. It is made up of 69% micro-hydro power plant, 30% wind and biogas electricity and 1% photovoltaic electricity.

For heat generation a wood pellets based heating system is in use. Advantages of the wood pellets based heating system are the reduction of CO_2 emissions, a reduction of the greenhouse effect, as well as the stable price of the wood pellets in comparison to the oil price over the last years.

3.3.3 Business trips and CO_2 consumption

Like most other companies, Kommunalkredit Austria AG generates unavoidable CO_2 emissions (primarily by business trips and heating). For this reason the Kommunalkredit Austria AG compensates these emissions by sticking to the procedures of Climate Austria. "*Climate Austria is a cooperation devoted to the voluntary offsetting of CO_2 emissions. This is achieved by investing your voluntary contribution in climate protection projects, primarily in Austria and, upon request, also abroad*". In this context CO_2 compensation means that in the ideal case per ton CO_2 emission caused by a company climate protection projects should be supported which avoid CO_2 emissions on the same extent.

Remarkable in this context are the "business bicycles". The company provides bikes for its employees (several normal bikes and one e-bike). The idea was born from a working group on "sustainability in every day working life". Members of this group suggested business bicycles be introduced for fast, healthy and environment-friendly work related journeys. This idea was adopted and implemented and has contributed to a culture where the car is left behind for short business trips.

3.3.4 Resource, waste and recycling management

Copy and printing paper in Kommunalkredit Austria AG are 100% recyclable. All-in-one printers are used to reduce the wastage of paper. Additionally all of these printers have a default setting double-sided print only.

Further we have identified the following environmental friendly policies: the company uses environmentally friendly stationary only and the same applies to advertising material. For company events fair trade products are used exclusively.

The recycling and waste management system had been identified as a weakness, but the waste management system has been modernised recently (shortly after our study had been conducted).

3.3.5 The staff's position

Company activities on environmental protection and CSR are not only important from an ethical or to put it more pragmatic from a PR point of view it is important to the employees as well. If a company takes responsibility for its action e.g. in the environmental field the staff members transfer this attitude to other fields and regard the company as more thrust worthy. Therefore corporate concepts of environmental protection have a great impact on the motivation of a company's employees. The survey has also shown, that even job applicants are influenced by the CSR related behaviour of their future company.

Shared values concerning environmental protection, sustainability and corporate social responsibility have a highly motivating effect on the employees. It is important that entrepreneurs know, that they should be aware of this effect. By acting sustainable a company can generate an additional immaterial value for its employees. Employees are extremely interested in how their company is behaving in these fields and they acknowledge appropriate actions. We can say that according to our investigation environmental protection is a particular concern to the employees of the Kommunalkredit Austria AG and therefore we can confirm a positive relationship between acting environmentally sound and highly motivated staff members.

4   Conclusion

The empirical study revealed that environmental protection, sustainable management and corporate social responsibility in general are of particular importance for a modern company. These issues have a major importance for the employees and therefore a positive impact on the motivation of a company's staff.

Sustainable management and acting according to CSR values in general influences the external and internal image of a company as well as its corporate culture. Assessing the motivation theories, incentives of the organisational field and the corporate culture play a very important role for the employees. Companies which are aware of these facts can create a positive impact on their staff. It might be reasonably assumed that a reduction or a rejection of that corporate environmental protection produces an employee's discouragement.

Activities concerning environment protection and sustainability are often very cost-intensive. Therefore the company has to do everything to get a return on these investments. Often these returns are not of a financial nature, the enhanced employee motivation is certainly such a non-financial return. Therefore companies have to put high effort on emphasising environmental related topics in internal communications. The employees must know about these activities and have to recognize their value. Otherwise the positive impacts on employee motivation cannot be utilized.

Based on the example of Kommunalkredit Austria AG it could be demonstrated that the sustainability, environmental protection and corporate social responsibility are not only euphemisms. Employees take these issues very serious. The corporation's environmental protection measures regularly have positive effects on the employees of this particular company. Employees feel more comfortable and need not to have a bad conscience towards the environment if the company acts environmentally sound and communicates to its staff members accordingly. Acting according to the principles of sustainable management and CSR is an important input which a company's management can provide to its personnel. The result is an increase of the employee's motivation.

References

[1] Pölzl, U., *Umwelt-Controlling für Industriebetriebe*, Dissertation, Graz, 1992.

[2] Bartik, D., Der Einfluss von unternehmerischen Umweltschutzkonzepten in Form von Coporate Social Responsibility auf die Motivation von MitarbeiterInnen am Beispiel der Kommunalkredit Austria, Thesis, Vienna, 2011.

[3] Crane A., Matten D., Laura J., *Corporate Social Responsibility, a global context,* Routledge, New York, 2008.

[4] Frederick, W.C. et al., Business and Society: Corporate Strategy, Public Policy, Ethics, 7th ed., McGraw Hill, 1992.

[5] Schneider, A., Reifegradmodell CSR – eine Begriffsklärung und - abgrenzung, in: Schneider, A., Schmidpeter, R. (eds.), *Corporate Social Responsibility*, Springer Gabler, Berlin Heidelberg, 2012.

[6] European Commission, A renewed EU strategy 2011-14 for Corporate Social Responsibility, COM (2011) 681 final, Brussels, 2011.

[7] Porter, M., Kramer, M.R., Corporate Social Responsibility, *Harvard Business Manager*, 29, 1-16, 2007.

[8] Ernste, D., Marktwirtschaft und Moral. Eine ordnungsethische Reflexion, Instituts-Verlag GmbH, Köln, 2007.

[9] Engelfried, J., *Nachhaltiges Umweltmanagement*, Oldenburg Wissenschaftsverlag GmbH, München, 2011.

[10] European Commission, Regulation (EC) No 1221/2009 of the European Parliament and of the Council of 25 November 2009 on the voluntary participation by organisations in a Community eco-management and audit scheme (EMAS), repealing Regulation (EC) No 761/2001 and Commission Decisions 2001/681/EC and 2006/193/EC, *Official Journal of the European Communities*, 2009.

[11] International Organisation for Standardization, *ISO 14001:2004, Environmental management systems – requirements with guidance for use*, http://www.iso.org/iso/home/store/catalogue_ics/catalogue_detail_ics.htm?csnumber=31807

[12] European Council, Council Regulation (EEC) No 1836/93 of 29 June 1993, allowing voluntary participation by companies in the industrial sector in a Community eco-management and audit scheme, *Official Journal of the European Communities*, 1993.

[13] Kaspar, H., Mayrhofer, W., *Personalmanagement Führung Organisation*, Linde Verlag, Wien, 2009.

[14] Hungenberg, H., Wulf, T., *Grundlagen der Unternehmensführung*, Springer Verlag, Berlin, Heidelberg, New York, 2007.

[15] Maslow, A.H., *A Theory of Human Motivation*, CreateSpace Independent Publishing Platform, 2013.

[16] Herzberg, F., *One More Time: How Do You Motivate Employees?*, McGraw-Hill Professional, 2008.

[17] Vroom, V. H., Manage people, not personnel: motivation and performance appraisal, Harvard Business School Press, 1990.
[18] Adams, J.S., Inequity in social exchange, *Advances in Experimental Social Psychology*, 62:335-343, 1965.
[19] Rosenstiel, L., *Motivation im Betrieb. Mit Fallstudien aus der Praxis*, Rosenberger Fachverlag, Leonberg, 2001.
[20] Climate Austria, https://www.climateaustria.at/en/home/, 2013.

Technical collaboration in international environmental assessment projects: a case study of the UNEP Environmental Assessment of Ogoniland Project

I. I. Kakulu[1], M. J. Cowing[2] & B. B. Fakae[1]
[1]Rivers State University of Science and Technology, Nigeria
[2]United Nations Environment Programme, PCDMB, Geneva

Abstract

Environmental Assessment projects range from very simple local projects involving the investigation of a single site to large and more complex international projects involving multiple locations; investigating multiple environmental media; and executed by a multi-cultural project management team. In the case of a post impact assessment survey, the goal is to gain access to impacted sites; collect relevant data; analyse the data and produce a report. In real life situations however, such a simple description does not match the complexity of the process as observed in actual field operations. The socio-economic and socio-cultural environment in which a project takes place presents its own challenges to a project management team and an understanding of the expectations of local community which is a key success indicator. In the absence of working knowledge and understanding of local expectations, complex international projects may depend on joint working relationships between independent bodies in the form of collaborative partnerships to achieve their set goals. Using this approach, the planning and implementation of the project's activities becomes joint responsibility of the partners and which may lead to the creation of new organizational structures and new implementation processes. This paper reviews the Technical Collaboration Partnership between the Post Conflict and Disaster Management (PCDMB) of the United Nations Environment Programme (UNEP) and the Rivers State University of Science and Technology (RSUST), Nigeria in the Environmental Assessment of Ogoniland Project, in Nigeria (2009 to 2011). The review adopts a philosophical framework

WIT Transactions on Ecology and The Environment, Vol 173, © 2013 WIT Press
www.witpress.com, ISSN 1743-3541 (on-line)
doi:10.2495/SDP130061

that is grounded in phenomenology; a qualitative case-study research strategy and participant observation as the primary data collection method including content analysis of field notes. The findings indicate changes to normative operational procedures as a result of the partnership and recommends replication of this approach in similar international EIA projects, particularly in developing countries.

Keywords: environmental assessment, project management, technical collaboration, EIA, Partnerships, socioeconomics, international projects, Ogoniland Project.

1 Introduction

In July 2006, the United Nations Environment Programme (UNEP) received a formal request from the Federal Government of Nigeria (FGN) to carry out a comprehensive assessment of the environmental and public health impacts of oil contamination in the four Local Government Areas (LGSs) of Ogoniland, and to suggest options for remediation and clean-up. Following protracted delays to the smooth take-off of the project; in excess of two years, the UNEP led Environmental Assessment of Ogoniland Project, otherwise called The "UNEP Ogoniland Project" effectively took off on a formal note with a training workshop held at the Rivers State University of Science and Technology (RSUST) on the 12th of October, 2009. The mandate and scope of the project was the assessment of soil contamination, groundwater contamination, surface water and sediment contamination in the creeks; adverse impacts on ecosystem due to oil related pollution from oil field infrastructure and activities. Other aspects of the study included exploration of potential changes to surface hydrology, vegetation; potential changes in agricultural productivity and fisheries due to contamination of soil, surface water and groundwater; possible impacts to public health and property due to oil field fires. In February 2010, UNEP entered into a Project Cooperation Agreement (PCA), RSUST-Department of Estate Management (RSUST/EM), for the purpose of *providing support services* in respect of the "UNEP Environmental Survey of Ogoniland, Nigeria". Collaborative activities which were jointly identified at the onset of the cooperation formed the basis of the services which RSUST/EM rendered in support of the Project which forms the basis of this case study. The PCA with RSUST/EM was executed following UNEP's recognition of RSUST as one of the leading academic institutions in the Niger Delta with regards to natural resources management and land access – two paramount issues, which had to be adequately addressed in order for the Ogoniland Assessment Project to succeed.

The cooperation allowed the parties to transfer skills and competencies related to the project as well as general capacity building in the field of sustainable management of natural resources. With the endorsement and operation of the PCA, RSUST/EM became the primary project implementation partner of UNEP during the "UNEP Ogoniland Project. Throughout the project, UNEP relied on RSUST/EM as its instrumental partner who facilitated interactions between various stakeholders of the project namely; the UNEP project management team; government entities; academic institutions; MOSOP; NGOs and local communities in Ogoniland. RSUST experts participated in various thematic areas which were led by UNEP International Experts according to individual qualifications, skills and expertise. Adhering to the multifaceted Terms-of-Reference (see section 3.3), RSUST provided the required support and assistance in virtually all aspects of the project, and where necessary, engaged staff of other relevant institutions like the Rivers State Polytechnic and the University of Port Harcourt to facilitate the work.

2 Literature review

2.1 Collaborative partnerships

Collaboration can take the form of joint ventures in the business world (Rounthwaite and Shell [1]) and it offers several advantages by bringing several perspectives to the discussion. Liyanage and Mitchell (1994) (cited in Pecas and Henriques [2]) refer that collaboration between academia and industry remains dependent upon cultural, organizational and management characteristics of the organizations involved in the process. Depending on the type of project, there is not one common definition of success. It is based on what a project has set out in its aim and objectives and more importantly, recognizing the fact that different people may judge the same project to be successful or unsuccessful (Turner [3]). Collaborative business relationships including strategic alliances, joint ventures, clusters and consortia are popular mechanisms for dealing with resource constraints, accelerating technological advancement (Palakshappa and Gordon [4]) amongst other benefits. Hamel (1991) (cited in Palakshappa and Gordon [4]), conducted a study to understand the extent to which collaboration could lead to a redistribution of skills among partners and identified three important determinants of learning within collaborative relationships: intent, transparency and receptivity. The intention or purpose of establishing the collaboration, the level of transparency of skills of either partner and the openness of each organization in the partnership to learn from each other are all vital in the overall success of a collaborative partnership. According to (Shelbourn et al. [5]), there are many factors that are likely to influence the success or failure of working collaboratively and it is important to realize that no two collaborations progress in exactly the same way. However the peculiarities of each particular project can provide learning outcomes for replication. (Shelbourn et al. [5]), recognize six key areas as being critical in collaboration, as vision; trust, stakeholder engagement; communication; process and technologies. Information sharing is also recognized as a key requirement for collaborative interorganizational relationships (Sheu et al. [6]). According to Doz and Hamel (1998) (cited in Ingirige and Sexton [7]), alliances provide opportunities for individuals terms and firms to gain mutual benefit from sharing skills and resources.

The objectives of collaborative partnerships for each party can be quite different. In academia, collaborative partnerships with industry or other organizations are viewed as rich sources of information for further research and academic publications. The success of collaborations between companies and universities (Sampson, 2007) (cited in Philbin [8]), can be highly contingent on the performance of information flow between the collaborators. Collaboration requires individual participants to adopt simplified standardized solutions based on common architectures and data models (Horvath [9]). Usually, collaboration enables participants to build capacity to complete a set of tasks that one sole organization would find difficult to achieve. To be successful, collaboration must be robust and correctly focused. Alliances such as that between UNEP and RSUST/EM are voluntary initiated cooperative agreements that involve exchange (Ingirige and Sexton [7]), sharing, or co-development. The UNEP Ogoniland Project by design and execution was a complex project and the fundamental principles of project management where at work throughout its duration. It benefited immensely from collaborative partnerships using an innovative approach that can be replicated to other similar project scenarios. In the field of Project Management, projects are successfully delivered through a process which involves contributions and participation of several parties. In order for a project to succeed, there are two components of project success, project success criteria and project success factors.

2.2 Project success criteria

Project success criteria refer to the qualitative and quantitative measures against which a project is judged to be successful and are dependent variables by which success is judged. Success criteria include the fact that it gives satisfaction to the financiers; achieves its purpose; satisfies the project owner, sponsors; customers and users as well as the project team. Project success factors on the other hand, are those elements which can be influenced to ensure the chance of a successful outcome and are independent variables through which we influence the achievement of project success. The critical success factors in the Ogoniland Project can be linked to its project management structure (Kakulu et al. [10]) and the use of partnerships. When managers contemplate entering into a partnership arrangement (Trim and Lee [11]), they need to think in terms of what constitute critical factors. Compatibility, commitment, communications and common aims (Lawton Smith and Dickson, 2003) (cited in Trim and Lee [11]), can constitute critical factors. One of the strengths in entering into partnerships is that a hybrid organizational structure is formed that is distinct and different from the initial separate groups of persons who come together to form the partnership. Collaborative partnerships benefit from the merging of ideas and experiences and formation of new organizational cultures. New partners (Trim and Lee [11]) bring with them different types of information that can lead to a broadening of an organizations scope and organizational value systems merge thus promoting temporary change in identity of an organization during the period of the partnership.

3   A case study on the UNEP Ogoniland Project

3.1 Methodology

A case study methodology was used and in-depth review of the collaborative partnership between RSUST and UNEP in the UNEP Ogoniland Project. Practical outcomes of the collaboration and prospects for replication in the future are also highlighted. Flowing from the terms-of-reference establishing the cooperation between UNEP and RSUST/EM through to its completion, there are learning outcomes which this paper seeks to highlight. Data is grounded in a series of project review meetings and progress reports which the authors contributed to as participants. Thus participant observation is the main data collection strategy adopted in this study.

3.2 The Ogoniland Project

Between October 2009 and August 2011, UNEP conducted a scientific assessment of Ogoniland and collected in excess of 4000 samples from more than 200 sites in the disciplines of contaminated land, forestry and agriculture, fisheries and the aquatic environment, socio-economics and public health. Extensive use was made of satellite images, photographs, interviews, physical samples backed by laboratory analysis and expert data management and analysis to build a picture of the state and extent of oil pollution in the area including historical impacts on health impact of drinking water, impact on livelihoods, depth and spatial extent of contamination as well as interactions between these phenomena. The UNEP project team surveyed 122 kms of pipeline rights of way and visited all oil spill sites, oil wells and other oil-related facilities in Ogoniland, including decommissioned and abandoned facilities, that were known and accessible to UNEP during the fieldwork period, based on information provided by the Government regulators, Shell Petroleum Development Company (Nigeria) Ltd (SPDC) and community members in and around Ogoniland (UNEP [12]).

The UNEP Ogoniland Project involved fieldwork using multi-disciplinary scientific teams which carried out site assessment and collected samples of water, soil, sediment, air quality, plant and animal tissue followed by laboratory analysis. Many stakeholders were involved in the project, including Nigerian officials at the Federal and Rivers State level, traditional rulers and chairmen of the four Ogoni local government areas, women and youth leaders, land holders, universities, polytechnics, NGOs, health Centres' and laboratories. The project was undertaken by UNEP with assistance from the United Nations Development Programme (UNDP). The project funding was negotiated to ensure the independence and integrity of the assessment. In line with the polluter-pays principle, the government, the Shell Petroleum Development Company (SPDC) of Nigeria and UNEP agreed the US$9.5 million project cost would be borne by SPDC (a joint venture between the government, Shell International, Elf/Total and Agip). A Presidential Implementation Committee (PIC) monitored the project while a Community Consultation Committee (CCC) advised UNEP project team and articulated inputs/concerns from the local communities. The CCC also served as a bridge between the people and UNEP.

Extensive preparation, which included frequent consultation with local communities, served to build trust between the multi-national assessment teams and the Ogoni people. The assessment findings were published in a report on August 4th (see http://www.unep.org/nigeria/), which was generally well received despite its hard-hitting nature. In fact, the UNEP assessment has been extolled as a cost-effective alternative to the adversarial approach used in similar complex situations where communities, environment and corporate interests are seemingly inextricably entangled: *"the UNEP Report is a brilliant model for fact-finding, whatever the fate of its grand proposals. Funded by Shell Nigeria but conducted by the U.N. with peer scientific review, the 14-month, $10 million, 4000-sample UNEP Report took a fraction of the time and money of the adversarial assessment conducted by Chevron and its foes in Ecuador, and— miracle of miracles—yielded authoritative results".*

The American Lawyer August 31, 2011

3.3 Nature of the cooperation between UNEP and RSUST

An extensive, complex and multifaceted project cooperation agreement (PCA) was executed between UNEP and RSUST/EM and the implementation of the UNEP Ogoniland Project. Extracts from the Terms-of-Reference (TORs) are outlined below as follows:

1. Applying the use of local expertise and knowledge to provide UNEP's project management (PM) team with political, institutional and social guidance and advice; identification and interface with relevant community groups and NGOs operational within the Ogoni communities and participation in the initial "ground-truthing" exercise.

2. Assisting with negotiating land access; participation in technical meetings with UNEP's PM team and project specialists for designing the field assessment work and with the provision of field training and workshops for UNEP's national staff and staff from national counterpart institutions.

3. Production of desk studies, relating to areas impacted by oil exploration and production and the establishment of base-line data from selected sites not previously impacted by oil exploration and production operations; design and execution of some of the technical protocols used for undertaking the scientific study in a few RSUST led sectors; and the quantifying and identifying the geographical extent of contamination/impact from oil exploration and production activities within all relevant media.

4. Assist UNEP with the assessment of the changes in biodiversity and productivity within the agricultural and fisheries sectors; undertaking of, public health and case study interviews; designing and implementing several awareness-raising initiatives to reach all sections of local

society; provision of periodic input to UNEP communication team and participation in regular community consultation committee meetings.

5. Provision of sampling support and logistics to convey the students to the field on a daily basis; engagement of local youth to work with the university team on a daily basis and provision of security personnel and additional police to cover routine operational and field activities; provision of support to community nominated representatives that were present during all field activities and the "sample custodians" who were charged with collecting, packing and shipping field samples to laboratories abroad as well as laboratory services for Soil Microbiology analysis.

6. Provision of regular and periodic feedback to the UNEP project management team on the progress against the ToRs.

These activities were implemented over the life of the project and some of them are explained in more detail in subsequent sections.

4 Collaboration activities

4.1 Political, institutional and social guidance

RSUST facilitated the interface between UNEP's Project Management Team and the Rivers State Government; the traditional rulers, Local Government Chairmen, and other stakeholders. Through continuous dialogue, the application of local knowledge and the experience of the RSUST team, several potential conflict areas were avoided. RSUST visible presence at all town-hall and public meetings improved the overall receptivity of the Ogoni's as well as the Government and people of Rivers State. The UNEP Project Management team initiated a standing Community Consultation Committee (CCC) to deepen and enhance the active participation of key stakeholders and partners. The CCC was a monthly forum for open discussion and exchange of ideas, including concerns from stakeholder constituencies, advice to UNEP and make recommendations to the Presidential Implementation Committee (PIC) – the principal decision making body of UNEP Environmental Assessment of Ogoniland Project. RSUST/EM was very active in the CCC and was well represented. In several cases, the RSUST team undertook and led high-powered "Door-Opening" missions that averted several bureaucratic stalemates and bottlenecks that arose in the course of the project. RSUST project team members participated in weekly and routine and technical project meetings. Several suggestions, constructive criticisms and useful contributions were made on a regular basis from the University team to UNEP's project management team and international experts, whenever or wherever this was required at every stage throughout the life of the project.

4.2 Training workshops desk studies and establishment of baseline data

RSUST collaborated in several training workshops throughout Ogoniland the project life span. An initial inaugural workshop was held to prepare the team for the ground-truthing and Reconnaissance phase of the project. A four-day 'Sampling Methodologies' workshop which involved wider international and national participation ahead of the Sampling Phase. Sampling Field Training was organized jointly by UNEP and RSUST for the students who were recruited to work with the contaminated land team as sampling field assistants. An end-of-project workshop held in December, 2010 which marked the official end of the sampling phase. The national experts on the RSUST team produced a number of desk studies thus bringing to bear a significant amount of local knowledge to the international team, in exchange for the wealth of experience and skills possessed by the internationals. The desk studies covered contaminated land, biodegradation of oil and oil products; long-term effect of spilled crude in several places. The hydrology in the Ogoni Section of the Niger Delta and the Hydrogeology of the Niger Delta formed part of the desk studies. Also covered in the desk studies was a summary of literature on large and complex oil spills in the Niger delta. The Ministry of Water Resources and rural development also provided a baseline survey of drinking water sources while RSUST national experts provided a meteorological review of Ogoniland and existing information on air quality. Desk studies on public health from part of the collaboration. The land ownership structure; use of water bodies and fishing rights in the study area 4 Ogoni LGAs was also documented. An interview report on the Social structure of Kings and Chiefs of the Ogoni People was also conducted. Desk study reports on fisheries, forestry and agriculture were compiled by both the RSUST fisheries; forestry and agriculture expert teams. These desk studies provided useful insight at the commencement of the project. Working closely with the international experts and using RSUST laboratory facilities and local knowledge, RSUST expert teams identified sites and selected sites not previously impacted by oil exploration and production operations. Sites in Okwale, Oyigbo and outside Rivers State were identified. Health reports and federal government health statistics were provided where needed in support of the field teams.

4.3 Geo-referencing and awareness raising

In the absence of detailed land use maps RSUST teams visited and geo-referenced hundreds of community wells and drinking water sources in the 4 Ogoni LGAs. Places of interest were also identified and geo-referenced and all the gathered information fed into the project database. UNEP data management team verified this data which was used to update different project maps. One of the success factors of the UNEP Ogoniland Project was effective communication with the local communities, traditional rulers, key stakeholders, the federal and Rivers State governments and their agencies, and partners both horizontally and vertically. The RSUST team provided invaluable inputs to shape the content and context of the UNEP's communication tool. In addition, the RSUST team worked productively with UNEP's Geneva Communications Unit, UNEP's Communications Adviser (Port Harcourt), the 4 UNEP CLAs for the 4 Ogoni LGAs, and especially with local youths whose capacities were transformed and strengthened and who helped in creating awareness and acceptance for the project in the communities.

4.4 RSUST expert teams and activities

Land access constituted one of the paramount issues which needed to be adequately addressed in order for the UNEP Ogoniland assessment project to succeed. RSUST Land Access Team (LAT) members participated in the development of a community entry strategy involving a logical step-by-step procedure for community entry during both the ground-truthing and sampling phases of the project, see (Kakulu and Nuhu [13]). Working closely with the UNEP project management team, the "field entry strategy" was developed to ensure unhindered access to oil spill sites, carry out necessary assessment and collect samples for laboratory analysis. The strategy for field entry involved a four-step field work procedure in order to allow for smooth transition and flow of field activities as well as guarantee zero-conflict in the communities, especially among landholders and areas where there are existing land disputes. The community entry protocol was based on an understanding of the traditional land access practices in Ogoniland. Thus, the role of RSUST LAT in the scientific study was very critical to the entire team's entry to spill sites in Ogoniland. LAT members, negotiated with appropriate community contact persons, youth leaders thus ensuring that the UNEP teams could gain access to the contaminated sites for assessment, and made all required financial compensation relating to site access and site clearance in a professional manner. Members of the Land Access Team also assisted in the verification and updating of the remote sensing material and maps, produced by UNEP experts.

The RSUST Contamination Land Team participated in the collection of soil, sediment and water samples for laboratory analysis. The team assisted in collecting soil, water samples and sediment samples from the field for shipment to various laboratories (international and national,) for analysis. The Fisheries and Aquatic Team assisted and supported the UNEP studies in collecting water and marine samples. They also as offered quality advice on the species of fish in Ogoniland and those that have been adversely affected by oil spills based on previous studies in the Niger Delta. The RSUST Public Health team provided useful practical health and safety tips that guided UNEP's field missions throughout the project. The team also facilitated field visits of the public health and air quality thematic group as well as accessing records in target healthcare centres and hospitals in the 4 Ogoni LGAs and within Port Harcourt City and its environs. They also assisted the UNEP team in organizing and arranging records collected from hospitals and healthcare centres into manageable data for analysis. With tremendous theoretical and practical experience, the RSUST Forestry and Agricultural Team provided UNEP's international and national staff/consultants with relevant background literature and useful advice on plants and livestock in Ogoniland and in the Niger Delta. They assisted the UNEP team to source and collect hundreds of plants and livestock samples in contaminated areas of Ogoniland and elsewhere in neighbouring Imo State for control-samples. Also, the tissues of these plants and livestock samples were analysed by experts in relevant laboratories at the RSUST.

4.5 Data management, topography survey and sampling support activities

RSUST played a lead role in the topographical survey to establish the elevations of drilled water quality monitoring wells, managed the logistics of this activity and established the ground elevations for 142 water monitoring wells. RSUST worked with consultants and were in the field to cover all sampling activities during which they worked closely with the UNEP Community Liaison Assistants (CLAs), community contact persons and identified five to six local labours from the community to work alongside the students. RSUST provided a team of 3 (three) sample Custodians who worked with the UNEP sampling team. The sample custodians, who were office based, were fully involved in sample management activities. They received samples from the field teams, documented the samples and prepared them for shipment. Samples were packed and labelled, and Chain of Custody forms were also prepared. The sample custodians were also responsible for preparing de-ionized water and ensuring that there was sufficient quantity to go into the field on a daily basis. All samples (soil, sediment, water, air quality, plant and animal tissues, etc.) collected in the field were sent to internationally accredited laboratories for analysis.

5 Benefits of the collaboration

In the area of collaboration, the Ogoniland Project provided ample opportunity for knowledge exchange between the partners. Working with a large team of counterparts, the international experts could focus on bringing their skills and expertise to the table without being distracted by issues which were possibly better handled by the national experts. From an academic perspective, the authors can confirm that the collaboration and the involvement of several persons from within the university has opened up new frontiers of research and academic publications. Collaboration calls for a merging of ideas and a great deal of flexibility is required. The flexibility on the part of UNEP led to the initiation of pilot studies on livestock sampling and analysis. Pilot surveys were conducted in each of the four Ogoni LGAs and it is expected that following extensive peer review, the findings will be disseminated as academic publications in conferences and through academic journals. Pilot studies were also conducted on the perception of local farmers on the effect of long term soil contamination on their farming practices (see Kakulu and Nuhu [13]).

6 Conclusion

The UNEP Ogoniland Project within the context of project success, achieved its purpose in the production of a credible environmental assessment report with strong recommendations for clean-up and remediation. The project success factors included the setting up of Technical collaboration partnerships with local institutions which facilitated knowledge exchange between the International team and national experts which this paper addresses. Collaborative partnerships provide an opportunity for acquiring new skills and competencies through participation in a relationship. The purpose of the collaboration was clearly one of knowledge transfer and this was achieved by both parties in the collaboration. The training workshops provided ample opportunity for learning new skills and this was further enhanced by actual participation on daily field activities. While the picture may appear somewhat rosy in the end, the initial friction between parties holding on to their convictions was very challenging to the project management team. Subsequently however, with the merging of ideas and several project briefings and meetings, grey areas became sorted which allowed gradual refinement of the process. Replication of this pattern of international collaboration is strongly recommended by the authors who were also participant observers.

Acknowledgement

The support of the School of Real Estate and Planning, Henley Business School, University of Reading, United Kingdom is hereby acknowledged.

References

[1] Rounthwaite, Tony, and Ian Shell. "Designing Quality Partnerships." *The TQM Magazine*, 1995.

[2] Pecas, P, and E Henriques. "Best practices of collaboration between University and industrial SMEs." *Benchmarking*, pp. 54–67, 2006.

[3] Turner, Rodney J. "Project Success and Strategy." In *Gower Handbook of Project Management*, 871. Aldershot: Gower, 2007.

[4] Palakshappa, Nitha, and Mary Ellen Gordon. "Collaborative business relationships: Helping firms to acquire skills and economies to prosper." *Journal of Small Business and Enterprise*, pp. 264–279, 2007.

[5] Shelbourn, M, N.M. Bouchlaghem, C. Anumba, and P Carrillo. "Planning and implementation of effective collaboration in construction projects." *Construction Innovation: Information Process Management*, pp. 357–377, 2007.

[6] Sheu, Chwen, HsiuJu Rebecca Yen, and Bongsug Chae. "Determinants of supplier-retailer collaboration: evidence from an international study." *International Journal of Operations and production management*, pp. 24–49, 2006.

[7] Ingirige, Bingunath, and Martin Sexton. "Alliances in Construction: Investigatiing initiatives and barriers for long-term collaboration." *Engineering, Construction and Architectural Management*, pp. 521–535, 2006.

[8] Philbin, Simon. "Measuring the performance of research collaborations." *Measuring Business Excellence*, pp. 16–23, 2008.

[9] Horvath, Laura. "Colaboration: The key to value creation in supply chain management." *Supply Chain Management: An International Journal*, pp. 205–207, 2001.

[10] Kakulu, Iyenemi Ibimina, Simeon Igbara, Isaac Akuru, and Nekabari Paul Visigah. "Land Access and Community Entry Challenges in Environmental Surveys Selected cases from Nigeria." *Proceedings, FIG Working Week 2013.* Abuja: FIG, 2013.

[11] Trim, Peter R.J., and Yang-Im Lee. "A Strategic Approach to Sustainable Partnership development." *European Business Review* **20(3)** pp. 222–239, 2008.

[12] UNEP. *Environmental Assessment of Ogoniland.* Technical Report, Nairobi: UNEP, pp. 257, 2011.

[13] Kakulu, Iyenemi Ibimina, and Mohamed Bashir Nuhu. "A Phenomenological Approach to Valuing Contaminated Farmlands in Nigeria." *The Estate Surveyor and Valuer*, pp. 16–22, 2012.

Concept of an ecologically balanced area based on Ecological Footprint

H. Chen, S. Ise & M. Taniguchi
Graduate School of Systems and Information Engineering,
University of Tsukuba, Japan

Abstracts

As environmental problems increase on a global scale, a framework must be established to achieve environmental balance. Because the power of local governments is rising as a result of decentralization in Japan, local governments must shoulder the responsibility of dealing with environmental consumption within a region and set up a suitable system for an area. This study examines an ecologically balanced area based on the balance of environmental productivity and consumption capacity. Using a case study approach examining Ibaraki prefecture in Japan, which has been influenced strongly by Tokyo because of its location in the national capital region, it is possible to explain how the concept promotes understanding of ecological productivity and consumption. The study evaluated the Ecological Footprint (EF) of all 44 municipalities in Ibaraki prefecture and connected municipalities with a high environmental load with a low environmental load as one area. To the lower one, the higher one pays for its obligation for environmental management. Results of a case study demonstrated a method to let the designed areas manage their environment voluntarily and to promote local production for local consumption through interregional cooperation. This concept used in environmental planning will improve the ecological balance. The conclusions show that most municipalities in Ibaraki prefecture are not ecologically balanced and that the environmental consumption of the area is influenced by the positional relation with Tokyo metropolitan district. The median value of environmental load excess ratio of all municipalities was designed as a reduction goal in ecologically balanced areas. Consequently, the 44 municipalities in Ibaraki prefecture were formed into 11 areas, with four municipalities left without matching with the others.
Keywords: Ecological Footprint, ecologically balanced area, urban planning.

WIT Transactions on Ecology and The Environment, Vol 173, © 2013 WIT Press
www.witpress.com, ISSN 1743-3541 (on-line)
doi:10 2495/SDP130071

1 Introduction

At the Rio Summit held in 1992, many countries participated to discuss issues related to the environment. In 2012, the United Nations Conference on Sustainable Development (Rio+20) was also held in Rio as a 20-year follow-up to the 1992 Rio Summit. However, 20 years after the Rio Earth summit, the environment of the planet is becoming worse, not better, according to a report from WWF [1].

For solving environmental issues, a framework should be established. Administrative power tends to be transferred from the central bureaucracy to local governments in Japan. Through decentralization, the power of local governments is rising and local governments must shoulder the responsibility to address environmental problems. Therefore, to achieve consumption within a region, it is necessary to propose a suitable concept and to set up a suitable system considering environment balance.

This report of our study proposed an ecologically balanced area based on an Ecological Footprint, which quantifies the productive environment and that of consumption. The paper describes a case study, choosing Ibaraki prefecture in Japan to reveal the applicability of the concept for other regions. Moreover, this study presents more features of interest and of greater possibility, such as changes of the area's shape or trading system inside the area.

2 Previous study

This study proposed a concept of ecologically balanced area using the EF indicator as an evaluation of environmental balance. The EF indicator represents the amount of biologically productive land necessary to supply the resources a human population consumes, and to assimilate associated waste. The EF indicator was developed by Wackernagel and Rees in the early 1990s [2], and applied by many researchers. The indicator has been calculated for 150 countries at the national level by WWF [3], and cities all over the world at a regional level [4, 5]. The EF indicator has been adopted as a proactive approach in England, such as for the environmental evaluation of project [6]. In Japan, the Ministry of the Environment provides the EF indicator as an assessment of progresses in the Basic Environmental Plan. The governments also introduce the indicator in the Regional Environmental Plan [7]. Application of the indicator has been limited to environmental evaluation or formulation of policies.

Furthermore, the EF applications in the literature are growing in number and diversity. Recently, land-use policies, specifically related to sustainable land resources, and a cap and trade systems using EF have been explored [8]. Even though studies about integrating urban planning with EF are insufficient, these studies have provided accumulations for the realization of ecologically balanced areas.

WIT Transactions on Ecology and The Environment, Vol 173, © 2013 WIT Press
www.witpress.com, ISSN 1743-3541 (on-line)

3 Methods

3.1 Calculation of EF

This study calculates the EF Value using the Ujihara Taniguchi Model 2010.3 (EF-Calc), developed by Ujihara (Okayama University) and Taniguchi [9]. The residents' consumption is calculated using this tool based on the environmental load generated during the daily life activities of residents. Data used in the Ujihara Taniguchi Model are all publicly available and easily obtainable. Consequently, the environment load generated by urban activity outside such region, such as the industrial and service-related load, is not included.

Table 1:   Method of EF indicator value calculation.

Components in the EF indicator		Formulas for calculation	Parameters
1) Farmland footprint	Food and feed	$$F_j^{\,k} = \sum_{n=1}^{10} p_n^{\,k} \cdot f_{nj}$$	$F_j^{\,k}$: Consumption of crop j in area k (t) $p_p^{\,k}$: Population of age bracket n in area k (person)
	Apparel		
2) Grazing land footprint	Meat and milk	$$EF_{fg}^{\,k} = \sum_{j=1}^{10} \frac{F_j^k}{\alpha_j}$$	f_{nj} : Consumption of crop j in age bracket n (t/person) α_j : Land productivity of crop j (t/ha)
	Wool		
3) Forestland footprint (paper)		$$EF_p^{\,k} = \frac{p_n^k}{p} \cdot r \cdot \sum_{m=1}^{3} \frac{w_m}{\beta_m}$$	w_m : Wood pulp and chip demanded for import m (m³) β_m : Growing stock amount of forest of each destination for import m (m³/ha) p: Population in Japan (person) r: Rate of household consumption (%)
4) Built-up land footprint		$$EF_b^{\,k} = \sum_{i=1}^{3} b_i^{\,k}$$	b_i^k : Built-up of land use i in area k (ha)
5) Energy footprint	Household	$$EF_h^k = \sum_{i=1}^{2} \sum_{j=1}^{4} C_{ij}^{\,k} / \gamma$$	C_{ij}^k : CO₂ emissions, type i of houses, and size j of households in area k (ton) r: Absorption efficiency of CO₂ (t-CO₂/ha)
	Private transportation	$$EF_t^k = p^k \cdot C^k k_c / \gamma$$	C^k : Automobile fuel consumption in area k (CC/person) k_c : Conversion factor

The EF indicator comprises the following components, which reference to Table 1. These components are referred from the compound EF methodology developed by Wackernagel and Rees [2].

1) Farmland needed to grow crops for food and feed (Farmland footprint).
2) Grazing land needed to graze animals for meat and milk (Grazing land footprint).
3) Forestland needed to obtain materials for use in paper production (Forestland footprint).
4) Built-up land needed to conduct urban activities (Built-up land footprint)
5) Forestland needed to absorb CO_2 from fossil fuels for household and private transport use (Energy footprint).

Biocapacity (BC) refers to the capacity of an area to provide resources and absorb wastes of each component in EF (such as productive land for farmland).

Moreover, r is defined as the environmental load excess ratio based on EF value association with residents' consumption, with reference to Table 1. The environment balance in each region is evaluated using r. The environmental load excess ratio in region "k" (r^k) is defined as follows.

$$r^k = \frac{EF^k}{BC^k}$$

(1)

EF^k: EF in region "k" (ha)
BC^k: Biocapacity in region "k" (ha)

3.2 Concept of ecologically balanced area

The ecologically balanced area proposed in this paper is a combination of a municipality with a high environmental load with that imposing a low environmental load as one area. Therefore, the dependence relation of environmental consumption is definite in terms of its area. The concept promotes the municipality with a high environmental load (consuming-municipality) to takes or pays the obligation of management by achieving environmental balance ($r \leq 1$). The consuming municipalities shoulder the responsibility to take an approach to a suitable system for the area.

4 Case study

4.1 Target region and EF value

This case study evaluated the Ecological Footprint (EF) of all 44 municipalities in Ibaraki prefecture to review the applicability of the ecologically balanced area for other areas.

Because the concept is assumed to be applicable to the entire country, the case study ought to select a widely diverse target region covering diversified municipalities to the greatest extent possible. Therefore, this case study selected Ibaraki prefecture with its different environmental balance such as small cities and big cities. Ibaraki, which has a population of 2.96 million, is located in the outer edge of Tokyo metropolitan area, stretching eastward to the Pacific Ocean.

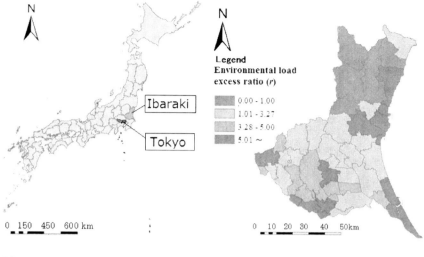

Figure 1:   Location of Ibaraki
            in Japan.

Figure 2: r values of 44
            municipalities   in
            Ibaraki.

The northernmost part of the prefecture is mountainous, whereas the southern part is within subway commuting distance of the capital region. Figure 1 presents the target region location.

The condition of environmental balance (r) in each municipality is calculated based on the EF value associated with residents' consumption, which is given in reference to Table 1.

Results shown in Figure 2 explained that the southern part of Ibaraki has a higher r, although the northern part had a lower one. This outcome occurred by reason that there is large acreage of forest to absorb wastes in the northern part. Furthermore, the urban development of the railroad line in the south caused a decrease of BC value and population concentration. In addition, the EF value is increased because of the concentration. This result certifies the applicability of choosing Ibaraki as a case study.

The medium environmental load excess ratio of Ibaraki is 3.27. Only 5 municipalities among all 44 municipalities are ecologically balanced ($r \leq 1$). Therefore, the design of an ecologically balanced area is difficult in Ibaraki prefecture.

4.2 Design of ecologically balanced area

Understanding of the ecologically balanced area is necessary to seek ways to design an area. Therefore, Tsukuba city is an example illustrating how to shape the area by one condition. The target city of Tsukuba, with 200 thousand people, has the largest population in Ibaraki prefecture. Figure 3 presents the location of Tsukuba city. Tsukuba developed rapidly as a result of development along the railway line, which attracted numerous commuters in the Tokyo metropolitan.

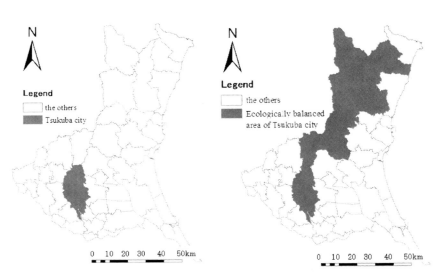

Figure 3:   Tsukuba city.

Figure 4:   Example of Tsukuba's ecologically balanced area.

This study sets a condition of connecting a consuming municipality and municipalities with a low environmental load ($\alpha \leq 3.27$) that reduces the r value mostly. Investigation of all possible conditions is difficult. Therefore, the case study assumed one condition to determine the feasibility. The most ecologically balanced area of Tsukuba city designed by this condition is shown in Figure 4.

However, the area expanding from Tsukuba city to the northeast and formed a bizarre shape just like a *Gerrymander* [9]. Moreover, the environmental load of the area is 1.28. Results show that r of the area cannot be decreased further, and that it is impossible to achieve ecological balance of every municipality in Ibaraki prefecture.

Therefore, the concept is conducted to set a target value (α) in the area to play an obligation on the consuming-municipalities. Several areas can be designed under the target value.

The target value (α) is a reference to the medium or median value. This case study set the medium value as 'α', considering the extremely high environmental load in each municipality.

4.3 Result

As discussed in chapter 4.2, the area of Tsukuba was designed. In this chapter, all 22 consuming municipalities in Ibaraki are designed simultaneously. The 22 consuming municipalities shown in Figure 5 have environmental loads that are greater than the target value (α =3.27). When matching with the consuming municipality, competition occurred in several municipalities with a low environmental load. In such cases, the consuming municipality matching the municipality that reduces the r value most. Results are shown in Figure 6.

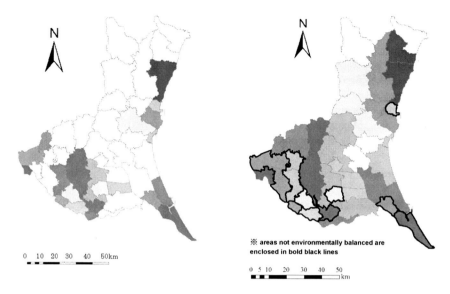

Figure 5:   Municipalities in Ibaraki   Figure 6:   Example of ecologically
with $\alpha \geqslant 3.27$.   balanced area in Abaraki.

Conclusions from these analyses show that the 44 municipalities in Ibaraki prefecture were formed into 14 areas, which included 32 municipalities. In addition, 11 municipalities were left without matching with the others, and 2 areas failed to be environmentally balanced ($r \geq \alpha$). These municipalities and areas, which are not environmentally balanced, are shown as surrounded by a bold black line in Figure 6. However, all municipalities can be designed into ecologically balanced areas using a flexible target value (α). The conclusion from this analysis is that districts such as Tokyo, with a high environmental load excess ratio, can apply the concept of ecologically balanced areas.

5   Discussion and conclusions

The concept of ecologically balanced area based on EF is expected to become a tool promoting environmental management in an area. This study proposed a tool to clarify the amount of environmental consumption and where it has been consumed by designing areas. Based on this tool, the concept played an obligation of environment management on the consuming municipalities by setting a target value (α) in the area. The study demonstrated the possibility that, even if most municipalities are not ecologically balanced, areas should be made by adjusting the target value.

However, this study merely proposed a method to design an ecologically balanced area and gave no consideration to the incentives of environmental management. A system to promote voluntary measurement intended for improvement of environment balance in the area should be considered in the future. In fact, an interregional cap and trade system using EF was developed by Ujihara and Tanaguchi [8]. A possible exploration is to combine an ecologically balanced area with the interregional cap and trade system. This structure can contribute to improvement of the environment balance in areas from the perspective of financial resources.

Moreover, environmental management inside the areas should be explored because the concept is established to achieve an environmental balance. Such an approach is applicable to studies of individual behaviors that interact and impact the environment to benefit environment management.

References

[1]   WWF, Living planet report 2012, http: //awsassets.panda.org/downloads/ lpr_2012_rio_summary_booklet_final_120509.pdf   (accessed   on   December 17, 2012).

[2]   Wackernagel, M. & Rees, W. E., Our Ecological Footprint: Reducing Human Impact on the Earth, New Society Publishers (Canada), 1996.

[3]   WWF, Living Planet Report 2008, http: //www.wwf.or.jp/activity/lib/lpr/

[4]   wwf_lpr_2008.pdf (accessed on December 17, 2012).

[5]   Best Foot Forward, City Limits A resource flow and ecological footprint analysis of Greater London, 2004.

[6]   Regional Progress, http: //www.regionalprogress.org/index.html, accessed on December 17, 2012.

[7]   Desai, P. and Riddlestone, S., Bioregional Solutions: For living on one planet, Greenbooks, 2002.

[8]   Okayama prefecture, New Okayama Basic Environmental Plan-Ecovision 2020, http://www.pref/okayama.jp/seikatsu/kansei/iso/ecovision2020.pdf, (accessed on December 17, 2012, in Japanese).

[9]   Ujihara, T. and Taniguchi, M., Trading system of environmental loads: interregional cap and trade system using an ecological footprint, Ed. by Brebbia, C.A. and Beriatos, E., Sustainable development and planning V, pp. 381–396, WIT Press, 2011.

[10]   Hale, N., Benjamin and Russell, J., Federalist Newspaper, 1812.

Identification of homogeneous areas from urban-environmental vulnerabilities: La Plata, Buenos Aires, Argentina

J. Esparza, G. Viegas & I. Martini
Research and Policy Institute of the Built Environment, La Plata Faculty of Architecture, La Plata National University, Argentina

Abstract

The urban growth of recent decades has created a significant imbalance between the environment, the territory and its inhabitants. This process therefore results in environmental issues such as pollution, overcrowding, excessive accumulation of debris and flooding of urbanized areas, among others. In this paper, the environment and the perception of the people (through surveys), are unmeasured and located in the territory, in order to recognize common ground between the three and to identify areas of urban-environmental vulnerability (AU-AV).

It explains a technical-instrumental system, developed from a relational methodology of information, forming a body of data with which to identify the issues raised. In this case, the analysis information, allowed discrimination: (i) the geographical location of the perception of the people; (ii) the degree of influence of territorial and environmental variables; (iii) identification of areas which are affected by this influence. Recalling that, given the complexity of collision, we must work from methodological triangulation, where information must respond to quantitative and qualitative methods whose implementation can be independent or combined.

The Inverse Distance Weight (IDW) interpolation method was used, pertaining to the program Arc Gis 9.3. This method incorporates the information of each survey territorialized (as information points) and calculates the value of its attribute depending on the information of the surrounding points, which allow for obtaining graphical results (maps). The maps have been a key figure input to identifying these areas. Variables submitted for appraisal of the perception of people, allowed us to obtain and identify certain detailed issues as intrinsic

WIT Transactions on Ecology and The Environment, Vol 173, © 2013 WIT Press
www.witpress.com, ISSN 1743-3541 (on-line)
doi:10.2495/SDP130081

directionality between the response and the observed and causal territorialization of them.

Keywords: urban/environmental vulnerability, technical/instrumental system, graphical results.

1 Introduction

Urban characteristics in recent times have been linked closely, through their study and intervention, with the environmental aspects. The dynamics of urban and population growth have generated considerable imbalances with respect to the surrounding medium. Consequently, supply systems and services (from the energy aspect to waste generation) have collapsed as a result of contemporary urban life. The resulting environmental damage or costs threaten future productivity, health and quality of life of its inhabitants [1]. Goytre explains: "On the basis of this situation (...), it is highlighted that (...) citizens have lost control of the ability of over many activities that occur in their urban environment. With the development of the modern state, and in an accelerated way in the second half of the twentieth century, decisions on urban activities(production, exchange and consumption), have been emancipated from the places where they occur, regardless of the needs both local natural capital as the human development of its inhabitants" [1].

This generalized urban-environmental crisis, suggests that the formulation of methodologies reliable and capable of understanding the urban system from its complexity, would minimize the different vulnerability levels. In the city, the *territorial vulnerability* arises from factors such as excessive population growth, modes of land use, exploitation of resources, but also by the functional, institutional and political lack and default. In relation to what is exposed above, it should add as synthesis, that the environmental issues have become the focus of the question and discussion of contemporary urban.

2 Methodology

The study of vulnerability can be invoked from different scales and interdisciplinary approach. In this case, the study of the territory can recognize, among other things, urban dynamics [3], mode and type of settlements, the behavior of networks and building infrastructure and communication modes.

Thus, it appeals to a *relational system* [2] based on the juxtaposition and overlap of variables from different systems and scales. This scheme, which appeals to the bidirectional processes, requires a comprehensive study based on the multiplicity of results. It can be said that if it count with a methodology and tools that enable the collection of systematic information, it will allow for recognizing on one hand, the contributions that are manifested in the observed reality and on the other an accurate diagnosis of the urban situation.

To this purpose it is necessary to develop a mechanism in order to obtain Homogeneous Areas of Urban-Environmental Vulnerability (HAU-EV) on which to act from a policy of comprehensive planning and management.

Therefore it is necessary to define and quantify the participation of each of the variables involved, from: (i) the conception of the variables as "layers", as perceived by each person; (ii) the conception of them as a data set to obtain measurable results in environmental urban order.

Variables such as "relatable" layers intersect generating different possible results. From the variables approach and main objective, it is proposed to obtain and identify HAU-EV from the superposition and juxtaposition of the different variables involved. They are presented in Table 1.

Table 1:   Outline of the object of study and the methodological and operational conceptualization.

Macro Variable	Variable	Relation value	Superposition method	Representation
V1. Territorial Variable	**V1a. Urban Consolidation**	Building Density	Mapping and geospatial analysis. First integration results	Graphic-numerical outputs (maps)
		Coverage of basic inf services		
	V1b. Road infrastructure	Primary and secondary corridors		
		Connectivity between areas		
	V1c. Socio-economic Level	Income of the population		
		Unsatisfied Basic Needs		
V2. Environ-mental Variable	**V2a. Pollution and environmental degradation**	Flood areas		
		Dumps areas		
		Noise Pollution		
		Air Pollution		
	V2b. Green Spaces	Squares and boulevards		
		Urban and Regional Parks		
V3. Subjective Variable	**V3a. Subjectivity**	Surveys	Mapping and Spatial Analysis	
		Newspaper clippings		

2.1 Study and processing of variables

When working with information from different media, it is necessary to incorporate a methodology called "methodological triangulation", from which the problem can be approached from qualitative and quantitative methods simultaneously. In this case, the implementation can be independent or combined, since each of the methods has advantages and disadvantages regarding the collection of information [3]. Consequently, the proposed variables are oriented to investigate territorial, environmental and perceptive aspects in the urban context, in this case La Plata City. The following systematization variables tools are used:

2.1.1 Geographic Information System (GIS)
The specialization of the variables proposed is via a numerical database, from a Geographic Information System (GIS), as an ArcView type, which allows viewing and obtaining results from a geographical-territorial context. Using this methodology instrumentation allows conforming different results maps, which enables viewing homogeneous areas characterized from each aspect and variable analyzed.

From the use of this tool, different maps were built that correspond to different "layers" containing information on the variables analyzed. As stated before, depending on the degree of information to be analyzed or crosslink, the layers allow obtaining graphical information. If for example, territorial and environmental aspects are superposed, such as urban consolidation and green spaces, it can begin to recognize through georeferenced results (GIS), the relationship between the built and natural environment.

This crossing will only recognize certain holistic data. In order to become part of a recognizable everyday reality, these data should be weighted or recognized by people. Here, it is reported the formation of the city of La Plata and its location with respect to the Autonomous City of Buenos Aires (Province of Buenos Aires) (see Figures 1–3).

Figure 1:   La Plata City and Autonomous City of Buenos Aires.

Figure 2:   La Plata City.

Figure 3:   La Plata City and surrounding area. Source: Google Earth.

2.2 Variables overlapping

To identify HAU-EV, certain patterns of "clustering" and juxtaposition of these variables should be known, and as noted above, from different approaches. Figure 4 shows the three territorial variables under study, their overlap and the defined areas in a first approximation level.

Figure 4:   Map of the juxtaposition of the environmental variables.

Analyzing the resulting map we can conclude that: (1) in the Central area, the three maximum values of the variables analyzed are shown: the high occupancy (urban consolidation), extremely busy main roads and those homes without UBN. In the same way, we can distinguish three areas: a central one, other in the far North, and the other in the extreme Southwest, where the mixture of situations begins to appear; (2) in the Northern suburbs (to Buenos Aires) an intermediate situation exists. Here, the consolidation is medium-low, but with the existence of busy roads, such as the "General Belgrano Road" and "Centennial Road" and a high percentage of homes without UBN; (3) in the South periphery (towards Villa Elvira), consolidation is mostly low, where the only way of concurrency is the 7th Avenue. In this case, there are a high percentage of households with UBN. Moreover, the issue related to the territorial transformations processes of recent times coexist, which the expansive phenomenon had occurred towards the Federal Capital. In this sense, if you look at the map of UBN, a vast difference between the two peripheries can be recognized.

The following step is to unfold the study of the environmental variables. It is important to remember that both the study of the environmental and territorial variables, the inhabitants' perceptions should be incorporated as the main point for the recognition of the observed reality (see Figure 5).

Analyzing the resulting map it can be concluded that: (1) there are two critical or vulnerable areas, mainly by the presence and convergence of two or more of these variables. In the center area, pathologies related to air pollution (produced by public transport, mostly) and sound pollution converge, by the existence of commercial and administrative area in that sector. Furthermore, the failure and lack of drainage system complicates the water running in rainy days. The system has been collapsed in the last years by the increasing pressure on the land cost; (2) in the area of the Northern suburbs (Gonnet, see Figure 3) pathologies such as floods, dump areas and sound pollution converge. The detailed study of the environmental aspects [4] has allowed us to highlight the reality state that exists between the objective data that we developed previously, and those related to the subjective one, where the opinion and/or perception of inhabitants allows verifying such situation (morning Journal "El Dia", 2009); (3) in the area of the Southern suburbs (Los Hornos, see Figure 3), pathologies such as dump areas and flooded areas converge. This is particularly due to poor waste collection system, since in the area occurs only three (3) times a week, not daily as in the Central area.

3 Homogeneous areas of urban environmental vulnerability analyzed from perception

The opinion (of subjective character) can become objective and measurable when it relates to certain parameters pertaining to the territorial and environmental variables. The subjective data collection tools are as follows:

3.1 Surveys

The survey was structured from what Corraliza [5] called "affective dimensions of the environment". It allows recognizing the degree of appreciation of respondents from "adjective pairs" qualifying the observed environment. In this research, these adjectives have been re-structured in terms of a better understanding for the respondents as a first test approach, many of the words used by Corraliza at work, were not included respondents from the local environment: (1) Pleasing Factor: "pleasant/unpleasant", "attractive/repulsive", "cozy/inhospitable"; (2) Activation Factor: "quiet/busy", "village/desert", "lively /discouraged", "silent/restless"; (3) Impact Factor: "significant/ insignificant", "colorful/indifferent", "flashy/discreet", "singular/regular"; (4) Control Factor: "comfortable/disturbing", "safe/unsafe", "care/careless", "light/dark".

To overlay information from different media (objective and subjective) is to use a rating system which has allowed the survey structure from the factors and variables mentioned and depending on the possible answers, where the ranges vary 0.1 to 1.0 [6]. For example, if the respondent believes that the environment is "Very pleasant" 0.1 as ceiling serious scale, "Pleasant", 0.3, "Little pleasant" 0.5 and "Unpleasant", would be 1.0.

3.2 Newspaper clippings

The press screening can be used as analysis method to evaluate the opinion of people. In this sense, it was proposed as an alternative methodology, the daily monitoring of the region, "The Day" to know what the readers assessments regarding these variables. In this evaluation system, the perceptions of local residents were assigned a value (and qualification) to each of the issues, which determine the level of satisfaction of the inhabitants. For the case of territorial variables, the assigned scale has values of 10 to 1, with 10 being the maximum ceiling of that scale (Good) 5.0 (Regular), 1.0 (Bad) and 0.0 (without data). In the case of environmental variables, the scale includes values from 0.1 to 1.0 determines the level of satisfaction of the inhabitants, the floor being 0.1 scale (very noticeable), 0.3 (Notorious), 0.5 (inconspicuous) and 1.0 (not perceive).

For this research, the degree of perception can be appreciated of the inhabitants of two of the variables coincident with those referred to in Table 1: air and sound pollution. It should be noted that as part of the implementation methodology, not only the opinions and/or perceptions by neighbors were required, but also the location and territorial reference point (Neighborhood and/or address of the respondent). Below are a series of maps that represent the perceptions of people in the city of La Plata in different parts of it (see Figure 6).

4 Results

As has been said, the opinion of people can be considered from two instruments: surveys and newspaper clippings. Accordingly, the opinions (subjective

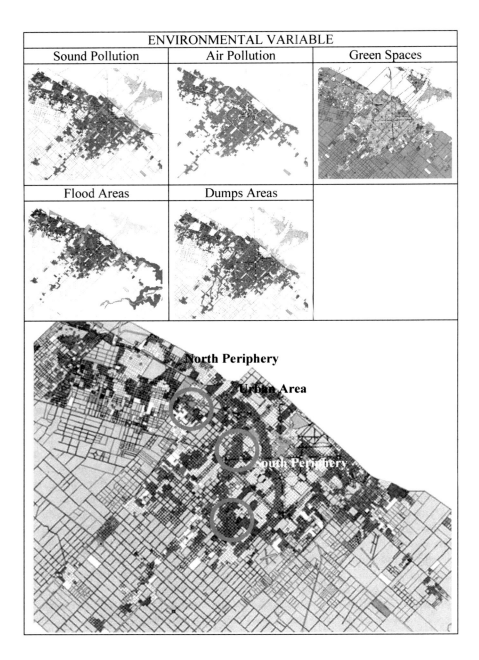

Figure 5: Map of the juxtaposition of the environmental variables.

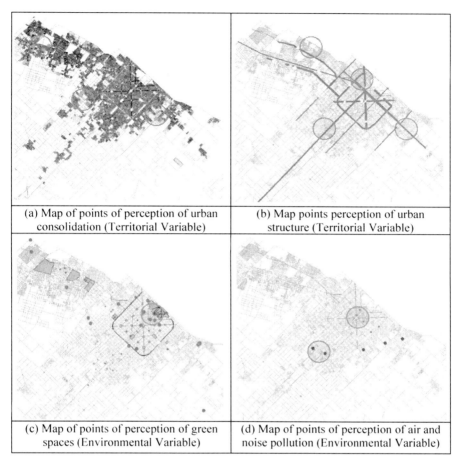

(a) Map of points of perception of urban consolidation (Territorial Variable)	(b) Map points perception of urban structure (Territorial Variable)
(c) Map of points of perception of green spaces (Environmental Variable)	(d) Map of points of perception of air and noise pollution (Environmental Variable)

Figure 6:   Maps of points of perception of (a) urban consolidation, (b) urban structure, (c) green spaces and (d) air and noise pollution.

character), were systematized in a data matrix, from which results are integrated with those "objectives" and standardized from attributes.

It was used the IDW interpolation method (gravitational or inverse distance), belonging to the extensions included in the Arc GIS 9.3. This method incorporates the information of each territorialized points (in this case, surveys) and calculates the value of its attribute depending on the information of the surrounding points.

In this sense the determination of the point to interpolate the greater the closer you are to another point in the same informative feature [7]. So, each of the subjective variables were "interpolate" through this system, obtaining areas of influence of the different responses obtained.

Surveys	Interpolation	Contours or areas of influence
This shows the total surveys and territorialization (geographic location). It is perceived that the largest number of responses have been obtained in the urban area.	It has allowed obtaining HA from the valuation given to each of the appreciations of the respondents. (Very Pleasant-0.1-, Pleasant-0.3-, Little Pleasant-0.5- and Unpleasant-1.0)	Interpolation also allows obtaining "contour" or a so-called "area of influence" of the response. This process clearly identifies the HA when subjectivity of survey overlaps with the other variables.

Figure 7: Location of respondents (surveys), the interpolation and identification of affected areas.

Only as a methodology, is developed "Activation Factor", which gathers the responses of the variables quiet, village, lively and silent. They made it possible to know whether or not respondents perceive the movements and dynamics of the city themselves, that is, those activities that at certain times, days or moments attract or disperse the population. This may depend on factors such as proximity to places and/or cultural events, commercial and administrative sectors or major public spaces (such as parks or walks).

The "Activation Factor" in its four variables was crisscrossed with urban consolidation and garbage dumps, allowing obtaining and identifying homogeneous areas in relation to the number of people affected by them. In this respects recognized the compatibility between responses and objective reality, where those unsatisfactory characters are located in areas where there are low consolidation or dumps. It is worth mentioning that these variables are particularly useful to identify which areas would be vulnerable, from which, acting from a management policy and integrated planning. Then village variable develops exemplary of the proposed methodology (see Figure 8).

In the graphical results was observed that most of the responses have been "village". In this case, they are located in areas of high and medium consolidation, both the central and the periphery areas (toward Villa Elisa). In Figure 9, the interpolations can be seen.

The answers "very village" is mostly, and consequently, in the greater consolidation area in the center of central area. Those who responded "little village", are located mostly in the northern periphery, and those who responded "desert", are located in the southern suburbs, where there is a low area of the city consolidation.

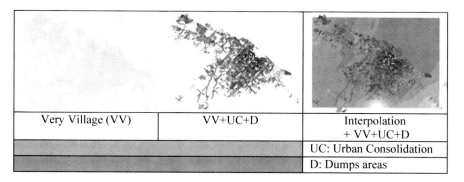

Very Village (VV)	VV+UC+D	Interpolation + VV+UC+D
		UC: Urban Consolidation
		D: Dumps areas

Figure 8:   Activation Factor – village variable.

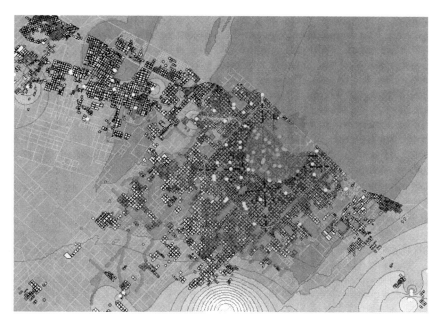

Figure 9:   Homogeneous areas of vulnerability from the village variable.

From these observations, two issues can be defined: first, the direct relationship between observed reality and the objective of territorial variable and, second, the relationship between the degree of consolidation and dumps areas. For example, in areas of high consolidation, garbage collection is performed daily while in certain sectors of the periphery only performed three times a week.

5   Conclusions

Both the territory and the environment and even perceptions of the inhabitants, as the weighting factor of the observed, have been unmeasured and located in the territory, in order to identify points of encounter between the three, and thus, to identify homogeneous areas.

In the synthesis of the variable map village, have identified two (2) homogeneous areas, which particularly are overlapped. One of them is the one that gathers responses located on the high and medium areas of consolidation, where converge the largest number of "village" and the second, over the area where the answers converge "very village" in the Central area.

In this regard, and as a general conclusion, in the studied region have been identified three (3) areas defined not only by the number of respondents, but the disparity in their answers. The first area, which encompasses the area consequently most people, is the center area where nucleate generally satisfactory responses, regulated by the improved situation of the objective variables. The second area is that in the northern periphery (Tolosa, Gonnet, City and Villa Elisa Bell (see Figure 3)). It is known that the growth and transformation of the territory has been given in an important pattern of land occupation, to this area. The third area, located in the southern periphery (toward Villa Elvira (see Figure 3)) gathers unsatisfactory issues, where factors such as lack of security, are highlighted.

The answer would be to generate comprehensive proposals from the various administrative and governmental estates, from decentralizations of cultural and social, as well as from those activities functional and livelihood of the entire studied territory. It is understood that each of these proposals requires some accompaniment of the inhabitants from their civic duty.

References

[1] Goytre, Félix Arias. (2001) Problemática Urbana Actual. Instituto Juan de Herrera. Madrid. España. ISSN: 1578-097x.
[2] Codd, E.F. (1970). Un modelo relacional de datos para grandes bancos de datos compartidos. IBM Research Laboratory, San Jose, California.
[3] Esparza, J.; Dicroce, L.; Martini, I.; Rosenfeld, E.; Discoli, C.; Ramirez Casa, J. (2008). Análisis metodológico de las herramientas de evaluación de la opinión/percepción en el marco de un Modelo de Calidad de Vida Urbana. Revista Avances en Energías Renovables y Medio Ambiente. Vol. 12, ISSN 0329-5184.
[4] Esparza, J.; Martini I.; Discoli, C. (2011). Metodología para el análisis detallado de los aspectos urbano-ambientales en la escala puntual de la ciudad. Revista Avances en Energías Renovables y Medio Ambiente. Vol. 15, ISSN 0329-5184.
[5] Corraliza Rodríguez, José Antonio. (2003). Emoción y ambiente. Psicología ambiental, Juan Ignacio Aragonés. Editorial Pirámide, Madrid.

[6] Rosenfeld, E. (2005). Modelo de Calidad de Vida Urbana. Determinación de índices y espacialización de áreas homogéneas. Revista avances en energías Renovables y medio ambiente. ISSN 0329-5184. Vol. 6. Tomo 1. pp. 01.41– 48. INENCO – UNSa, Salta.

[7] Dicroce, L.; Discoli, C.; Martini, I.; Esparza, J.; San Juan, G.; Rosenfeld, E. Aplicación de un Modelo de Calidad de Vida Urbana (MCVU) con datos oficiales extraídos del censo nacional. (2009). Revista Avances en Energías Renovables y Medio Ambiente. Vol. 13, ISSN 0329-5184.

[8] Domingo Gómez Orea (1999). Evaluación del Impacto Ambiental. Un instrumento preventivo para la gestión ambiental. Ediciones Mundi-Prensa, Editorial Agrícola Española.

From order to (dis)order in the land reform programme of Zimbabwe: was environmental sustainability retained?

E. Kori
Department of Geography and Geo-Information Sciences,
University of Venda, South Africa

Abstract

Land reforms have occurred throughout the world for different reasons including the need to change patterns of land ownership or land use. In Africa, such reforms aim to redress the discriminatory colonial land policies by providing the poor and disadvantaged with arable land. To be successful, land use options within a land reform programme should incorporate not only social and economic viability, but environmental sustainability as well. One of the vexing challenges facing policy makers is how to redistribute land and at the same time ensure productivity and ecological sustainability. Critics of the Fast Track Land Reform Programme (FTLRP) in Zimbabwe have often characterised this challenge as a remnant of the government's move from the orderly willing buyer willing seller to the 'disorderly' command driven approach. Using the Ecological Footprint accounting approach, this paper endeavours to determine whether the change from willing-buyer-willing-seller to FTLRP compromised the environmental sustainability of the resettled areas. Data were collected from both primary and secondary sources in Chirumanzu District, Midlands Province of Zimbabwe through household questionnaires and key informant interviews. Results reveal that despite the change in the land reform approach, there is a generally environmentally sustainable situation prevailing in both the orderly and the (dis)orderly FTLP resettled areas. Contrary to popular view, both areas produced an ecological reserve. Such results may lead one to conclude that although there was a major shift in the land reform approach, the orderliness was not lost hence environmental sustainability was retained.
Keywords: land use, ecological resources, resettlement, land reform.

WIT Transactions on Ecology and The Environment, Vol 173, © 2013 WIT Press
www.witpress.com, ISSN 1743-3541 (on-line)
doi:10.2495/SDP130091

1 Introduction

Zimbabwe is a predominantly rural country where access to productive land resources is essential for social and economic development. However, between 1893 and 1980, the colonial government passed segregatory legislation such as the Land Husbandry Act of 1930, which deprived the majority of the Africans of the right to own productive land. This divided the country into prime land for Europeans and largely infertile and inhospitable land as "Native Reserves" for Africans. The result was that 3 per cent of the population got entitlement to about 39 per cent of the national total arable land [1–3]. African economic and social development was, therefore, stunted. Thus, the new government implemented land reforms after independence from Britain in 1980 to address these anomalies. However, land reform in Zimbabwe has been piece-meal and reactive in approach [4] culminating in environmental sustainability challenges.

Land reforms aim to promote noble ideas central to human livelihoods. Musyoki [5] and Mohamed-Katerere [6] observe that to be successful, land use options within a land reform programme should incorporate not only social and economic viability, but environmental sustainability as well. Environmental sustainability issues are among a host of vantage points taken by Zimbabwe government critics when it abandoned the intensive package approach. The intensive package approach entailed the provision of adequate basic support services such as access roads, water, and sanitation facilities, dipping tanks, clinics, schools and rural service centres, before or as soon as settlers had occupied the redistributed land [7–9]. The associated comprehensive planning done before the settlers' relocation ostensibly guaranteed environmental sustainability.

The new approach adopted in 2000 entailed the relocation of settlers to new settlement areas before basic social services and infrastructure had been established [10]. It became known as The Fast Track Land Reform Programme (FTLRP). It was a radical and controversial exercise. Existing landowners were sometimes forcibly removed from their hitherto farms. Methods of land acquisition, beneficiary selection and resettlement support changed to a completely command-driven approach [11]. Beneficiaries occupied farms before any provision of basic infrastructure and Government officials followed at a later stage to "demarcate" the land [12]. Critics viewed this approach as retrogressive and a recipe for serious ramifications on, among others, the sustainability of the environment in resettled areas. As a result there is a host of publications condemning the land reform programme in Zimbabwe.

2 Environment and land reform debate

Different publications [4, 13–15] point to environmental sustainability challenges in resettlement areas in Zimbabwe. However, according to the Zanu (PF)'s National Congress Report [16] one of the objectives of the FTLRP was to reduce pressure on land and enhance environmental sustainability. The Land Reform Task Force [10] identifies the intention to "promote environmentally sustainable utilization of land", as one of the objectives of the FTLR. Manjengwa [14] however, observes that there was some "environmental degradation occurring as a result of accelerated resettlement causing conflicts over natural resource use..." This is supported by Murombedzi's [15] observation that "...settlers are ...asset strippers, cutting down trees, hunting wild animals and exploiting other natural resources so as to open up new lands for agriculture, reduce competition and protect their livestock from predation, but also to source capital to invest in their new agriculture enterprise." Furthermore, the Zimbabwe Environmental Research Organization (ZERO) [4] argues that the post-colonial era in Zimbabwe has been characterised by growing levels of environmental degradation and, to date, land reform has done little to improve the environmental sustainability of rural land use practices. Adopting the fast track approach was worsening the already bad environmental situation.

Clover and Eriksen [9] add that despite the stated intention of addressing some of the problems of overcrowding and inequality, land reform in Zimbabwe has paradoxically failed to address overcrowding and resource scarcity on marginal lands, but instead precipitated new ecological, social and economic challenges. ZERO [4] observes that the pace of environmental degradation has nowhere been quicker than in resettlement areas. Compounding the situation is that environmental sustainability is not mainstreamed in the land reform process [13].

Harts-Broekhuis and Huisman [17] point out that resettlement schemes have been implemented in some comparatively vulnerable and agro ecologically poorly endowed regions of the country. Serious environmental degradation tailed demographic and economic changes that have produced a semblance of communal areas in resettlement schemes [18, 19]. Estimates suggest that resettlement resulted in deforestation ranging between 100,000 and 320,000 hectares per year [20].

Gold panning along Zimbabwe's rivers also mushroomed since the beginning of the FTLRP. Panning takes place unsustainably and unsystematically, usually in riverbeds, banks and flood plains with no concern for the environment [14]. The concern is the ability of such a scenario to sustain the ecosystem services which humanity will always need for survival.

Most of the above arguments emanate from the belief that for a sustainable environmental situation to prevail, humanity should extract ecological resources from, and release waste to the environment in quantities that the biophysical environment has the capacity to supply and absorb, respectively. In this context, environmental sustainability is considered in terms of the natural resources available to support life (biocapacity) against what humanity is extracting (Ecological Footprint) from nature. That is the point of departure for this paper.

While many of the publications cited above cite obvious human activities ostensibly causing environmental degradation in resettled areas, none of them supports their views with a robust scientific study. Their main basis is that the FTLRP lacked planning. However, Chaumba et al. [21] contend that order was never lost and that the FTLRP was a planning mishap is media propaganda. It is the aim of this paper to present results of a scientifically robust and transparent calculation of the demands humanity places on the natural environment from a scientific study of the resettled areas of Chirumanzu District of Zimbabwe. This should reveal the environmental sustainability status obtaining after the implementation of the FTLRP. The adoption of a natural resource supply and consumption approach affords the accomplishment of this aim as presented in the following section.

3   Methods

It is possible to track the majority of the resources people consume and the wastes they produce. These resources consumed and the wastes generated can be measured in physical terms [22]. This paper considers environmental sustainability in terms of the natural resources available to support life against what humanity is extracting from, and returning as waste to, the ecosystem. This is done through tracking the regenerative capacity of an ecosystem in terms of natural resource flows using the Ecological Footprint (EF) tool. These resources and waste flows are measurable in terms of biologically productive areas necessary to maintain the flows

The EF accounts for exploitation of the environmental renewable resources and the assimilative capacity by a given population over specified time [23, 24]. EF is a measure of sustainability, and use of *interest* rather than *capital*. The system compares the demand on ecological services (EF) to the available supply, biocapacity (BC) [25, 26]. The EF is the area of ecologically productive land needed to maintain a population's consumption patterns and absorb its wastes with the prevailing technology [27–31].

The assumption of the EF tool is that all resources consumed by humanity can be traced to an area of land, in global hectares (gha), on the earth's surface. The EF tool captures natural resource flow and clearly reveals where there are ecological deficits and reserves [29]. This is done through the calculation of the EF and BC of each land use category. These disaggregated calculations are then condensed into a final consumption (EF) and supply (BC). A comparison between the EF and the BC determines the environmental sustainability status of the specific land use type or the overall area. A BC larger than EF gives an ecological reserve signifying a sustainable environment. Conversely, a BC less than EF give an ecological deficit, signifying an unsustainable environment.

Pursuant to the foregoing, four land use types: cropland, grazing land, forests for timber and firewood, and built up land [25, 26, 29] are considered in this paper. Each land use type has a supply side (BC) computed using formula 1 and demand side calculated by employing formula 2 [25, 32].

$$BC = A * YF * EQF \qquad (1)$$

where
A = the area available for a given land use type,
YF and EQF are yield factor and equivalence factor, respectively, for the land use type in question.

$$EF = \frac{P}{Y_D} * EQF \tag{2}$$

where

EF = Ecological Footprint
P = the amount of a product harvested or waste emitted
YD = district average yield (t wha^{-1}yr^{-1})
EQF = equivalence factor for the land use type in question.

It is important to emphasise that the EF tool traces resource flows. Therefore weather the land used to produce goods falls within the physical boundary of the consumer or not, the ecological demand is placed under the consumer. The tool computes land used to produce goods within the resettled areas. It also calculates the land area embodied in the goods imported into or exported out of the district. This culminates in EF of Production (EF$_P$), Imports (EF$_I$) and Exports (EF$_E$) to cater for the ecological land used in the production of goods within the resettled area, land as well as embodied in imported goods as well as exported goods, respectively. To get the actual ecological land consumed in the district, the EF of consumption (EF$_C$), production and imports are added together and exports subtracted.

Both primary and secondary statistics were collected for the EF tool to determine environmental sustainability. Primary data was collected through the administration of questionnaires to sampled households. Government offices provided secondary data across all the four land use classes. The EF tool uses a year as a temporal unit of measurement. Therefore, all the data collected for this study was for the year 2010 as ten years are long enough for human activity to have a measurable influence on the ecosystem.

Consequently a sample size of 150 households represented the 5167 households in the resettlement areas (95% at 7.89 confidence). The sample was taken from both new and old resettlement areas as shown in Table 1. The household figures are as at April 2010. The household interviews solicited for biophysical information from the respondents. Statistics such as area (ha) put under different land uses, production from different land uses, grazing resources, livestock resources and crop production were gathered.

Key informant interviews with officials from the Ministry of Lands and Rural Resettlement, AGRITEX, Veterinary Services as well as the District Administrator provided secondary statistics. Both primary and secondary data were then captured into the Microsoft Excel worksheets for computation of the environmental sustainability of the resettled areas. Following the application of the above formulae, BC and EF of the old and new resettlement were compared to find the ecological reserve (or deficit as the case may be). The following section deals with the results and their implications on environmental sustainability. In addition the section reveals whether the critics of the FTLRP were correct or off the mark.

Table 1:   The sample size.

Resettlement type		Old Resettlement	New Resettlement	Totals
Households	Number	861	4306	5167
	Per cent	15.7	84.3	100
Sample size (households)		24	126	150

4 Results and discussion

The results presented here follow the elaborate calculation outlined above. Both old and new resettlement areas reveal an ecological reserve. However, it is important to delve into the individual land uses to shed more light into the environmental sustainability case at hand. Built up land cannot practically produce an ecological deficit as construction is done on land physically available in the resettled areas. As such no attention will be directed at the built up land footprint.

While it is noted that land reform has increased household crop production and improved livelihoods [33, 34], and income [21, 35] the cropland and grazing land EF should not be misconstrued to be referring to that. The EF is concerned with the degradation of once productive land. The Footprint refers to the environment's regenerative capacity exploited in the production of the said crops and livestock.

Environmental sustainability is concerned with maintenance of the ability of the ecological environment to continue providing that capacity indefinitely. The maintenance of ecological sustainability will ensure that resettled farmers will not find themselves living in a land base with ever decreasing biocapacity. Thus, in terms of cropland use, therefore, the population is living unsustainably and this has a negative impact on food security in the future.

Interestingly, both old and new resettlement areas show an ecological deficit as shown in tables 1and 2. This supports the observation by ZERO [4] that environmental management has always been poor in the resettled areas of Zimbabwe. Worth noting is that many households have extended their arable land in the hope of increasing production. This could be the most plausible explanation for the ecological deficit. Chirumanzu is in agro ecological region III where crop production has to be under irrigation. Rain-fed subsistence farming by the resettled farmers does not produce satisfactory crops.

Table 2:   Chirumanzu District Old Resettlement Ecological Footprint Account.

Demand Type	EF $_P$	EF $_I$	EF $_E$	EF $_C$	Biocap	BC-EF$_C$
[-]	[gha]	[gha]	[gha]	[gha]	[gha]	[gha]
Cropland	54358.39	1329.59	1847.61	53840.36	11007.64	-42832.72
Grazing Land	1367.18	391.52	418.87	1339.83	190073.52	188733.69
Forest Land	314.36	0.00	0.00	314.36	2408.33	2093.97
Built up Land	13994.23	-	-	13994.23	15554.04	1559.82
Total	70034.15	3823.32	4515.54	69341.93	219043.53	149701.60

Be that as it may, an examination of the grazing land footprint can shed more light on the cropland footprint. The household interviews revealed that only 35% of the sampled households own some form of livestock. Out of that 31% own less than 10 livestock species. The dominant livestock species are fowl and goats, which use very little biocapacity. This can be argued to have contributed to the large ecological reserve.

Additionally, the government demands that beneficiaries in both new and old resettlement take effective occupation' of the allocated land. Effective occupation is personified by activities on the land. Therefore, the beneficiaries without livestock resort to crop cultivation and illegal arable land extension as a sign of effective occupation. Therefore this eats into the cropland biocapacity while leaving out a large ecological reserve in the grazing land use. Consequently, the grazing land ecological reserve can be termed *livestock limited* environmental sustainability.

Table 3:   Chirumanzu District New Resettlement Ecological Footprint Account.

Demand Type	EF_P	EF_I	EF_E	EF_C	Biocap	$BC-EF_C$
[-]	[gha]	[gha]	[gha]	[gha]	[gha]	[gha]
Cropland	72889.53	1329.59	2891.93	71327.18	59104.71	-12222.47
Grazing Land	16121.69	2493.73	2667.93	15947.49	190073.52	174126.02
Forest Land	1966.48	0.00	0.00	1966.48	2408.33	441.86
Built up Land	1527.24	-	-	1527.24	15554.04	14026.80
Total	92504.94	3823.32	5559.86	90768.39	267140.61	176372.21

The EF tool traces resource flows. A comparison of the grazing land imports and exports reveals that both the old and the new resettlements export more grazing land than they import. This exported biocapacity is considered under the importing areas. Such a scenario contributes to a larger ecological reserve in the grazing land use. The large grazing land ecological reserve contributes significantly to the overall ecological reserve revealing the overall environmental sustainability of the resettled area.

A further examination of the results also shows a similar trend between the newly resettled areas and the old ones. Both have an ecological deficit in cropland use and a large ecological reserve in grazing land use. It can be argued therefore, that, the new resettlements are a continuation of the old resettlement system in as far as environmental resource consumption is concerned. At the end both resettlement schemes depict a *livestock limited* environmental sustainability situation.

5 Conclusion

Livelihoods, crop production and household income have improved and order was never lost in the new era of resettlement [21, 34]. This paper has revealed that there is a generally environmentally sustainable situation prevailing in both the old and the new resettlement areas. The introduction of the FTLRP was not as detrimental to the environment as the popular view puts it. It is concluded that adopting the FTLRP did not result in the environmental sustainability being compromised. Rather environmental sustainability that prevailed in the old resettlement areas was retained.

References

[1] Chitsike, F., A Critical Analysis of the Land Reform Programme in Zimbabwe, Paper presented at the *2nd FIG Regional Conference*, Marrakech, Morocco, December 2–5, 2003.

[2] Moyo, S., Land Policy, Poverty Reduction and Public Action in Zimbabwe Institute of Social Studies (ISS)/ UNDP Land, Poverty and Public Action Policy Paper No. 11, 2005.

[3] Mushimbo, C., *Land Reform in Post-Independence Zimbabwe: A Case of Britain's Neo-Colonial Intransigence?* Master of Arts Thesis, Graduate College of Bowling Green State University, 2005.

[4] Zimbabwe Environmental Research Organization (ZERO), *Untitled*, ZERO official website, 2005.

[5] Musyoki, A., *Land Reform and the Alleviation of Poverty: towards Sustainable Rural Development,* Inaugural Professorial address presented at University of Venda, 19 May 1999.

[6] Mohamed-Katerere, J., Legal and Policy Studies for Shared Forest Management. Harare: *Report Produced For Forestry Commission/ DFID Shared Forest Management Project*, 2000.

[7] Moyo, S., *The Land Question in Zimbabwe*, Harare: Sapes Trust, 1995.

[8] Zimbabwe Farmers Union (Z. F. U.), *Resettlement Programme in Zimbabwe: Options for the Future*, Unpublished Conference Report, 1995.

[9] Clover, J., and Eriksen, S., The effects of land tenure change on sustainability: human security and environmental change in southern African savannahs. *Journal of Environmental Science and Policy,* **12** pp. 52–70, 2009.

[10] Land Reform Task Force, *Inception Phase Framework Plan: 1999–2000*, Harare: Government Printer, 1999.

[11] Chiremba, S., and Masters, W., The Experience of Resettled Farmers in Zimbabwe, African Studies Quarterly 7, no. 2&3: [online] viewed 15 June 2010 URL: http://web.africa.ufl.edu/asq/v7/v7i2a5.htm.

[12] Muyengwa, S., and Sango, D., *Decentralizing Land Reform: Lessons Drawn from Zimbabwe,* Harare: Centre for Applied Social Science, University of Zimbabwe, 2008.

[13] Manjengwa, J., *Natural resource management and land reform in Southern Africa,* Harare: Centre for Applied Social Sciences, University of Zimbabwe, 2006.

[14] Manjengwa, J., *Environment and Development issues in Zimbabwe, since 2000 and beyond*, Harare: Centre for Applied Social Sciences, University of Zimbabwe, 2009.

[15] Murombedzi, J. C., *Environment and sustainable development in Zimbabwe*, Harare: International Union for the Conservation of Nature (IUCN), 2004.

[16] ZANU (PF), Report by The Chairman Of National Land Acquisition Hon. J. W. Msika (MP) at ZANU (PF) Congress 15/12/2000. Unpublished.

[17] Harts-Broekhuis, A., and Huisman, H., Resettlement revisited: land reform results in resource-poor regions in Zimbabwe, *Geoforum*, **32 (3)** pp. 285–298, 2001.

[18] Mukwada, G., Unlocking Resources: The Impact of Land Reform on Sustainability of Forest and Woodland Resources and Rural Livelihoods – The Case of Mufurudzi Resettlement Scheme (Zimbabwe), Ph.D. Thesis, Wits University, South Africa, 2007.

[19] Sikor, T. and Muller, D., The Limits of State-Led Land Reform: An Introduction, USA: Elsevier Ltd, 2008.

[20] Ministry of Lands, Land Reform and Resettlement (Government of Zimbabwe), *Land Reform and Resettlement Program Revised Phase II*, Harare: Ministry of Lands, Agriculture and Rural Resettlement, 2004.

[21] Chaumba, J., Scoones, I. and Wolmer, W., From Jambanja to Planning: The Reassertion of Technocracy in Land Reform in South-eastern Zimbabwe, *The Journal of Modern African Studies*, **41(4)**, pp. 533–554, 2003.

[22] Monfreda, C., Wackernagel, M., and Deumling, D., Establishing national natural capital accounts based on detailed ecological footprint and biological capacity accounts, *Land Use Policy*, **21**, pp. 231–246, 2004.

[23] Lewan, L., and Simmons, C., (eds). *A short Primer on the Ecological Footprint,* London: Earthscan Publications, 2001.

[24] Weidmann, T., and Lenzen, M., On the conversion between local and global hectares in ecological footprint analysis, *Ecological Economics*, **60**, pp. 673–677, 2007.

[25] Ewing, B., Reed, A., Rizk, S.M., Galli, A., Wackernagel, M. and Kitzes, J., *Calculation Methodology for National Footprint Accounts, 2008 Edition,* Oakland: Global Footprint Network, 2008.

[26] Ewing, B., Moore, D., Goldfinger, S., Oursler, A., Reed, A., and Wackernagel, M., *The Ecological Footprint Atlas 2010,* Oakland: Global Footprint Network, 2010.

[27] Wackernagel, M., and Rees, W., *Our Ecological Footprint. Reducing Human Impact on the Earth,* Gabriola Island, BC: New Society Publishers, 1996.

[28] Wackernagel, M., and Rees, W. E., Perceptual and structural barriers to investing in natural capital: economics from an ecological footprint perspective, *Ecological Economics*, **20** pp. 3–20, 1997.

[29] Wackernagel, M., Schulz N. B., Deumling, D., Callejas Linares, A., Jenkins, M., Kapos, V., Monfreda, C., Loh, J., Myers, N., Norgaard, R. and Randers, J., *Tracking the ecological overshoot of the human economy,* USA: National Academy of Science, 2002.

[30] Moldan, B., Hak, T., Kovanda, J., Havranek, M. and Kuskova, P., "Composite Indicators of Environmental Sustainability." Statistics,

Knowledge and Policy – *OECD World Forum on Key Indicators, Palermo* 10–13 November 2004.

[31] Mayer, A. L., Strengths and weaknesses of common sustainability indices for multidimensional systems, *Environment International*, **34**. pp. 277–291, 2008.

[32] Kitzes, J., Wackernagel, M., Loh, J., Peller, A., Goldfinger, S., Cheng, D., Tea, K., Shrink and share: humanity's present and future ecological footprint, *Philosophical Transactions of the Royal Society* **B 363**, pp. 467–475, 2008.

[33] Deininger, K., and May, J., Can there be growth with equity: an initial assessment of land reform in South Africa, **1**, *Policy, Research working paper, no. WPS 2451*, 2000.

[34] Scoones, I., Marongwe, N., Mavedzenge, B., Murimbarimba, F., Mahenehene, J., and Sukune, C., *Zimbabwe's Land reform: myths and Realities,* Harare: Weaver Press, 2010.

[35] Zikhali, P., Fast Track Land Reform, Tenure Security, and Investments in Zimbabwe, *Environment for Development Discussion Paper Series, June, 2008.*

Sustaining abundance and distributional patterns of benthic diatoms from streams in Kentucky, USA

K. M. Manoylov[1,2], R. J. Stevenson[1] & Y. K. Wang[1,3]
[1]Department of Zoology, Michigan State University, USA
[2]Current address: Department of Biological and Environmental Sciences, Georgia College and State University, USA
[3]Current address: Department of Ecological Sciences and Technology, National University of Tainan, Taiwan

Abstract

A sustainable approach to the preservation of natural aquatic communities requires detailed understanding of primary producers in those communities. Diatom species abundance depends on the ecological conditions and species' ability to distribute and grow at conditions close to its optima. The abundance-distribution relationship of diatom species was studied along an anthropogenic gradient in Kentucky streams. Mean relative abundance of diatoms found in reference streams decreased with an increase of nutrients and chloride, while distribution remained wide. Diatoms from the non-reference streams had higher diversity, but even with wide distribution, they had low abundance. Species that were most common and most abundant were species that occurred in streams in low human impact watersheds. Relative abundance of these species decreased with the increasing of nutrients and chloride concentrations; however, they persisted in habitats with high human disturbance. Non-reference sites had higher diversity, higher richness and lower evenness than reference sites. These results do warrant concern in regards to conservation, where the native low nutrient, low diversity sites in the State of Kentucky are the desired attribute.
Keywords: periphyton, diatoms, community structure, reference and non-reference streams, low nutrient streams.

1 Introduction

The relationship between species abundance (relative, absolute or percent cover) and distribution has been studied for many years [1–3] on the premise that dynamics of resource exploitation by species in local communities are connected with their regional distribution. Almost without exception [4], species with wide distribution, i.e. present at a large proportion of sites in a defined region, tend to be more abundant than species with restricted distribution [5, 6]. In this context, abundance is the average abundance at sites, where the species population is observed. For scenarios where all species can exist in all sites, either positive [5] or no [7] correlation between abundance and distribution of species has been observed in many groups of organisms [7]. A positive correlation between species abundance and distribution contradicts the presumed relationship if ecological specialization was important. Specialization is the ability of a species to exploit and maintain populations in unique environmental conditions [6]. Specialists have higher mean abundances at unique sites, which would result in no or negative correlations between species abundance and distribution in a region.

Microbial bioassessment and algal conservation are valued tools in current applied ecology [8]. Study of the abundance-distribution relationship in periphyton is needed because species abundance changes greatly along environmental gradients and relative abundance is often reported in large-scale surveys [9]. Survey studies report algal species distribution patterns, but distribution refers to the correspondence between abundance and environmental characteristics. In those studies usually dominant species are weighted more than species with lower abundance in an ecoregion [10]. Periphyton abundance and distribution are a result of complex interactions [11], physical disturbance [12]), substrate conditions [13], grazing [14], and nutrient concentrations and ratios [15]. Addressing relationships between species abundance and distribution (as frequency of occurrence) could be valuable for the understanding of changes in ecosystems.

Diatoms are an excellent group for testing the abundance-distribution relationships, because they are mostly microscopic, wildly distributed and every species has the potential of establishing populations under a given set of environmental conditions, while presenting species specific traits along environmental gradient n [16]. Diatom species composition is sensitive to environmental changes [17]. Consideration of both ecological preferences and historical occurrences could provide the accurate understanding of diatom abundance and distribution [18]. The abundance and distribution relationship of periphytic diatoms within an ecoregion have not been addressed.

Species in streams with minimal human impact can be defined as reference species [16]. Diatoms from those streams are likely to be reference diatoms of the area or region. Those diatoms presumably existed in streams prior anthropogenic alterations. Reference species are expected to have a broad niche under reference conditions, while specialists (potentially introduced to a region) will have narrow distribution, according to the fundamental niche differentiation [19]. Diatoms are a very diverse group of algae with an estimated hundreds of thousands number of species [9]. It is unrealistic to expect few diatom species to be declared 'most valuable' for protection, rather in current bioassessment, the desire to protect and restore reference communities and conditions, regardless of their diversity, is considered an important ecological goal [20].

The goal of this study was to describe the relationship between relative abundance and distribution of diatom species in streams along a human disturbance gradient. Diatoms with high mean relative abundance were expected to have a narrow distribution at a small number of sites due to specialization (species specific autecology). Diatom community organization in reference streams was predicted to be similar, while diatom communities between reference and non-reference streams were expected to differ.

2 Material and methods

Samples from 44 streams from the Knobs ecoregion (northwestern Kentucky and southeastern Indiana) were collected during the April–June periods in 1996 and 1997 (Table 1 and Fig. 1). A total of 69 statistically independent samples were analyzed for the abundance – distribution pattern. Four streams were designated as reference sites and were sampled during both years (Table 1). Those sites were completely enclosed in nature preserves or human disturbance in the watersheds was low.

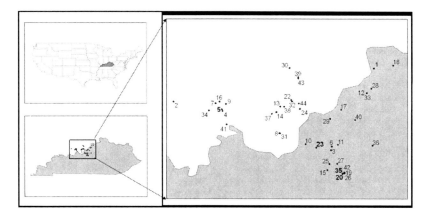

Figure 1:   Map USA, the State of Kentucky and of Knobs ecoregion (northwestern Kentucky and southeastern Indiana) with sampling sites given as numbers, reference sites in bold, sites correspond with numbers in Table 1.

Each stream was visited weekly for 8 weeks. At each visit, pH and conductivity (CON) were measured with a YSI meter (YSI Incorporated, Yellow Springs, Ohio, USA); water temperature was determined with a thermometer;

and canopy cover (CAN) was assessed with a spherical canopy densiometer. Samples for chloride and nutrients were collected in 2 125-mL acid-rinsed polyethylene bottles. Water in one sample was filtered in the field through 0.45 μm pore-size filters to measure dissolved nutrients. Nutrient samples were stored on ice until returning to the lab where they were frozen until analysis.

Table 1: Site locality and identification for sites samples each year in Knobs ecoregion US, sites in bold are considered reference.

ID	SITE NAME	site	WATERSHED	STREAM	COUNTY	LAT	LONG	1996	1997
1	Barebone Creek	BBCR	Ohio River	Barebone	Trimble	38.59	85.4		•
2	Bird Hollow	BIHO	Little Blue River	Bird Hollow	Crawford	38.36	86.77	•	•
3	Bluelick Creek	BLCR	Ohio River	Bluelick Creek	Bullitt	38.03	85.69	•	
4	Bogard Creek	BOCR	Little Blue River	Bogard Creek	Crawford	38.29	86.43	•	•
5	**Brushy Creek**	**BRC**	**Little Blue**	**Brushy**	**Crawford**	**38.31**	**86.44**	•	•
6	Brooks Run	BRRU	Ohio River	Brooks Run	Bullitt	38.05	85.69	•	
7	Brownstown	BTCR	Little Blue River	Brownstown	Crawford	38.35	86.48	•	•
8	Buck Creek	BUCR	Buck Creek	Buck Creek	Harrison	38.14	86.04	•	•
9	Camp Fork Creek	CAFO	Little Blue River	Camp Fork	Crawford	38.34	86.41	•	•
10	Cain Run	CARU	Ohio River	Cain Run	Jefferson	38.07	85.87	•	
11	Cedar Creek #1	CEC1	Salt River	Cedar Creek	Bullitt	38.06	85.65	•	
12	Cedar Creek #2	CEC2	Salt River	Cedar Creek	Bullitt	38.42	85.45	•	•
13	Corn Creek	COCR	Indian River	Corn Creek	Harrison	38.33	86.04		•
14	Crandall Branch	CRBR	Indian River	Crandall	Harrison	38.29	86.07	•	•
15	Crooked Creek	CRCR	Salt River	Crooked	Bullitt	37.89	85.72	•	•
16	Dog Creek	DOCR	Little Blue River	Dog Creek	Crawford	38.36	86.45	•	•
17	Goose Creek	GOCR	Ohio River	Goose Creek	Jefferson	38.3	85.62	•	
18	Hardy Creek	HRCR	Ohio River	Hardy Creek	Trimble	38.61	85.27		•
19	Harrison Fork	HAFO	Ohio River	Harrison Fork	Nelson	37.87	85.6		•
20	**Harts Run**	**HAR**	**Salt River**	**Harts Run**	**Bullitt**	**37.86**	**85.61**	•	•
21	Hite Creek	HTCR	Ohio River	Hite Creek					•
22	Jersey Park Creek	JPCR	Indian River	Jersey Park	Floyd	38.37	85.96	•	•
23	**Knob Creek**	**KNC**	**Ohio River**	**Knob Creek**	**Bullitt**	**38.04**	**85.79**	•	•
24	Little Indian Creek	LIIN	Indian River	Little Indian	Floyd	38.31	85.91	•	
25	Long Lick Creek	LLCR	Salt River	Long Lick	Bullitt	37.93	85.71	•	•
26	Lower Wilson	WICR	Salt River	Lower Wilson	Nelson	37.87	85.61	•	•
27	Lickskillet Creek	LSCR	Salt River	Lickskillet	Bullitt	37.93	85.65	•	•
28	MB Harrods	HACR	Ohio River	MB Harrods	Oldham	38.45	85.42		•
29	MF Beargrass	MFBG	Ohio River	MF Beargrass	Jefferson	38.24	85.7		•
30	MF Blue River	MFBL	Blue River	MF Blue River	Washingto	38.59	85.98		•
31	MF Buck Creek	MFBU	Buck Creek	MF Buck	Harrison	38.14	86.04	•	•
32	MF Indian Creek	MFIN	Indian River	MF Indian	Floyd	38.36	85.96		•
33	NF Harrods Creek	NFHA	Ohio River	NF Harrods	Oldham	38.42	85.45		•
34	Otter Creek	OTCR	Little Blue River	Otter Creek	Crawford	38.3	86.53	•	•
35	**Overalls Creek**	**OVC**	**Salt River**	**Overalls**	**Bullitt**	**37.87**	**85.6**	•	•
36	Pryors Fork	PRFO	Ohio River	Pryors Fork	Trimble	38.06	85.41		•
37	Racoon Branch	RABR	Indian River	Racoon	Harrison	38.28	86.1	•	•
38	Richland Creek	RICR	Indian River	Richland	Floyd	38.32	86.01	•	•
39	SF Blue River	SFBR	Blue River	SF Blue River	Washingto	38.53	85.92		•
40	Stinking Fork	STFO	Little Blue River	Stinking Fork	Crawford	38.23	85.53	•	•
41	Turkey Fork	TUFO	Little Blue River	Turkey Fork	Crawford	38.2	86.4	•	•
42	Upper Wilson	UWIL	Salt River	Upper Wilson	Nelson	37.87	85.6		•
43	Whiskey Run	WHR	Ohio River	Whiskey Run	Washingto	38.52	85.92		•
44	Yellow Fork	YEFO	Indian River	Yellow Fork	Floyd	38.35	85.91		•

Benthic algae were sampled during 1 of the 8 weeks of sampling, which was timed so that algae had greater than 7 days to recover after the last storm event.

Benthic algae were removed from five 3-rock clusters in riffles with a spoon and toothbrush placed into a container and split for chlorophyll *a* and enumeration. Subsamples for chlorophyll *a* were stored on ice until returning to the lab, where they were frozen until processing. Algal samples (n=69) for enumeration were preserved with M3 in the field [21]. Rock surfaces from which benthic algae were scraped were measured in the field.

2.1 Laboratory assays

Water samples were analyzed for chloride, nitrate (NO_3), and ammonium (NH_4) using a Skalar® auto-analyzer. Soluble reactive phosphorus (SRP) was measured using a Hitachi® U-2001 spectrophotometer. Alkalinity (ALK) was assessed according to standard methods APHA [21]. Silica was determined with ascorbic acid method on a Skalar® auto-analyzer [21]. To determine total phosphorus (TP) and total nitrogen (TN) concentrations, particulate matter in water samples was oxidized with persulfate and analyzed for SRP and NO_3. Chlorophyll *a* was measured was measured spectrophotometrically after extraction from the periphyton samples with 90% buffered acetone [21].

Algal subsamples were analyzed for diatom species composition. Permanent diatom slides were prepared by acid-cleaning to increase the clarity of observing diatoms and mounting in Naphrax resin (RI 1.74, Northern Biological Supplies L., Ipswich, UK). A minimum of 600 diatom valves were identified and counted in each slide. Correct taxonomic identification in the dataset was ensured following a QAQC protocol. A second analyst independently counted samples from the reference streams and four random streams in each year. Proportional relative abundances of diatom taxa in each sample were determined.

Diatoms from reference streams are species that occurred naturally in Kentucky (or not introduced). In the reference sites, human disturbance is considered negligible [20], so diatoms from those sites were defined as reference taxa. Those species are the species that occur in many water bodies, fossil records and habitats. Extensive counts were performed to account for as many rare taxa as possible in the four reference streams. After the original 600 count and the QAQC count, a third count continued until at least five taxa were enumerated with 100 valves (which in diverse sites reached a count of >2500 valves). This protocol ensured accounting for all dominant taxa (more than 5% relative abundance in each count), allowed observation of more taxa in the count and was independent of a predetermined number count.

2.2 Data analyses

The relationship between species abundance and distribution was tested with regression analysis. Following the terminology of the core-satellite hypothesis [5], a core species was a common diatom that appeared in more than 90% of the sites, while a satellite species appeared in less than 10% of the sites. Species in the middle (found in more than 10 % and less than 90% of the sites) were called intermediate, but those intermediate taxa had the potential to become part of the later categories. We varied those categories increasing the sites for core species up 4 folds (more than 80%, 70% core and 60% core) and followed characteristics of the newly classified number of species in each category. Based on the number of species in each category, different distribution patterns are discriminated (skewed to the left or right, unimodal, or bimodal). All categories can vary in abundance.

The physico-chemical differences between reference and non-reference sites were tested with a Mann-Whitney nonparametric test. Average species similarity (aveS) within reference and non-reference sites or dissimilarity (aveδ) between the two groups of sites was evaluated with SIMPER procedure (Primer-E Ltd. [22]). This allowed examining the contribution of each diatom species to either similarity within or dissimilarity between reference and non-reference sites. Standard deviation of the means were estimated for S and δ, respectively SD(S) and SD(δ). For both measures, how consistently a diatom species contributes to either aveS or aveδ was measured with the ratios aveS/SD(S) and aveδ/SD(δ) respectively. When SD(S) and SD(δ) were small the ratios were large and the respective diatom species not only contributed much for the similarity or dissimilarity, but was also consistent in doing so. Diatom species with high discriminating ratios (either aveS /SD(S) or aveδ/SD(δ)) were called discriminating species [23] and are reported. Statistical analyses were performed with SYSTAT[®] version 10 [24] unless stated otherwise.

3 Results

3.1 Species abundance-distribution relationship

A positive relationship was observed between diatom species abundance and distribution in the survey, more abundant species occupied a larger percent of the sites than less abundant species (regression analysis: $R^2 = 0.68$, p<0.01; Fig. 2a). A total of 189 diatom species were recorded. Three taxa were observed in more than 90 % of the sites sampled. *Achnanthidium minutissimum* was observed at all sites and had the highest mean relative abundance in the survey (20.8%). The other two core species in this study, *Nitzschia dissipata* and *Gomphonema angustatum*, had 6.5 and 15.5% mean relative abundances, respectively. Sixty-nine percent of the observed taxa were defined as rare because they appeared in less than one percent of sites. All rare taxa had mean relative abundances less than 4.2% (Fig. 2b).

The observed positive relationship between abundance and distribution was not due to sampling error or aggregation. The coefficient of variation was negatively related to species distributions (Table 2). Regression analysis: Model: $R^2=0.98$, $F_{2, 188}=5095.22$, $p<0.0001$. Diatoms with high abundance were found in more sites and had smaller coefficient of variation. The analysis showed that the parameters differed from zero.

Table 2: Test of the influence of sampling on the abundance-distribution relationship for Kentucky stream diatoms. Species-specific coefficient of variation (CV) and average abundance (x_{all}) were calculated across all sites. SE- standard error, p – significance level.

Variable	Estimate	SE	p
Intercept	0.04	0.09	0.66
$\ln(\ln(x_{all}))$	0.99	0.03	<0.0001
$-2*\ln(CV)$	1.99	0.03	<0.0001

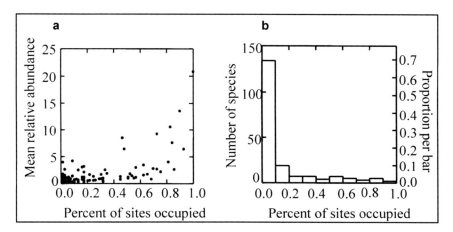

Figure 2: Relationship between diatom species abundance and distribution (as percent of sites occupied) in the survey for all samples (n=69); a. A scatter plot of mean relative abundance for the sites occupied; b. A histogram number of species and percent sites occupied (second y axes represents the proportion of taxa in the bars) against their distribution.

3.2 Relation of core-satellite species to ecological conditions

Temperature, canopy cover (measure of light) and pH were not different between the reference and non-reference streams. Silica was higher in the reference streams. All other physico-chemical variables in the reference sites were significantly lower compared to sites with human influence (Table 3). Multiple regression analysis: Model R^2=0.43, $F_{2, 188}$=71.93, p<0.0001. Conductivity and chloride were 1.5 times higher in the non-reference sites compared to the reference sites. Nutrients were several orders of magnitude higher also.

In reference streams taxa observed (richness) in counts varied from 15 to 26 taxa (mean evenness 0.55± 0.03 SE, range 0.41 to 0.66), while in sites with human influence there were 14 to 45 diatom taxa were observed (mean evenness 0.67± 0.01 SE range 0.36 to 0.82). Diatom species membership at reference sites was less diverse than at all sites.

 WIT Transactions on Ecology and The Environment, Vol 173, © 2013 WIT Press
www.witpress.com, ISSN 1743-3541 (on-line)

Table 3:   Physicochemical measurements in reference and non-reference sites. Mann-Whitney test, p= significance level.

Variables	Reference sites				Non-reference sites				
	mean	±SE	min	max	mean	±SE	min	max	p
air temperature °C	15.9	2.1	6	32	15.8	0.7	3	36	n.s
water temperature °C	13.6	1	6.8	19.7	14.3	0.5	5	25.9	n.s
canopy cover (%)	24.36	3.69	0	87	29.02	1.3	0	88	n.s.
conductivity (µS cm-1)	220	17.9	107	322	345	16	105.2	804	<0.001
alkalinity (mg L-1)	75.3	7.6	51	120	113.5	6.3	12	208	0.02
pH	8	0	8	8	8.1	0	7	9	n.s
Chloride (meq L-1)	2.5	1	0.8	7.1	7.3	0.7	1.6	21.3	0.01
NO3(µg L-1)	204.7	67.9	27.8	789.6	957.0	123.9	19.2	6645.2	0.01
NH4 (µg L-1)	12.7	2.4	2.1	32.6	23.9	3.5	3.8	263.0	<0.001
TN (µg L-1)	308.1	75.5	2.6	876.0	1131.8	131.0	38.0	7358.0	0.04
SRP µg L-1	6.6	1.4	1.0	20.6	31.6	11.7	0.0	940.9	<0.001
TP (µg L-1)	9.3	1.9	2.6	27.1	51.1	16.7	2.3	1379.9	0.01
SI (mg L-1)	8.9	0.8	5.0	12.0	6.5	0.3	1.0	17.0	0.01
NP (molar ratio)	86.3	24.5	0.5	298.0	107.0	18.2	4.6	688.0	n.s

In reference and non-reference sites, *Cymbella affinis* occurred in 80% of the samples, but had mean relative abundance of 14.9% and 8.8% respectively (Tables 4 and 5). *Achnanthidium deflexum* appeared in 82% of non-reference and 88% of reference sites. *Achnanthidium deflexum* and *Achnanthidium minutissimum* were the most abundant taxa in reference streams. Only *A. minutissimum* and *Cymbella* sp. *K* appeared in all reference samples, but differed in mean relative abundance 38% to 2.8% respectively.

The observed differences in species richness between reference and non-reference sites contributed to 68% dissimilarity between the two groups. Twenty-seven taxa (15% of all identified) contributed for 90% of the dissimilarity, with 50% of it contributed by four taxa (Table 4). The highest discriminating species in the between sites dissimilarity was *Cymbella affinis* (ratio 8.67). Additional dissimilarity was contributed by *Gomphonema angustatum*, *Achnanthidium minutissimum* and *A. deflexum*. All four discriminating taxa appeared in both reference and non-reference taxa.

Within non-reference streams, average similarity among sites was lower, 31% (Table 5a). Thirteen taxa accounted for 90% of the accounted similarity. *Achnanthidium minutissimum* accounted only 30.6% of similarity among the non-reference sites. Three discriminating species in non-reference sites had high similarities and low standard deviations: *A. minutissimum*, *G. angustatum* and *Cymbella affinis* (discriminating ratios 9.15, 6.75 and 5.60 respectively, Table 5a). Average similarity among reference streams was 48%. Four taxa contributed to 90% of the similarity, with over 60% contributed by *A. minutissimum* alone (Table 5b). *Achnanthidium minutissimum* and *Gomphonema angustatum* were the two discriminating species in reference sites, because of their high similarity and low standard deviation measures (discriminating ratios 16.44 and 8.38 respectively, Table 5b). Low nutrient taxa decreased only 13 % with 4 fold increase of the core sites, while the satellite species were predominantly high nutrient taxa (Figure 3).

Table 4:   Diatom species average dissimilarity (ave δ) between non-reference and reference sites, contribution from each species; species are ordered in decreasing contribution with 90% cumulative contribution (Cum%) as a cut-off percentage; meanRAnr- mean relative abundance in non-reference sites, compare with mean RA in reference sites Appendix B; (SD)δ – standard deviation of the δ (*i*th species) values; aveδ/SD(δ) - discriminating ratio, highest in bold; ∑(aveδ)% - average percent contribution to similarity by the (*i*th species).

Taxon	meanRAnr	ave δ	ave δ (SD)	δ/δSD	∑ave δ%	Cum%
Achnanthidium minutissimum	18.6	12.67	1.79	**7.08**	18.7	18.7
Gomphonema angustatum	11.6	8.42	1.08	**7.80**	12.5	31.2
Cymbella affinis	8.8	6.85	0.79	**8.67**	10.1	41.3
Achnanthidium deflexum	5.9	5.97	1.36	**4.39**	8.8	50.1
Gomphonema olivaceum	7	3.27	0.75	**4.36**	4.8	54.9
Nitzschia dissipata	6.6	3.04	0.93	3.27	4.5	59.5
Nitzschia inconspicua	4.5	2.25	0.41	**5.49**	3.3	62.8
Rhoicosphenia abbreviata	6.5	1.75	0.47	3.72	2.6	65.4
Navicula veneta	3.5	1.75	0.67	2.61	2.6	68
Cymbella sp. K	1.8	1.57	1	1.57	2.3	70.3
Synedra rumpens	0.1	1.41	0.59	2.39	2.1	72.4
Navicula cryptotenella	3.5	1.22	0.6	2.03	1.8	74.2
Navicula minima	2.5	1.17	0.52	2.25	1.7	75.9
Amphora pediculus	2.8	1.13	0.53	2.13	1.7	77.6
Navicula gregaria	1.9	0.95	0.25	**3.80**	1.4	79
Encyonema silesiacum	0.6	0.94	1	0.94	1.4	80.4
Surirella minuta	1.8	0.92	0.66	1.39	1.4	81.8
Achnanthes ventralis	0.2	0.86	0.56	1.54	1.3	83
Cymbella delicatula	0.2	0.77	0.92	0.84	1.1	84.2
Gomphonema minutum	1	0.69	0.48	1.44	1	85.2
Meridion circulare	0.4	0.68	0.84	0.81	1	86.2
Diatoma vulgaris	1.8	0.64	0.45	1.42	1	87.1
Reimeria sinuata	1	0.52	0.73	0.71	0.8	87.9
Nitzschia frustulum	1	0.49	0.31	1.58	0.7	88.6
Fragilaria vaucheriae	0.3	0.48	0.47	1.02	0.7	89.3
Synedra ulna	0.7	0.45	0.51	0.88	0.7	89.9
Nitzschia sociabilis	1.2	0.37	0.64	0.58	0.6	90.6

4   Discussion

In this study a positive abundance-distribution relationship was observed for benthic diatoms.   The observed patterns were due to the species-specific abundance and distribution relationship of relatively small number of diatom species.   *Achnanthidium minutissimum* had highest mean relative abundance in

Table 5: Diatom species average similarity (aveS) contributed from each species for: a. non-reference sites, and b. reference sites; species are ordered in decreasing contribution with 90% cumulative contribution (Cum%) as a cut-off percentage; (SD)S – standard deviation of the S (ith species) values; aveS/SD(S) – discriminating ratio, highest in bold; $\sum$(aveS)% – average percent contribution to similarity by the (ith species).

Taxon	aveS	SD(S)	aveS/SD(S)	$\sum$aveS%	Cum%
a.					
Achnanthidium minutissimum	10.43	1.14	**9.15**	30.62	30.6
Gomphonema angustatum	4.86	0.72	**6.75**	14.28	44.9
Nitzschia dissipata	3.21	0.93	3.45	9.44	54.3
Cymbella affinis	2.91	0.52	**5.60**	8.55	62.9
Gomphonema olivaceum	2.57	0.68	3.78	7.53	70.4
Achnanthidium deflexum	1.79	0.49	3.65	5.26	75.7
Navicula veneta	1.14	0.6	1.90	3.36	79.1
Navicula cryptotenella	0.71	0.52	1.37	2.09	81.1
Navicula minima	0.66	0.49	1.35	1.92	83.1
Cymbella sp. K	0.62	0.54	1.15	1.81	84.9
Surirella minuta	0.59	0.62	0.95	1.74	86.6
Nitzschia inconspicua	0.59	0.22	2.68	1.73	88.3
Amphora pediculus	0.59	0.46	1.28	1.73	90.1
b.					
Achnanthidium minutissimum	29.26	1.78	**16.44**	61.5	61.5
Achnanthidium deflexum	6.86	0.9	7.62	14.4	75.9
Gomphonema angustatum	6.03	0.72	**8.38**	12.7	88.6
Cymbella sp. K	0.82	0.48	1.71	1.7	90.3

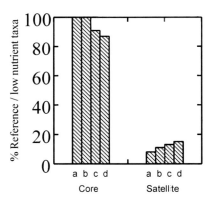

Figure 3: Distribution of species membership low nutrient (reference) requirements in different site number designations of core (C) and satellite species (S): a. C>90%, S<10%; b. C>80%, S<20%; c. C>70%, S<30%; and d. C>60%, S<40%.

the survey and was found at all sites. Core species comprised only 2% of the diatom community, while the majority of diatoms were satellite species. The large number of rare taxa observed did not change the positive correlation between abundance and distribution.

Diatom communities from reference streams had low diversity and high similarity. Reference and non-reference diatom communities were highly dissimilar. A relatively small number of diatom taxa contributed to the observed dissimilarity. Diatoms observed in the reference sites were observed in many non-reference sites, but in significantly lower abundance. All non-reference diatoms were in lower abundance regardless of the number of sites they appeared.

With an increase in nutrients, eutrophic species grow faster when compared with diatom species from the reference community. The robustness of the pattern was confirmed with the experimental results. In the abundant literature addressing the abundance-distribution relationships, only one relates to algae. Lewis [25] found an asymmetric relationship for phytoplankton, which was skewed to the right with most taxa in a few sites. That distribution was independent of mean abundance and resource supply. The relationship was specific for green algae, bluegreen algae, and diatoms and varied with grazer conditions. In the present study we found a strong positive relationship between abundance and distribution, common taxa were most abundant and had wider distribution.

Biologically the appearance of *Achnanthidium minutissimum* at all sites and with high mean relative abundance can be explained with the relatively fast growth of this diatom and high tolerance for low nutrient concentrations. Tradeoff theory suggests that there should be optimal conditions, so if *A. minutissimum* was at optimal growth in the reference sites, different taxa should have high abundance at the non-reference sites. The mean abundance of *A. minutissimum* in the reference sites was significantly higher compared to all sites.

The observed pattern did not follow the core-satellite hypothesis [5], which predicts a bimodal abundance-distribution pattern. This pattern has been observed in different organisms and along multiple gradients [26, 27], but it was not evident for benthic diatoms. Diatoms with high abundance were found in more sites and had a smaller coefficient of variation. Thus, the predictions of ecological specialization were not supported [28]. Sample collection, sampling area, and the number of samples were appropriate to study the abundance-distribution relationship [27]. However, the degree of environmental heterogeneity was minimized by sampling only riffles, rocks, and streams within an ecoregion.

Diatom species with high mean relative abundance had the widest distribution. Species were expected to be most abundant in relatively few habitats in a region if species specialized with optimal performance in specific environmental conditions. Contrary to this prediction, a positive correlation was observed between diatom abundance and breadth of their distribution in the Knobs ecoregion of Kentucky and southern Indiana. A positive relationship between relative abundance and distribution was observed. Few taxa were abundant and they had broad distributions, the majority (79%) of the observed diatom species had low abundance and appeared in few sites (less that 10% of sites).

Acknowledgements

We would like to thank Drs S. T. Rier (Bloomsburg University) and C. M. Riseng (University of Michigan) for collecting the samples as part of the STAR-EPA grant to RJS and Carrie DeJaco (Queens University of Charlotte) for initial sample identification. The manuscript benefited from the critical reviews of Drs D. Hall, G. Mittelbach and T. Burton (Michigan State University). This research was done and presented as partial fulfillment of the dissertation research of KMM at Michigan State University.

References

[1] Adrewartha H.G., Birch L.C. The distribution and abundance of animals. University of Chicago Press, Chicago, 1954.
[2] Brown J.H. On the relationship between abundance and distribution of species. *Am Nat*, **124**, pp. 253-279, 1984.
[3] Gotelli N.J., Simberloff D. The distribution and abundance of tallgrass prairie plants: a test of the core-satellite hypothesis. *American Naturalist*, **130**, pp. 18-35, 1987.
[4] Hanski I., Gyllenberg M. Two general metapopulation models and the core-satellite hypothesis. *American Naturalist*, **142**, pp. 17-41, 1993.
[5] Hanski I. Dynamics of regional distribution: the core and satellite species hypothesis. *Oikos*, **38**, pp. 210-221, 1982a.
[6] McNaughton S.J., Wolf L.L. Dominance and the niche in ecological systems. *Science, 167*, pp. 131-39, 1970.
[7] Levins R. Some demographic and genetic consequences of environmental heterogeneity for biological control. *Bull Entomological Society America*, **15**, pp. 237-240, 1969.
[8] Stevenson R.J., Smol J. Use of algae in environmental assessment. In: Wehr JD and Sheath RG (eds.) Freshwater algae of North America. Academic press, New York, 2003.
[9] Pan Y., Stevenson R.J., Hill B.H., Herlihy A.T., Collins G.B. Using diatoms as indicators of ecological conditions in lotic systems: a regional assessment. *J North American Benthological Society*, **15**, pp. 481-495, 1996.
[10] Patrick R. A study of the numbers and kinds of species found in rivers of the Eastern United States. *Proceeding of Academy of Natural Sciences of Philadelphia*, **113**, pp. 215-258, 1961.
[11] Stevenson R.J. Scale-dependent determinants and consequences of benthic algal heterogeneity. *J North American Benthological Society*, **16**, pp. 248-262, 1997.

[12] Humphrey K.P., Stevenson R.J. Responses of benthic algae to pulses in current and nutrients during simulations of subscouring spates. *J North American Benthological Society*, **11**, pp. 37- 48, 1992.

[13] Peterson C.G., Stevenson R.J. Substratum conditioning and diatom colonization in different current regimes. *Journal of Phycology*, **25**, pp. 790-793, 1989.

[14] Steinman A.D. Effects of grazers on freshwater benthic algae In: Stevenson RJ, Bothwell ML, Lowe R.L. (eds.) Algal Ecology. Academic Press, San Diego, pp. 341-374, 1996.

[15] Peterson C.G., Grimm N.B. Temporal variation in enrichment effects during periphyton succession in a nitrogen-limited desert stream ecosystems. *J North American Benthological Society*, **11**, pp. 20-36, 1992.

[16] Stevenson R.J., Rier S.T., Riseng C.M., Schultz R., Wiley M.J. Comparing effects of nutrients on algal biomass in streams in two regions with different disturbance regimes and with applications for developing nutrient criteria. *Hydrobiologia*, **561**, pp. 149-165, 2006.

[17] Van Dam H. On the use of measures of structure and diversity in applied diatom ecology. *Nova Hedwigia*, **73**, pp. 97-115, 1982.

[18] Stoermer E.F., Julius M.W. Centric diatoms. In: Wehr JD, Sheath RG (eds.) *Freshwater algae of North America*, pp. 559-594, 2003.

[19] Whittaker R.H. Communities and ecosystems, 2nd ed. MacMillan, New York, 1975.

[20] Karr J.R., Dudley D.R. Ecological perspective on water quality goals. *Environmental Management*, **5**, pp. 55-68.

[21] APHA. Standard methods for examination of water and wastewater. Washington DC, American Public Health Association, 1998.

[22] Clarke K., Gorley R.N. Primer v5. Primer Ltd, Plymouth Marine Lab. UK, 2001.

[23] Clarke K., Warwick R.M. A taxonomic distinctness and its statistical properties. *J Applied Ecology*, **35**, pp. 523-531, 1998.

[24] Wilkinson L. Systat: The System for Statistics. Evanston, 1989.

[25] Lewis W.M. Ecological significance of the shapes of abundance-frequency distributions for coexisting phytoplankton species. *Ecology*, **58**, pp. 850-859, 1977.

[26] Gibson D.J., Ely J.S., Collins S.L. The core-satellite species hypothesis provides a theoretical basis for Grime's classification of dominant, subordinate, and transient species. *J Ecology*, **87**, pp. 1064-1067, 1999.

[27] McGeogh M.A., Gaston K.J. Occupancy frequency distributions: patterns, artifacts and mechanisms. *Biological Review*, **77**, pp. 311-331, 2002.

[28] Telford R.J., Vandvik V., Birks H.J. How many freshwater diatoms are pH specialists? A response to Pither and Aarssen. *Ecology Letters*, **9**, E1-E5, 2006.

Allometric equations to estimate carbon pool in soil and above-ground biomass in mangrove forests in Southeast Mexico

J. J. Guerra-Santos, R. M. Cerón, J. G. Cerón, A. Alderete-Chávez, D. L. Damián-Hernández & R. C. Sánchez-Junco
Centro de Investigación de Ciencias Ambientales,
Universidad Autónoma del Carmen, Mexico

Abstract

This paper reports the results of carbon stored in soil and aboveground biomass from the most important area of mangroves in Mexico with dominant vegetation of Red mangrove (*Rhizophora mangle* L.), Black mangrove (*Avicennia germinans* L.), white mangrove (*Laguncularia racemosa* Gaertn.) and button mangrove (*Conocarpus erectus* L.) in three sites located in the Atasta Peninsula, Campeche, Mexico. Samples were taken in 2009 and 2010 during the dry season from soils with high fertility. To determine tree biomass (AGB), allometric equations were used. Greater values of AGB were found for button mangrove (253.18 ± 32.17 t ha^{-1}) and lower values were found for Black mangrove (161.93 ± 12.63), intermediate carbon storage were found in the other two species Red mangrove 181.70 ± 16.58 t ha^{-1}), and white mangrove (206.07 ± 19.12 t ha^{-1}). Carbon stored in soil at the three sites was measured in a range of 36.80 ± 10.27 to 235.77 ± 66.11 t C ha^{-1}. The Tukey test ($p < 0.05$) showed significant differences exist between Black mangrove and button mangrove. The button mangrove trees evaluated had a higher AGB compared with other species, and black mangrove trees have a relatively lower AGB, because they grow in hypersaline environments which reduce their development, while for buttonwood mangrove growing on higher ground, their soils are better able to obtain nutrients. AGB tends to be relatively low in areas near the sea and rise as the forest location is closer inland. In the case of a black mangrove, usually these individuals are growing on recently deposited sediments; the Tukey test indicated no significant differences among the sample sites. These results show that all sites have good potential to store carbon for long periods of time. The

WIT Transactions on Ecology and The Environment, Vol 173, © 2013 WIT Press
www.witpress.com, ISSN 1743-3541 (on-line)
doi:10.2495/SDP130111

carbon stored in the three sampling sites in the state of Campeche Mexico is higher than that reported by other authors in different places in the world.

Keywords: carbon storage, Rhizophora mangle, Laguncularia racemosa, Avicennia germinans, tree biomass.

1 Introduction

Carbon Dioxide (CO_2) is emitted to the atmosphere both naturally and anthropogenic, is the most important greenhouse gas and its large quantities contribute 55% of global warming The concentration of CO_2 in the atmosphere has increased from 280 ppm in 1750 to 367 ppm in 1999 (31%), the observed increase is predominantly due to the oxidation of organic carbon from burning fossil fuels and deforestation [1]; The main C stocks in forest ecosystems are soil, vegetation and humus, this is because the vegetation has the ability to assimilate carbon and incorporate it into its structure, to be fixed and stored for long periods of time, through photosynthesis. That is why forests are important carbon sinks [2]. The foliage of the trees adds organic matter to the soil when the leaves are decomposed; they incorporate CO_2 into the soils then gives rise to stable humus which, in turn, brings again CO_2 [3].

Wetlands are known to be an important carbon sink despite occupying only about 5% of the planet's surface, contain much of the reservoir of carbon stored in the world [4]; their soils stored carbon for a long period of time, due the phreatic groundwater, high productivity and low decomposition by the slow diffusion of oxygen [5].

Field studies for the determination of biomass and productivity in mangrove forests are quite difficult due to muddy soil conditions. There are 3 commonly used methods that have been developed to estimate forest biomass: 1) the destructive method, 2) the average tree method and 3) the allometric method; in mature forests, trees can reach up to several tons in weight, so in the destructive method, trees would be harvested for data, so it is not practical in these cases and is difficult to reproduce the results. The average tree method usually applies only in forests with a homogeneous distribution of sizes in the trees, as in the case of plantations (Komiyama *et al.* [4]); The allometric method on the other hand, is used to estimate the partial or total weight of a tree from measurable dimensions such as Diameter at Breast Height (DBH) and height of the individual, using allometric equations [6]. In this work it was decided to use this method because it has the advantage that it is not a destructive method and is therefore useful to estimate temporal changes in forest biomass through subsequent measurements, for instance the diameter of the tree is easily measured and the weight of the tree is much more difficult to determine, this alternative method is a relatively easy to estimate the biomass in forests

The state of Campeche ranks first nationally according to their protected area with the largest expanses of mangrove coverage, more than 259 000 ha, are located in the area of protection of Flora and Fauna "Laguna de Términos" is considered the most important wetland area in the Gulf of Mexico. The Atasta Peninsula is located in this area, where different economic activities, such as agriculture, aquaculture, oil industry and population growth are the main threats to these mangrove forests [7]. Therefore, due to the ecological and economic importance of mangrove forests located in the study region, this paper reports results of the carbon stored in soil and tree biomass estimated from allometric equations in a mangrove forest located in the Peninsula Atasta in Campeche, Mexico.

2 Methodology

2.1 Site description

The study area is located northwest of the state of Campeche, is part of the municipality of Carmen, the geomorphology of the area consists of wetlands and floodplains at elevations between 0 and 20 m. The soils of the region are characterized by heavy clay with high fertility and are associated with predominant vegetation of mangrove forest as *Rhizophora mangle* (Rm), *Avicennia germinans* (Ag), *Laguncularia racemosa* (Lr) and *Conocarpus erectus* (Ce) [7].

The climate regime of the area has three well defined seasons: dry (February to May), rainy (June to October) and "North" (November to February). The selected stations (Table 1) were as follows:

Puerto Rico (PR) located at 18°36'55"N and 91°56'35"W, at an altitude of 11 meters. The classification of this is the type mangrove basin as described by Lugo and Snedaker [8], the plots are located inland, have a minimum slope of land and water turnover very slow floodwaters accumulate in depressions; to others, by its terms, these sites correspond according to Twilley *et al.* [9] to a cycle of organic matter and nutrients in a closed ecosystem; on this site were recorded *Avicennia germinans*, *Laguncularia racemosa*, and *Rhizophora mangle*.

Table 1:   Description of study sites: mangrove species occurring, geographical coordinates, maximum diameter at 1.30 m (Max. DBH), annual rainfall, duration of the dry season and forest type.

	Study site		
	Puerto Rico	Xicalango	Nuevo Campechito
Species	Rm, Lr, Ag	Lr, Ag, Ce	Rm, Lr, Ag, Ce
geographical coordinates	18° 36'55"N, 91°56'35"W	18°37'02 "N, 91°58'20"W	18°38'28"N, 92°27'29"W
Maximum. DBH (cm)	49.8	2.93	7.80
Rainfall (mm/year)	1680	1680	1680
Months of the dry season	4	4	4
Type of forest	Wet mangrove	Wet mangrove	Wet mangrove

Xicalango (XC): located 18°37'02"N and 91°58'20"W, at an altitude of 12 meters. The mangrove forest settled in this site corresponds to a mixed stunted mangrove as proposed by Rico-Gray [10]. On this site we found a mixture of mangrove species such as Ag, Lr and Ce, the plots were located inland near a stream that connects the lagoon system Pom-Atasta. The soil is yellowish brown and has high activity of aquatic fungi and bacteria, with a low concentration of salinity. It is a very dense mangrove, the height of the individuals ranged from approximately 3 to 6 m with exposed aerial roots that made complicated the access

Nuevo Campechito (NC) located 18°38'28"N and 92°27'29"W, with a height of 1 m. Like PR, the mangrove forest is the type of basin [8], grows in a coastal plain with poor drainage, selected plots were bordered by two small lakes, major mangrove species found were Ar, Lr and Ce

2.2 Method of sampling and forest inventory

Soil samples were collected at the three sites described above located in areas of mangrove forest Atasta Peninsula. The sample collection was conducted during the dry season in 2009 and 2010. Each site was chosen selectively, seeking representation in the region, considering factors such as vegetation, accessibility and hydrology. At each sampling site plots were 18 m^2, 6 plots were established for the PR, and in NC and XC 3 plots at each site. In each of the plots were collected 3 samples distributed in a transect, taken at 0.30 m depth using a corer of 193.3 cm^3, to include a variation of organic matter per site; After extraction, each sample was labelled, sealed and processed in the laboratory for analysis. The forest inventory was conducted in 12 plots of 200 m^2 distributed in a rectangular shape in the three sampling sites. Data were recorded at 1.30 m in diameter (DBH) for all species, in the case of Rm the DBH was measured at 1.30 m above the adventitious roots and a total of 321 trees data were collected.

In the laboratory, samples were removed the shells, bits of organic material (roots, leaves and branches), then air-dried and passed through a sieve of 2 mm. For quantification of Organic Carbon (CO) was used the method of loss on ignition, which consists in determining the organic matter by heating at 550°C for 4 h (Heiri *et al.* [11]) and converted to CO by multiplication with 0.4   (Craft *et al.* [12]).

2.3 Analytical procedure

To determine the bulk density (Da) a plastic tube assay was used, which consists in passing the dry sample through a sieve of 2 mm; the weight of the plastic test tube of 50 ml was obtained after that 20 to 50 g of sieved soil were added, then placed on a firm surface and given 30 strokes with a rubber mallet in a vertical path from 0.20 to 0.30 m. Finally, record the volume occupied and the weight of the sample.

To calculate Carbon stored (CA) was carried out by the following eqn (1):

$$C = CO\% \times Da \times Pr \tag{1}$$

where: C = carbon stored (Ton ha^{-1}); CO% = percentage of carbon in the soil, Da = apparent density (t/m^3) and Pr = the depth (m) (Gonzalez *et al.* [13]).

The electrical conductivity (EC) was measured by a conductometer CL 35 in an extract suspended in a 1:5 soil: water solution (NOM-021-RECNAT-2001). Statistical development compares and relates the statistical analysis for carbon storage by compartment and EC data. The average values were obtained for the different determinations. The hypothesis made was evaluated by the method of one-way ANOVA to determine significant differences between sampling station and plots. The evaluation was conducted by testing standardization and homogeneity of variances (p <0.05) by Tukey's method, using the Statistica software version 7.

Allometric models were used to estimate tree biomass (AGB), these models were developed from destructive sampling for different mangrove forests around the world (Table 2), the model used in this study calculated with equation (2), is based on samples of a total of 2.410 trees of different tropical forests, including 27 study sites distributed in the tropics (Chave *et al.* [14]):

$$AGB = p \, (\exp(-1.349 + 1.980 \, Ln \, (DBH) + 0.207 \, (Ln \, (DBH))^2 - 0.0281 \, (Ln \, (DBH))^3) \quad (2)$$

where p, is the density of the wood, and DBH is the diameter of the stems at breast height. This model assumes a constant ratio between the diameter and height, which is useful because the height of the trees was a missing data in our forest inventory. The density of the wood was extracted from the database Global Wood Density (Zanne *et al.* [15]). For species not included in the

Table 2: Allometric equations for estimating tree biomass (AGB in Kg) for mangrove forests with DBH = Diameter at 1.30 m, p = wood density (t m-^{3}). The densities are: *Avicennia germinans* = 900, *Laguncularia racemosa* = 762, *Rhizophora mangle* = 1000, and *Xylocarpus granatum* = 700.

Equation	Specie	Area	Source
AGB=0.140DBH$^{2.40}$	*Avicennia germinans*	French Guyana	Fromard *et al.* (1998)
AGB=0.140DBH$^{2.54}$	*Avicennia germinans*	Guadeloupe, French Antilles	Imbert and Rollet (1989)
AGB=0.102DBH$^{2.50}$	*Laguncularia racemosa*	French Guyana	Fromard *et al.* (1998)
AGB=0.209DBH$^{2.24}$	*Laguncularia racemosa*	Guadeloupe, French Antilles	Imbert and Rollet (1989)
AGB=0.178DBH$^{2.47}$	*Rhizophora mangle*	Guadalupe, French Antilles	Imbert and Rollet (1989)
AGB=0.0823DBH$^{2.59}$	*Xylocarpus granatum*	West Australia	Clough and Scott (1989)
AGB=0.251pDBH$^{2.46}$	Common	Tropical Forest in America, Asia, and Oceania	Komiyama *et al.* (2005)
AGB=p(exp(-1.349+ 1.980Ln(DHB)+0.207(Ln (D))^2-0.0281(Ln(DHB))^3)	Common	Southwest of Asia	Chave *et al.* (2005)

database is considered the density of the wood to any member of the same botanical family. The carbon content of the biomass was evaluated at 50% dry weight of biomass (Basuki et al. [16]).

3 Results and discussion

3.1 Importance value

In all sites the importance value (defined as the sum of the relative frequency plus relative density, plus relative dominance divided into 3) was calculated (see Table 3). In Puerto Rico (PR), A. germinans, had the highest importance value, and L. racemosa the minimum value, similar results had been found for A. (NC) L. racemosa obtained the maximum value and even A. germinans germinans in plots located in other areas of Laguna de Terminos in mangrove forests of the river type (Day et al. [17]), in contrast in Nuevo Campechito corresponded to the minimum value of importance. Puerto Rico had the lowest density of trees; however, were found largest diameter trees and basal area. On the other hand, Xicalango (XC) had the minimum values of diameter and basal area, while in NC, was the site with the highest density of trees. Note that in XC, the three species present (Ag, Lr and Ce) have the same value of importance shown in Table 3.

Table 3: Composition of trees in mangrove forests of Puerto Rico, New Campechito and Xicalango (trees > 1 cm DBH).

Site/species	Density (stem ha^{-1})	Frequency[1]	DBH mean (cm)	basal area (m^2 ha^{-1})	Importance value[2]
Puerto Rico					
Avicennia germinans	9050	78.06	11.09	13.31	78.06
Laguncularia	1100	9.71	9.74	3.69	9.71
racemosa	1400	12.23	11.33	1.77	12.23
Rhizophora mangle	11550			18.77	100
Total					
Nuevo Campechito					
Avicennia germinans	2780	7.42	6.46	3.47	7.42
Laguncularia	12220	33.83	2.49	2.37	33.83
racemosa	7780	25.42	2.2	1.96	25.42
Rhizophora mangle	10000	33.33	1.28	1.30	33.33
Conocarpus erectus	32780			9.10	100
Total					
Xicalango					
Avicennia germinans	6667	33.33	1.64	1.41	33.33
Laguncularia	13889	33.33	1.14	1.42	33.33
racemosa	3333	33.33	1.19	0.37	33.33
Conocarpus erectus	23889			3.2	100
Total					

[1]Percentage of total number of trees.
[2]Importance value is the sum of the relative frequency, relative density and relative dominance divided into 3.

3.2 Estimating tree biomass (AGB)

The higher average of AGB was found in C. erectus (253.18 ± 32.17 t ha^{-1}) and lowest in *A. germinans* (161.93 ± 12.63 t ha^{-1}), species with intermediate tree biomass were R. mangle (181.70 ± 16.58 t ha^{-1}) and *L. racemosa* (206.07 ± 19.12 t ha^{-1}) (Figure 1) Similar values were found for tree biomass (AGB) in a forest of *Avicennia* (193 t ha^{-1}) in Sri Lanka (Amarasinghe and Balasubramaniam [18]), and lower values (35.1 t ha^{-1}) in French Guyana, in the this study found similar data for *Laguncularia* associated with *Avicennia* (188.6 t ha^{-1}) (Fromard et al. [19]), on the other hand, in India were found somewhat similar values for *Rhizophora* (214 t ha^{-1}) (Mall et al. [20]).

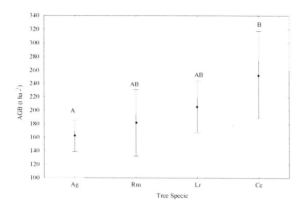

Figure 1:   Mean values for the content of tree biomass (AGB/t ha^{-1}) of the four species (Ag = *Avicennia germinans*, Rm = *Rhizophora mangle*, Lr = *Laguncularia racemosa* and Ce = *Conocarpus erectus*). Means with the same letter are not significant $p < 0.05$.

The Tukey test showed significant differences between Ag and Ce (ANOVA, $p < 0.05$), which means that trees of C. erectus evaluated, had a larger AGB compared with other species, and trees of A germinans showed a relatively lower AGB, according to previous reports, this may be because the trees grow in hypersaline environments, which can reduce their development as proposed by Komiyama et al. [6].

While *C. erectus* grows up in higher areas, the soils have better conditions for nutrients. AGB tends to be relatively low in areas near the sea and rise as forest location is closer inland. In the case of *A. germinans*, these individuals are usually growing on recently deposited sediments, however, besides this factor, there are others such as soil properties and nutritional status (Komiyama et al. [4]) which may affect the rate of growth in biomass of mangrove forests.

3.3 Carbon stored

The Tukey test showed no significant variation in the carbon stored on site in both the AGB (fig 2) and soil (fig 3). However, for carbon in tree biomass, XC present the maximum value (114.37 ± 12.74 t ha-^{1}), while the minimum value was obtained in PR (77.46 ± 9.17 t ha^{-1}). In this case, measured trees had similar diameter sizes, the highest density of Ce was found in XC, which explains the increase recorded.

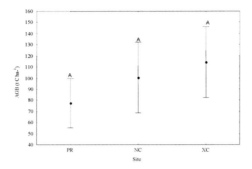

Figure 2: Mean values of carbon in tree biomass (AGB, t C ha^{-1}) at different sampling sites. Means with the same letter are not significant $p<0.05$.

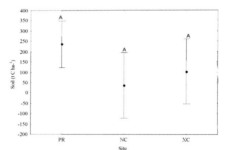

Figure 3: Mean values of carbon content in soil (t C ha^{-1}) at different sampling sites. Means with the same letter are not significant $p<0.05$.

The carbon stored in the soil of the three sites was within a range of 36.80 ± 10.27 to 235.77 ± 66.11 t C ha^{-1} showing superior performance to that reported by authors such as Arreaga [21] as well as Webb [22], the maximum value was found in Puerto Rico (235 ± 66.11 t ha^{-1}) and the minimum value in Nuevo Campechito (36.00 ± 10.27). The plots in Puerto Rico had the highest density of A germinans, a species that sits on land that has high organic matter accumulation due to low rates of decomposition in the soils by being continuously flooded and present high concentrations of salts also inhibit decomposition, this would explain its contents as high carbon in the soil and also its low forest development.

The carbon stored in AGB as shown in Table 4, differed significantly between forest plots (p <0.05), averaging 174.08 ± 8.86 t C ha^{-1} in mangrove

Table 4:   Mean of tree biomass (AGB), carbon content in AGB, and soils of mangrove forests at Atasta Peninsula, Campeche, México.

Site	Plot	AGB (t ha^{-1}, mean±ES)*	AGB (t C ha^{-1}, mean±ES)	Soil (t C ha^{-1} mean±ES)
PR	P1	116.45±7.22	58.22±3.61	64.18±10.52
PR	P2	145.46±14.68	72.73±7.34	73.46±7.89
PR	P3	165.29±46.10	82.65±23.05	480.26±30.34
PR	P4	236.90±47.76	118.45±23.88	356.02±77.30
PR	P5	113.80±6.69	56.90±3.34	202.89±49.58
PR	P6	151.67±15.36	75.84±7.68	237.82±10.49
NC	P7	169.56±45.58	84.78 ±22.79	54.85±17.52
NC	P8	162.03±21.29	81.01±10.64	33.61±5.60
NC	P9	269.80±41.79	134.90±20.90	19.53±13.18
XC	P10	279.72±29.00	139.86±14.50	116.88±26.16
XC	P11	203.24±23.75	101.62±11.88	74.10±4.16
XC	P12	203.25±27.60	101.63±13.80	119.50±20.40
Mean		174.08±8.86	87.04±4.43	152.76±24.16

ES= Standard Error

*Allometric equation based on Chave et al. [14].

forests, in Plots (P) 4, 9 and 10 were significantly high compared to other plots. P9 and P10 are dominated by Ce and Lr, respectively, while P4 has an association of Ag with Rm, which is known for a high abundance of relatively large trees in these specific communities. Plots 1, 2 and 5 are not significantly different, but showed significant differences with P4, P9 and P10; the lowest values were observed in P1, P2 and P5, the three plots dominated by Ag, and were the most disturbed. While P3, P6, P7, P8, P11 and P12 showed no significant differences among them. The results of plot 4 were higher than those reported by Fromand et al. [19] in forests with *Rhizophora* and *Avicennia* association (143.3 and 122.2 t C ha^{-1}) in French Guyana, the carbon content in the biomass follows the same trend as the AGB. The plots P3, P4, P5 and P6 show the highest values of carbon stored in soil in a range of 202.89 ± 49.58 to 480.26 ± 30.34 t C ha^{-1}, however, P3 and P4 show significant differences ($p<0.05$) with P5 and P6. This condition can be given because of the high productivity of the species associated with these soils as a result of defoliation, which incorporate a high content of organic matter to soils, in addition to the flooding conditions prevailing at the sites, which induces to store large amounts of carbon. The remaining plots averaged soil carbon of 19.53 ± 13.18 to 119.50 ± 20.40 t C ha^{-1}. It can be inferred that the topographical and hydrological conditions are the cause of these values.

There were differences between the content of carbon stored in the studied plots, mangrove forests are considered as major reservoirs of carbon in their soils, this is influenced by topographical and hydrological conditions, for example, soils with higher waterlogging (P3, P4, P5, P6) had the largest stores of carbon, compared to the driest (P8 and P9), despite having low values of carbon content in AGB, P3 and P4 plots showed the higher contents of total carbon, while the lowest at P1 and P8 (fig 4). There are high variations in AGB when comparing different allometric models, this indicates the need to develop allometric models specific to mangrove forests.

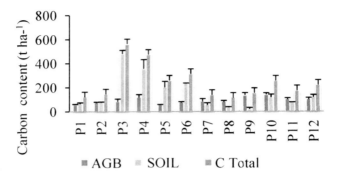

Figure 4: Carbon content in soil and tree biomass (AGB) and the total carbon (C Total) in the different plots for the mangrove forest in Campeche, Mexico. The bars indicate the standard error.

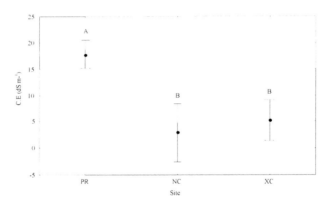

Figure 5: Mean values of EC (dS m⁻¹) of the three sites (PR = Puerto Rico, NC = New Campechito and XC = Xicalango). Means with the same letter are not significant.

All sites showed high values of EC 2.93 ± 0.35, 5.18 ± 0.26 and 17.78 ± 1.77 dS m⁻¹ to NC, XC and PR, respectively (Figure 5). The EC values are indicators of salinity. Therefore indicate a high salinity for PR, and moderate for XC and NC, the high salinity in PR is probably attributed to the low permeability of the soil, which contributes to the accumulation of water by increasing the concentrations of Na and contributing to a low activity of microbiota. It is noteworthy that Ag tolerates higher concentrations of salinity; reason turns out to be the most abundant species at this site.

4 Conclusions

All sites have good potential to store carbon for long periods of time also prevalent in the high productivity of mangrove forests are a source of nutrients that work synergistically with the low rate of decomposition and hydrology, resulting in high storage rates. The maximum content of carbon storage were found in soils at the site of Puerto Rico The results of this study is one of the few measurements of tree biomass and carbon storage in mangrove forests of the humid tropics of Mexico, in particular in the state of Campeche, showing that the soils are good reservoirs of carbon. The AGB values found are influenced by associations of mangrove species present in each of the plots in the study sites. It was found that plots with predominance of *Conocarpus erectus* showed higher values of AGB while those plots with associations predominating *Avicennia germinans* showed lower values of tree biomass,

References

[1]   IPCC (Intergovernmental Panel on Climate Change), *Climate Change: The Scientific Basis*. Cambridge Univ. Press, Cambridge, UK, 2001.

[2]   Ordoñez, J.A. and Masera, O. *Captura de carbono ante el cambio climático*. Madera y Bosques, 7: 3–12, 2001.

[3]   Ordoñez, J. A. *Captura de carbono en un bosque templado: el caso de San Juan Nuevo, Michoacán* 1ra. Edición electrónica. www.ine.gob.mx/ publicaciones/consultaPublicacion.html?id_pub=296 1998.

[4]   Komiyama, A., Ong J. E., and Poungparn, S. *Allometry, biomass, and productivity of mangrove forests: a review*. Aquatic Botany 89: 128–137, 2008.

[5]   Whiting, J. G. and Chanton, J. P. *Greenhouse carbon balance of wetlands: methane emission versus carbon sequestration*. Tellus 53B: 521–528, 2001.

[6]   Komiyama, A., Poungparn, S., Kato, S., *Common allometric equations for estimating the tree weight of mangroves*. J. Trop. Ecol. 21: 471–477, 2005.

[7]   INE, *Programa de Manejo del área de protección de flora y fauna "Laguna de Términos";* SEMARNAT, 1997.

[8]   Lugo, A. and Snedaker, C. 1974. *The Ecology of Mangroves*. Annual Review of Ecology and Systematics, 5: 38–64.

[9]   Twilley, R.W., Lugo, A.E. and Patterson-Zucca, C. *Litter Production and Turnover in Basin Mangrove Forests in Southwest Florida. Ecology. 67:* 670–683, 1986.

[10] Rico-Gray, V., *Estudio de la vegetación de la zona costera inundable del noroeste de Campeche, México: Los petenes*. Biótica, 7: 171–188, 1982.

[11] Heiri, O., Lotter, A. F., and Lemcke G. *Loss on Ignition as a method for estimating organic and carbonate content in sediments: reproducibility and comparability of results*. Journal of paleolimnology 25: 101–110, 2001.

[12] Craft, C. B., Seneca, E.D. and Broome S.W. *Ignition and kjeldahl digestion for estimating organic carbon and soils: Calibration with dry combustion*. Estuaries. 14: 175–179, 1991.

[13] Gonzalez, M., Etchevers, B. and Hidalgo, M., *Carbono en suelos de ladera: factores que deben considerarse para determinar su cambio en el tiempo.* Agrociencia [online]. 42:7, 741–751, 2008.

[14] Chave, J., Andalo, C., Brown, S., Cairns, M.A., Chambers, J.Q., Eamus, D., Fölster, H., Fromard, F., Higuchi, N., Kira, T., Lescure, J.P., Nelson, B.W., Ogawa, H., Puig, H., Riéra, B., and Yamakura, T., *Tree allometry and improved estimation of carbon stocks and balance in tropical forests.* Oecologia 145: 87–99, 2005.

[15] Zanne, A.E., Lopez, G.G., Coomes, D.A. Llic, J., Jansen, S.L., Lewis, S.L., Miller, R.B., Swenson, N.G., Wiemann, M.C., and Chave, J., *Global wood density database. Dryad. Identifier*: http://hdl.handle.net/10255/dryad.235, 2009.

[16] Basuki, T.M., van Laake, P.E., Skidmore, A.K. and Hussin, Y. A., *Allometric equations for estimating the above-ground biomass in tropical lowland Dipterocarp forest.* Forest Ecology and Management, 257: 1684–1694, 2009.

[17] Day, J.W., Conner, W.H., Ley, L.F., Day, R.H., and Navarro, A.M., *The productivity and composition of mangrove forests, Laguna de Terminos, Mexico.* Aquat. Bot. 27: 267–284, 1987.

[18] Amarasinghe, M.D., and Balasubramaniam, S., *Net primary productivity of two mangrove forest stands on the northwest coast of Sri Lanka.* Hydrobiol 247: 37–47, 1992.

[19] Fromard, F., Puig, H., Mougin, E., Marty, G., Betoulle, J.L., Cadamuro, L. *Structure above-ground biomass and dynamics of mangrove ecosystems: new data from French Guiana.* Oecologia 115: 39–53, 1998.

[20] Mall L.P., Singh V.P. and Garge A., *Study of biomass, litter fall, litter decomposition and soil respiration in monogeneric mangrove and mixed mangrove forest of Andaman Island.* Trop. Ecol. 32: 144–152, 1991.

[21] Arreaga, W., *Carbon storage in forest with a management program in the natural reserve "Maya Peten", Guatemala.* Thesis M.Sc. CATIE, Turrialba, CR. 86, 2002.

[22] Webb, A., *Pre-clearing soil carbon levels in Australia.* National carbon accounting system technical report No. 12. Australian greenhouse office, Canberra, 204, 2002.

Section 3
Environmental policies
and planning

Floodplains and sustainable development

F. Rochford
La Trobe University, Australia

Abstract

Australian floodplains are environmentally significant, carrying high biodiversity loads. International conventions, state and federal laws protect them to an extent. However, since Australian flood events, when they occur, can affect massive areas of farmland, and cause significant damage to urban private property and state infrastructure, floodplain management is a balance of competing interests. The management of flooding events and conservation of water has resulted in a legacy of structures that capture, divert or restrain floodwaters, resulting in a range of environmentally damaging effects.

This paper considers the impact of infrastructure on recent flooding in northern Victoria, considering the degree to which flooding followed the natural flow of water, and what constrained its flow. It considers particularly the impact of regulations and planning decisions on floodplain management. It also considers the impact of the implementation of environmental watering requirements under the *Water Act* 2007 (Cth) and the potential impact of environmental watering on state liability for flood damage of private infrastructure.

Keywords: environment, law, planning, infrastructure.

1 Introduction

Extensive floodplains characterise the Australian geography, and the management of floodplains from ecological and planning perspectives attracts significant literature. Balancing the needs of an ecosystem reliant on intermittent but extensive flooding with private and public infrastructure is an acknowledged problem in Australian natural resource management. However, to date much literature has been devoted to the amelioration of the effects of natural flood events, and the management of liability risks arising from infrastructure

WIT Transactions on Ecology and The Environment, Vol 173, © 2013 WIT Press
www.witpress.com, ISSN 1743-3541 (on-line)
doi:10.2495/SDP130121

planning. The risk generated by environmental watering by government authorities is an issue of relatively recent provenance.

This paper first considers the role of floodplains in Australia's ecosystems, noting broadly the consensus as to the need to provide Environmental Water Allocations to periodically water significant floodplains. It sets out the legislative framework within which Environmental Water Allocations are to be provided, concentrating in particular on the provisions of the *Water Act* 2007 (Cth), which imposes requirements on the states to create environmental flows.

The potential liability of state and federal agencies for non-natural flooding of public and private infrastructure must be considered in the context of the statutory machinery established to facilitate environmental flooding. This paper will consider the statutory framework and the common law rules to ascertain potential litigation risk, and concludes that far more needs to be done to detail the consequences of environmental flooding regimes.

2 Litigation risk factors

As recent flood events have indicated, much of inland Australia is subject of flooding. The massive extent of inland flooding, much like the recent catastrophic drought period, illustrates the limits on the human capacity to control, or even ameliorate, severe weather events in Australia. Within those limits, however, measures have been taken to live and work on Australian floodplains. Indeed, the fact that they are floodplains means that these are some of the more fertile areas of the Australian inland. The extent of flooding also cautions that it is a nonsense to suggest without caveat that there should be no development on floodplains.

Nevertheless, floodplain development must occur with reference to a number of factors: the risk of inundation and the consequent destruction of public and private infrastructure, the risk to life, both in the initial period of inundation and as a consequence of the increased risk of disease due to inundation, stock losses and business losses as a result of flooding, and the risks to natural floodplain ecosystems if inundation is modified or reduced. This can translate into potential litigation risk, particularly to public authorities, whose planning decisions and frameworks have enabled construction and whose response to risks can come under scrutiny.

There are second-level risks, too. If development occurs on floodplains the risks need to be managed, and the management of those risks tends to lead to unintended – if not unanticipated – consequences. The inundation of private assets, particularly in townships, requires massive investment in levees and drainage works and rescue and recovery operations, and the role of this infrastructure is necessarily going to push floodwater into areas into which it would not otherwise have gone. The construction of flood mitigation dams leads to the potential for catastrophic flood events if the dam fails or dam releases result in flooding, as occurred in the case of the Wivenhoe Dam in Brisbane.

The steering role of insurers to define, manage, spread and shift risks has been demonstrated in the aftermath of recent flood events, with some insurers relying on distinctions between riverine and non-riverine flooding to deny claims, and others applying significant premium increases to properties in regions considered to be subject to inundation.   The expected response of insurers to the findings of the Commission of Enquiry into the operation of the Wivenhoe Dam is likely to be legal action against the dam authority, which shifts losses to the public through Queensland's arrangements for maintaining infrastructure.

Finally, and problematically, the recent policy imperative to create and design a satisfactory framework for environmental flows has created a new set of litigation risks.   Holding environmental water increases the risk that a dam will spill or overtop its banks, and the release of an environmental flow increases the potential for inundation.   In the current legislative framework, the risk sharing arrangements between the Federal and State governments and landholders are a significant planning feature.

3   The significance of Australian floodplains

The environmental significance of floodplains is long-established.   Australian ecosystems have adapted to intermittent inundation to the extent that controlling inundation has the capacity to diminish ecosystem health.   The importance of flooding events to the ecosystem is dependent, however, on the context.   As Kingsford and Thomas note, '[l]arge floodplain rivers are dynamic ecosystems with enormous spatial and temporal complexity.   Flood channels, backswamps, braids, marshes, distributories, billabongs and wetplains make up the floodplain of a large lowland river' [1].   Interference with this pattern of inundation on a basin scale has occurred through the regulation of rivers to reduce flood events and to conserve water for irrigation and stock and domestic use, the extraction of water, mainly for irrigated agriculture, more effective drainage, reducing the length of inundation periods and increasing inflows into rivers, and infrastructure on floodplains, including roads and railways, irrigation channels, drains, private and public levee banks, and irrigation check-banks.

It should be noted that the comparative importance of the ecosystem and anthropogenic values of floodplains is an essentially political decision; as recent flood events demonstrate, humans could not sustain a settled population in inland Australia without managing the catastrophic effects of flooding; any more than they could survive without ameliorating the effects of drought.   Whilst drought and flooding are necessary components of Australian ecosystems as they have evolved, the necessary consequence of having a non-nomadic and growing human population in Australia is some regulation of extreme weather events. The comparative importance of ecosystem values and human production assets has shifted over time, as has the attitude to shifting and sharing the risk of loss.

Accordingly, when the ecosystem values of Australian floodplains are discussed, they should be assessed not on a general basis, but on a system of optimal ecosystem preservation values.   However, because floodplain connectivity is also an issue, ecosystem preservation is both a local and an integrated issue.   The 'maintenance of natural patterns of longitudinal and lateral connectivity is essential to the viability of many riverine species' [2]. However, in arid regions, low-relief topography, increased evapotranspiration and variability in rainfall and runoff, and the El Nino/Southern Oscillation effects 'combine with the complex riverine landscape to produce highly variable levels of connectivity' [2].

Australia's obligations to protect floodplain ecosystems commence with International Instruments to which Australia is a party. Australia is signatory to the Ramsar Convention on Wetlands of International Importance (the Ramsar Convention), the Convention on Biological Diversity, the Convention on the Conservation of Migratory Species of Wild Animals (the Bonn Convention), the Convention Concerning the Protection of the World Cultural and Natural Heritage (the World Heritage Convention), the World Charter for Nature, and Agenda 21. Whilst legislative authority to manage most environmental matters resides with the states, the Federal government attracts legislative competence through the external affairs power in s.51(xxix) of the *Constitution*, and has exercised this power through the *Environment Protection and Biodiversity Conservation Act* 1999 (Cth). The *Water Act* 2007 (Cth) is also based in part on the external affairs power, and the objects of that Act specify in particular that the Act is to '(b) give effect to relevant international agreements…, and (c) in giving effect to those agreements, to promote the use and management of the Basin water resources in a way that optimises economic, social and environmental outcomes.'

Leading commentators have argued, therefore, that consistency with international conventions will be required to ensure legislative competence [3]. Thus, priority must be given to environmental sustainability in implementing the provisions of the Act and the making of the Murray-Darling Basin Plan. Section 21(1) of the *Water Act* 2007 (Cth) makes this clear:

The Basin Plan … must be prepared so as to provide for giving effect to relevant international agreements (to the extent to which those agreements are relevant to the use and management of the Basin water resources).

Assessing the relevance of floodplains to Australia's responsibilities as signatories to these Conventions is critically important. But this gives rise to massive difficulties of definition and scale. As Australian floodplains extend over almost half of the continent, but the recharge of wetlands depends on their continued interconnectivity, political questions arise as to the protection of infrastructure and public and private investment consistent with the preservation of wetlands. The precautionary principle has been explicitly included in the political agreements that inform the legislative program [4] and in Australian common law [5], and this demands that 'a lack of scientific certainty should not prevent the implementation of measures needed to prevent irreversible or serious environmental damage' [4], but a high degree of variability is something to which the ecosystem has evolved, and is something which should be replicated in attempting to remediate the effects of floodplain development.

Accordingly, environmental water holders in both state and federal jurisdictions attempt to ameliorate the effects of altered water flow regimes by targeted environmental watering. This requires a complex reallocation of rights and duties between the states, with the primary responsibility for the administration of water, and the Commonwealth bodies empowered by the federal Act to effect environmental watering. The Commonwealth Environmental Water Holder manages the Commonwealth's water holdings pursuant to s.105(1) of the *Water Act* 2007(Cth) and has a duty to manage water holdings in accordance with the environmental water plan – which is part of the Murray-Darling Basin Plan still in preparation – other relevant plans, operating rules and environmental water schedules (s.105(4)). Section 106 prevents the disposition of water other than in accordance with those instruments unless the water is not necessary to meet the objectives of an environmental water plan.

Clearly, however, this requires consequential reallocation of risks, since the infrastructure required to store and deliver environmental water holdings is administered by the states, and the infrastructure risks as a result of running the reservoir at a greater capacity, or instituting a spill, or piggy-backing on a high-flow, are in the hands of the states.

This is not merely theoretical. Disputes have already arisen between the Snowy Hydro, the administrator of the Snowy Mountains Hydroelectric Scheme and the dams in the Snowy Mountains, and the New South Wales Water Commissioner.

Snowy Hydro proposed an environmental release of to relieve 'uncomfortably high dam levels,' but the NSW Water Commissioner initially refused 'because of a technical accounting dispute over who would notionally pay for the water, and to conserve water in case global warming comes good' [6]. The 'airspace' issue, which relates to the amount of free space in the dam to mitigate the possibility of overtopping or dam failure, was also an issue in the management of the Wivenhoe Dam in Queensland. The dam was originally built as a flood mitigation measure, and water storage capacity was to be augmented by the planned construction of new facility. This facility was never built, and at the time of the Brisbane flooding in January 2011 the dam was the primary water supply facility for Brisbane, and after a major drought it has been theorised that flood mitigation was not then a priority. As a result of massive inflows during January 2011 the dam was at risk of overtopping and failing. A Commission of Inquiry has recently been concluded, finding that SEQ Water, the instrumentality charged with administering the dam, did not comply with its operating manual. The outgoing Queensland Premier, Anna Bligh, conceded that legal action against the state was likely [7].

4   Common law background

The common law rules apportioning liability for damage as a result of flood events are of long standing, but are not always clear. Liability is primarily assessed through the common law of nuisance and negligence. The common law distinguished between floodwater and the drainage of surface water, although this distinction is difficult to draw.

Common law authorities were unclear as to whether landowners were able to use any measures necessary to protect their land, or whether landowners were permitted to take such measures as were reasonably necessary as long as they used reasonable care and skill. The rules were set out in *Gartner v Kidman* (1962) 108 CLR 12, however much of those rules could be set to be obiter, because the case itself only required resolution of a dispute in which a lower landowner was entitled to obstruct the flow of surface water in a depression [8]. The facts of that case are typical of supply issues – where the parties are concerned about rights to the flow of water. The same law could apply, however, where the nuisance or negligence arises from the excessive flow of water; whether because of obstructions placed into the path of water which diverts water onto previously unaffected land, or the construction of works which move water more quickly onto affected land. Nuisance and negligence principles may also apply where water which has been tainted by chemicals, hormones, genetically modified organisms or other substances and affects crops or animals on land.

Nuisance has historically applied to emanations from land. It is the unreasonable interference with another person's use and enjoyment of land. This is a question of degree, and takes into account considerations such as the nature of the interference, its intensity and duration or frequency, and its cause.

In *Munro v Southern Dairies Ltd* [1955] VLR 332 the court noted that private nuisance is

> 'An unlawful interference with a person's use or enjoyment of land, or of some right over, or in connection with it,' but that definition of itself is so wide that it is necessary to add to it and qualify it in order to set out clearly what it is that will constitute an actionable private nuisance of the kind here complained of. In the first place, there must be a substantial degree of interference with the comfort and convenience of the occupier who complains of a private nuisance, or with some other aspect of the use or enjoyment of his land. The interference must be so substantial as to cause damage to him.

This can be applicable to water escaping from land in a number of contexts, particularly due to obstructed drains, as in *Sedleigh-Denfield v O'Callaghan* (1940) AC 880, or damaged pipes, as in *Montana Hotels Pty Ltd v Fasson Pty Ltd* (1987) Aust Torts Reports ¶80-109. Nuisance has traditionally also applied to pollution of groundwater.

In some jurisdictions nuisance was applied to artificial erections which cause floodwaters to flow onto neighbouring land: *Broder v Saillard* (1878) 2 ChD 692; *Hurdman v North Eastern Railway Co* (1878) 3 CPD 168. This would be a significant principle to apply to the widespread channel, rail and road infrastructure that blocks or impedes the flow of floodwaters across the enormous Australian floodplains. Of course, it would also apply to levy banks deliberately erected to protect towns and infrastructure from floodwaters. Floodplain development can cause ecosystem problems by severing wetlands from rivers and preventing the flooding of floodplains [9]. It can also cause damage to land caused by flooding where that land would not naturally flood. The reform of planning provisions to allow development of land with recognised 'flood overlays' both alters the flow of water and increases the potential for private and public infrastructure loss. However, Australian authorities applied that English rule relating to obstruction of flows only where the artificial erection was not a natural or reasonable use of land: *Kraemers v AG* [1966] Tas SR 113; *Furness v Clarke* (1970) 1 SASR 359 (Chamberlain J).

In the context of the *escape* of large quantities of water, as in for instance, the case of a dam breach, the principles were derived from *Rylands v Fletcher* (1868) LR 3 HL 330. That case applied the statement of Blackburn J in *Fletcher v Rylands* (1866) LR 1 Ex 265 to the effect that:

> the person who for his own purposes brings on his lands and collects and keeps there anything likely to do mischief if it escapes, must keep it in at his peril, and, if he does not do so, is prima facie answerable for all the damage which is the natural consequence of its escape. He can excuse himself by shewing that the escape was owing to the plaintiff's default; or perhaps that the escape was the consequence of vis major, or the act of God; but as nothing of this sort exists here, it is unnecessary to inquire what excuse would be sufficient.

In application to the escape of water, a large accumulated mass of water stored in a reservoir satisfied the 'mischief' or 'danger' test for the purposes of the rule.

However, that case has more recently been subsumed into the general Australian law of negligence by *Burnie Port Authority v General Jones Pty Ltd* (1994) 179 CLR 520. In application to water stored on land, therefore, if a person uses their land to carry on a dangerous activity, or to allow another so to do, they may be liable under a normal rules of negligence but with a heightened standard of care, amounting in relevant cases to a non-delegable duty – a duty which is not discharged by the appointment of reasonable contractors.

Of course, however, the statutory context in which the reservoir was operated is relevant to liability if the dam is operated by the State: *Crimmins v Stevedoring Industry Finance Committee* (1999) ALR 1. In *Graham Barclay Oysters Pty Ltd v Ryan* (2002) 211 CLR 540 the court said:

> An evaluation of whether a relationship between a statutory authority and a class of persons imports a common law duty of care is necessarily a multi-faceted inquiry. Each of the salient features of the relationship must be considered. The focus of analysis is the relevant legislation and the positions occupied by the parties…

Whereas State authorities are unlikely to be made liable for matters of policy, they may be liable for implementation of policy. It is clear that, for instance, that 'the purposes or functions peculiar to government' will not give rise to liability: *Maguire v Simpson* (1977) 139 CLR 362, 393-395 (Stephen J), 408 (Murphy J); *Commonwealth v Evans Deakin Industries Ltd* (1986) 161 CLR 254. Courts perceive themselves to be incompetent to review decisions based on value judgments, policy judgment and decision, particularly since

> almost all acts of government hurt someone, and it would be utterly impracticable to assess and order compensation for every injury inflicted by government. Even if one were to limit such compensation to injuries caused by government fault, the impracticability of complete compensation remains. ... [C]omplete liability would inhibit governments from acting. ... [A] complete fault-liability scheme would be an enormous force for conservatism [10].

State legislation demonstrates the manner in which liability can be managed.

5 Legislative framework

Where state authorities artificially create flooding to provide ecosystem benefits, or maintain dams at an artificially high level to retain water for environmental flows and the dam is subsequently forced to spill, inundating private land, state liability may be determined by reference to the common law of nuisance and negligence. However, the common law principles are to be determined by reference first to the legislative framework. In the Australian federal context, competence for water management is largely a state matter.

> State-based organisations can be classified according to their role in policy development, resource allocation, administration, distribution, and monitoring and enforcement. Some of the bodies have exclusively judicial or quasi-judicial functions, while others operate on a policy or allocation principle level, and are thus unlikely to be affected by potential litigation in tort [11].

Thus, in Victoria, Division 2 of the *Water Act* 1989 (Vic) circumscribes the extent of state liability in some circumstances. Section 16 makes it clear that liability can arise from the unreasonable flow of water from land onto another's land, but s.17 specifies that no civil liability for an unreasonable flow of water arises except under the Act. Section 20 sets out the matters relevant to the question of whether a flow of water is unreasonable, and s.21 sets out the matters relevant to the question of liability for management of public works.

However, the federalisation of Australian water policy pursuant to the *Water Act* 2007 (Cth), although still leaving implementation matters in the hands of the States in deference to federal Constitutional restrictions, introduces major shifts in potential state liability. It requires states to implement the environmental flow requirements settled by the Murray Darling Basin Plan under the authority of the *Water Act* 2007 (Cth). The Plan, when it is finalised, will require environmental flows through an environmental watering plan. Section 28(2) of the *Water Act* 2007 (Cth) requires the specification of objectives and targets and the identification, prioritisation and management framework by which the environmental outcomes are to be achieved.

The mechanisms by which 'environmental watering' is to be achieved are still inchoate and are currently run in conjunction with state environmental watering plans. Environmental water holders at state and federal level obtain and store water in reservoirs and release that water for targeted environmental purposes, typically 'piggy-backing' on natural flood events or irrigation flows. The extent of the targeted flooding events is not clear, but if attempts are made to reinstate natural flooding regimes on floodplains the damage to private and public infrastructure will be marked. Politically it is likely that flood events will initially be restricted to targeted wetlands still attached to river systems, such as the Barmah Forest or Coorong Lake systems, which have the benefit of also being state-owned.

As more ambitious flooding regimes are proposed, risk assignment under the legislation is significant. The National Water Initiative focused on the allocation of risks due to water allocation changes, assigning risk according to whether it was due to drought, climate variation, bona fide changes in knowledge, or government reallocation. The *Water Act* 2007 (Cth) incorporates risk assignment mechanisms in Part 2, Division 4.

Significantly, however, the National Water Commission has concluded that there is uncertainty in the interpretation and implementation of the risk assignment terms in the National Water Initiative [12]. Whereas the risk factors specifically identified in the Act and in the National Water Initiative have tended to be in relation to the reduction in water entitlement, and risks have been apportioned between water access entitlement holders, relevant state governments and the federal government, the risks due to massive flood events do not appear to have been considered in great detail.

6   Conclusion

Justice Holmes, who conducted the Commission of Inquiry into the Wivenhoe Dam, noted in the preface to the report:

> Years of drought did not promote rigour in flood planning, whether in relation to disaster response, dam management, or land use... Complacency about flood prevailed, at least in parts of the state, over many years. And there is a risk that the recommendations made here will be enthusiastically taken up in the short term, but, absent another flood disaster in the next few years, priorities will drift and the lessons will be forgotten [7].

A similar set of priority shifts arise in relation to management of environmental water in a long wet period after a significant dry period. Whereas the law has been enacted and the policies formulated, the massive problems of implementation appear to have been taken as capable of solution.

References

[1] Kingsford, R.T., Thomas, R.F., 'Use of satellite image analysis to track wetland loss on the Murrumbidgee River floodplain in arid Australia, 1975-1998' (2002) 45 *Water Science and Technology* 45-53, p.45.

[2] Catherine Leigh and Fran Sheldon, 'Hydrological changes and ecological impacts associated with water resource development in large floodplain rivers in the Australian tropics' (2008) 24 *River Research and Applications* 1251-1270, p.1252.

[3] Paul Kildea and George Williams, 'The Water Act and the Murray-Darling Basin Plan' (2011) 22 PLR 9.

[4] *Intergovernmental Agreement on the Environment* May 1992.

[5] *Rowe v Lindner* (No 2) [2007] SASC 189.

[6] Ean Higgins, 'Nature swamps Snowy's 'drop in a bucket' flow' *The Australian,* March 14, 2012.

[7] Sean Parnell, 'Anna Bligh says legal action likely over floods in the way of inquiry findings' *The Australian* March 19, 2012.

[8] John Adams, *Drainage of Surface Waters: Common Law Rights and Victorian Legislation* [unpublished Master's thesis] 1976, p.93.

[9] CMM Steinfeld and RT Kingsford, *Floodplain Development and Vegetation Health on the Macquarie River Floodplain of the Murray-Darling Basin* (Wetlands and Rivers, School of Biological, Earth and Environmental Sciences, University of New South Wales, 2008), p.3.

[10] M Aronson and H Whitmore, *Public Torts and Contracts* (1982), p.59.

[11] Francine Rochford, 'Liability in negligence of water authorities for contaminated water' (2005) 10 *The Australasian Journal of Natural Resources Law and Policy* 39-80.

[12] National Water Commission, *Australian Water Reform 2009: Second Biennial Assessment of Progress in Implementation of the National Water Initiative* (National Water Commission, Canberra, September 2009), p.193.

Planning low volume forest road-net for sustainable development in a coastline area in Chalkidiki

A. Stergiadou[1], S. Theodoridou[2], G. Zachou[3] & A. Karagiannidis[4]
[1]*Institute of Mechanical Science and Topography,*
Faculty of Forestry and Natural Environment,
Aristotle University of Thessaloniki (AUTh.), Greece
[2]*Biology School, AUTh, Forester and Environmentalist, Greece*
[3]*Forester and Environmentalist, AUTh, Greece*
[4]*Forest Services of Drama Prefecture, AUTh, Greece*

Abstract

Mountains have been an important part of environmental sciences. Understanding and effectively addressing the complex challenges; faced by mountain population in an era of global change requires carefully designed and implemented research involving scientists from a range of disciplines. To address the mountain problems associated with inaccessibility, fragility, and marginality; we can suggest a number of measures such as: improvement of road net; sustainability of natural resources and regulation of their usage. Furthermore, we can adopt consumption activities in order to fulfil the environmental and decentralized needs of the residents in order to develop eco-tourism to a semi mountainous area. The aim of this paper is: a) to record the current situation of Cassandra's road net in a semi mountainous area, b) to propose places that can be further developed and; c) to develop an estimating method of parametric system based on environmental impact assessment. The results of our research are based on; how until now this area has been managed and how we are going to reform it by our proposals; by the usage of road net and the rural development. We used a route; which passes through several forest stands and is preferred compared to the provincial highway which is used as a connecting axis between the cities of Cassandra and Fourka. Another ultimate aim is to propose structures that could improve these sections of forest land to

WIT Transactions on Ecology and The Environment, Vol 173, © 2013 WIT Press
www.witpress.com, ISSN 1743-3541 (on-line)
doi:10.2495/SDP130131

upgrade the area; to increase the percentage of forest road crossing and the multiple-use by hikers and visitors. As a goal is the visit ability of this semi-mountainous area by pupils with low incomes or by more affluent groups. Finishing this task, we believe it contributed even slightly to the sustainable development of the area of Cassandra; while such projects should be provided and assistance is granted by the Prefecture and local governments to expand the horizons of development of non-urbanized areas.

Keywords: planning, low volume forest road-net, sustainable development, semi mountainous area, environmental impact, Cassandra, Greece.

1 Introduction

Forested areas are almost 65.130.000 ha $\cong$ 49.5% of Greece and that makes them important for the environmental sciences [1]. We address the mountain specified problems associated with inaccessibility, fragility, and marginality, so that we can suggest a number of measures such as: improvement of road net; sustainability of natural resources and regulation of their usage. Furthermore we can adopt interactive activities in order to fulfil the environmental and decentralized needs of the residents. That can develop eco-tourism to a semi mountainous area.

Sustainable management is in harmony with environmental protection from both quantitative and qualitative terms, since the objective is to use the resources of the planet to the point of tolerance [2]. The concept of sustainable development as determined through an exhibition Brutland is not limited to the sustainable use of natural resources and natural systems, but extends to political and economic factors, and also recognizes the need for global action with the cooperation of all countries [3]. Sustainable development is closely linked to the sustainable management of natural resources of the planet, but also with care to satisfy the developmental and environmental needs of future generations [4]. Sustainable development means that it preserves the overall quality of life, sustainable use of natural resources through a process where the flow for materials in various stages of processing consumption and use should facilitate or encourage optimum reuse and recycling [5].

Overcrowding combined with unpleasant environmental conditions and lack of adequate quantity and quality, green outbreaks in urban centres led the people to seek leisure near nature in suburban forests, forming a forestry recreation. By default, forest recreations are all forms of outdoor recreation that takes place in forest areas; where the forest has a preponderant role in recreational activities. Many factors affect the demand for forest recreation such as the population size, place of residence, living zone, occupation, economic factor, transportation factor, time, etc. Satisfying the demand for recreation requires the availability of an area; and the pupils' interest for those places. The factors which are affecting the value of the proposed sites and their suitability for development of forest recreation; can be classified into three categories factors: a) natural, b) biotic and c) cultural.

2 Research area

The low volume forest road is located in the prefecture of Chalki-iki, in the Municipality of Cassandra. This road starts from Cassandra village (23°24'50.98" east of Greenwich and 40° 2'23.81" north of the Equator), and ends just before the entrance to the village of Fourka (23°25'15.92" east of Greenwich and 40°0'37.79" north of the Equator) (Map 1).

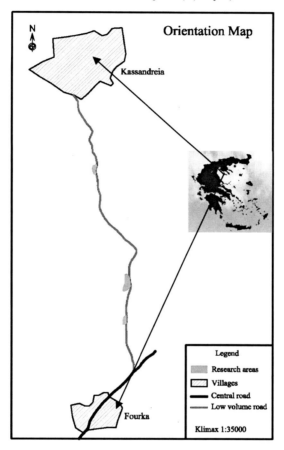

Map 1: Orientation map.

The reference to the conditions of the road accessibility, are considered good as it is accessible from both Fourka's and Cassandra's villages, while leading rural roads as a low volume street of the central axis.

The average gradient along the route of the road ranges from 35% to 50%. The soil is sandy and deep and there are a small number of irrigation wells. The soils in Cassandra are sand-clay and clay, angular with strong granular structure. It is typical for these territories to have a high ph and magnetite. Particular clusters are characterized by sedimentary loam, silt-sand sedimentary rocks and sometimes alluvial sediments. The climate of Cassandra in coastal areas is temperate but also in inland areas, it's not rough.

The vegetation of the area is rich with the dominant forest species: Pinus halepensis, Fagus silvatica and Picea abies. Other species scattered or in small groups and sessions mixed forest species in the ecosystem, are broadleaves, Pistacia lentiscus, Arbutus unedo, Myrtus communis, Arbutus andrachne and Erica arborea. Moreover, outweigh the understudy, the Quercus ilex and Fraxinus ornus, found in northern and north-western cluster of reports, which are aside the low volume road net. The forest type which constitutes the area is mainly the same aged cluster, semi-planted and trees of different ages. The largest number of trees commonly found in the lower age class. The ecological setting of the area is quite good to moderate.

The Mediterranean climate of coastal regions where there are extensive olive groves is characterized by mild winters and cool summers. The microclimate in lowland areas contributes to the absence of frosts or excessively high temperatures. The coldest months are February and March but without creating problems where the average minimum temperatures are above 0°C. The average annual rainfall ranges from 500–600cm. The majority of rain falls during the period from October until April. The winds that blow in the area are mainly from north–northeast while south winds blow mainly during the summer.

3 Methods

The equipment which we have used and helped us to the termination of our research includes: topographical map with the forest types in the research area, describing sheets clusters along the way, literature data related to forest recreation and improvement of forest roads, rangefinder (TruPulse 360/360B), photographs of the area and constructions. We used the program AutoCAD for the accurate mapping and design, both engineering structures in the region.

The first stage was the data selection in the studied area. We visited the area and walked along the low volume road net so as to identify the positions, where the proposed construction projects of recreation can be built. The principles which have been taken in order to choose recreation areas are: guest satisfaction, management and access to forest and the ratio of natural resource to visitor. We selected the locations by taking into account some basic principles and specific factors affecting the site. These elements can be applied to each site selected for forest recreation.

This was followed by recording and processing the data, of the positions which were selected for further development using the rangefinder (TruPulse 360/360B). The laser range sensor determines distance by measuring the time it takes for each pulse to travel from the rangefinder to the target, and back. In each selected area measured on the coordinates and the perimeter in order to provide the best accuracy and acquisition distance (Table 1, Map 2).

In the next step, projects for improvement were proposed for the selected places, such as recreational structures (kiosks, view positions, etc.) and suggestions for improvement of the route along the road (with technical works

Table 1:   Coordination measurement with TruPulse 360.

A/A	X	Y	A/A	X	Y	A/A	X	Y	A/A	X	Y
0	449592.75	4432456.90	16	450558.52	4428951.17	32	450280.70	4429070.23	48	450320.39	4429811.06
1	449711.85	4432112.94	17	450571.75	4428832.10	33	450267.47	4429176.06	49	450280.70	4429758.15
2	449910.29	4431782.21	18	450479.14	4428686.58	34	450241.02	4429242.21	50	450280.70	4429877.21
3	450001.89	4431332.42	19	450360.08	4428567.52	35	450280.70	4429308.35	51	450307.16	4429956.59
4	449976.43	4431028.15	20	450307.16	4428488.14	36	450293.93	4429348.04	52	450333.62	4429983.04
5	449989.66	4430869.40	21	450201.33	4428435.23	37	450373.31	4429324.81	53	450293.93	4430022.73
6	450241.02	4430657.73	22	450121.95	4428329.39	38	450346.85	4429361.27	54	450333.62	4430075.65
7	450492.37	4430366.69	23	450161.64	4428461.69	39	450280.70	4429572.94	55	450413.00	4430128.56
8	450479.14	4430300.54	24	450267.47	4428527.83	40	450320.39	4429665.54	56	450426.23	4430234.40
9	450413.00	4430247.63	25	450439.45	4428673.35	41	450346.85	4429692.00	57	450439.45	4430300.54
10	450386.54	4430088.88	26	450518.83	4428818.87	42	450360.08	4429692.00	58	450479.14	4430327.00
11	450399.77	4429784.61	27	450505.60	4428911.48	43	450360.08	4429692.00	59	450399.77	4430419.61
12	450320.39	4429533.25	28	450505.60	4428937.94	44	450386.54	4429731.69	60	450280.70	4430591.59
13	450452.68	4429255.44	29	450532.06	4428977.62	45	450360.08	4429797.83	61	450214.56	4430657.73
14	450479.14	4429162.83	30	450413.00	4429228.98	46	450360.08	4429827.52	62	450042.58	4430737.11
15	450558.52	4429017.31	31	450333.62	4428990.85	47	450346.85	4429877.21	63	450002.89	4430869.40

A/A	X	Y
64	449989.66	4431213.36
65	449953.20	4431372.11
66	449870.60	4431451.48
67	449923.52	4431544.09
68	449963.20	4431583.78
69	449936.75	4431689.61
70	449936.75	4431689.61

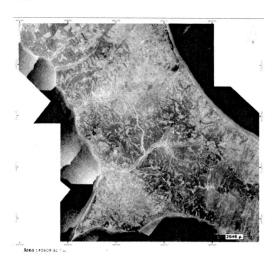

Area 145609.61 τ.μ.

Map 2:   Topographical diagram based on the Greek surveying system. (Source: www.ktimanet.gr.)

such as better road pavement, traffic signs, etc). We made an exact selection of proposed projects in these places along the way of low volume road, after careful review and assessment of the current situation in the region.

The region which we examined is characterized by a clear change of the local population in the past few years (1998–2002). The town of Cassandria has 3,500 inhabitants and in the summer with the summer settlements is a big city of 25,000 inhabitants. The population of the region in 1998 amounted to 7,415 inhabitants, while in 2002 increased to 10,269 inhabitants [6]. In particular, the forest road Cassandra–Fourka, after the research we conducted showed that it's most frequently used by residents of these areas, in comparison with the main road.

In the research area we noticed that there are several places that could be used to enhance sustainable development in the region. These are mainly from the right side (heading towards Fourka) of the road where there are uncovered areas surrounded by lush vegetation that makes these areas ideal for further development. So, at such locations we suggest a number of technical projects that will enhance their respective landscapes while attracting more people to visit them for activities.

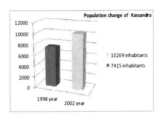

Figure 1:   Hellenic statistical authority [6].

Practical criteria have been held in order to evaluate the absorption of the impact. The grading of these criteria depends on the following principle: We accept a situation as ideal (=100%) for the forest protection from construction. This ideal situation will be described by criteria. The following parameters have been considered: a) the duration of the negative effect, b) the influenced area, c) the sensitivity of the general public to the effect as well as the social impact and political desire. The evaluation of the latter parameters will be difficult and therefore the description of an EIA in a profile form will be a necessary addition [7–10]. The identification and the rating of criteria for assessing environmental impacts of the proposed constructions through impact absorption will allow for comprehensive evaluations of every construction according standards set by EU directions. The equation for compatibility of the proposed constructions and the natural environment of these biotopes is: $C = MA \times ME$, where: C (%) = Compatibility, MA (%) = Mean Absorption, ME (%) = Mean Intensity [11, 12].

4   Planning and study results

4.1 Criteria of absorption

The capacity of optical absorption of landscape shows the possibility of landscape to "acquiring" procedures such as human constructions or intense management interventions. This feature depends on topography, the forest species, the change of vegetation, etc. The gradation of absorption criteria are based on: the kind of terrain conditions and the distance between the selected sites for the constructions and other interesting locations. The values of Weights are: 1= **min** (not important), 2=**med** (important) and 3=**max** (very important). It is also well known that the absorption can be measured by: the type of Forestall plants (pinus, acer, etc), the topography of the location and so on. In Table 2 we measured the terrain conditions for the road constructions and for the nature and the distance of our research areas from important places (villages, bus station, etc), in order to calculate the average clause by deviate the sum of each selected area with the weights of our criteria.

Table 2:   Criteria of absorption at the selected areas.

Criteria of absorption						
1. Terrain conditions	**Weights**	**Selected Area 1**		**Selected Area 2**		**Selected Area 3**	
		GRADE %	SUM	GRADE %	SUM	GRADE %	SUM
1.1 Forest	3	100	300	100	300	100	300
1.2 Mixed forest	3	70	210	70	210	65	195
1.3 High forest	3	60	180	100	300	70	210
1.4 Selection forest	3	50	150	50	150	50	150
1.5 Mean height	3	80	240	90	270	80	240
1.6 Side quality	3	50	150	50	150	50	150
1.7 Productivity	3	-	-	-	-	-	-
1.8 Slope	2	25	50	25	50	25	50
1.9 Relief	2	100	200	100	200	90	180
2. Distance from							
2.1 Tourist places	2	100	200	100	200	100	200
2.2 Highway	1	80	80	75	75	80	80
2.3 Railway	-	-	-	-	-	-	-
2.4 Archaeological sites		-	-	-	-	-	-
2.5 Town	1	90	90	90	90	100	100
2.6 Village	1	100	100	100	100	100	100
2.7 Path way	1	100	100	100	100	100	100
Sum	**31**		**2050**		**2195**		**2055**
Average clause (%): weight/sum			**66,12**		**70,806**		**66,29**

4.2 Environmental study on wooden and concreted constructions

It is recommended to use timber as a material of construction works, because it is a natural product. Especially in a forest, technical construction uses "composite wood" because it is 40% stronger than the rigid timber has 360 kp/m^2 strength and weight nearly 480kg/m^3. The ratio weight and strength of wood is better than conventional construction materials (Table 3) [13].

Wood is the best environmental option as it is a natural and recyclable material. In each country which is encouraged to support sustainable development, the only material available that meets the above criterion for the construction projects is wood.

4.3 Recommended projects and technical features

In all the selected locations it is proposed to establish wooden garbage bins (B) as well as fire safety signs (FS). The observance of cleanliness for recreational

Table 3:   Ratio of weight and durability of wood.

Material	Strength (bending) kg/cm²	Density kg/m³	Ratio of resistance
Glulam	140	490	0.285
Structural steel St37	1400	7800	0.179
Full timber	85	550	0.155
C12 concrete	80	1800	0.045

areas with the collection and disposal of waste is a serious problem [14], especially in our country where environmental awareness in the community hasn't developed. What should first be sought is the discharge of waste with well-established positions. So, it is necessary to place wooden garbage bins (1–2), because anyone can combine a walk with a rest for an outdoor lunch (picnic). The wooden garbage bins can be used to prevent the pollution created by the scattering of rubbish in the areas. Moreover, it is necessary to put up signs of fire hazard warning. Because of the increased risk of fire especially during summer months, forest areas are required to place signs to prevent and suppress such disasters. This increases the responsibility of the visitor towards the environment.

Furthermore, besides these, in every region, recommended sustainability plans are proposed depending on the capabilities and needs of each of these in the context of forest recreation. At the same time we propose technical works associated with each area:

4.3.1 First area
This first place is indicated as an area of recreational exercise, since it is located within a short distance from Cassandra, which is accessible by walking. It could be seen as a nearby recreation area due to its proximity to the permanent residence of the locals and the short time required visiting the place. Combined with the above is that the road permeates the area has good flow.

The projects proposed for this area are (Design 1):
a) Football field 5x5: in the first place soccer 5x5 serving young people since it offers them sport and exercise, stimulating and fun for exercisers and audience, increases social behaviour, gives the opportunity for training camps within the physical education lessons. The area where this stadium is proposed is sufficiently large for such technical project while being easily accessible. We recommend a small football field with a plastic surface such as turf, which has prevailed for several reasons. The main reason is the difficulty to maintain although of the natural grass due to the climate, but it does not offer the same flexibility to absorb vibration of the body as the turf one.
b) Kiosk: near the location of the stadium a wooden pavilion can be made, that will serve some rest to the visitors. The wooden pavilion that offers: rest and relaxation, protection from sudden weather conditions (rain, storm, etc.), offers shade from the sun and it can be a place for a snack or picnic. The proposed material for that forestalls construction is wood. The wood is environmentally friendly and more suited to forest landscapes.

c) <u>Faucet (F)</u>: the area where we propose to construct the soccer field and the kiosk will not constitute a comprehensive recreation site without a faucet. Since in the area there is a natural source, it is easy to provide water to the tap from this source. It is proposed to be stone built in order to blend aesthetically with the surroundings (2).

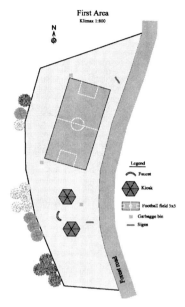

Design 1:   First area.

4.3.2 Second area

The second section is 2.3 km from Kassandreia near the church of St Marina, where a festival takes place from 19 to 20 July. The recommended construction (Design 2) is:

a) <u>Configuring the region for the festival</u>: with folding fabric awnings.

b) <u>Compost bins</u>: in compost bins, organic waste (fruits, vegetables, leaves, etc.) are converted into a rich organic mix, which acts as soil conditioner and fertilizer. By composting we can reduce all of our household waste by 35% and reduce the trash going into landfills. This has multiple benefits: (a) reduce overall quantities of waste; (b) significantly prolong the life of the landfill after receiving less waste; (c) protect the planet from global warming; (d) and another problem that solves the composting organic waste is desertification of soils. The compost, which is the product of composting, returns to the soil, necessary for the soil's fertility, organic and inorganic substances. In addition to compost bins, it would be useful to place recycling bins for other inorganic materials (paper, plastic, glass, cans, etc).

c) <u>Parking with natural shading from trees</u>: the space is sufficient for about 30–40 cars and buses. It would be also useful to place near the street, a wooden sign for parking.

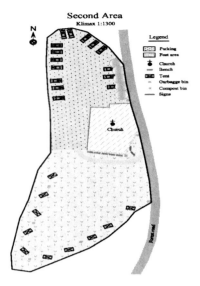

Design 2:   Second area.

4.3.3 Third area

The third place is at the end of the route and may be a small recreation area. At this point a faucet and water troughs already exist, so there could be placed some structures (Design 3):

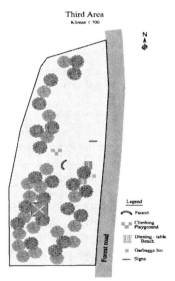

Design 3:   Third area.

4.4 Along the road the following constructions are proposed

1. Informative signs, Kalambaka type (type A): It is proposed to place (6) notices of type A at a distance of 20m before the following points: in the 5x5 football field, at the Church of St. Marina, in the third region (interactive site). An information sign will include the elements of the service and the names of the respective points.

2. Directional information signs: it is proposed to place two (2) notices of direction, type A, which are signs of general information. The summary of proposed projects is shown in Table 4.

Table 4:   Summary of proposed project.

SELECTED AREA	CONFIGURATION OF SCOPE									
	Football field 5x5	Kiosk	Composting bins	Wooden climbing multi-instrument	Observatory of Wild Fauna	Benches for rest/ dining	Faucet (F)	Garbage bins (B)	Informative signs/ Fire signs(FS)	Parking
1st	✔	✔				✔	✔	✔	✔	✔
2nd		✔	✔			✔		✔	✔	✔
3rd				✔	✔	✔	✔	✔	✔	

5   Conclusions and proposals

With the staging of our work, we separated it in the three main pieces: a) Field Work (select one area of forest road, walking on the forest road, identifying potential points for improvement, etc.) b) recording and processing of selected data points c) designing of the proposed projects and d) presentation of final proposals to study the sustainable development of the region.

The average values for the optical absorption capacity of each selected areas for regeneration, are about the same (66.12%, 70.806% and 66.29%) and over 50% is necessary because that makes acceptable our proposed development. In the second selected area (S.A.2) the percentage is higher (71%) because the site is already formed to some extent; since there is the church of Saint Marina where during the summer there is a festival. So there the terrain slope is nearly 5% and the accessibility conditions are very good.

Our proposals refer to the improvement of certain parts at the right side of the road, with forest recreation structures based on the principles of sustainable use. We believe that this structural plan can be accepted for funded from the Prefecture because it has low cost and was designed based on the sustainable rural development criteria. That can give employment of local population and the growth of tourism at a pace commensurate with the physical development and not with the speed desired by the short-term economic forecasts.

References

[1] Minagric 2012, *The value of the forest.* www.minagric.gr/greek/agro_pol/dasika/forests/forests1.htm

[2] Stergiadou A., 2007. *Sustainable development of coastal forested areas by using an environmental opening up strategy*, CEMEPE Proc. of SECOTOX Conference on Environmental Management Engineering, Planning and Economics, v.1, pp. 739–744, Thessaloniki.

[3] United Nations. 1987. *Report of the World Commission on Environment and Development*, General Assembly Resolution 42/187, 11 December 1987. Retrieved: 2007-11-14.

[4] WCED (World Commission on Environment and Development), 1987. *Our Common Future*. Oxford, UK: Oxford University Press.

[5] Stergiadou A., 2001. *Promotion, sustainable development and forest open up of the mountain region (regions: Grevena, Ioannina and Kilkis)*, Doctoral Thesis in Geotechnical School, A.U.Th., Greece. http://phdtheses.ekt.gr/eadd/handle/10442/22812.

[6] Hellenic statistical authority, 2012. *Human population*, www.statistics.gr

[7] Eskioglou P. and Efthymiou P., 1995. *Alternative stabilization methods of forest roads for an efficient and gentle mechanization of wood harvesting systems*, http://www.fao.org/documents/en/docrep.jsp (6.05.2012).

[8] Koutsopoulos N. and Yang Q., 1992. *Modelling requirements for emerging transportation system operating environments*. Report DTRS-57-88-C-0078, TTD 29, John A. Volpe National Transportation Systems Center, Cambridge, MA.

[9] Koroneos C., Bouras A., Mousiopoulos N., Balla C. 1999. *Life Cycle Analysis: A Comprehensive Approach*. Proceedings of Heleco 1999: "Environmental Technology for the 21st Century", Vol. II, Third International Exhibition and Conference (3–6 June 1999, Thessaloniki), TEE, Athens.

[10] Doucas K., 2004. *Forest Construction*, Giachoudis press, pp. 346, Thessaloniki, Greece.

[11] Stergiadou A., 2006. *Environmental impact assessment (E.I.A.) for the evaluation of forest roads in mountainous conditions (case study: Valia Kalda)*, Proceedings of International Conference "Sustainable Management and Development of Mountainous and Island Areas", 29th Sep.–1st Oct. 2006, Island Naxos, Greece, Pub: D.U.Th., pp. 125–129, Orestiada.

[12] Stergiadou A., 2007. *Sustainable development of "Smixi" using environmental impact assessment*, Sustainable Development and Planning III, Vol. 2, pp. 281–291, WIT press Transaction on Ecology and the Environment, Vol. 102, ISSN:1743-3541 (on-line).

[13] Democritus University of Thrace (DUTh.), 2012. http://diocles.civil.duth.gr/links/home/museum/mater/wood/wood7.html

[14] Liakos L., 1977. *The recreation in forests*. Aristotle University Press, pp. 365, Thessaloniki, Greece.

[15] Papageorgiou N.K., *Game Breeding*, University Studio Press, Thessaloniki, 1996.

Urban agriculture in Dar es Salaam: a dream or reality?

H. S. Mkwela
Norwegian University of Science and Technology (NTNU), Norway

Abstract

The paper focuses on the policy issues concerning urban agriculture (UA) in Dar es Salaam city. It argues that the process of formalisation and/or including UA in the city master plan takes longer than expected despite efforts by local and international stakeholders including the UN Habitat and United National Environmental Program (UNEP). The two agents jointly launched the Sustainable Dar es Salaam City Project (SDCP) in 1992 which became operational in 1993. The project idea was to make Dar es Salaam one of exemplary sustainable cities in Africa. Urban agriculture was identified as one of the priority for the Project; because a sustainable city should be able to feed its residents by using local resources. By the time the project was completed in 2003, still, there was no clear UA policy in the country. In support of UN Habitat and UNEP initiatives for a Sustainable Dar es Salaam City Project, national and international funded UA development projects have been implemented at different times and scales. One of these programmes is the on-going Sustainable Cities International Network-Africa Programme (SCINAP) which is aimed at promoting legitimization of UA in the city. These projects have had a number of proposals concerning inclusion of UA in the city's master plan which are yet to be implemented by the authorities. These delays have left the hapless urban farmers with no alternative but to invade institutional and hazardous land leading to insecurity of tenure and environmental degradation. The paper is aimed at identifying and analysing the sources of delay in formalisation and inclusion of UA in the master plan. It is based on the in-depth literature and analysis of the published works, policies related to UA and official reports from the government of Tanzania. It would appear from the gathered evidence that among other barriers for the timely formalisation and inclusion of UA in the master plan in Dar es Salaam city is related to urban authorities' perceptions of the activity.
Keywords: urban agriculture (UA), sustainable city, Sustainable Dar es Salaam Project, UA policy, UA dream, UA reality.

WIT Transactions on Ecology and The Environment, Vol 173, © 2013 WIT Press
www.witpress.com, ISSN 1743-3541 (on-line)
doi:10.2495/SDP130141

1 Introduction

Urban Agriculture (UA) is regarded as one of the fastest growing employment and income generation industries in most developing countries (Mougeot [1]). The Town and Country Planning (Urban Farming) Regulations (1992) defines Urban farming as *'the carrying out of plant and animal husbandry activities within statutory township boundaries as provided in the schedule'*. The schedule defines six (6) areas to fall within the UA category ranging from cultivation of crops to serpentaria and forestry and rearing of animals. In Mougeot's [1] view, UA is often located within (intra-urban) or on the fringe (peri-urban) of a town, an urban Centre, a city or metropolis, which grows or raises, processes and distributes a diversity of food and non-food products, (re-) using mainly human and material resources, inputs and services found in and around that urban area, and in turn supplying human and material resources, outputs and services largely to that urban area. Earlier on, Sawio [2] defined UA in Dar es Salaam as the carrying out of farming activities in the built-up and peri-urban areas, where un built land is available, as well as keeping livestock such as dairy cattle, goats, sheep, pigs and fowl. While the first definition is more inclined to purportedly allowable activities that are likely to take place within the defined boundaries, the second and third definitions covers the actual activities that are taking place within townships both urban and peri-urban areas. In this study UA is taken to mean the practice of agricultural activities in the city and its surroundings.

The dream of making Dar es Salaam a sustainable city through the formalisation and managing of agricultural activities seems to be contrary to what is taking place on the ground i.e. the reality. The dream can be traced back from 1992 when UN Habitat and United National Environmental Program (UNEP) introduced the Sustainable Dar es Salaam Project (SDP); the project took off in November 1993 (Mwalukasa [3]). Among other environmental concerns, UA was identified as one of the major environmental issues in the city which needed special attention [3–5]. The project had a responsibility to develop a new Strategic Urban Development Plan (SUDP) for integrating UA into the city management plans [5]. In this respect, a special working group for UA was formed aiming at promoting sustainable UA. By the time the project was completed in 2003, there was no clear urban agriculture policy and UA was not included in the City's Master Plan. It would appear that this dream has not been realized (Mkwela and Banyani [6]).

The reality surrounding UA activities in Dar es Salaam is contrary to the sustainability dream initiated by the SDP and advocated by Sustainable Cities International Network-Africa programme (SCINAP). To-date, UA is regarded as an informal activity; existing without proper plans, designated areas or a guiding policy. UA has been subjected to criticisms from planners, policy makers and researchers. A vivid example is a paper by Mlozi [7] in which UA has been linked to severe health threats, environmental, social and security concerns. Considering this view, UA has more sustainability problems than benefits. Due to the overriding criticisms and negative attitude, UA has not gained a place in the master plan nor in the hearts of the city planners and decision makers

(Schmidt [8]). As a consequence, farmers face issues related to land access, tenure and security. The National Samples Census (URT [9]) has shown that only 5% of the estimated 36,551 farmers surveyed in Dar es Salaam have certificate of ownership. The remaining 95% tend to own land through customary law, rented, borrowed, shared or purchased from other inferior right holders. Agricultural activities in the city are subjects of occasional abuse by the authorities which can take the form of crops destruction and/or evacuation.

The paper is aimed at identifying and analysing the sources of delay in inclusion of UA in the master plan and formulation of the policy guiding UA activities in Dar es Salaam City while taking into consideration of the questions in the paragraph below. It focuses on the policy issues concerning Urban Agriculture (UA) in Dar es Salaam city but while doing so it also makes reference to published UA research works and official reports. In the current situation, it is not very clear what is guiding UA activities in the city due to varieties of policies and other instruments. It is also not clear whether UA is practically accepted or not despite the fact that donors and international researchers have worked for years to outline the guidelines for UA in Dar es Salaam city as shown in the previous discussion. There is an indication that effort to showcase Dar es Salaam city as sustainable city has not yielded the expected outcome. The process of formulating UA policy and/or including UA in the city master plan has taken longer time than expected. These delays have left the hapless urban farmers who are yet to be recognized officially by the city authorities with no alternative but to invade institutional and hazardous land leading to environmental degradation and insecurity of tenure.

The basic questions which remain to be answered could be: "Is there a possibility that UA will be formally recognized in the city?"; How long will the process to formalize UA take?"; "Who is holding back the process?"; "What is the current policy position on urban agricultural activities?"

2 Methodology

The paper is based on in-depth analysis of the content of the policies, published works and official reports with the intention of identifying the sources of delay in formalisation and incorporation of UA in the city's master plan. It critically analyse policies related to or which affects urban agriculture (UA) as a land use in Dar es Salaam city, Tanzania. The analysis seeks to uncover meanings and understandings of the broad interrelationships between policies and the practice of UA in the city. It compares specific provisions of the policies with the intention to identify their similarities and differences. In carrying out the analysis of the content of the policies, the paper adopts the hermeneutic approach [10–12]. Gummesson [13] noted that hermeneutic approach uses a personal interpretive process in order to understand reality. The author states "*language takes on a central role, qualitative assessments partially replace quantitative data, and general characteristics become lesser interest than specific features*". Jaspers [11] notes that, hermeneutic approach analyses and reflects upon texts and words in the need to uncover and find meaning. It can be used to criticise or support the content of a written word.

The paper identified specific provisions and articles within different policies which are meant to guide and manage urban agriculture in the city. It also evaluated published works and official reports which were directly associated to or reported on UA issues. Subjects of these various provisions articles and the content of the published research and official reports were critically analysed. The analysis was intended to single out the position, contribution, and impact of a specific instrument or report in the formalisation and inclusion of UA in the master plan. This intention guided the choice of the documents used in the analysis. The choice was based on the purposive convenient sampling (Kumar [14]). Documents which were pre-reviewed were chosen due to their rich information and ease of access or availability. The analysed policies include the Land Policy, 1995; Agricultural and Livestock Policy, 1997 and National Human Settlements Development Policy, 2000. The study also evaluated the impact of the content of the Town and Country Planning (Urban Farming) Regulations, 1992. In some instances the paper revised the content of official websites of key organisations such as government ministries and development programme.

One of the drawbacks of this method is the possibility of leaving a key document(s) that would otherwise provide more insight on the subject matter in case it was not within the reach of the researcher. Another possible challenge can be biasness related to interpretation of the text and words. The research addressed the two issues by (i) conducting of in-depth review of the existing literature, (ii) concisely define the objectives of the study and (iii) the paper was exposed to rigorous peer review after the initial drafts.

3 What are the current policies positions regarding UA?

Apart from the Town and Country Planning (Urban Farming) Regulations, 1992 there is no single explicit document for the management and regulation of the conduct of UA in Tanzania. Presently, UA is deemed to be regulated and managed using specific ministerial or sectorial policies and regulations as well as local government by-laws. Table 1 provides a summary of three policies and one regulation that has a direct impact in the operation of UA practice in Dar es Salaam. The list may not be exhaustive but it includes the key machineries which are intended to guide the orderly conduct of the UA practice.

It has been observed that three policies in Table 1 were promulgated to deal with other primary issues not urban agriculture. For example the National Land Policy, 1995 was intended to deal with general issues related to land management and administration. The Agricultural and Livestock policy of 1997 was intended to deal with broad agriculture and livestock development issues in the country. The National Human Settlements Development Policy, 2000 was intended to provide the orderly planning, management and regulation of human settlements developments. While dealing with these primary objectives, each of the policies found itself encompassing some provisions dealing with UA. The Town and Country Planning (Urban Farming) Regulations, 1992 explicitly deal with the conduct of UA in the country. It defines UA, set conditions and enumerates a number of activities that fall under it. The policies have been identified to include provisions which have an impact on UA in terms of tenure, land rights and the general conduct.

While these policies and regulations are country-wide; their scope of application in this paper has been delimited to Dar es Salaam city. In the following discussion, the paper analyses the similarities and differences within and between the selected three policies and later on, the regulations. The idea is to determine the positions of these policies towards UA in Dar es Salaam City.

Table 1:   The summary of provisions in policies and regulations.

National Land Policy 1995	Agricultural and Livestock Policy, 1997	National Human Settlements Development Policy, 2000	The Town and Country Planning (Urban Farming) Regulations, 1992
S. 6.1.2 (i): Measures to limit the loss of agricultural land to urban growth by controlling lateral expansion of all towns	S. 3.3.2 (i) Agriculture is not a principal function of towns but when properly organized urban agriculture has the potential to provide employment, income and is a supplementary source of food supply	S.4.3.7.2(i) The government shall designate special areas within planning areas whereby people will be granted legal rights to engage themselves in agricultural activities	S. 78. 3 (1): No person shall occupy or use more than three acres of land for urban farming
S. 6.7.0(i): Agriculture is not a principal function of towns but when properly organized, urban agriculture has the potential to provide employment, income, and is a supplementary source of food supply		S.4.3.7.2(ii) Continue to regulate and research on the conduct of urban agriculture, this will ensure that it does not disrupt planned urban development	S.78.3 (2): No person shall, except where that person practices zero grazing, graze his animal in urban area
S. 6.7.0 (ii): In their present form agricultural activities often conflict with the proper planning of urban land uses	S.3.3.2 (ii) The government will continue to regulate the conduct of UA and will ensure that it does not disrupt planned urban development	S.4.3.7.2(iii) Review the existing laws to facilitate planned urban agriculture	S.78.4. From the date of coming into effect of these regulations, any farming activity which may be deemed to constitute a nuisance in the form of noise or smell or pose a physical danger to the safety of the public shall not be permitted in the areas other than those zoned for urban farming
S. 6.7.1: The government will continue to regulate the conduct of urban agriculture and will ensure that it does not disrupt planned urban development		S.4.3.7.2(iv) Facilitate the construction of appropriate infrastructure to mitigate/prevent land degradation, water pollution, and health and safety hazards in the areas whereby agriculture is permitted	

The analysis has shown the existence of consensus and similarities between and within the policies in some aspects; not all. One of the agreements between the three policies is the idea that *"UA has to be regulated in order to avoid its disruptions to planned urban development"*. This position has been explicitly stated under article 6.7.1 of the National Land Policy, 1995 article 3.3.2 (ii) of the Agricultural and Livestock Policy, 1997 and article 4.3.7 (ii) of the National Human Settlements Development Policy, 2000 as shown in Table 1. This statement suggests that; UA is a marginal land use which is not part of the planned urban development and likely to disrupt the important ones. This has been augmented by the National Land Policy which states that *"In their present form agricultural activities often conflicts with the proper planning of urban land uses"*

This interpretation is supported by the first part of the provisions in the National land Policy, 1995 and Agricultural and Livestock Policy that, *"Agriculture is not a principle function of towns....But when properly organised UA has the potential to provide employment, income and is a supplementary source of food supply"*. Ideally, since UA is not a principle function of towns (urban areas) which is likely to disrupt or conflict with the planned land use, it has no need to claim a place within the towns and cities boundaries. It has to stay where it belong i.e. in the rural areas. With this type of policies driving the mind-sets of the professionals and decision makers alike it has been difficult for UA to be accepted within towns or urban areas including the city of Dar es Salaam.

The preceding discussion has shown one of the two sides of the policies related to UA in Tanzania. The interpretation of the provisions has suggested that agriculture is less favoured compared to planned land uses in urban areas. However, in some instances these policies have shown a different stance. For example the second part of the provisions in the National land Policy, 1995 and Agricultural and Livestock Policy 1997 which states that, *"....But when properly organised UA has the potential to provide employment, income and is a supplementary source of food supply"* recognises the enormous contribution which can be made by UA to urban environment.

It comes with no wonder therefore, when the same National Land Policy, 1995 states under article 6.1.2 (i) it intentions "to devise measures which will limit the loss of agricultural land to urban growth by controlling lateral expansions of all towns". The provision not only recognises the contribution of UA to urban areas but also the need to ensure the availability of arable land by limiting other urban land uses. This article in a way contradicts with the other provisions within the same policy which were discussed earlier on with a stance that, agriculture is not a principle function of towns and it tends to disrupt other planned urban land uses. The need to set land aside for UA open up opportunities for discussion and its inclusion in the planned urban development. Conspicuously, this provision supports the existence of agriculture as a land use in urban areas.

It would appear that; this provision of the National Land Policy, 1995 was taken into consideration when formulating the National Human Settlements Development Policy in 2000. The 2000 policy has three statements all in favour of UA as follows:

(i)   The government shall designate special areas within planning areas whereby people will be granted legal rights to engage themselves in agricultural activities.

(ii)   The government intended to review the existing laws to facilitate planned UA.

(iii) Government has an intention to facilitate the construction of appropriate infrastructure to mitigate/prevent land degradation, water pollution, and health and safety hazards in areas whereby agriculture is permitted.

If these provisions are taken to mean the government commitment towards UA, then the future is promising. It shows that government has; on top of recognising the contribution of UA decided to embrace it in its urban areas by ensuring that farmers are allocated land which ensures security of tenure and even market of their produce. It also suggests that the government has identified the compatibility between UA and other planned urban developments in contrary to the position held in the National Land Policy, 1995 and Agricultural and Livestock Policy, 1997.

While the wording of the three statements is positive and promising the available evidence indicates that none of the three issues covered has been implemented. For example, Mkwela and Banyani [6] have shown that no agricultural land was set aside in the 20,000 Plot Delivery Project that was implemented between 2002/2003 to 2005/2006 in the Dar es Salaam city. The project acquired 76sq. km of land which was formerly used as agricultural land and converted it into a 37,000 residential plots. The consequence has been for the farmers to continue with agricultural activities in the buffer zones illegally (see figure 1). This serves as a warning that the mere policy commitment is not enough; there is a need to implement these provisions in fully when development projects are being designed.

The Town and Country Planning (Urban Farming) Regulations, 1992 is another instrument which has been developed to regulate the practice of UA in

Figure 1: UA in the buffer zone of 20,000 plots delivery Mbweni area – Dar es Salaam.

Figure 2: Herd of goats crossing the road, Kinondoni – Dar es Salaam.

urban areas. The regulations provide three conditions within which UA should be practised as shown in Table 1. The regulations limits the acreage held for any urban farmer to 3 acres and restricts the livestock keeping to zero grazing. It also, restricts the carrying out of any agricultural activity that will be deemed to constitute a nuisance. While the provisions of the regulations are relatively good, they are seldom implemented. There are people legally holding land with more than 3 acres within the city that are put under agricultural use [4, 9]. Zero grazing has also proved to be difficulty; herds of goats can simply found roaming the city of Dar es Salaam and interferes with the traffic flow (see figure 2).

4   Formalization of UA in Dar es Salaam city

The discussion on the positions of policies which have direct impact on UA has revealed both, the support and opposition. However, the most recent policy, i.e. the National Human Settlements Policy, 2000 has more provisions which support the practising of UA and it even indicates the government intention to review other pieces of legislations in order to enable the practise to be planned. This forms part of the broad dream of UA in the city which is not as yet realised i.e. the possibility that the practice can be legitimised and incorporated in the city's master plan. The discussion below traces the various processes that had followed this dream.

Efforts to formalize UA in the city were initiated by the Sustainable City Programme in 1992. UNEP and UN HABITAT selected Dar es Salaam as one of the demonstration project for urban sustainability. A Sustainable City Programme (SCP) initiated in the 1990s was a response by UN Habitat to implement Agenda 21. The programme had an emphasis on strengthening the capacity of local city authorities in controlling environmental hazards and management of city resources in a sustainable way. Through its Sustainable Dar es Salaam Project (SDP) the project initiated the Environmental Planning Management (EPM) as a tool that involved various stakeholders to identify key environmental issues in the city. One of the urban environmental issues identified in Dar es Salaam was Urban Agriculture. A total of US $5,615,000 was spent making the SDP the largest project of all SCP [5].

UA working group was created by the SDP consultation meetings to deal with UA issues in the city. The group composed of academic institutions, municipalities, ministries, financial institutions, urban citizens, informal and formal businesses, livestock owners and farmers met in 1993 [3]. The aim of the group was mainly to suggest ways of sustainable UA and to facilitate the inclusion of UA in the city's master plan. In 1993, the UA working group set out some strategies on how to improve the practice of UA; the group came up with three main ideas, integration of UA in the city master plan (A mixed land use strategy), preparation of the action plan, and implementation of demo projects. Out of these ideas, a UA demo project was successful launched [3].

The idea of mixed land use strategy and inclusion of UA in the city's master plan is further advanced by The Sustainable Cities International Network-Africa Programme (SCINAP). SCINAP is working with the local municipalities in Dar es Salaam city to formulate strategic plans on urban agriculture (SCINAP, 2011). The successful prepared strategic plans at the municipal level will be forwarded to the Ministry of Lands, Housing and Human Settlement Development (MLHHSD) for inclusion the city's 2010 to 2030 Master Plan. Due to the organizations commitment and collaboration with the municipalities, one of the three Dar es Salaam city's municipality has already formulated its strategic plans on urban agriculture and has been forwarded to the ministry for approval.

Demonstration projects are one of the ideas suggested by UA working group in Dar es Salaam under the SDP. One of a successful demo project is the Mbutu Agriculture Society (MAS) with 120 members. The project was registered in 1993; the main objectives of the project were to provide food security, encouraging gender equality and poverty alleviation activities. Other projects facilitating UA include Mikocheni vocational school gardening and composting project, The Kesho Trust and Kisiwani Environmental Group.

5 Reflections

The process to formalize and include UA in the city's master plan is faced with many challenges and takes longer than expected. The main questions posed earlier in this paper can be answered based on the in depth analysis of policies, regulations and efforts by local and international organization in the process of formalization and inclusion of UA in the city's master plan which has been discussed above. The main questions were, is there a possibility that UA will be formally recognized in the city? how long will the process to formalize UA take? Who is holding back the process? What is the current policy position on urban agricultural activities? Discussions below provide some reflections and way forward in regard to UA formalization in Dar es Salaam city.

5.1 Is there a possibility of formalisation of UA in Dar es Salaam city?

There is always a possibility and hope that UA will eventually be formalized in Dar es Salaam. However, ambiguous trends behind the process to include UA in the city's Master Plan reveal a major disregard of UA activities. Dar es Salaam city Municipalities are working on the Strategic Urban Development Plans (SUDP) that takes into consideration UA management. The plans will be forwarded to the Ministry of Lands and Human Settlement Development for approval and eventually inclusion in the city's future Master Plan 2010–2030.

5.2 How long will the process to formalize UA take to be finalised?

The process looks simple and easy, however, the bureaucracy behind the process is frustrating. For over two decades, many local and international organizations in favour of UA have put their effort in persuading the decision makers to formally recognize UA with little success. It is not clear at this moment, how long will the process be finalized.

5.3 Who is holding back the process?

Most of Dar es Salaam city residents have a negative attitude towards UA. People's perception on UA contributes to its drawback. City planners and law makers, realize the potential of UA to some of its residents, mainly, the jobless and the poor. However, agriculture is regarded as a rural activity and a disgrace of a proper urban planning. This attitude is hidden in the people's hearts and can only be manifested in the whole planning and decision making process regarding UA. People who could positively defend UA have a stigma that UA has no place in the city i.e. it is a shame, old fashioned, dirty, not proper, and uncivilized.

5.4 What is the policy position on urban agricultural activities?

The country as a whole does not have UA policy to guide the activity. At the moment UA is indirectly depicted by other National policies; as a result UA is not adequately represented. Further discussion on this item has been covered in section 3 of this paper.

6 Conclusions

The reality surrounding agriculture in Dar es Salaam city and many urban areas of the country is the same. UA in the city is considered as an informal activity at times a source of nuisance. Agriculture has been used as a short term strategy to cope with food shortages, economic, social, climatic and political instabilities that occur in different periods. Furthermore, UA is recognized by its importance in providing food security, employment and a source of income for urban residents, especially the poor. However, this recognition is not enough for the activity to be officially recognized and included in the city's long term plans. The dream of sustainable agricultural activities in the city will be uncertain, until the moment it will be formally recognized, regulated and supported by all stakeholders. From the analysis of the policies the following recommendations can be made:

- There is a need for a single policy document resulting from the harmonization of various policies related to or which affects UA activities in the city in order to realise an orderly conduct of the practice.
- Inclusion of UA in the master plan and other short term or ad-hoc city plans and projects.
- Educating the policy makers and the general public by emphasizing on the change of their attitude and perception regarding UA. More research on how much UA contributes to food security; employment and social economic stability need to be portrayed through exemplary projects. Initiation of a TV and early school programmes that promotes UA will also be important in changing people's perception and implanting good image of UA to children.
- The use of road reserves and way-leaves is recommended as a short term solution or strategy against scarcity of arable land. It is proposed that

temporary licences be granted to co-operatives/peer or women groups/farmers groups to produce short cycle crops.

References

[1] Mougeot, L., *Urban Agriculture: Definition, Presence, Potential and Risks, Main Policy Challenges.* CFP Report No. 31.IDRC. Canada, 1999.

[2] Sawio, C., *Managing urban agriculture in Dar es Salaam city*, Cities Feeding People Initiatives, IDRC Canada, Report 20, 1998.

[3] Mwalukasa, M., Institutional aspects of urban agriculture in the city of Dar es salaam, *Growing Cities, Growing Food, Urban Agriculture on the Policy Agenda*, eds. N. Bakker., M, Dubbeling., S, Guendel., U, Koschella., H, de Zeeuw., RUAF: Netherlands, pp. 99–117, 2000.

[4] Mlambo, A., Institutionalizing urban agriculture in Dar es Salaam city through the EPM process *Proc. Of the E-Conf. On Appropriate Methods for Urban Agriculture. Research, Policy development, Planning, Implementation and Evaluation,* RUAF: Netherlands, pp. 1–10, 2002.

[5] Nnkya, T. *The Sustainable Cities Programme in Tanzania 1992–2003*: From a City Demonstration Project to a National Programme for Environmentally Sustainable Urban Development. UN HABITAT. Nairobi-Kenya, 2004.

[6] Mkwela, H., Banyani, M., *Urban Farming: A Sustainable Solution to Reduce Solid Waste Problems in Dar es Salaam, Tanzania.* RICS publication. UK, 2008.

[7] Mlozi, M., Impacts of urban agriculture in Dar es Salaam, Tanzania. *The Environmentalist*, **17(2)**, pp. 115–124, 1997.

[8] Schmidt, S., Urban agriculture in Dar es Salaam, Tanzania. #7-12, *Food Policy for Developing Counties: Case studies*, ed. P. Pinstrup-Andersen., F. Cheng., Cornell University, pp. 1–10, 2011.

[9] United Republic of Tanzania (URT), National sample census of agriculture 2002/2003, vol. vg *Regional Report: Dar es Salaam region*, Dar es Salaam, 2007.

[10] Ticehurst, G.W., Veal, A.J., *Business Research Methods: A Managerial Approach*, Longman Person Education Pty Limited, 1999.

[11] Jaspers, D., *A Short Introduction to Hermeneutics*, Westminster John Knox Press, Kentucky, 2004.

[12] Thiselton, A.C., *Hermeneutics: An Introduction*, Wm. Eerdmans Publishing, Michigan, 2009.

[13] Gummesson, E., *Qualitative Methods in Management Research*, Sage Publications Inc, Newbury Park, CA, 1991.

[14] Kumar R., *Research Methodology: A Step by Step Guide for Beginners*, London, Sage Publications, 1999.

Policies and regulations

United Republic of Tanzania (URT), The National Land Policy, 1995, www.tanzania.go.tz

United Republic of Tanzania (URT), Agricultural and Livestock Policy, 1997, www.tanzania.go.tz
United Republic of Tanzania (URT), National Human Settlements Development Policy, 2000, www.tanzania.go.tz
The Town and Country Planning (Urban Farming) Regulations, 1992, http://faolex.fao.org/cgi-bin/faolex.exe.rec_id=005242

Section 4
Regional planning

Identifying social-ecological couplings for regional sustainability in a rapidly urbanizing water-limited area of western Canada

M. E. Tyler[1] & M. S. Quinn[2]
[1]Faculty of Environmental Design, University of Calgary, Canada
[2]Institute for Environmental Sustainability,
Mount Royal University, Canada

Abstract

Regional planning for sustainability is predicated on an ability to create and maintain resilient social-ecological systems that are adaptable in the face of surprise and change. One of the central challenges is to understand, articulate and manage the connections between social systems and the physical environment. Over the last fifty years economic 'booms' associated with abundant oil and gas resources have driven rapid regional population growth and large scale landscape change in the Calgary region. However, the region is a semi-arid and temperate area where growth-related land use planning is quite literally water dependent. Climate change modeling suggests even warmer and drier conditions in the region making the critical relationship between land-use and water increasingly acute. A voluntary regional partnership of local municipal governments has emerged over the past six years to address common land use planning concerns emerging from the rapid anthropogenic and natural changes affecting the region. In this paper we explore some of the critical social-ecological couplings that have emerged as drivers for sustainability and resilience in the Calgary region of southwestern Alberta, Canada. We posit critical social-ecological and spatial couplings involving: 1) the intersection of built infrastructure (transportation, irrigation and utility corridors) and ecological infrastructure (landscape connectivity), and 2) regional ecohydrology and human water use.
Keywords: social-ecological systems (SES), coupled human and natural systems (CHANS), resilience, regional planning, sustainability, ecohydrology.

WIT Transactions on Ecology and The Environment, Vol 173, © 2013 WIT Press
www.witpress.com, ISSN 1743-3541 (on-line)
doi:10.2495/SDP130151

1 Introduction

Social-ecological systems (SES) are a 'synthesis' of human and ecological processes, interactions and interconnections. They are 'emergent' systems insofar as they are not simply a social system + an ecological system and, as such, cannot be modelled as analogous to either an ecosystem or a socio-economic system.

Liu *et al.* [1] define coupled human and natural systems (CHANS) as "integrated systems in which people interact with natural components." CHANS are characterized by nonlinear human and ecological process interactions and complex reciprocal feedback loops that are socioecological as well as socioeconomic. In a CHANS framework, integrated human-ecological process interactions function as co-regulators of SES functional dynamics in time and space. Human activities do not just exist 'outside' of ecological systems and have impacts upon them; they are an integral part of ecological system function and are becoming increasingly dominant. A co-regulators approach differs significantly from a conventional impact model such as the EEA [2] Drivers-Pressure-State-Impact-Response effect chain. In a CHANS framework, system dynamics and threshold effects are characterized by nonlinearity. SES drivers and responses represent reciprocal anthropogenic and ecological (abiotic-biotic) processes. Human and natural systems co-evolve and co-regulate change, instability and mutual adaptation across scales.

To date, much of the research into CHANS and SES has focussed on rural and indigenous social-ecological systems (Berkes and Folke [3], Berkes *et al.* [4]). However, Lui *et al.* [1] suggest, urban social-ecological systems and couplings are substantively different insofar as they "are mediated by factors such as the urban form, built infrastructure, and location and consumption patterns of heterogeneous households and businesses." Social innovation, technological innovation, economic opportunity and changes in sociocultural organization and preferences have resulted in rapid urbanization and growing city regions together with massive rural to urban land use transitions (Lambin and Meyfroidt [5]). While such human drivers of environmental change may initially appear to be exogenous to ecological systems, their reconciliation over time will depend upon co-regulation by endogenous social-ecological couplings.

Crutzen and Stoermer [6] proffered the term 'Anthropocene' to describe a new geologic period in which humankind is the dominant force in the biogeoclimatic transformation of our planet. While there has been some controversy regarding this term, the dominant influences and functions of human activities on the function and evolution of the Earth system is becoming increasingly recognized (Steffen *et al.* [7], Vitousek *et al.* [8], Zalasiewicz *et al.* [9]). For example, in 2012, a new international scientific journal named 'Anthropocene' was founded to address the nature, scale, and extent of the influence that people have on Earth (Elsevier [10]). Similarly, Zalasiewicz *et al.* [9] are unequivocal in stating that addressing the Anthropocene "is now arguably the most important question of our age – scientifically, socially and politically. We cannot think of a greater or more urgent challenge."

Scheffer *et al.* [11] state it is becoming increasingly clear that many complex systems, including CHANS, have "critical thresholds – so-called tipping points – at which the system shifts abruptly from one state to another." Such abrupt state shifts or critical transitions are potentially catastrophic. Therefore much of the international research focus on resilience theory is to identify possible warning signs of such transitions. The potential large scale negative socioeconomic consequences of critical transformations is part of the current rationale for incorporating resilience theory and resilience thinking into adaptive ecosystem management and sustainable urban and regional systems governance (Stockholm Resilience Centre [12]).

The growing acknowledgement of increasingly tight couplings between human and natural sub-systems within the overall planetary system is fostering research to understand and ultimately manage resilience and sustainability (Jahn *et al.* [13]). The research we describe in this paper is in the context of a rapidly growing semi-arid region and is intended to identify clues for identifying critical regional SES couplings and manage them at a regional landscape scale.

1.1 Social-ecological couplings across scales

The 'regional analysis of social-ecological systems' (RASE) is one approach to understanding CHANS that has emerged in the context of environmental monitoring for environmental management (Bourgeron *et al.* [14]). The general steps in a RASE approach are illustrated in Fig. 1. According to Bourgeron *et al.* [14], there are three fundamental stages involved in RASE development; and five region-specific knowledge requirements. These can be produced through the analysis and interpretation of available data and maps of historical and current biological conditions and human activities and include:

- Identification of key inter-relationships among ecosystem components and integration of socioeconomic, land use and biological data.
- Identification of scaled relationships between RASE data acquisition and strategic scenarios.
- Identification of spatial scales for six types of boundaries used in RASE (including: assessment area, characterization area, analysis area, cumulative impact area, reporting unit).
- Description of SES as a whole, including coupling of components and system properties such as disturbances and resilience.

The substantive nature of these information requirements requires detailed and specialized information not always readily available. There is also a high degree of subjective interpretation and expert opinion required for identification of important or critical social-ecological couplings and their thresholds. However, as hypothetical as a RASE approach may be, it has regional to local cross-scalar application (as illustrated in Fig. 2).

Walker *et al.* [15] state: "A regional SES does not consist of just one kind of cycle at one scale. It functions as a nested, hierarchical structure, with processes

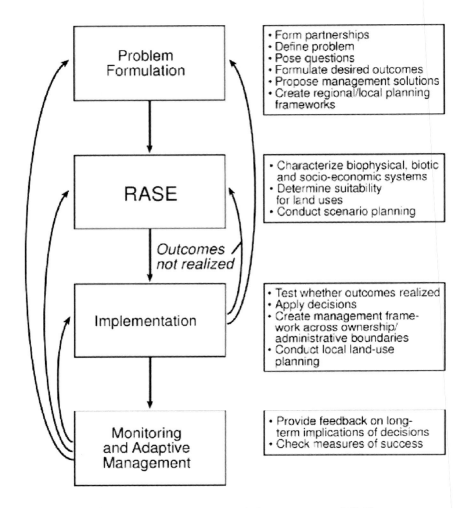

Figure 1:   RASE approach (Bourgeron *et al.* [14]).

clustered within subsystems at several scales." Likewise, Gunderson and Holling [16] stress the importance of multi-scale approaches. Therefore, the identification of social-ecological couplings needs to recognize and reflect these various scales and rates in terms of fast and slow variables and stages in adaptive cycles.

Cross-scalar processes are also important because of the significance of, and potential for, cascading effects. As described by Peters *et al.* [17]: "Cascading events that start at small spatial scales and propagate non-linearly through time to influence larger areas often have major impacts on ecosystem goods and services." Cascading events are often driven by linked ecological and human processes across scales which illustrate the critical linkages between land use decisions and ecosystem dynamics. They also demonstrate "non-linear

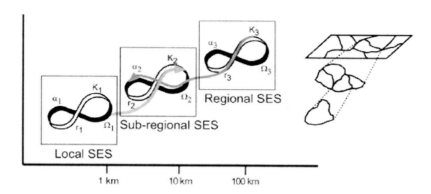

Figure 2:   Cross-scalar application of RASE approach (Bourgeron *et al.* [14]).

aggregation of fine-scale processes with unanticipated effects at broader scales" [17]. Therefore, it becomes increasingly critical to identify and understand such cascading effects within CHANS.

Attempts to identify critical social-ecological couplings have illustrated that there is a disconnection between human decision-making and complex system variability.   This disconnection is addressed by Milly *et al.*'s [18] declaration that "stationarity is dead."   This refers to the traditional practice in water resource engineering of assuming stationarity ("the idea that natural systems fluctuate within an unchanging envelope of variability") in water resource planning and management.   Unfortunately, there is evidence of increasing uncertainty rather than predictability which has rendered stationarity 'dead' because "substantial anthropogenic change of Earth's climate is altering the means and extremes of precipitation, evapotranspiration and rates of discharge of rivers" [18]. Therefore, new approaches are necessary for engaging uncertainty and nonlinearity in order to assist human adaptation to unpredictable climate system dynamics. Holling and Meffe [19] have previously described this disconnection problem in terms of the pathology of command and control approaches to natural resource management.   These approaches to system modelling are disconnected from the nonlinear and uncertain behaviour of the complex adaptive systems being managed which has resulted in surprise.

One proposition for the study of SES is that the social and ecological domains can both be handled in a common framework (Walker *et al.* [20]).   In the case studies presented by Lui *et al.* [1], these couplings exhibited variance and nonlinear system dynamics which suggests that the couplings themselves may provide much of the critical information needed to understand social-ecological systems.   Therefore, an initial heuristic approach to identify propositions for social-ecological couplings was suggested by Walker *et al.* [20] as a starting point for dealing with system complexity uncertainty. In this paper, we posit two initial heuristic relationships and regionally significant 'clues' for the Calgary metropolitan region in western Canada.

2 A role for network analysis

Network approaches to social-ecological systems have the potential to provide a common language that could be used to integrate the study of social and ecological systems (Janssen *et al.* [21]). Network analysis techniques have been used in resilience and robustness assessment as a proxy for resilience in social-ecological systems (Janssen *et al.* [21], Anderies *et al.* [22]). A network construct can represent the components of any system and the relationships between them. Components are represented as nodes and the relationships are represented as links or edges and its composition depends on the attributes of the system and the purpose of the analysis. In an SES context, nodes can represent either social or ecological components or a mix of the two (Janssen *et al.* [21]). It is this ability to mix social and ecological links that shows promise for network SES analysis. However, integration is one of the greatest challenges in network analysis and as yet there is no clear consensus on a single method (Cumming *et al.* [23]).

A network can be used to model the flow of water through a system (Bodini [24]). A purely ecological implementation would include only water bodies in the network. A social network can also be built to represent human modifications of vegetation cover, flow control measures, water withdrawals, and influence on other human actors (Stein *et al.* [25]). By including human flow diversions (wells, agriculture, etc.) the network can represent interactions between water-related social and ecological components. Resilience in SES does not refer to specific aspects or measurements of system characteristics. Rather, it represents a framework for thinking about system dynamics in order to gain insights into how they behave (Anderies *et al.* [26]). However, specific ways of analysing social-ecological system dynamics using networks have emerged. Connectivity and centrality metrics are applicable to any type of network. These methods are well documented in the network analysis literature (e.g., Bodin *et al.* [27], Janssen *et al.* [21]). We have selected connectivity metrics, specifically permeability and centrality, for SES application in the Calgary region.

3 Critical social-ecological couplings in the Calgary region

The work represented here is part of a larger transdisciplinary research program we are involved in with the Calgary Regional Partnership. The partnership is a voluntary consortium of municipalities with the goal of regional sustainability. Our approach is to employ a social-ecological systems (SES) approach to co-create an ecological governance framework for integrating land use planning and water management into strategic regional planning. This is demonstration research aimed at advancing both theory and practice in sustainable regional planning. AtKisson [28] suggests: "Sustainable development always begins, formally or informally, in a confrontation with information." The critical social-ecological couplings described below are an attempt to confront the information available at a regional or landscape scale. Subsequent analyses will be required to further explore the connections at sub-regional and local scales. The overall intent is to identify critical areas of focus in a sea of potentially useful information. In the following sections of the paper, we focus on critical social-ecological couplings in the context of regional ecohydrology and landscape connectivity.

3.1 Water: social-ecohydrological connections

The Calgary metropolitan region of western Canada is located in a landscape characterized by an elevation, topographic and hydrologic gradient that extends from the Rocky Mountain Continental Divide east to the mixed-grass plains. The land decreases in elevation (3,400 m to 800m), relief (mountainous to flat) and precipitation (~950 mm/yr. to ~350 mm/yr.) from west to east. The western-most portions of the region occur in the rugged Rocky Mountains and contain the headwaters for surface and groundwater systems that supply moisture to the prairies. The city of Calgary (population 1.2 million) is situated approximately in the centre of the region (see Fig. 3). The rain shadow effect of the Rocky Mountains results in a semi-arid continental climate as the landscape east of the foothills has an annual evaporation rate that exceeds the rate of annual precipitation. Water availability is the limiting factor for primary productivity in the region and is thus the critical regulating variable for all associated ecological goods and services.

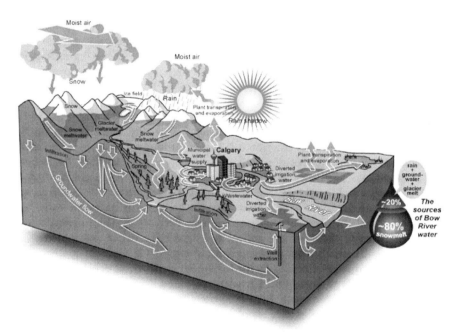

Figure 3:   Stylized depiction of the Calgary regional hydrologic system and the elevation, topographic and hydrologic gradients (Turner *et al.* [29]).

In a semi-arid region, water is also a primary limiting factor for human development. A recent report on water in the region sums up the situation succinctly: "While Alberta's economy is fuelled by hydrocarbons, it runs on water" (Alberta Water Smart [30]). The hydrological basin in which the Calgary region is located (South Saskatchewan River Basin) is recognized as being fully allocated with respect to water licenses; the provincial regulator has deemed that no new allocations will be granted (Alberta Environment [31]). Two significant trends are expected to exacerbate the current water limitations in the Calgary region: 1) human population growth, and 2) climate change.

The growth rates of communities within the Calgary regional are among the highest in Canada. The current annual growth rate of 1.5% will result in a doubling of the population in the next 50 years. The increase in population will have concomitant demands on the hydrologic system; not only through direct withdrawals, but through alteration of hydrologic flows via land-use expansion and intensification.

Analysis of tree-ring data for drought severity indicates that the drought conditions experienced in western North America between 2000 and 2004 were the most severe in the past 800 years (Cook and Spray [32]). Climate change modelling suggests that this type of drought "will be commonplace through the end of the twenty-first century. Furthermore, projections suggest that this drought is likely to become the 'wet' end of a drier hydroclimate period in the latter half of the twenty-first century" (Schwalm et al. [33]). Climate change is also expected to have an effect on the timing and nature of regional precipitation. Specifically, mountain snowpack currently accounts for approximately 80% of the annual flow in the Bow River, a primary water source in the region and the most significant reservoir in the regional hydrologic system. Future projections suggest a decline in mountain snowpack due to a seasonal shift to more precipitation falling as rain. This could have significant detrimental effects on the Bow's current flow regime (Bow River Project Research Consortium [34]). Finally, glacial melt is currently contributing a relatively small amount of the annual flow. However, this contribution arrives during low flow stage late in the summer when human and ecological demand is highest. Therefore, the decline and eventual loss of glacier input during late summer low flows could result in water shortages and lethal low flow conditions for river biota. This could have a major impact on the River's recreational trout fishery and its economic value.

We posit that the social-ecological couplings between regional ecohydrology and anthropogenic water use are critical and need to be better understood. The following are the most salient characteristics of regional hydrologic context: 1) water is the primary limiting factor for the regional social-ecological system, 2) the water supply is already fully (over) committed, 3) the demand for water is likely to increase with expected regional population growth, 4) climate change projections suggest that water supply will decline significantly, and 5) the temporal flow regime may be negatively affected.

The most obvious and direct SES coupling in the regional hydrological cycle is the withdrawal of water for domestic, agricultural and industrial purposes. In 2010, the combined water allocation (maximum licensed removal) from the Bow

River was 2,801 million m^3 (approximately 65% of the annual flow) (Bow River Basin Council [35]). Irrigation and other agricultural uses accounted for 71% of the allocation, followed by municipal use (18%), industrial (2%), fish and wildlife habitat (7%) and other (2%). The allocation values do not represent the net removal of water from the system because: 1) not all of the allocations are used, and 2) some of the water is returned (e.g., sewage treatment from municipalities, storm water return and irrigation return flow [35]). Understanding water withdrawal and diversion from a systems perspective helps to identify the feedbacks to other parts of the social-ecological system. From social, economic and political perspectives, the availability of water for human use (growth) constitutes the most challenging and contentious arena of debate in the region. This is recognized in the Calgary Regional Partnership's most recent Metropolitan Plan, which identifies water and watershed management as the Plan's first principle (Calgary Regional Partnership [36]). Alteration of natural flows and the return of water with thermal and/or chemical pollution also have synergistic and cascading ecological effects. For example, decreased dissolved oxygen, nutrification (phosphorous), sedimentation, increased water temperature and an increase in toxic chemicals and pharmaceuticals (endocrine disrupters) have all been identified in the Bow River and present significant risks to the resilience of the system (Alberta Environment [37], Chen *et al.* [38]). Feedbacks between social and ecological water subsystems are diverse and complex and represent essential intervention opportunities for planning and management as well as triggers for initiating system change.

A second critical coupling at the regional scale is represented by the link between ecohydrology and land-use (Wilcox *et al.* [39]). Although planners and managers tend to focus primarily on the allocation of surface water flows (blue flow), approximately 65-70% of water in the semi-arid environs of the Calgary region is entrained in soil moisture and vegetation (green flow) (Falkenmark and Rockstrom [40]). As a result, land-use is a direct mechanism for managing water. A regional ecohydrological perspective allows for the identification of key leverage points in the system. For example, Fig. 4 illustrates site specific hydrological alterations at the local level. When occurring cumulatively over hundreds of square kilometres, these alterations have a much larger and significant hydrological effect. Spatial land use planning could influence such cross-scalar ecohydrological effects and feedbacks. Although residential development due to population growth is a key variable in the ecohydrological system, significantly more water is utilized in regional agricultural activities. Water withdrawals and evapotranspiration losses through irrigated agriculture represent a particularly potent leverage point in the SES.

4   Landscape connectivity: anthropogenic infrastructure and ecological flows

The term 'landscape connectivity' is applied in a variety of ways in the conservation biology, land-use planning and landscape ecology literatures. Taylor *et al.* [41] originally defined landscape connectivity as the degree to

Figure 4:   Photograph from the Calgary region showing a new subdivision development, a secondary highway and the alteration to existing wetland hydrology.

which the landscape facilitates (or impedes) the movement of populations, species and genes among resource patches. This definition incorporates both the physical dimensions and patterns of the landscape (structural connectivity) as well as the behavioural responses of organisms to that structure (functional connectivity). Thus, landscape connectivity is an 'emergent property' of species-landscape interactions. Taylor et al. [42] posit that landscape connectivity is "a dynamic property that is assessed at the scale of landscape (with particular organisms or suites of organisms in mind) and is not simply an aggregate property of a set of patches within the landscape." This species focus has engendered a proliferation of highly valuable applied research focused on modeling and measuring the ability of species (or groups of species) to utilize landscapes (Hilty et al. [43]). This is useful to understanding the effects of land-use change and fragmentation on biodiversity. However, for the purpose of understanding social-ecological system couplings, we have adopted a slightly different meaning for connectivity which Biggs et al. [44] have described as "the manner by which and extent to which resources, species, or social actors disperse, migrate, or interact across ecological and social 'landscapes'." This expanded definition includes, but goes beyond an individual species focus to include ecological flows and processes as well as social processes. Defined in this way, connectivity is one of seven key principles for maintaining the capacity of social-ecological system to sustain the production of desired ecological goods and services [44].

We use connectivity as a tool to illustrate the essential nexus of social and ecological systems processes with the Calgary region. These flows of organisms, water, and nutrients are critical to the persistence of the natural systems that support the region (including ecological goods and services). Landscape connectivity intersects with an anthropogenic network of human activities and related infrastructure that supports the movement of people, materials, energy and information. The spatial intersection of these two systems creates a network of nodes and hubs and generates a series of natural and anthropogenic feedbacks. The long term efficiency and persistence of both systems is predicated on understanding and working with the critical points of interface or coupling and their associated feedback loops at the regional scale.

We employ a method to explore the structural and functional connectivity of the Calgary regional landscape based on the intersection of anthropogenic infrastructure or human 'footprint' with the natural landscape features in a GIS environment. The study area used is the Calgary Regional Partnership's 2007 boundary plus a 10 km buffer. The buffer zone was added to produce a rectangular shape in order to avoid edge effects in calculations. We used percolation theory and least-cost distance methods for network analysis (Theobald *et al.* [45], Landguth *et al.* [46], Beyhan [47]). Procedural steps included: 1) a human footprint layer (H; all anthropogenic features mapped at a resolution of 2 m) was processed to be used as a base-map; 2) conductance in the study area was estimated by using the reciprocal mean of H locations (a measure landscape naturalness) with a transition matrix that represented the traversing cost to go from one location to an adjacent one; 3) landscape permeability was estimated as the mean of a series of iterations representing the accumulated traverse adjacency cost of each location; 4) energy routes representing the flow through a least-cost path were derived from the permeability layer using the landscape permeability as a surrogate for an elevation model; and, 5) configuration of the landscape permeability was analyzed using network analysis over a least cost network obtained by using a factorial approach. A detailed description of the methods we are using is presented in Quinn *et al.* [48].

Mapped results from these analyses are summarized in Figs 5 and 6. The road network depicted in Fig. 5 is provided as a surrogate for human footprint as it is the dominant anthropogenic feature in the landscape. The city of Calgary is clearly visible in the centre of the figure and the predominantly square grid of the agricultural road network can be seen in the eastern 2/3 of the study area. Fig. 6 provides an overall illustration of the natural connectivity network. It is worth noting that the dendritic pattern occurring in the prairie landscape differs significantly from the more linear routes running perpendicular to the mountains and foothills to the west. Finer scale analysis will yield critical spatial points for management intervention reflecting natural and anthropogenic connectivity. To date, regional connectivity has focused on the river corridors and associated riparian zones that run west to east in the Calgary metropolitan landscape. However, application of our connectivity approach clearly demonstrates the importance of non-river north-south connectivity patterns on the west side of the study area. For example, the patterns generated in Fig. 5 provide can provide initial input into regional spatial planning by illustrating critical local leverage points for regional intervention. We are also in the process of combining

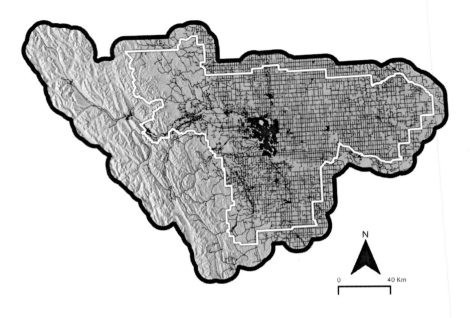

Figure 5:   The road network within the Calgary regional partnership boundary (white line) and the greater study area (outside black boundary).

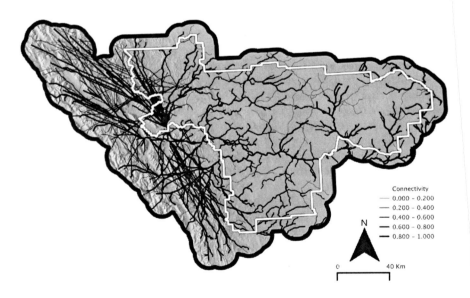

Figure 6:   Connectivity within the Calgary regional partnership boundary (white line) and the greater study area (outside black boundary).

regional socio-ecohydrology with landscape connectivity analyses. We anticipate being able to identify potentially critical SES feedbacks based on ecohydrological connectivity (Miller *et al.* [49]).

5   Conclusions

Traditional land use planning has been used as a control mechanism for ensuring certainty by "attempting to exclude instability and non-linearity as much as possible" (Timmermans *et al.* [50]). However, spatial planning offers significant potential for integrating natural and human system interactions and dealing with scale and subsystems. A number of sources, including Portugali [51] and Manson and O'Sulllivan [52], have dealt with uncertainty and complexity in terms of spatial planning. However, spatial planning in this context is neither technical nor communicative. Rather, it emerges as "mitigation" or "adaptive" planning which has also been referred to as 'swarm' planning. This concept of spatial planning represents an adaptive response to uncertainty that uses warning signs to anticipate uncertainty (Timmermans *et al.* [50]). A specific example of this approach is the "floodable landscape" of the Eemsdelta region in The Netherlands (Roggema [53]). Similarly, Rogemma *et al.* [54] suggest that network theory holds the key to identifying spatial location. In the context of our work in the Calgary region SES, we believe connectivity analysis provides a set of network metrics for adaptive spatial planning that can inform the identification and management of water and transportation couplings.

Scheffer *et al.* [11] have suggested four general warning signals for major system transitions. The fourth signal is "types of spatial patterns" and specifically includes "scale-invariant distributions of patch sizes and increased spatial coherence." In addition to warning signals, Roggema *et al.* [54] suggest identifying "starting points" for system change based on network theory: "some nodes in networks are more suited to the ignition of change than others." Some key network characteristics of these starting points include (Newman *et al.* [55]): "enough edges, high level of clustering, fitness of nodes (based on increased connectivity) and node connections". Research into identifying network points with the greatest potential for change has used two primary methods for network analysis (Roggema *et al.* [54]): "(1) the density of individual networks such as water-energy-or transport network, and (2) the number of different network types colliding at one physical location." In other words, networks with the most node density and the most connected networks are the most likely starting points for change. Based on our work to date, we believe that our landscape connectivity analysis has demonstrated spatial patterns of increased spatial coherence and edge effects within the Calgary SES. We also suggest the interface of human water use and regional ecohydrology is a critical system coupling. Together with our current in-progress SES network analysis, we believe this will enable spatial identification of clustering, fitness of nodes and node connections at a regional scale for water and transport couplings that will lead to an increased ability to undertake adaptive spatial planning in a regional governance context.

Acknowledgements

This work was supported through grants to the authors from the Canadian Social Science and Humanities Research Council, the Calgary Regional Partnership, the Samuel Hanen Foundation and an anonymous private foundation. We are grateful for the substantive spatial modelling and analysis contributions of Dr Pablo Poujol Pina and GIS support from Greg Chernoff.

References

[1]   Lui, J., Dietz, T., Carpenter, S.R., Alberti, M., Folke, C., Moran, E., Pell, A. N., Deadman, P., Kratz, T., Lubchenco, J., Ostrom, E., Ouyang, Z., Provencher, W., Redman, C.L., Schneider, S.H., and Taylor, W.W. Complexity of coupled human and natural systems. *Science* 317, pp. 1513–1516, 2007.

[2]   EEA (European Environment Agency), *Information for Improving Europe's Environment*, EEA: Copenhagen, 1999.

[3]   Berkes, F. and Folke, C. (eds), *Linking Social and Ecological Systems*, Cambridge University Press: Cambridge and New York, 2000.

[4]   Berkes, F., Colding, J. and Folke, C. (eds), *Navigating Social Ecological Systems*, Cambridge University Press: Cambridge and New York, 2003.

[5]   Lambin, E. F. and Meyfroidt. P., Land use transitions: Socio-ecological feedback versus socio-economic change. *Land Use Policy* 27, pp. 108–118, 2010.

[6]   Crutzen, P. and Stoermer, E.F., The "Anthropocene", *IGBP Newsletter*, 41, pp. 12, 2000.

[7]   Steffen, W., Sanderson, A., Tyson, P.D., Jager, J., Matson, P.M., Moore, B., Oldfield, F., Richarson, K, Schnellnhuber, H.J., Turner, B.L. and Wasson, R.J., *Global Change and the Earth System: a Planet under Pressure*, The IGBP Book Series. Springer: Berlin, Germany, 2004.

[8]   Vitousek, P.M, Mooney, H.A., Lubchenko, J. and Melillo, J.M. Human domination of the Earth's ecosystems. *Science*, 277 (5325), pp. 494–499, 1997.

[9]   Zalasiewicz, J., Williams, M., Haywood, A. and Ellis, M., The anthropocence: a new epoch of geological time? *Philosophical Transactions of the Royal Society A*, 369, pp. 835–841, 2011.

[10] Elsevier. Anthropocene, http://www.journals.elsevier.com/anthropocene/

[11] Scheffer, M., Bascompte, J., Brock, W.A., Brovkin, V., Carpenter, S. R., Dakos, V., Held, H., van Nes, E. H., Rietkerk, M. and Sugihara, G., Early-warning signals for critical transitions. *Nature*, 461, pp. 53–59, 2009.

[12] Stockholm Resilience Centre, www.stockholmresilience.org/

[13] Jahn, T., Becker, E., Keil, F. and Schramm, E., Understanding Social-Ecological Systems: Frontier Research for Sustainable Development. Implications for European Research Policy, Institute for Social-Ecological Research (ISOE): Frankfurt/Main, Germany, 2009.

[14] Bourgeron, P. S., Humphries, H. C., and Riboli-Sasco, L., Regional analysis of social-ecological systems. *Natures Sciences Sociétés*, 17, 185–193, 2009.

[15] Walker, B., Carpenter, S., Anderies, J., Abel, N., Cummings, G., Janssen, M., Lebel, L., Norberg, J., Peterson, G. D. and Pritchard, R., Resilience management in social-ecological systems: a working hypothesis for a participatory approach. *Ecology and Society,* 6(1), pp. 14, [online] URL: http://www.consecol.org/vol6/iss1/art14/, 2002.

[16] Gunderson, L., and Holling, C. S., (eds). *Panarchy: understanding transformations in human and natural systems*, Island Press: Washington, D. C., USA, 2002.

[17] Peters, D. P. C., Sala, O. E., Allen, C. D., Covich, A. and Brunson, M., Cascading events in linked ecological and socioeconomic systems. *Frontiers in Ecology and the Environment*, 5(4), pp. 221–224, 2007.

[18] Milly, P.C.D., Betancourt, J., Falkenmark, M. Hirsch, R.M., Kundzewicz, Z.W., Lettenmaier, D.P., *et al.*, Stationarity is dead: whither water management?, *Science*, 319, pp. 573–574, 2008.

[19] Holling, C. S. and Meffe, G. K., Command and control and the pathology of natural resource management. *Conservation Biology*, 10(2), pp. 328–337, 1996.

[20] Walker, B. H., Gunderson, L. H., Kinzig, A. P., Folke, C., Carpenter, S. R. and Shultz, L., A handful of heuristics and some propositions for understanding resilience in social ecological systems. *Ecology and Society*, 11(1): pp. 13, [online] URL: http://www.ecologyandsociety.org/vol11/iss1/art13/, 2006.

[21] Janssen, M.A., Bodin, O., Anderies, J.M., Elmqvist, T., Ernston, H., McAllister, R.R. J. *et al.*, Toward a network perspective of the study of resilience in social-ecological systems. *Ecology and Society,* 11, p. 15, http://www.ecologyandsociety.org/vol11/iss1/art15/, 2006.

[22] Anderies, J. M., Janssen, M. A. and Ostrom, EA framework to analyze the robustness of social-ecological systems from an institutional perspective. *Ecology and Society,* 9(1):18. [online] URL: http://www.ecologyandsociety. org/vol9/iss1/art18/, 2004.

[23] Cumming, G. S., Bodin, Ö., Ernstson, H. and Elmqvist, T., Network analysis in conservation biogeography: challenges and opportunities. *Diversity and Distributions,* 16, pp. 414–425, 2010.

[24] Bodini, A., Building a systemic environmental monitoring and indicators for sustainability: What has the ecological network approach to offer? *Ecological Indicators*, 15, pp. 140–148, 2012.

[25] Stein, C., Barron, J. and Ernstson, H., A social network approach to analyze multi-stakeholders governance arrangement in water resources management: Three case studies from catchments in Burkina Faso, Tanzania and Zambia. *Proceedings of the XIVth World Water Congress*, 25–29 September, at Porto de Galinhas, Pernambuco, Brazil, 2011.

[26] Anderies, J. M., Walker, B. H. and. Kinzig, A.P., Fifteen weddings and a funeral: Case studies and resilience-based management. *Ecology and*

Society, 11(1), p. 21, [online] URL: http://www.ecologyandsociety.org /vol11/iss1/art21/, 2006.

[27] Bodin, Ö., Crona, B. and Ernstson, H., Social networks in natural resource management: What is there to learn from a structural perspective? *Ecology and Society*, 11(2), [online] URL: http://www.ecologyandsociety.org/vol11 /iss2/resp2, (2006).

[28] AtKisson, A., The Sustainability Transformation: How to Accelerate Positive Change in Challenging Times, Earthscan: London, 2011.

[29] Turner, R.J.W., Franklin, R.G., Grasby, S.E., and Nowlan, G.S., *Bow River Basin Waterscape*, Geological Survey of Canada: Ottawa, Miscellaneous Report 90, 2005.

[30] Alberta Water Smart, South Saskatchewan River Basin Adaptation to Climate Variability Project: Initial Assessment of the Current State of the Foundational Blocks to Support Adaptation in the SSRB, Alberta Water Smart, Climate Change Emissions Management Corporation and Alberta Innovates: Edmonton, 2012.

[31] Alberta Environment, Approved Water Management Plan for the South Saskatchewan River Basin (Alberta), Alberta Environment: Calgary, 2006.

[32] Cook, B. R. and Spray, C.J., Ecosystem services and integrated water resource management: Different paths to the same end? *Journal of Environmental Management*, 109, pp. 93–100, 2012.

[33] C. R. Schwalm, C. A. Williams, K. Schaefer, D. Baldocchi, T. A. Black, A. H. Goldstein, *et al.*, "Reduction in carbon uptake during turn of the century drought in western North America," *Nature Geoscience*, 5, pp. 551–556, 2012.

[34] Bow River Project Research Consortium, *Bow River Project: Final Report*, Alberta Water Research Institute: Calgary, 2010.

[35] Bow River Basin Council, *Bow River Basin: State of the Watershed Summary 2010*, Bow River Basin Council: Calgary, 2010.

[36] Calgary Regional Partnership, *Calgary Metropolitan Plan*, Calgary Regional Partnership: Calgary, 2012.

[37] Alberta Environment, *South Saskatchewan Regional Plan: Water Quantity and Quality Modelling Results*, Edmonton: Government of Alberta, Alberta Environment, 2010.

[38] Chen, M., Ohman, K., Metcalfe, C., Ikonomou, M.G., Amatya, P.L. and Wilson, J., Pharmaceuticals and endocrine disruptors in wastewater treatment effluents and in the water supply system of Calgary, Alberta, Canada. *Water Quality Research Journal of Canada*, 41, pp. 35–364, 2006.

[39] Wilcox, B.P., Seyfried, M.S., Breshears, D.D. and McDonnell, J.J., Ecohydrologic connections and complexities in drylands: new perspectives for understanding transformative landscape change. *Ecohydrology*, 5, pp. 143–144, 2012.

[40] Falkenmark, M. and Rockstrom, J., The new blue and green water paradigm: Breaking new ground for water resources planning and management. *Journal of Water Resource Planning and Management*, 132, pp. 129–132, 2006.

[41] Taylor, P.D., Fahrig, L., Henein, K. and Merriam, G., Connectivity is a vital element of landscape structure. *Oikos,* 68, pp. 571–572, 1993.

[42] Taylor, P.D., Fahrig, L. and With, K.A., Landscape connectivity: a return to basics (Chapter 2). *Connectivity Conservation,* ed. K.R. Crooks and M. Sanjayan, Cambridge University Press: New York, pp. 29–43, 2006.

[43] Hilty, J.A., Lidicker, W.Z. Jr. and Merenlender, A.M. Corridor Ecology: The Science and Practice of Linking Landscapes for Biodiversity Conservation, Island Press: Washington, 2006.

[44] Biggs, R., Schlüter, M., Biggs, D., Bohensky, E.L., BurnSilver, S., Cundill, G., *et al.,* Toward principles for enhancing the resilience of ecosystem services. *Annual Review of Environment and Resources,* 37, pp. 421–448, 2012.

[45] Theobald, D.M., Reed, S.E., Fields, K. and Soulé, M., Connecting natural landscapes using a landscape permeability model to prioritize conservation activities in the United States. *Conservation Letters,* 5, pp. 123–133, 2012.

[46] Landguth, E. L., Hand, B.K., Glassy, J., Cushman, S.A. and Sawaya, M.A., UNICOR: a species connectivity and corridor network simulator. *Ecography,* **35**(1), pp. 9–14, 2012.

[47] Beyhan, B. Developing Graph Theoretic Analysis Tools in FOSS4GIS: An Experiment in OpenJUMP with a Specific Focus on Space Syntax. FOSS4G-CEE and Geoinformatics: Prague, 2012.

[48] Quinn, M.S., Pina Poujol, P. Tyler, M.E. and Chernoff, G. Modeling the ecology of a rapidly urbanizing regional landscape: Connectivity assessment of natural integrity for ecological flows. *In prep.*

[49] Miller,G. R., Cable, J.M., McDonald, A.K., Bond, B., Franz, T.E., Wang, L., *et al.,* Understanding ecohydrological connectivity in savannas: a system dynamics modelling approach. *Ecohydrology,* 5(2), pp. 200–220, 2012.

[50] Timmermans, W., Lopez, F. O., Roggema, R., Complexity Theory, Spatial Planning, and Adaptation to Climate Chang (Chapter 3). *Swarming Landscapes, the Art of Designing for Climate Adaptation,* ed. R. Roggema, Springer: Dordrecht, pp. 43–66, 2012.

[51] Portugali, J., Complexity theory as a link between space and place. *Environmental Planning A,* 38, pp. 647–664, 2006.

[52] Manson, S., O'Sullivan, D., Complexity theory in the study of space and place. *Environmental Planning A,* 38: pp. 677–692, 2006.

[53] Roggema, R., Swarming landscape (Chapter 8). *Swarming Landscapes, the Art of Designing for Climate Adaptation,* ed. R. Roggema, Springer: Dordrecht, pp. 167–193, 2012.

[54] Roggema, R. Vermeend, T., Timmermans, W., *Transition and Transformation* (Chapter 4). *Swarming Landscapes, the Art of Designing for Climate Adaptation,* ed. R. Roggema, Springer: Dordrecht, pp. 67–90, 012.

[55] Newman, M., Barabasi, A-L., Watts, D.J., (eds). *The structure and dynamics of networks.* Princeton University Press, Princeton/Woodstock, USA, 2006.

National planning in South Africa: a critical review

J. E. Drewes & M. van Aswegen
North-West University, Potchefstroom Campus, South Africa

Abstract

According to the European Regional/Spatial Planning Charter (1983), "Regional/spatial planning gives geographical expression to the economic, social, cultural and ecological policies of society. It is at the same time a scientific discipline, an administrative technique and a policy developed as an interdisciplinary and comprehensive approach directed towards a balanced regional development and the physical organisation of space according to an overall strategy". It is against this background that this study reviews past spatial planning policy and how it gave "geographical expression" to economic, social and cultural policies in South Africa

This paper aims to provide a critical and objective perspective on national spatial planning since the inception of the concept in South Africa in the 1970s till the most recent directive in 2012. The paper will discuss the understanding of national planning in South Africa in terms of the economic approach and spatial implementation of each plan.

It is argued in this paper that over the past three decades the national space has been left open for interpretation in terms of economic growth and development, which has led to a lack of execution of the well-intentioned spatial guiding documents from the various levels of government. It could be interpreted that spatial planning in South Africa has come full circle since the 1970`s, being once again politically driven, this time by social policy, and not economic policy. The paper proposes that national spatial planning should, once again, start to focus on giving clear guidance on how, where and when the magnitude of social and economic goals should be reached.

Keywords: national planning, spatial planning, regional planning; South Africa planning history.

WIT Transactions on Ecology and The Environment, Vol 173, © 2013 WIT Press
www.witpress.com, ISSN 1743-3541 (on-line)
doi:10.2495/SDP130161

1 Background

During the most recent history of national spatial planning in South Africa there has been a definite drive towards economic growth, which overshadowed all other developmental goals. During the 1970s till 1991 development was primarily driven by industrial development in specific areas earmarked for concentration. The focus was on extracting and maximizing the potential of the vast natural resource pool of the country. The reasoning behind this specific era's development was, however, dominated by the political ideology of separate development and centred around these principles.

Throughout the history and evolution of spatial planning and policy in South Africa, three main perspectives are evident. In the latter part of the previous millennium, economic growth was seen as the all-encompassing goal in national development. National policy, although founded on political ideology, was based primarily on industrial development in areas earmarked for concentration. An emphasis shift occurred in the early 1990s towards a balanced policy approach, whereby a participative or people-centred approach replaced the previous 'fordist' approach to development. In the mid-1990s, the principles of resource management or environmental sustainability were also accepted as being part of the spatial planning and policy formulation process. The latter two approaches to development are clearly process-driven, i.e. the integration of principles, community participation and environmental sustainability in spatial planning, are of utmost importance. In contrast, the end result of economic growth and separate development was the main goal in the previous regime's approach to spatial policy formulation up to the 1990s in South Africa. In the new millennium the "geographical expression" of spatial planning is again focused on social and political issues.

It is the aim of this paper to give insight in the evolutionary development of national development policy is South Africa. This paper will analyse the relevant policies influencing the development of the national space as implemented over the past five decades. South Africa is quite a unique example because of its policy of separate development instigated in 1948 by the Nationalist Party, up to the present socialist-oriented democratic government.

2 Chronology

The spatial planning milieu in South Africa has changed drastically over the past 40 odd years. From the first spatial policy initiative, the National Physical Development Plan (1975) radical changes have occurred in the approach to national planning. Since 1975, South Africa has seen the Good Hope Plan (1981), the Regional Industrial Development Programme (1991), Reconstruction and Development Plan (1994), Urban and Rural Development Frameworks (1997), SMME development (1996), Spatial Development Initiatives and Industrial Development Zones (1999), and two National Spatial Development Perspectives (2002 and 2006). The most recent spatial planning directive in South Africa is the National Development Plan (2012), which has a diverse approach with political, social and economic goals. During this time national planning policy and directives have moved through balanced and unbalanced growth approaches, from a top-down approach with rigid area-specific directives to a bottom-up more adaptable, socially-oriented and interpretation-based approach in recent years. The main pillars of spatial policy in South Africa have always been the development and deconcentration of the industrial sector. This remained the focus of this type of policy until the early 1990s, when smaller industries and the services sector were also added to national policy. South Africa's spatial policy has evolved from a policy dominated by political objectives in the 1960s, to a policy supposedly based only on economic principles of a free-market system; from one of strong government intervention to one of little intervention.

2.1 National physical planning: 1975 -1991

In the National Physical Development Plan (NPDP) (1975) the Decentralization Board identified growth points through a top-down approach (SA [2]). This plan contained various planning instruments aimed at the arrangement of the physical development according to specific development and political ideals. Fair [3] divided the report into two parts. First, a growth centre strategy was proposed in order to obtain more balanced spatial poles. Secondly, a framework which divided the country into 38 planning regions was proposed. The NPDP could therefore be regarded as the overall framework through which the decentralization policy was implemented (Bos [4]). Many of the officially proclaimed industrial points were located in sparsely populated areas as well as in the peripheral economic space of the country. However, numerous studies have indicated that the development of sparsely populated areas should take place in stages, emanating from a strong economic core. Efforts to 'plant' a growth point away from a national or regional economic core have proven fruitless (Stern [5]; Bloch [6]). The proposed development initiatives in both instances (growth poles and growth points) primarily aimed to create work opportunities. Industrial development, however, is stimulated in the growth points by means of extended infrastructural development (Bos [4]). Therefore, the NPDP aimed to focus national planning in a spatially unbalanced manner, as well as targeting economically unbalanced development (Rosenstein-Rodan [7]) through its focus on industrial development.

The beginning of the eighties witnessed a marginal shift from the extreme practices of White paternalism of the past (Geyer [8]) with the Good Hope Plan (GHP). After deliberations between the government and private sector, the GHP was announced in 1981. The plan contained a number of industrial development guidelines, a framework through which the Government, in a top-down approach, intended to implement its new industrial decentralization policy. Altogether, a total number of 47 'industrial development points' and 11 'deconcentration points' were designated to be developed simultaneously (SA [9]). 'Deconcentration points' were identified adjacent to metropolitan regions to relieve pressures of industrial concentration in these areas (SA [9]). Similar to the NPDP, almost all of these 'deconcentration points', as well as the overwhelming majority of the 'industrial development points' were located within peripheral areas. Apart from their impractical locations from an economic point of view, too many of these points had been identified, incentives has been spread over too many geographical areas and the dispersed pattern of too many growth points also raised doubts as to whether such a strategy could ever be implemented successfully (Stern [5]). This plan could, therefore, be summarized as having an economically unbalanced as well as a spatially unbalanced approach and intent.

From the first two national plans it is evident that decentralization policy, implicating a certain growth centre strategy, played a major part in development thinking in South Africa since its inception in peripheral region development in the 1950s. A major shift in decentralization policy occurred in 1991 with the implementation of a new, apolitical, Regional Industrial Development Programme (RIDP [10]), based on a uniform development approach (Rosenstein-Rodan [7], Baldwin [11], Hirschman [12]). Proposals by the Development Bank of Southern Africa were made regarding the nature of a new profit/output-based incentive scheme, its level of incentives, and the specific spatial application of the incentive scheme. Because of the supposedly limited achievement of self-sustaining growth at industrial development points and the assumption of the inability of the growth centre to support the above-mentioned principles (SA [13]), the RIDP was proposed and implemented in 1991 (SA [10]). According to Bell [14] the 1991 RIDP represented a fundamental split from the past. Its professed aim is mainly economic, in particular, promotion of 'the self-sustaining economic growth and development of integrated economy' (POE [15]). In view of the alleged inability of the previous approach to give effect to the accepted principles and a declared policy of a greater democratisation of the economic processes, a spatially uniform approach (Friedmann [16]) was formulated based on the above-mentioned guidelines. Again, however, two implicit assumptions were repeated, i.e. that metropolitan areas are over concentrated and that the promotion of secondary industry is the most effective means of achieving development (Luiz and van der Waal [17]). A distinction was made between three levels of incentives according to the development status of an area. Accordingly, entrepreneurs settling in the major metro's (Gauteng complex and the Durban core area) received no incentive for industrial development, while new developers in the emerging metro's (Cape Peninsula, Durban-Pinetown-Pietermaritzburg, greater Durban functional region and the area surrounding the Gauteng region) received 60 per cent of the calculated establishment allowance (100 per cent after two years). The rest of the South African spatial area rendered the new industrial developer eligible for 100 per cent of the established allowance for the five year period (SA [10]). The primary advantage of this RIDP, namely locational freedom, allowed the new industrial developer to pick a site of his choice anywhere in the country - save in metropolitan regions - and receive 100 per cent establishment incentives (Ligthelm and Wilsenach [18]). The second primary advantage of the RIDP was its 'political correctness' (Black and Roux [19]). This issue was emphasised by Luiz and van der Waal [17], who indicated that the government tried to appease all interest groups by making the incentive nationally applicable and avoided making tough decisions. In fact, except for the 'restrictions on new development' in metropolitan regions, the government essentially implemented a laissez-faire approach (Drewes and Bos [20]).

2.2 Sectoral national planning initiatives: 1994 - 2010

After coming into power in 1994, the African National Congress (ANC) undertook to ensure equal access in all sectors by creating and implementing the Reconstruction and Development Programme (RDP) (1994). The RDP was the first economic/spatial programme after the apartheid era and is regarded as a bridge between the apartheid and post-apartheid era (ANC [21]). From this point the approach of national planning changed drastically. The RDP was an integrated socio-economic policy framework that aimed to "mobilize all the people and our country's resources towards the final eradication of apartheid and the building of a democratic, non-racial and non-sexist future" (ANC [21]). The RDP's integrated approach to developing and implementing policy was the first of its kind in the political history of South Africa, which brought with it a whole new paradigm shift which conveyed new challenges. The six basic principles the RDP was founded on was (ANC [21]): (i) integration (ii) people- driven process (iii) peace and security. (iv) build the nation (v) link reconstruction and development (vi) democratization. To improve and accelerate the development linked with the RDP the Development Facilitation Act (DFA) was created. This was a fast-track approach to development in order to have more effective decision-making and delivering (SA [22]). The DFA bypassed all apartheid legislation and initiated development planning through land development objectives. Accordingly the RDP was spatially balanced, and in theory everybody had equal access to economic activities. The RDP was a programme and did, however, not have a physical spatial plan indicating where development should take place.

One of the first attempts since the 1980's at national spatial planning was initiated by the RDP Office in the form of the National Spatial Development Framework (NSDF) in 1995. According to Oranje [23] this framework was an 'outcome of concerns about uncoordinated expenditure and a lack of shared standards in infrastructure investment'. It was foreseen that the framework would commence with the mapping of the whole country through GIS in order to stimulate dialogue on future investment localities. The 'framework', however, never got past the stage of initial mapping and died a still death. The NSDF came to abrupt end with the closure of the RDP offices in 1996 (Oranje [23]).

Following the above approach, the Growth Employment and Redistribution (GEAR) strategy in 1996 announced an economic reform programme directed towards: (i) competitive fast-growing economy; (ii) redistribution of income opportunities; (iii) capable society; and (iv) safe environments and productive workplaces (SA [24]). These principles went on to form the macro-economic framework within which the Rural Development Framework (1997) and Urban Development Framework (1997) was established. Robbins [25] confirms that GEAR 'limited itself to focusing on traditional macro-economic policy instruments and did little to explore the ramifications of such national choices'. The GEAR strategy was regarded as being spatially and economically balanced, and being driven from the top-down, although being informed by the people's needs. The GEAR strategy did not emanate a specific spatial approach linked to locations or using planning mechanisms and is regarded as an economic strategy, rather than a spatial one.

A key document providing the leading perspective on rural development is the Rural Development Framework (RDF) of 1997 (SA [26]), which was borne out of the relative inactive RDP. It highlights the RDP's role as embodying the commitment of government to the eradication of poverty in a rapidly growing economy and in the context of an open, peaceful and democratic society. The RDF was established in order to provide a counterbalance to the Urban Development Framework (UDF) (SA [27]). Therefore, this framework can be classified as a spatially unbalanced framework with its focus on rural areas and aiming to provide a more balanced rural economy. Rural South Africa came with its own unique set of difficulties, referring to high poverty levels, the multi-sectoral nature of rural development, marginalised economies and in some instances having a high environmental sensitivity (SA [26]). The Framework acknowledged that to balance out the rural economic space it had to improve and develop the relevant institutional capacity and infrastructure.

The Urban Development Framework (UDF) of 1997 was specifically aimed at developing urban nodes (SA [27]). The Framework had a vision of spatially and economically integrated centres, providing the inhabitants economic and social opportunities, good housing and infrastructure in a participative fashion. The UDF accordingly, further strived towards environmental sustainability with vibrant urban governance, and an integrated approach to various land uses. It mainly has four key programs, (i) integrating spatially segregated and sprawling cities; (ii) improving housing and infrastructure; (iii) promoting urban economic development; and (iv) creating institutions for ensuring delivery of basic services and support. Urbanizing centres created many challenges and realities, i.e. a large and growing urban population, inequality and poverty, financial pressure on municipalities, a vibrant and dynamic urban society, and immense economic and financial potential for urban revitalization. The UDF was regarded as a framework aiming to provide a balanced urban economy, while being spatially unbalanced, focussing only on urban South Africa.

The policy of Spatial Development Initiatives (SDIs) was accepted in 1996 to supposedly address fragmented development patterns, and to promote equity, integration and efficiency (SA [28]). The SDI approach was developed based on the lessons learnt on regional development in the European Community (Oranje [23]). Robbins [25] affirms that the launch of the SDI 'heralded something of a shift in thinking towards some measure of recognition of the benefit of more spatially differentiated national policies and programmes'. Developmental regions, axis's and projects identified by their inherent under-utilised economic potential, aimed at sustainable employment creation, by identifying and facilitating new investment opportunities. Private and public investment were stimulated through infrastructure, manufacturing, mining, small business

(SMME), tourism, agriculture, housing and the provision of water to achieve the advantages of agglomeration (Wiese [29]). With the establishment of the SDIs, the approach reverted back to the principles of earlier policies of 1960 and 1982. The aim was, once again, to create employment near people's homes, especially in the rural areas, to ensure balanced development – with all the associated linkage benefits. (Drewes and Kleynhans [30]) SDI policies were outward orientated, aimed at the supply and demand of commodities of which South Africa was said to have a comparative advantage. Businesses, with large backward and forward linkages, were encouraged in order for more industries to develop in a centripetal action and create more employment (Drewes and Kleynhans [30]). The identification of possible clusters also played an important role in the development of SDIs. The former government was accused of establishing industries in the homelands without supplying the necessary infrastructure, however, SDI projects were identified wherever potential exists and the authorities ensure that necessary infrastructure are provided and developed, making this a spatially and economically unbalanced initiative.

The Integrated Sustainable Rural Development Strategy`s (ISRDS) main thrust was to ensure that government departments had a common platform and approach for implementing rural development strategies and programs (2001). It also put emphasis on the relationship between rural and urban economies, and furthermore affirmed that a sustainable economic growth can be achieved if it is premised on linking exploitation of rural assets and redistribution. It stated that agriculture, for example, has strong forward and backward linkages into the rest of the economy, and together with SMME and Tourism had the capacity to create labour intensive jobs as well as in related industries, giving rise to income distribution in the national economy (SA [31]). The objective of the ISRDS was to improve the quality of life of rural citizens through alleviating poverty and providing sustainable livelihoods. It outlined the following key policy issues, i.e. (i) obstacles inhibiting rural development; (ii) employment creation and economic development; (iii) building rural infrastructure; (iv) prioritise the needs of the vulnerable groups; and (v) building local government capacity. As part of the ISRDS, the President identified 13 Nodal Development Points throughout the country. They served as pilot projects to fast-track rural development in selected areas. The ISRDS was a spatially as well as economically unbalanced strategy.

On-going concerns about the spatial impact of apartheid on existing towns and cities led to the formulation of the National Spatial Development Perspective (NSDP), in 2003 (SA [32]) and again in 2006 (SA [33]), to provide guidance in the spatial planning and provision of infrastructure. 'In terms of the Cabinet's approval of the first NSDP (2003) it was not only meant to be an indicative tool for all spheres of government to guide development and expenditure, but also acted as a platform for discussion and debate regarding national planning (Oranje [23]). According to the NSDP, infrastructure investment should primarily support localities that will become major growth nodes in South Africa and the SADC region to create regional gateways to the global economy. According to Hughes [34] the NSDP placed 'far greater emphasis on people than places' as a direct result of the spatially distorted legacy of apartheid, and plays an important social role to uplift the socially exclude and equalize all people. The NSDP principles facilitated structured and rigorous analysis that enabled comparison between places and sectors, and assisted all spheres of government in weighing up trade-offs, making clear choices and maximising the impact of scarce state funds. The NSDP categorises the municipalities of South-Africa according to their economic potential and also their human need. According to Oranje [23] an 'unease' regarding the second version of the NSDP (2006) arose due to it being perceived as having a more unbalanced approach. Oranje states that the NSDP is often referred to as being 'ant-rural', stimulating growth only in urban areas of high potential and lower need, as opposed to rural areas mostly characterised by low potential and high need. The NSDP was the first policy/perspective to focus on the whole space economy since the GHP of 1981. The NSDP envisioned a spatially balanced South Africa by providing unbalanced economic support to specific areas of need and potential. However, it must be noted that the NSDP didn't include any physical plan and compliance to the framework was voluntary.

In 2010 the New Growth Path (NGP) set a target of creating five million jobs over the next decade, through reducing unnecessary red-tape, improving competition in the economy and stepping up skill development (SA [35]). The NGP regarded investments in five key physical and social infrastructure areas – energy, transport, communication, water and housing – as being a critical factor in growing the economy. The government believes that high levels of public investment in these five areas would create the required jobs in construction, operation and maintenance of infrastructure. The target of the NGP is to reduce unemployment which can only be achieved if the social partners and government work together to address key structural challenges in the economy. As a first step, government would have focused on unlocking the employment potential in six key sectors and activities, i.e. infrastructure, agriculture, mining, green economy and manufacturing. The macro-economic approach entailed more active monetary policy interventions to achieve growth and jobs targets, inter alia through a more competitive exchange rate and a lower cost of capital, with a more restrained fiscal stance and reprioritisation of public spending to ensure sustainability over time. The micro-economic approach involved targeted measures to support jobs and competitiveness, which in turn should have made the macro-economic strategy sustainable and viable. This approach is regarded as aiming for balanced spatial and economic development. It could be argued that national planning in South Africa returned to its origins of the 1990s, being once again politically driven, this time by social policy, and not economic policy.

2.3 A new direction in National Development Planning: 2012

In 2012 a need was identified for the coordinated and focused implementation of a plan on national level to eradicate poverty and exclusion in South Africa, from which the National Development Plan (NDP) (2012) was borne (SA [36]). The main argument of the National Planning Commission (NPC) regarding the need for a national plan referred to the poverty cycle and exclusion of the majority of people from opportunities for further education. The report outlined nine major challenges that South Africa faces, which fall under two major focus areas namely the need to eliminate poverty and reduce inequality. The following issues has been identified as obstacles inhibiting transformation, i.e. (i) Poor education outcomes (ii) High unemployment (iii) High disease burden (iv) A divided society (v) Public services that often fail the poor (vi) Parts of the country where people are locked into poverty (vii) Crumbling infrastructure (viii) inefficient use of natural resources (ix) Corruption. The NDP aims at creating a virtuous cycle whereby opportunities are expanded, leading to building the capabilities of the nation, resulting in a reduction in poverty and community development, ultimately giving rise to higher living standards and completing the cycle where opportunities for the next generation is expanded. The intended result of the NDP can be summarised as follows: (i) Creating jobs and livelihoods; (ii) Expanding infrastructure; (iii) Transitioning to a low-carbon economy; (iv) Transforming urban and rural spaces; (v) Improving education and training; (vi) Providing quality healthcare; (vii) Building a capable state; (viii) Fighting corruption and enhancing accountability; (ix) Transforming society and uniting the nation. The NDP supposedly recognizes the need for leadership on all levels (from national to community). At the core thereof lies the dire need for growth and development, supported by strong leadership, capable state and sacrifice on all levels of participation, this plan aims to gain national consensus and social cohesion.

From a physical planning perspective, the NDP also proposes the development of a national spatial framework (NSF) involving government, business and civil society to create a collective vision. This hasn't been done yet, but the NSF will target a number of spatial areas, of which the following are mentioned: national competitiveness corridor; nodes of competitiveness; rural restructuring zones; resource-critical regions; transnational development corridors; special intervention areas. This will be first official national planning framework, giving specific and definite geographic expression to the use of financial resources to influence the space-economy of South Africa since the Good Hope Plan of 1981.

3   Concluding remarks

National planning in South Africa has left somewhat of a sour taste in the mouths of politicians and the public alike, due to its history of enforcing separate development through spatial planning tools. South Africa seems to have been planning on a first-world level (social goals) instead of on a third-world level (focusing on economic growth and infrastructure development). It is known that social goals are not attainable without true economic growth. Is economic growth then obtainable if "geographic expression" is not given through national spatial planning? As so eloquently put by Tony Blair "It is not an arrogant government that chooses priorities, it's an irresponsible government that fails to choose."

It is the argument of this paper that over the past three decades the national space has been left open for interpretation in terms of economic growth and development, which has led to a lack of execution of the well-intentioned spatial guiding documents from the various levels of government. The expertise does not exist on the provincial and local municipal levels to give expression and influence economic development with the wide range of social goals given in more recent spatial planning guidelines. Only in the most recent initiative, the National Development Plan (2012) has the concept of geographical-ordering and influencing the physical development of the country by means of spatial planning tools become acceptable and an approachable subject. By means of the National Spatial Framework (as proposed in the National Development Plan) planning in South Africa will probably be able to break through the past barriers and formally plan for growth and development in an organized and recognized manner. It can only be hoped that this time a national level plan will be able to guide and assist local and provincial authorities more clearly and specifically on the physical translation and manifestation of social goals. The new National Spatial Framework should aim to find the golden path between being too rigid and autocratic and being a wish-list of unattainable desires, leaving the space-economy open for interpretation of unattainable social goals. In his most recent State of the Nation Address (February 2012) President Jacob Zuma identified five major geographically-focussed programmes, as well as projects focusing on health and basic education infrastructure, information and communication technologies and regional integration, covering the national space. These projects, if successfully implemented, should be the launch of a new era in national spatial planning for South Africa.

References

[1]   Council of Europe, European Regional/Spatial Planning Charter (Torremolinos Charter). Strasburg: CoE, 1983.
[2]   South Africa. Department of Planning and the Environment, *National physical development plan,* Pretoria: Government Printer, 1975.
[3]   Fair, T.J.D, The National Physical Development Plan (NPDP): a summary and review, *South African geographical journal,* **57(2)**, pp. 126–133, 1975.
[4]   Bos, D.J, *Ruimtelike ekonomiese implikasies van nywerheidsontwikkeling.* Potchefstroom PU for CHE. (Dissertation – M. Art. et Scien.), 1987.
[5]   Stern, E., Developing the inter-metropolitan periphery, *Town and regional planning,* **20,** pp. 4–10, Sep, 1985.
[6]   Bloch, R., Post-war regional planning: theory and record, *The South African Journal of Economics,* **58(2),** pp. 139–156, Jun, 1989.
[7]   Rosenstein-Rodan, P. Problems of industrialisation of Eastern and South-eastern Europe. *Economic journal, LIII,* pp. 202–211, 1943.
[8]   Geyer, H.S, Industrial development policy in South Africa – the past, present and future, *World development,* **17,** pp. 379–396, 1989.
[9]   South Africa, Department of Foreign Affairs, *Good Hope Plan,* Pretoria: Government Printer, 1981. SA *see* South Africa.

[10] South Africa, Board for Regional Industrial Development, *Regional Industrial Development Programme (RIDP)*, Incentive scheme introduced on 1 May 1991, Midrand: DBSA, 1992.

[11] Baldwin, R.E, *Economic development and growth*. New York: Wiley. 150 p, 1972.

[12] Hirschman, A.O, *The strategy of economic development*, New York: Norton, 1958.

[13] South Africa, Office for Regional Development, *National Regional Development Programme: general overview*, Pretoria: Government Printer, 1991.

[14] Bell, T. South African Regional Industrial Development Policy: Critical issues, *Transformation*, 32, pp. 1–30, 1997.

[15] Panel of Experts, Evaluation of the regional industrial development program as an element of the regional development policy in South Africa, Midrand: Development Bank of Southern Africa, 1989.

[16] Friedmann, J, Regional policy: a case study of Venezuela. Cambridge, MA: M.I.T. Press, 279 p, 1966.

[17] Luiz, J.M. and van der Waal, C.S, Re-evaluating South Africa's Regional Industrial Development Programme: case studies from Brits and Nkowankowa, *Urban forum*, **8(1)**, pp. 61–79, 1997.

[18] Ligthelm, A.A. and Wilsenach, A, A preliminary evaluation of the new RIDP and its impact on regional development in South Africa, *Development Southern Africa*, **10(3)**, pp. 361–381, Aug, 1993.

[19] Black, P. and Roux, A, The spatial dimension of regional policy selectivity versus uniformity, *Development Southern Africa*, **8(4)**, pp. 445–488, Nov, 1991.

[20] Drewes, J.E. and Bos, D.J, The Regional Industrial Development Programme: an evaluation, *South African journal of economics*, **63(2)**, pp. 247–270, 1995.

[21] African National Congress. *The reconstruction and development programme*, Johannesburg: Umanyano, 1994.

[22] South Africa, *Development Facilitation Act, no. 67 of 1995*. Pretoria: Government Printer, 1995.

[23] Oranje, M, Post-apartheid national spatial development planning in South Africa – a brief history, *European Spatial Research and Policy* **17(2)**, pp. 55–70, 2010.

[24] South Africa, Department of Finance, Growth, Employment and Redistribution Strategy, 1996.

[25] Robbins, G, Reflecting on South Africa's post-apartheid experience with spatially informed economic development programmes, Think piece for TIPS Forum October, 2008.

[26] South Africa, Department of Land Affairs, *Rural Development Framework*, Pretoria: Government Printer, 1997.

[27] South Africa, Department of Housing, *Urban Development Framework*, Pretoria: Government Printer, 1997.

[28] South Africa, Department of Trade and Industry, *Spatial development initiatives*, 1999.

[29] Wiese, H, *Regional industrial development strategies: A comparison of South African countries*. Paper delivered at the EBM Research Conference. 27-28 November 1996. University of Port Elizabeth, 1996.

[30] Drewes, J.E. and Kleynhans, Re-evaluation of the Platinum SDI: a critical commentary, *Town and Regional Planning*, **53**, pp. 1–9, 2008.

[31] South Africa, The Presidency, Integrated Sustainable Rural Development Strategy, 2000.

[32] South Africa, The Presidency, *National Spatial Development Perspective*, Government Printer: Pretoria, 2003.

[33] South Africa, The Presidency, *National Spatial Development Perspective*, Pretoria, 2006.

[34] Hughes, S, The role of intergovernmental harmonization as a national policy response to promote sustainable service delivery and development in South Africa, Unpublished paper, 2005.

[35] South Africa, Economic Development Department, *New Growth Path*, 2010.

[36] South Africa, The Presidency, *Draft National Development Plan*, 2012.

Underused land, brownfields, future use and effects: Browntrans Project outputs

D. Vojkovská, B. Vojvodíková & B. Macečková
Faculty of Civil Engineering VŠB, Technical University of Ostrava, Czech Republic

Abstract

The Czech Republic is one of the smaller states in Central Europe with about 10 million inhabitants. In the frame of problematic of regional development and regional planning issues interregional differences are solved. With regard to the fact Czech Republic is a relatively small country; the conception of regional development by the principle of subsidiarity is transmitted to the level of municipalities. One of the monitored effects, which influence sustainable development, is also the existence of underused land or also previously used land (brownfields). Non-governmental or non-profit institutions may participate in the regeneration or re-using of these areas. The consequences of existence of these areas in concrete municipality are analyzed. The possibility of how these process regenerations were solved in the Czech Republic are indicated in the frame of this article on the example of several localities indicated. An important part of the contribution is devoted to effects which this successful regeneration brought to their surroundings. Examples were deliberately chosen not with investments having the expectation of future profit but with inputs of small financial funds and big enthusiasm which achieved significant regional effects.
Keywords: brownfields, cultural heritage, municipality, regeneration, redevelopment, subsidies.

1 Introduction

Among other goals, the cohesion policy of the European Union aims at reducing disparities between regions. In the Czech Republic, the principal activities concerning development (since development is considered as a necessary condition for reduction of disparities) are carried out at the level of regions and

WIT Transactions on Ecology and The Environment, Vol 173, © 2013 WIT Press
www.witpress.com, ISSN 1743-3541 (on-line)
doi:10.2495/SDP130171

big cities. Smaller municipalities remain in the background, although more than half of the Czech population live in smaller towns and villages [1].

Just like big cities, such smaller municipalities have to deal with sites, which have ceased to perform their functions. Point out, for example, in nearly every municipality in the Votice micro-region (situated in Central Bohemia) there is at least one site, which can be defined as a brownfield site [2]. Before 1990, these sites used to house factories, agricultural buildings or cultural centres. Until 1990, many of these sites had been the principal source of work opportunities for locals and their removal had a considerable impact on the local architecture, and even more so, on the population and its demographic composition. Concentrated on the Tanvald region (situated in North Bohemia), and compared the situation between the years 1990, 2000 and 2011, for example in Klusáček *et al.* [3]. The first decade was a period of social changes associated with a dramatic increase in unemployment rate, and over the following ten years municipalities tried to redevelop the abandoned sites and restore them to their former functions, which consequently led to the reduction of the unemployment rate.

Therefore it is obvious that the re-use of so-called brownfield sites is one of the crucial tasks in regional development. To incorporate the redevelopment of brownfield sites into the regional land management is one of criteria, as defined by Pahlen *et al.* [4], for sustainability of land use and urban design. The Project BROWNTRANS Brownfield Regeneration Know-How Transfer – focuses on sharing experience of redevelopment of brownfield sites or underused lands.

The following text about three sites in Northern Moravia should illustrate the significance of locating some firms in small municipalities. It also shows how NGOs or the municipalities can undertake restoration and transformation of abandoned sites. In one of the cases, the municipality performs the role of the developer (thus not only initiating the project, but also executing it). By way of conclusion, each article sums up the principal impact of redevelopment, based on interviews with people involved in each case. The following section presents three particular cases of redevelopment of lands and buildings that had ceased to perform their function and became a burden for the environment. In none of the three cases the redevelopment process was carried out by a private firm aiming at making profit. Although the three sites differ from each other in their present state and past function, their redevelopment has always been primarily aimed at improving the life of people in the neighbourhood.

2   Old colliery "František" in Horní Suchá

2.1 What were the past benefits derived from the site? What was its past function? What was done by way of development?

The old and now unused coal mine "František" is located in Horní Suchá. The Municipality of Horní Suchá stretches to an area of about 10 km^2 and has 4,500 inhabitants. It is one of the smaller towns of the Ostrava-Karviná agglomeration, which has been connected with the coal mining industry for centuries.

The municipality was founded in 1305. As Figure 1 shows [5], it was a rather small, agricultural village, with a population of several hundred people. When the coal mine "František" was opened in 1911, it significantly affected the agricultural character of the municipality and the composition of its population.

Figure 1: Horní Suchá – I. military maps – era of Joseph II 1764–1768.

Figure 2: Horní Suchá in 1957.

The construction of the coal mine created a need for labour force, and it was mostly newcomers who started working there. The number of miners changed over the years, and while the mine was in operation there were between 1,200 and 2,500 miners [6]. Figure 2 shows the population density in 1957 [7]. In the northern part of the municipality we can see massive construction of mining houses. In the 1960s the population settled on the current number of 4,500 inhabitants.

2.2 When did the site ceased to perform its function? How did it affect the environment?

The coal mine "František" was closed in 1999. Ever since the mining activity was terminated, the unemployment rate was significantly increasing – in comparison with 1997 it was twice as much: 18.60% and over the following years it rose to 20%. In 2004 the situation got even worse, with the unemployment rate shooting up to 24.10%, the highest number in history so far [8]. Between 1999 and 2002 the premises of the old coal mine were unused. The coal mine was still a property of OKD (a private, coal mining company, which acquired the property in the process of privatization after the fall of communism). By that time most of the coal mines in the Ostrava basin (e.g. the coal mine "Alexander") were closed, which meant that there was a surplus of abandoned or unused coal mines. The unemployment rate in the entire region was extremely high, large companies were reducing their production and the State was supporting constructions of new industrial parks built on greenfield land. The result of such situation was that private owners were not induced to redevelop these sites in any way; on the other side, they were very eager to get rid of them. Thus, in 2002 the old coal mine went in the hands of DIAMO, state enterprise, which acquired the coal mine "František" together with other premises of old coal mines for a symbolic price of 1 CZK. Although the State had been well aware of the difficult economic situation in the region, it still continued to support industrial parks built on greenfield land and reduction of unemployment in bigger cities. During these years, the municipality had to struggle with unemployment as well as with the social pathological phenomena connected with unemployment, e.g. increase in crime. By the end of 2002 and in 2003 intense negotiations over the possibility of transferring the property to the municipality were conducted. It was also agreed that useless buildings were to be demolished. However, due to the fact that the security guards were dismissed, in a very short time scrap metal collectors devastated the buildings and the public utilities.

2.3 Who undertook the redevelopment? What were the sources of finance for the redevelopment?

In 2005 the old coal mine was transferred to the municipality. The municipality intended to build an industrial park on the site, thus compensating for the lack of work opportunities. The whole project has been managed by the municipality, which receives money from government budget but which also has to spend money within the municipality budget on co-financing and other costs. For more detail on the investments and investors see Table 1 [8].

On 4th May 2010 there was the grand opening of the entire industrial park.

Table 1:   Principal investing activities prior to the opening of the industrial park.

Years	Investments in	Investors	Investments
2006–2007	Restoration of the administrative building	OPIE	800,000€
2007–2008	Construction of the new hall	EU Structural Funds	800,000€
		Government budget	800,000€
		Municipality	800,000€
2006–2007	Infrastructure of the industrial park – project planning	OPIE	800,000€
	Infrastructure of the industrial park	Government budget of the Inter-Departmental Committee on the Redevelopment of the MSR	800,000€

2.4 What were the effects of the redevelopment?

The entire transformation of the brownfield site into the industrial park had a significant impact on the population. The unemployed inhabitants were enlisted as constructions workers. In 2008 the unemployment rate had already dropped to 13.2 % [1] and it has been going down even more.

2.5 Actual impact – present function

This part is based on an interview with Jan Lipner, Mayor of Horní Suchá. From the very beginning, the municipality intended to transform the old coal mine "František" into an industrial park, which had been in compliance with the land-use plan. Also, there were not many other possibilities. The inhabitants were rather sceptical about any plans for transformation. The project of transformation of the old coal mine "František" into an industrial park originally provided for 1,000 people working in the park. Due to increasing workforce productivity and taking into consideration current modern technologies, it seems more probable that the number of people employed in the industrial park will be about 500. There is no law, which would provide for preferring the employment of local residents of Horní Suchá, nevertheless, due to the commute costs the number of locals working in the park is significantly increasing. A considerable benefit derived from the project has been the employment of the long-term unemployed, who got the opportunity to work on the construction site. It turned out that a useful solution for the municipality is to hire the long-term unemployed to do community work.

Over time, the citizens of Horní Suchá have become more interested in the issues concerning the industrial park, yet their efforts often lead to a reduction of finances; the municipality must invest in the management of the industrial park. Although the park is two-thirds full, it is still slightly passive and its operation has to be subsidized by the municipality. However, in the near future the situation should improve.

3 Old colliery "Alexander" in Kunčičky

3.1 What were the past benefits derived from the site? What was its past function? What was done by way of development?

The old coal mine "Alexander" is located in Kunčičky, originally a solely agricultural municipality (it is now an administrative part of the city of Ostrava). The coal mining activity started in 1898 and the coal mine then employed 938 people. Together with the coal mine many mining houses were constructed. In ten years 90 new houses were built. The development of coal mining and the related iron and steel industry brought about significant changes in the local socio-economic environment. In a few decades the farmers turned into industrial workers. Following industrialization in the second half of the 19th century the number of inhabitants rapidly increased (nearly twenty times) [9]. Within twenty years, from 1890 to 1910, following the construction of the mine shaft "Alexander", the population of Kunčičky increased three times (in 1910 it was 4,607 people). In the inter-war years the number of inhabitants still continued to grow. However, population of Kunčičky got to its historically highest number in 1940 (it was 5,646 inhabitants) [11].

3.2 When did the site ceased to perform its function? How did it affect the environment?

The mining activity in the coal mine "Alexander" was definitively terminated on 31st December 1992 and all activities connected with coal mining were stopped in 1994.

During the period of subdued activity, the look of the coal mine "Alexander" changed significantly. Whereas some of the changes were positive (the demolition of the preparation plant – return to the original layout), other changes corrupted the historic value of the site (demolition of the engine rooms and compressor plant). In 1993, nine buildings together with both mine shafts were proclaimed cultural heritage of the Czech Republic and listed in the Central Register of Cultural Heritage. For a long time, the entire site had been abandoned. The possibilities of redevelopment of the site were made more difficult owing to the fact that the premises were cut off from public utilities and quite far from infrastructure. Also, the expected requirements and demands of the heritage department were a matter of concern. And last but not least, the financial demands of the owners (OKD and, later, DIAMO) were an important issue, too. In 2000 most of the buildings were in extremely poor condition. The site became a popular destination with scrap metal collectors. In 2005 some of the buildings were listed among the most endangered monuments.

3.2.1 Who undertook the redevelopment? What were the sources of finance for the redevelopment?

When the period of subdued activity ended, the site was taken over by DIAMO, a state enterprise, which retained some of the buildings and rented out or sold the rest of them. Events took a turn for the better, when, in March 2002, the Blacksmith Shop together with the adjacent land was transferred to the St. Alexandr's Charity, an NGO. The Charity started using both parts of the building as its headquarters and as sheltered workshops (for textile workers and carpenter helpers). The Blacksmith Shop was donated to the Charity by the *Charity of the Diocese of Ostrava-Opava*, which acquired it in 1998 from the OKD coal mining company for the price of one million CZK [12].

In 2008, DIAMO transferred two buildings, the Coach House and the Administrative Building, including the adjacent land, to the city of Ostrava. In June 2008 the city of Ostrava transferred the property to the St. Alexandr's Charity for free.

The restoration of all three buildings was rather expensive and the Charity was absolutely unable to finance the restoration works from their internal sources. Substantial financial aid was provided by various subsidy programs, etc. Thanks to this support the Charity was able to bring back to life this outstanding industrial monument, which is no longer condemned to dilapidation and decay, unlike many other monuments. Table 2 shows the total costs associated with properties of St. Alexandr's Charity [3].

Figure 3: The "Coach House" Figure 4: The "Coach House"
prior to restoration – after restoration –
2003. 2010 (photos by B.
Vojvodíková).

Table 2:   Total reconstruction costs "Alexander".

Donor	Costs
External sources (MSR, MoLSA, City of Ostrava, MoC, The OKD Foundation, The CIVILIA Foundation, The TIPSPORT Foundation, ROP)	585,983€
Internal sources	166,013€
% of external sources	77.92%
Total costs	751,996€

3.3 What were the effects of the redevelopment?

The restoration of the buildings actually meant that an industrial monument was saved at the last minute from possible complete decay. The fact that the properties were transferred to a charity, which intends to restore the buildings and start using them as sheltered workshops or sheltered housing for people with disabilities, means that the investment has a significant impact on reduction of unemployment of this particular group of people.

The restoration of these buildings also has a positive effect on the entire site. Since the buildings are located near the entrance to the premises, they also put in a negative light the owners of small businesses occupying other buildings on the site. Their clients no longer fear to enter the premises. It thus improves the condition of the small business, which, in return, can offer work opportunities to others.

3.4 Actual impact – present function

This part is based on an interview with director of the St. Alexandr's Charity. The positive effects can be divided into three main groups. First benefit is the possibility of employing people with disabilities. Yet, such institution could well work in any other place. The second significant effect is the fact that an industrial monument has thus been saved. However, this has not been a place of interest for tourists, although the number of visitors, who come to look at these buildings is increasing every year. The third, and most probably the most significant effect is that the citizens of Ostrava have gradually stopped considering this place as uninteresting and not worth moving to. Over the last three years the old mining houses in the neighbourhood have been restored, firms have started coming in, a riding hall has been built. Kunčičky is no longer a place, which one should avoid, on the contrary, the municipality starts drawing universal attention, which is a first step towards redevelopment of the area.

4 Vošárna in Raduň

4.1 What were the past benefits derived from the site? What was its past function? What was done by way of development?

Vošárna is a baroque building with a unique mansard roof dating back to the 18th century. It originally served as a washhouse for the local gentry at the Raduň chateau. It is located in Raduň, a municipality with a population of about 1,000 people. In the past, due to the location of the original castle, later the chateau, the municipality was one of the most important towns in the Opava Region. Vošárna was constructed between 1785 and 1820. It was built on land belonging to the chateau and offered work opportunities to locals [13].

4.2 When did the site ceased to perform its function? How did it affect the environment?

The building ceased to perform its function when the local gentry left the chateau in 1949. Over the years the chateau housed an agricultural high school and a warehouse. No one showed any interest in the Vošárna building, not even after the chateau was transferred to the National Heritage Institute in 1990 [14].

4.3 Who undertook the redevelopment? What were the sources of finance for the redevelopment?

For a long time the dilapidated building of Vošárna was a blot on the landscape of Raduň. Considering the poor condition of the building the National Heritage Institute listed it among the most endangered monuments in the Czech Republic. In 2007 the decaying building was bought by Rostislav Müller, a native of Raduň, who cared about what would become of the building. The Vošárna Civic Association, which was created to save the building, carried out the initial repair works. Afterwards, a project was set up to save Vošárna.

The project aims to restore the monument, which fits the definition of a brownfield site, and to transform it into a community centre (more information about system of reconstruction Václavík *et.al.* [15]). Table 3 shows the total costs associated with the restoration of the dilapidated historic monument [17].

Table 3:   Total costs reconstruction Vošárna.

Donor	Costs
External sources (MoC, ROP, SAIF)	266,053€
Internal sources (Vošárna, civic association, civic association in Opava, sponsors)	23,408€
% of external sources	91.91%
Total costs	289,460€

Since Vošárna is listed among the national cultural monuments, all restoration works were watched by the National Heritage Institute, which oversaw that the restoration works did not corrupt the historic integrity of the building. Each month, during days of supervision, there were discussions about the construction works and about further steps, which were to be taken in compliance with the project. The important aspect was the cooperation with a construction company, which has extensive experience in restorations of cultural monuments.

4.4 What were the effects of the redevelopment?

The aim and the output of the project is the restored building of a community centre in Raduň. Vošárna is the centre of cultural and social life in Raduň and Vršovice, which is a neighbouring village. It is a place where people can do amateur sports, hold meetings of various clubs, societies and associations, and where cultural events can be organized. The targeted group are the inhabitants of Raduň and Vršovice.

Figure 5:   Building prior to restoration in 2007.

Figure 6:   Stage 2 – restoration of the building (photos by R. Frgala).

4.5 Actual impact – present function

This part is based on an interview with Mr Müller. The principal benefit of the restoration of Vošárna is its social impact. The social life in Raduň and Vršovice has long suffered from the lack of a place where people could meet and gather for group activities. Nowadays, the majority of the people living in Raduň leave the village in the morning (to go to work or to school) and come back home in the evening, which slowly weakens social interactions and community ties. So, the fact that Vošárna offered a place for a maternity centre, for activities for smaller and bigger children, and for social gatherings contributes to better interpersonal relationships. And another significant benefit is naturally the fact that a valuable monument has been saved and is no longer a blot on the landscape of the village.

5 Conclusion

We could draw the following conclusion from the three examples. Small municipalities too have to deal with problems associated with disuse of some of their land. The problem is all the more serious if the previous development of the municipality was tightly connected with the original use of the land. Abandoned, decaying buildings do not generate any profit and present a blot on the landscape, hinder the possible development of the municipalities and constantly remind the inhabitants of the once glorious past. If the negative impression is corrected, further development is possible. The industrial park built on the site of the old coal mine "František" has new buildings, people are getting jobs and there are other services needed for the operation of the park and for the people who work there. The positive impact is also significant in the case of the old coal mine "Alexander". When the coal mine was closed, Kunčičky lost work opportunities as well as part of its population. The ugly, dilapidated buildings destroyed every hope of a future development and the interest of locals. Little by little, the restored buildings sparked the interest of the locals, as well as the interest of investors and business owners, who are slowly coming back to the region. As far as Vošárna is concerned, the principal benefit is not the creation of new work opportunities but the strengthening of interpersonal relationships in the village. A positive permanent development of a municipality has always been based on traditional relationships between the inhabitants. The Vošárna building helps to build up such relationships, which help keep the village from becoming merely a place to sleep in, without any interest extending beyond one's house; which would be unsustainable with regard to sustainable development. When the Czech Republic became a member of the European Union, it got the possibility of drawing money from European Union structural funds, which enabled NGOs and municipalities to undertake the redevelopment and restoration of old and unused buildings. However, it is necessary to emphasize the fact that at the beginning, the NGOs or municipalities had to invest their own money (as it was in the case of Vošárna, which was financed by a private person or in the case of the old coal mine "Alexander", which was financed by a charity). These persons or organizations invested their money without knowing in advance that they would receive subsidies. Thus, it was them alone who took the risk in being unable to finish the restoration works. In this context we must see that the role

NGOs play in the development of municipalities is significant, indispensable, and nowadays also irreplaceable.

List of abbreviations:

MSR   – Moravian-Silesian Region.
MoLSA   – Ministry of Labour and Social Affairs of the Czech Republic.
MoC   – Ministry of Culture of the Czech Republic.
ROP   – Regional Operational Programme Moravia-Silesia.
SAIF   – State Agricultural Intervention Fund.
OPIE   – Operational Programme Industry and Enterprise.

Acknowledgements

This paper is prepared thanks to the project Brownfield Regeneration Know-How Transfer BROWNTRANS, Project number: 11310 1614 which is supported by the Leonardo da Vinci Fund.

References

[1] Statistical office, www.czso.cz
[2] Bergatt-Jacson, J., Votoček, J. Inventatization brownfields sites in area Votice, 2003. www.brownfields.cz/wp-content/uploads/2007/11/inventarizace_votice.pdf
[3] Klusáček, P., Krejčí, T., Kunc, J., Martinát, S., Nováková, E.: *The post-industrial landscape in relation to local self-government in the Czech Republic.* Moravian Geographical Reports, 2011 Vol. 19, No. 4, pp. 18-28.
[4] Pahlen, G., Glöckner, S., *Sustainable regeneration of European brownfields sites, in Brownfield Sites II*, Assessment, Rehabilitation and Development, WIT Press, 2004, ISBN:1-85312-719-1.
[5] Czech cadastral office, www.archivnimapy.cuzk.cz
[6] Coal mining in Ostravsko- Karvinském district, Anagram, Ostrava, 2003, ISBN 80-7342-016-3.
[7] Old maps, www.oldmaps.geolab.cz
[8] Horní Suchá, www.hornisucha.cz/prumyslova-zona-frantisek.html
[9] Matěj, M., Klát J. & Korbelářová I., *Cultural monuments in the Ostrava-Karvina district,* National Heritage Institute, Department of regional planning in Ostrava, 2009, ISBN 978-80-85034-52-3.
[10] Regional Council of the Moravia Silesia Cohesion REGION (ROP MS). Realization of the projects, www.rr-moravskoslezsko.cz/realizuji-projekt/z-radunske-vosarny-bude-spolecenske-centrum
[11] Martinát, S., Dvořák, P., Frantál, B. & Kol., in *Brownfields – context and opportunities, Colliery Alexander – mirror of the past, opportunity of the future in Kunčičky*: VŠB – Technical University of Ostrava, 2012. ISBN 978-80-7431-089-8.

[12] Colliery Alexander second life; Czech Television, Rusty beauty. Online. www.ceskatelevize.cz/porady/10318003501-zrezivela-krasa/412235100091001-alexandruv-druhy-zivot/
[13] In village Raduň saved Vošárna; Czech Television, Regional news, Online. www.ceskatelevize.cz/ct24/regiony/97504-v-raduni-zachranili-vosarnu
[14] VOSARNA, www.vosarna.webnode.cz
[15] Václavík, V., Dvorský, T., Kušnerová, M., Daxner, J., *Polyurethane Foam as Aggregate for Thermal Insulating Mortars and Lightweight Concrete*, Środkowo-Pomorskie Towarzystwo Naukowe Ochrony Środowiska, 2012, ISSN 25-50-1506218X.
[16] Folta, P., Personal communication, 10 December 2012, Director of the St. Alexandr's Charity, Ostrava, Czech Republic.
[17] Müller, R., Personal communication, 20 November 2012, Founder NGOs Vošárna, Raduň, Czech Republic.

Section 5
Cultural heritage

Cultural heritage tourism research: a sustainable community-based design project for the San Antonio Mission Historic District

S. Doganer
College of Architecture, The University of Texas at San Antonio, USA

Abstract

This paper discusses how to provide maximum efficiency in the economical, historical, social, and cultural dimensions of tourism with sustainable development practices in order to support heritage tourism of the San Antonio Missions and development in South San Antonio.

The Missions of San Antonio are on the US "tentative list" to be advanced as possible UNESCO World Heritage Sites. The area designated as the Mission Historic District, located along the San Antonio River in the south section of the city, originally attracted both prehistoric Indian and historic Spanish and Anglo populations because of the prevalence of unique natural resources. The historic San Antonio River has long served as the heart of the city. Each year the world-renowned River Walk draws millions of visitors, yet miles of urban river with untapped potential lie beyond downtown and the famed Paseo del Rio. A comprehensive, multi-year project is underway to restore and enhance 13 miles of the San Antonio River both north and south of downtown. A multi-phase project to develop the full potential of the San Antonio River is focusing on improving two sections of the river -Museum and Mission Reaches- that pose different challenges. The Mission Reach segment overlays with the research area of this paper, and provides a strong connection between the area and downtown. Mission Portals will connect San Antonio's four historic missions – Mission Concepcion, Mission San Jose, Mission San Juan and Mission Espada – to the San Antonio River.

This research investigates and analyzes the potential of the San Antonio Mission Historic District towards community-based cultural heritage tourism. The connections of Missions to the river will feature historic and artistic interpretations of the story of the missions and highlight their social and cultural

 WIT Transactions on Ecology and The Environment, Vol 173, © 2013 WIT Press
www.witpress.com, ISSN 1743-3541 (on-line)
doi:10.2495/SDP130181

importance to the area. This will reinforce the importance of the river to the missions and encourage visitors to circulate between the Mission Reach and the river. Accelerating tourism in Mission Historic District will be a considerable economic and social benefit through the workforce, income and infrastructure developments. This research provides a legacy of positive development within the Mission Historic District, especially as the San Antonio moves towards World Heritage designation. This paper will also promote cultural and environmental sustainability at the local or neighborhood level while giving tourists an option to experience the cultural heritage of the region.

Keywords: cultural heritage tourism, sustainability, community-based design.

1 Introduction

Tourism is one of the world's fastest-growing industry and business. International tourist arrivals grew by over 4% in 2011 to 980 million, according to the latest UNWTO World Tourism Barometer. The Americas (+4%) saw an increase of 6 million arrivals, reaching 156 million in total. North America, with a 3% increase, hit the 100 million tourists mark in 2011 [1]. According to the Economic Impact of San Antonio's Hospitality Industry report, from 1998 to 2008, the economic impact of the hospitality industry increased by more than 70%. In San Antonio alone, hospitality industry employs more than 113,000 workers who annually generate $12.2 billion dollars back into the local economy; making tourism one of San Antonio's largest industries [2].

San Antonio is one of the State's top tourist cities. The city has a rich and unique historic urban landscape characterized by its river with its famous 'Riverwalk', historic neighborhoods and major landmarks such as San Antonio Franciscan Missions which are on the US "tentative list" as possible UNESCO World Heritage Sites. It is expected that the river improvement project will also reinforce the connection to the San Antonio Missions, and encourage visitors to circulate along the river beyond the downtown area.

This research investigates and analyzes the potential of the San Antonio Mission Historic District towards community-based cultural heritage tourism. Accelerating tourism in San Antonio Missions Historic District brings considerable economic and social benefit through workforce, income and infrastructure developments. This paper proposes a project to support and connect community small business owners to the existing heritage tourism economy, and assist them in renovating and reusing their existing structures and properties. The purpose of the study is to foster prosperity for residents of the district. This in turn, will sustain the community's cultural heritage. Proposed project will capitalize on the existing plans for improvements of the San Antonio River and is timely as the current consideration for World Heritage designation of the San Antonio Missions will bring international attention to the district.

2 Cultural heritage tourism in the San Antonio Mission Historic District

Cultural heritage tourism is "traveling to experience the places and activities that authentically represent the stories and people of the past and present" [3]. It is an economic development tool designed to attract visitors to an area based on the unique aspects of the locality's history, landscape and culture. This not only boosts regional and local pride but is also a good source of revenue for a community and creates jobs. Historic preservation is a tool for preserving a historic place, incubating small businesses, revitalizing downtowns, generating local jobs, and creating improvements in a community. It is estimated by World Tourism organization UNWTO in 2006 that between 35 and 40 percent of tourism today represents cultural tourism or heritage tourism.   Lyon and Wells [4] states "As an alternative to mass tourism, cultural and heritage tourism offer opportunities for place-based engagement that frames contexts for interaction with the "lived space" and "everyday life" [5] of other peoples as well as sites and objects of global historical significance."

San Antonio Missions play an important role in defining the city's culture. In 2009, over 1.7 million people visited Missions Concepción, San José, San Juan, and Espada while 26 million people visiting the city San Antonio in total. Collectively, these missions and associated features – including *acequias* (irrigation canals), *labores* (farm lands), dam and aqueduct, and the single remaining *rancho* (mission ranch) – comprise the San Antonio Missions National Historical Park [2].

San Antonio River was the lifeblood of the missions located within easy reach of its banks. San Antonio River Improvements Project (SARIP) will also affect the park by restoring the river's natural features, re-creating and preserving the natural ecosystem for the enjoyment of the area's residents and visitors. It is expected that the river improvement project will reinforce the connection to the San Antonio Missions, and encourage tourists to circulate along the river beyond the downtown area [2].

2.1 San Antonio Mission Historic District

The Catholic Church and the Spanish government established five mission compounds and a small military base in the 18th century that established today's San Antonio, Texas. These missions blended native traditions with newly adopted Spanish ways, and created a very unique culture. The communities still remain in the area is a very important part of San Antonio's rich cultural heritage [6].

San Antonio Mission Historic District, located along the San Antonio River in the south section of the city, includes the lower four missions (Listed from north to south: Concepcion, San Jose, San Juan Capistrano, and Espada), their *acequias* and fields. The area was originally attracted both prehistoric Indian and historic Spanish and Anglo populations because of the prevalence of unique natural resources. The abundant water, game, and other natural foods seem to have provided prehistoric Indians with an ample non-agricultural subsistence type of lifestyle based upon hunting, gathering, and fishing. The area was utilized for agricultural purposes as well as local industries after the establishment of the Spanish Missions [7].

The World Heritage Site (WHS) nomination is expected to be reviewed in 2015. Recognition as a World Heritage Site would put the missions in the company of fewer than 1,000 places around the world that are recognized for outstanding historical, artistic, scientific, or natural values [8]. WHS status can bring enhanced resources for conservation and additional funding and investment, and benefit nearby communities from increased visitation and tourist spending. These communities can also contribute to local economic development and revitalization. The new report on potential economic impact of WHS designation funded by Bexar community indicates that WHS designation could be both an outstanding promotional opportunity and a high-profile catalyst for developing more significant cultural and heritage tourism in the area [6].

2.2 Demographics

The San Antonio River South Area Coordinated Management Plan (2010) defines the demographic profile of the River South area as below:

"Between 1990 and 2008 the population within this area decreased slightly (-1%) while San Antonio increased by 37%. Residents within the corridor are 5% of the City's total population (approximately 66,000) and density averages 4.92 persons per acre. The median age is 32.7 years, slightly younger than San Antonio's average of 34 years. Almost 43% of the population 25 years and older, in this area has not completed a high school education... Educational attainment ties with income potential and discretionary spending. This area earns $30,630, nearly $11,000 less than the City average... Housing data shows that most residential structures account for 23% of the land use. They were built during the post WWII era and have a current median value of $54,843 compared to the City of San Antonio average of $113,988. Other major land uses in the area include parks 21%, institutional 22%, and commercial and vacant land both at 14%." [9]

Analysis reveals numerous challenges to the area such as: declining population, lower educational levels, median income and higher poverty levels when compared to overall City data. Currently of great concern in the River South neighborhoods, is the crime rate. This alone has caused many neighborhood areas to rally and work for expanded team efforts with schools, churches, civic organizations and the City for revitalization to strengthen its viability and discourage criminal activity.

2.3 Current planning studies and projects

Current planning studies and investments around the Mission Historic District are San Antonio River Improvements Project/Mission Reach Ecosystem Restoration and Recreation, River South Area Coordinated Management Plan, South Central San Antonio Community Plan, Roosevelt Corridor Reinvestment Plan, and Citywide Design Guidelines for Historic Districts.

2.3.1 San Antonio River Improvements Project: Mission Reach ecosystem restoration and recreation

Each year the world-renowned River Walk draws millions of visitors, yet miles of urban river with untapped potential lie beyond downtown and the famed Paseo del Rio. A comprehensive, multi-year project is underway to restore and enhance 13 miles of the San Antonio River both north and south of downtown. A multi-phase project to develop the full potential of the San Antonio River is focusing on improving two sections of the river -Museum and Mission Reaches-that pose different challenges. These enhancements are expected to have far-reaching benefits for all of San Antonio, from increased economic development to cultural resources and recreational opportunities connecting neighborhoods. The Mission Reach segment provides a strong connection between the area and downtown. The Mission Reach Ecosystem Restoration and Recreation Project is transforming an 8 mile stretch of the San Antonio River into a quality riparian woodland ecosystem. As the Mission Reach project restores the natural ecosystem of the river, it will also reconnect the river to the historic Missions that relied on it hundreds of years ago. Mission Portals will connect San Antonio's four historic missions – Mission Concepcion, Mission San Jose, Mission San Juan and Mission Espada – to the San Antonio River. These connections will feature historic and artistic interpretations of the story of the missions and highlight their social and cultural importance to the area. This will reinforce the importance of the river to the missions and encourage visitors to circulate between the Mission Reach and the river. River Improvements Project planners are also working closely with the National Park Service San Antonio Missions National Historic Park to ensure that there is a seamless transition between the Mission Reach and the historic missions, and the proposed project helps to strengthen this transition [9].

2.3.2 River South Area Coordinated Management Plan

River South is an 8-mile stretch of the San Antonio River, adjacent neighborhoods and home to four of the San Antonio Missions. The investment of time, funding and improvements at both the street and River levels is key to this area realizing its full potential as an attractive, viable corridor. The project encourages economic diversity and job creation, which are compatible with San Antonio's natural and cultural resources; preserves and revitalizes existing housing through community heritage-based economic development and promotes targeted infill for new housing neighborhood improvements [9].

2.3.3 South Central San Antonio Community Plan

The South Central San Antonio Community Plan, adopted in 1999 and updated in 2003, covers the northern portion of River South to SW Military Drive. Plan elements cover neighborhood and community development, community facilities, transportation and quality of life. Emphasis is on infill development, housing stock and improving the quality of commercial corridors. A chief goal is to "enhance and improve the Missions, parks and the San Antonio River" through strategies aimed at zoning, safety, accessibility and restoration [9].

2.3.4 Roosevelt Corridor Reinvestment Plan

The Roosevelt Corridor Reinvestment Plan, adopted in 2009, includes four registered neighborhood associations in River South – Roosevelt Park, Riverside South, Mission San Jose and East Pyron/Symphony Lane. The goal for the Corridor is to encourage reinvestment in the Roosevelt corridor; Launch community-based initiatives to improve quality of life, Link existing business and property owners with funding sources, Create investment opportunities [9].

2.3.5 Citywide Design guidelines for historic districts

The Citywide Design guidelines provide to historic district residents, property owners, professionals working with historic properties, and potential construction applicants an understanding of architectural design principles and guidelines.

Besides these ongoing projects, National Park Services has also proposed and developed couple studies that would support the cultural heritage tourism activities and sustain the communities and the culture that the missions helped spawn. Some of these initiatives are "A Day in the Life of the Missions" hands-on cultural demonstration programming at Mission San José, a Spanish colonial demonstration farm on mission *labores* land at Mission San Juan, which will entail both new construction and new programming, and building a new park headquarters and research center, and restoring the landscape around Mission San José [2].

3   A sustainable community-based design project for the San Antonio Missions District

The concept for this project proposed is to engage Mission Historic District residents in small business development. The purpose of this project is to create prosperity for residents of San Antonio's Mission Historic District. It means to promote the continuity of heritage through the benefits which come from cultural heritage tourism. The project aims to provide technical preservation guidance and cultural heritage tourism knowledge to potential small business owners in reuse of existing, historic buildings and properties for new businesses. Prospective entrepreneurs will receive training and professional support to tap into the tourist economy that flows right past their front doors, and in turn, their efforts will support and sustain the cultural heritage of their community.

The proposal addresses the issues of cultural and environmental sustainability at the local or neighborhood level while giving tourists an option to experience the cultural heritage of the region. Studying the potential of the San Antonio Mission Historic District and encouraging sustainable cultural heritage tourism and related small-scale economic activities in the area will promote sustainable local economic development.

This project focuses on the potential of new business uses for existing buildings and properties in the Mission Historic District, while planning sustainable, opportunity rich, and economically competitive communities. Proposed project promotes cultural and environmental sustainability at the local or neighborhood level while giving tourists an option to experience the cultural heritage of the region.

This proposed project aims to provide individual property owners with a package of offerings. Highlights include:

- training workshops on Cultural Heritage Tourism including coverage of the financial aspects of Heritage Tourism;
- training workshops on historic preservation and re-use of existing buildings;
- business plans for small business owners, including marketing plans, social media, and information on area micro-lenders;
- community planning meetings and workshops;
- architectural design as well as workshops and services geared to revitalization efforts.

3.1 Proposed geographic area

In order to accommodate needs and expectations, this plan is scaleable and flexible. The project group will integrate with the ongoing efforts of other city agencies and with the community's interests to designate the locations best suited for implementation of the project. Targeting zones such as portals to the river and other key areas will be a vital component of the project.

3.2 Method

In order to create a plan with the greatest opportunity for success, the project group would engage with the local community to ensure that professional and scholarly collaboration is led by the community's vision for their own prosperity. The project includes three components which utilize public participation in every level of the project. Architecture and planning, tourism, and business groups will work together to develop a successful community-based cultural heritage tourism project in the Mission Historic District.

3.3 Objectives

This is a three year project. The objectives of the full life of the project are: to effectively communicate the values of heritage tourism; the conservation of cultural resources and the inclusion of community in decision-making.

The objectives for year one are to:

- identify the target area(s);
- determine the capacity, value and potential re-use of structures and properties within the proposed area;
- identify resident entrepreneurs for participation in the project;
- provide entrepreneurs with business tools for success.

The objective for year two is to take the project from planning to implementation. The project group will assist the selected participants by providing architectural design plans, and planned business and marketing strategies, in order to foster and nurture sustainable small business practices.

The objective for the third and final year of this project is to implement all aspects of the project, including administration and monitoring of construction, business plans and outreach to tourists.

3.4 Deliverables

A summary of deliverables of the proposed three year project is shown in Table 1.

Table 1:   Summary of deliverables of the project.

Year 1	PROJECT REPORT • Site Design Analysis • Cultural Heritage Tourism Market Analysis • Identification of the Project Target Area • Architectural Inventory: An Assessment and Evaluation of the Selected Properties in the Target Area PROJECT INFORMATION WEB PAGE EDUCATION AND TRAINING • Community meetings on Cultural Heritage Tourism • Business Plan Training LIST OF POTENTIAL RESIDENT ENTREPRENEURS
Year 2	ARCHITECTURAL DRAWINGS BUSINESS CONSULTANCY COMMUNITY TRAINING SEMINARS
Year 3	CONSULTANCY ON IMPLEMENTATION OF THE PROJECTS DESTINATION MARKETING STUDIES FINAL REPORT

Year one

The deliverables for year one will include project report, project information web page, education and training opportunities, and list of potential resident entrepreneurs.

Project report

The project group will compile a comprehensive report that includes the sections detailed below. Each section will also be submitted for review as work is being completed. The project report will include a brief narrative of the historic context of the district and findings from previous analyses. The report will include photographs and maps, site design analysis, cultural heritage tourism market analysis, identification of the project target area, and architectural inventory.

• **Site design analysis** This will be the first step in identifying the potential for heritage tourism businesses in the Mission Historic District as well as determining the area(s) best suited for the project. It will consist of two elements:

a. Review of previous planning studies: the proposal aims to build on the comprehensive regional plans for the Mission Historic District in order to augment the community vision. An analysis of existing documents will aid in identifying the locations best suited to the project. The documents for this analysis include, but are not limited to: the "Roosevelt Corridor Reinvestment Plan," the San Antonio River Improvements Project's "Mission Reach Ecosystem Restoration and Recreation Project," the "River South Area Coordinated Management Plan," and the "South Central San Antonio Community Plan." Guidelines issued by the City of San Antonio Office of Historic Preservation and recommendations from the San Antonio City Design Center will be included in the analysis.

b. Field survey and research around the missions (concentrated radius around the missions and mission portals within the Mission Historic District): the architecture and planning group will conduct a field survey of the area surrounding the missions in order to gather visual data on existing structures and properties. Observations from the field survey and analysis of GIS maps will provide information on qualities such as authenticity, historic significance, unique features, existing conditions, site infrastructure, and cultural heritage tourism potentials. The survey will include photographs and generated GIS maps.

• **Cultural heritage tourism market analysis** Concurrent with the site design analysis, the tourism group will conduct a market analysis to determine the nature of current cultural heritage activity and potential future activity.

The analysis will have two components:

a. A survey of visitors to the missions: a visitor survey will be conducted of visitors to the missions (excluding the Alamo) to determine a visitor profile and obtain visitor perceptions of the tourism facilities and services. Visitor surveys will be performed at the four missions and other high volume areas within the heritage district. Information gathered from the visitor survey will be used to provide recommendations for promoting tourism for the Mission Historic District.

b. Focus group(s): a focus group of 10 to 12 people, including managers of the historic mission sites, local community leaders, and managers of other tourism operations in the district will be held to gain a better understanding of their strategies, perceptions of heritage tourism, and the current status of research efforts regarding tourists. If necessary, a second group will be held to accommodate all interested parties.

• **Identification of the project's target area(s)** The project group will identify the target area(s) for the proposed project in collaboration with city and county officials and community residents. Identification of the area will be determined using information gathered from the field survey and meetings with community residents.

• **Architectural inventory** Upon determination of the target area, the architecture and planning group will prepare an architectural inventory of selected (up to 25) properties in the target area. The inventory will include: address, estimated date of construction, property type, historic significance, unique features, size, structural and nonstructural systems and materials, existing conditions, site infrastructure, and architectural and historical integrity of the surveyed properties. This inventory will be used to assess and evaluate the potential re-use of the properties.

Project information web page

Project progress as well as the final report will be made available on a project website, for better community awareness. Limited quantities of printed editions of the report will also be made available for those without Internet access.

Education and training

• **Community meetings on Cultural Heritage Tourism** The focus groups (see Market Analysis) will be followed by one or more "town hall" meetings, with local community leaders, managers of tourism operations in the district, and district residents. Findings from the Site Design and Market Analyses will be presented at these meetings. The objectives of the meetings are to raise awareness of the benefits of Cultural Heritage Tourism, obtain information regarding community perceptions of the tourism industry in the district, determine if there are any areas of concern, seek potential entrepreneurs, identify the project's target areas and ensure the community is involved in decision-making in developing and implementing the project.

• **Business plan training** Potential and existing entrepreneurs will be given the opportunity to attend business plan training seminars. The aim of these seminars is to provide small business owners with the knowledge needed to start and grow a business. The training will include how to write a business plan and find financing. The training will be open to public participation, but limited to 100 participants.

List of potential entrepreneurs

The project group will identify and recommend ten to twelve candidates and their properties for the next phases of the project (Years Two and Three). The candidates will be identified based on results from the business planning seminars, the site analysis and the building inventory.

Year two

The deliverables for year two will include architectural drawings, business consultancy, and community training seminars.

Architectural drawings

Ten to twelve architectural projects including plans, sections and elevations will be provided to the selected potential entrepreneurs. Drawings will be suitable for submission to the Historic and Design Review Commission (HDRC).

Business consultancy

Advanced training and consultancy will be given to the ten to twelve selected potential entrepreneurs.

Community training seminars

Training seminars will be provided to selected business owners and service employees of tourism and hospitality organizations. Potential and existing entrepreneurs will also be given the opportunity to attend the essentials of starting a business seminar (open to public, but limited to 100 participants).

Year three

The deliverables for the third and final year of this project will include consultancy on implementation of the projects, destination marketing studies, and final report.

By the end of the third year, selected entrepreneurs will be trained on how to run a small business on cultural heritage tourism, financially assisted and supported, and ready to start up their own businesses. They will also be done with the construction and/or renovation of their own properties.

4 Conclusion

While 1.7 million people visit the Missions, the impact of those visits has not translated to positive economic development for the local community. Identification of the cultural and historical assets, inventory of the existing landscape and buildings, and determination of the adaptive reuse will emphasize and highlight the real potential of the site. Real opportunities do exists to capitalize on the Missions and the new public investment into the river improvements.

The proposed survey, study and analysis of the proposed project area should encourage the revitalization of the Mission Historic District. The area will regain its sense of identity and share its treasures of history, culture and heritage with all who visit and those who decide to stay.

World Heritage designation of the San Antonio Missions will bring international attention to the district. The Harbinger Consulting Group [6] states, "Cultural travelers, whether domestic or international, look for experiences that are unique to a place. The World Heritage Site can be used to capture the attention of these potential visitors, but they will be looking for other high quality, engaging, authentic cultural experiences to augment their WHS visit. Use WHS designation as a catalyst for developing and connecting other heritage tourism opportunities and local businesses." In this respect, this project proposal is very important and timely in order to support and connect community small business owners to the existing heritage tourism economy. Finally the success of projects completed will encourage other local business entrepreneurs on their initiatives. It is expected that successful local business in the area will cause a ripple effect, and create prosperity for the residents in the area while sustaining the community's cultural heritage.

Acknowledgements

I would like to thank UTSA Center for Cultural Sustainability, William Dupont, Claudia Guerra, and David Bojanic for their support and collaboration on this project proposal.

References

[1] Kester, J.G.C., 2012. *2011 International Tourism Results and Prospects for 2012*, UNWTO News Conference, HQ, Madrid, Spain, 16 January 2012. http://dtxtq4w60xqpw.cloudfront.net/sites/all/files/pdf/unwto_hq_fitur12_jk_2pp_0.pdf (accessed 03/03/2012).

[2] UTSA Institute for Economic Development's Center for Community and Business Research in conjunction with The Harbinger Consulting Group, 2011. *Economic Impact of the San Antonio Missions*, National Historic Parks, http://ccs.utsa.edu/pdf/EconomicImpactMissions.pdf (accessed 03/03/2012).

[3] National Trust for Historic Preservation, Heritage Tourism, http://www.preservationnation.org/information-center/economics-of-revitalization/heritage-tourism/#.UTO_fTk_644 (accessed 03/03/2012).

[4] Lyon, S.M. and Wells, E.C., 2012. "Ethnographies of Global Tourism: Cultural Heritage, Economic Encounters, and the Redefinition of Impact", *Global Tourism: Cultural Heritage and Economic Encounters*, AltaMira Press, UK, pp. 1-21.

[5] Lefebvre, Henri. 1974. *The Production of Space,* Wiley-Blackwell, London, UK.

[6] The Harbinger Consulting Group, 2013. Building on a Strong Foundation: Potential Economic Impact of World Heritage Site Designation for the San Antonio Missions, http://www.bexar.org/whs/Missions_WHS_Report.PDF (accessed 03/03/2012).

[7] City of San Antonio, Office of Historic Preservation, Local Historic Districts, Mission, http://www.sanantonio.gov/historic/Districts/Mission.aspx (accessed 03/03/2012).

[8] UNESCO World Heritage Centre, Tentative List: San Antonio Franciscan Missions, http://whc.unesco.org/en/tentativelists/5247/ (accessed 03/03/2012).

[9] San Antonio River South Area Coordinated Management Plan, Protect-Promote-Coordinate, 2010. http://www.sanantonioriver.org/images/River_South_Management_plan_12_08_2010.pdf (accessed 03/03/2012).

Research on intensive utilization of land and settlements protection under rural housing reconstruction in Chengdu Plain

B. Shu[1], T.-N. Gao[1] & Y.-X. Zhao[2]
[1]School of Architecture, Southwest Jiaotong University, China
*[2]Sichuan Southwest GuaXia Architectural Design Institute
Corp. Ltd., China*

Abstract

Land consolidation and settlement protection is a very important part of urban and rural integration development. The way of analyzing the causes of the Chengdu Plain traditional settlement genesis, forms, and positive aspects, as well as negative impacts on the settlements in the process of land consolidation; the important issues under rural housing reconstruction and what has to be considered in new rural design in the future, are summed up. These strategies do benefit on raising land utilization level in rural residents and avoiding the destruction of the traditional settlement. Furthermore, these experiences help people to plan and design the new rural construction on the premise of protecting traditional culture so as to achieve a win-win situation of land use and construction of a new rural area.
Keywords: Lin Pan, settlement pattern, intensive utilization, rural houses, tradition.

1 Introduction

Urban and rural development means to consider the city and the countryside, agriculture and industry, farmers and citizens as a whole, and solve related issues into the plan for social and economic development integrally. The economic and intensive use of land is significant to improve the efficiency of land resources utilization, alleviate the contradiction between supply and demand of urban and rural land and promote the long-term development of the national economy. Meanwhile, it provides reasonable theoretical proof for the reconstruction project

WIT Transactions on Ecology and The Environment, Vol 173, © 2013 WIT Press
www.witpress.com, ISSN 1743-3541 (on-line)
doi:10.2495/SDP130191

of rural houses in an earthquake stricken area. Chengdu plain is a demonstration of rural and urban development. In the process of implementing the "three concentrations", the supply of land resources becomes the core issue of rural and urban development. Therefore, promoting the intensive utilization of rural construction land has profound meaning in dealing with this issue. Especially in post-disaster reconstruction work, only by adopting effective planning and strategies, is the intensive economy capability improved. Therefore, a good living environment and perfect infrastructure can be successively created. Based on this, the traditional settlement in Chengdu Plain should be emphasized and protected; its pattern should be regarded as a critical principle of crackage reconstruction and new rural construction, so as to guarantee the simultaneous formation and harmonious development of the social economy and traditional characteristics when making highly-effective use of the land. By improving the level of economical use of land-intensive and strengthening the living protection of traditional settlements, accumulating the design, management, engineering experience, then summarizing planning and design strategies for crackage reconstruction, to people can provide reasons for decision-making and practical guidance in the process of new rural construction.

2 The formation of a traditional settlement in Chengdu plain

Land readjustment will inevitably lead to intensive utilization of land. Farmers can get economic compensation through the principle of land replacement, so they agree to transfer their land use rights. In addition, at the same time, the rural residential pattern also changes from the original relatively scattered village layout into a concentrated placement. This shift has great influence on the settlement form in Chengdu plain. Lin Pan, which is full of characteristics, surrounded by tall bamboo and green water will cease to exist. The earth landscape will change greatly, too. As one of the highly developed regions of farming civilization in our country, rich and beautiful Chengdu plain has been described in the pre-Qin ancient books named Legends of Mountains and Seas.

Settlement is the place where people live in compact communities. The settlement layout form in our country mainly has two characteristics: the centralized model in northern regions and decentralized model in southern regions. The most representative settlement form in Chengdu plain is the "LinPan" layout – villages dispersed into individual settlements, clear and running water in front of separated families, houses are surrounded by forests and plants, thatched cottages are nestled in the bamboo forest. Just as poet Fan Cheng-da said, that West Sichuan is a place: everywhere canals and bamboo surround the homesteads. This type of homestead is called "LinPan" [1]. The village consisting of LinPan is a typical decentralized model of village structure, also an important part of the Chengdu plain ecological system, which is a comprehensive product of a long-term ecological process and non ecological process and constitutes a stable ecological system with farmland, drainage and so on. Meanwhile, LinPan is an important carrier of history and regional culture [2, 3].

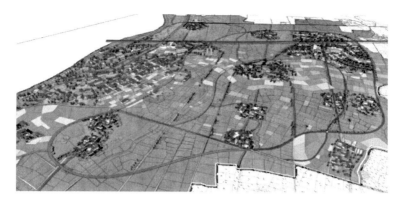

Figure 1:   Typical settlement in Chengdu plain.

2.1 Formation reasons

The traditional settlement seems to form naturally. In fact it is the results of people's selection in specific natural conditions, and adapted to the specific climate, mode of production and life style [4]. The formation of a Chengdu plain traditional settlement form mainly has the following key factors:

2.1.1 Physioclimate feature
The climate of Chengdu plain is moist and it is burning hot in summer. Because it is located at the bottom of Sichuan basin, the wind is very light and wind speed is 2.0 m/s below. Such a climate requires that houses should be adequately ventilated as the humidity is so intense. And there are a lot of tall bamboos around the house. They cannot only be used as building material, but also provide good shading effects, so make the living comfortable in burning hot summer.

2.1.2 Dujiangyan irrigation project
The Dujiangyan irrigation project, built more than 2260 years ago, helped Chengdu plain form a good gravity irrigation system. Plenty of rivers, ponds, ditches constitute a dense water network on the plain. This kind of terrain accords with the standards of site selection described in the Chinese ancient book GuanZi.: a place which is not at the foot of a high mountain, should be above a wide river, can be in highland but not near dry land, so the water is enough, in low places but not near water, then people need not pay attention to impermeability. Construction land is relatively homogeneous; families can get water nearby independently as there are many ditches around, so villages are dispersed into individual settlements. This kind of layout is quite different from the large centralized and street-style in the northern area in nature.

2.1.3 The influence of immigration
In the late Ming and early Qing dynasty, Sichuan suffered from wars; plummeting popularity accelerated the speed of population migration. From the

mid-Shunzhi period in the Qing dynasty, the Qing government set the policy to recruit people for land reclamation. Thus formed a large-scale immigration destined for Sichuan. The number of each family is generally not too big, and then there are not so many families of the same clan or same race. Usually, there are at least one or two families of one clan or six to seven families at most. The families of one clan formed a Lin Pan. Therefore, each Lin Pan is not large scale.

2.2 Settlement characteristics

The forms of traditional Lin Pan do not share the same layout. The differences are tightly tied to topography, landform and drainage of settlements, and the final settlement form is closely related to these factors. Essentially, there are two ways to form the settlement.

2.2.1 Linear structure
The growth pattern of the LinPan along rivers and roads is linear. The villagers decided to live along rivers and roads to enjoy the convenience of transportation and irrigation. Then houses are joined into a single piece along the gallery as time passes. Thus the linear distribution of LinPan is the layout. This kind of LinPan generally exists in areas with plenty of water. Since the size of the settlement is enlarged step by step, and the paths of river systems are linear overall, so settlements built by people who live in accordance with the water formed a linear layout spontaneously.

2.2.2 Radial growth
Most of such LinPan expands in all directions with the central courtyard as the basic point, form courtyards like irregular polygons, such as triangle or trapezium, etc. Generally, this kind of Lin Pan locates in the comparatively remote areas of villages, does not have an obviously convenient outer environment, so it grows into a group structure.

3 The utilization of land and the necessity of intensive utilization

Through analysis of Lin Pan, the historical background of the formation of this kind of special settlement can be learned. It was formed under the conditions of small-scale peasant economy, occupied a larger homestead, and was suitable in ancient times when there was vast territory with sparse population. Because of the development of productivity, farming practice and industrial types changed a lot, and the population exploded, residential land became in great demand. A traditional settlement also faces the problem of a large occupation area and difficulty in management [5, 6].

3.1 Problems of the utilization of a traditional settlement

3.1.1 Problems of homestead
Because in ancient times there were fewer people in one place, a traditional Lin Pan settlement usually took up too much area. Sometimes a four-person family homestead is more than 400 m² and traditional rural settlements in Chengdu plain are generally dispersed, so there is a lot of room for agriculture between them. Therefore the settlement can be expanded without limitation. Actually, construction of housing is a significant reason why the agricultural land is reducing. In addition, when villagers move out or choose another homestead, the original homestead cannot be withdrawn in time and they are then left unused. These are all the problems that a traditional settlement is faced with.

3.1.2 Developed construction technology makes better usage of vertical space
Since the dwellings before only had one storey, when there is expansion, it must be a plain one, otherwise it would take up too much room. As the development of construction, there is no problem to building storied houses and making better use of vertical space. Therefore, more land can be vacated.

3.2 The influence of intensive utilization of land upon settlement

From the above questions, the necessity of the intensive use of land and its influence upon the traditional settlement should be noticed. The new rural construction is planned and designed according to these questions. But the newly-designed communities still have some negative problems.

3.2.1 Changes of the layout of village
In order to make intensive use of the land, peasants' houses have to be centralized in contrast to the former dispersed ones. The traditional settlement formed spontaneously, and there was no interference from government. While the government's guidance played an important role in the process of new rural construction, at present, the design in a new rural community always abandons the characteristics of traditional construction, and copies the arrangement mode in an urban residential district. This adoption completely changes the village style in west Sichuan. With the appearance of these centralized large-scale communities, the layout of villages is changed a lot from the original form. It has no relation to the former, lost the primary ecological and organic features and shows many signs of over urbanization.

3.2.2 Changes of single building
Construction forms in some new rural communities are all in the same key. They take no consideration of regional, aesthetical or contextual factors in architectural styles. And designers just work hard without making deeper communication with villagers, even employing many design methods of modern construction. This kind of modern building which is isolated from traditions has nothing special. And this abrupt variation makes it hard for the villagers to get used to; the building itself has no life either.

Residences, besides living rooms we usually use now, also include other spaces out of agricultural necessity, such as yards, sties, patios or store rooms for farm tools. While, after the unification of multi-story building, those rooms are gone and this change has brought much inconvenience to villagers' lives.

3.2.3 Changes of village space

Many interfacial transition zones in the village have disappeared because of the appearance of these communities. The eaves and bilevel design of traditional rural houses offer a public place along the alleys – most beautiful scenes in the village happen here. New rural houses after land consolidation are self-built or constructed in a systematic way. Even both of the two ways are under the guide of integrated planning, they form quite different styles. The difference mainly falls on the connection with villagers. The users' voices must be listened to in the planning process because whether villagers are satisfied is the very criterion to measure whether a construction is successful.

Lin Pan blends the life of human beings and nature, makes living harmonious. It suits the productive and living needs of the agricultural age in Chengdu plain. It attaches importance to saving resources, making use of nature and the layout of waters. This ecological thought and the layout which is full of the spirit of country life are worth reserving and employing. But how to resolve the contradiction between modern and tradition, under the condition that the settlement in the village is not destroyed, residences of villagers are centralized and promote the intensive utilization of land to a certain extent, and the living standard of villagers' space is improved? Some practical examples show that new rural planning and design has paid attention to this issue.

4 Planning and design strategies based on intensive utilization and settlement protection

4.1 Planning strategies

4.1.1 Gather or scatter according to the condition of land

Actually, this strategy inherited the traditional construction principle. Although the self-built rural houses built by previous farmers seem to be located arbitrarily, from their point of view, the result is on the contrary. They are not designed from the general layout as is done now. The whole settlement is indeed a dynamic growth progress. It is not accomplished in one action or finished at one time. Therefore, whether it should be get-together or scatter has something to do with topography, landform, river system, climate and geomancy. This design principle should be followed deservedly. Then, to promote the intensive utilization of land, build a livable and ecological living environment.

4.1.2 Assemble appropriately

This rule is trying to avoid forming large communities like in cities after villagers have assembled in great number. Because the villagers' work radius has a close relation with population density, if the density is excessive, there must be a larger area of land being taken up, and the distance between their residences and cultivated land is increased. Then it is rather inconvenient to do farming. So the assembly scale should be controlled.

4.1.3 Keep the yard
Practically, individual labor and meticulous farming are still the main working patterns in Chengdu plain. The yard, including some functional spaces such as drying cereal, storing tools and spaces of sty, etc. is worth keeping.

4.1.4 The reflection of construction features
In the designing of monomers, the digging of the traditional settlement form and spirit in Chengdu plain must be emphasized. The construction form does not come from nothing in the historical evolution of thousands of years. Its formation is indispensible from local climate, productive mode, and construction level. And each settlement is formed by gathered monomers. Its texture, layout and landscape influence the form of final settlement. If the monomer has no cooperation with tradition, a completely different and with no regard to residents' living habits construction form and space is forced exist; the style of the whole settlement and villagers' living level will be affected.

4.2 Sample schemas

The new rural design is offered by Sichuan Sanzhong Architectural Design Co., Ltd. By collecting planar forms of traditional settlements from aerial photographs, designers can master the planning form better. And they would not copy the design technique of urban community. These are all worth learning. The new rural planning of Xi Yu village demonstrates that the designer endeavored to keep a traditional settlement style. Redesigned planning follows the original layout and texture of a traditional settlement in the resolution of the entire style, promoting the intensive utilization of land as well as retaining the settlement of Lin Pan, adopting modern technique in monomers, extracting elements of dwellings, reserving spaces in yard and improving the villagers' living standard greatly. It seems better than the former hard modern design of community.

5 Conclusions

Through the analysis on the change of settlement in Chengdu plain, it can be realized that promoting intensive utilization of land is the basic platform of protecting farming land and increasing land efficiency. Centralized communities after adjustment become the new residential form. Certainly, the development of productivity has brought variations to the village. However, the traditional settlement also contains some disadvantages left by the backward production mode. When regarding the construction capital and utilization of land, although the construction of a centralized community can not completely employ the original scattered layout, it should still adopt the outstanding design technique of a traditional settlement. The traditional Lin Pan layout relates closely to nature.

Its personal scale, spatial identifiability, variable and interesting layout has conformed to the terrain make the settlement pleasant and full of life.

Therefore, how to maintain balance among improving the spatial standard of reconstructed rural houses, keeping the traditional settlement and promoting the intensive utilization of land needs the designer to undertake well-constructed site survey beforehand. On the one hand, the condition of the site, the traditional form and the residential space should be well understood, for fear that the design will be over exaggerated and incompatible with the integrated environment. On the other hand, in order to avoid subsequent serial utilization problems after reconstruction, communication between designers and villagers should be paid attention to. Only by taking users' experiences and benefits into consideration, a win-win situation between land adjustment and a new residential construction of villages can be achieved.

Acknowledgement

Supported by the National Natural Science Foundation of China (No.51278421).

References

[1] Duan Peng, Liu Tian-hou. LinPan [M].Chengdu: Sichuan Publishing House of Science and Technology, 2004. (In Chinese) 段鹏，刘天厚. 林盘 [M], 成都：四川科学技术出版社. 2004.11.

[2] Zhao Yuan-xin. Chengdu Plains Traditional Settlements Evolution and Update Research on Morphological Perspective [D]. Chengdu: Southwest Jiaotong University, 2011. (In Chinese) 赵元欣, 形态学视野下成都平原传统聚落演进与更新研究[D].成都：西南交通大学硕士论文 2011.

[3] Shu Bo. Research on the Agriculture Landscape of Chengdu Plain [M]. Chengdu: Southwest Jiaotong University Press. 2012. (In Chinese). 舒波, 成都平原的农业景观研究 [M]. 成都：西南交通大学出版社, 2012.

[4] Wu Liang-yong. Integrated Architecture [M]. Beijing: Tsinghua University Press, 1990. (In Chinese) 吴良镛, 广义建筑学 [M]. 北京：清华大学出版社, 1990.

[5] Zhao Rong-ming. Research on Problems and Solutions of the Farmland Settlement Planning on Chengdu Fringe Area [D]. Chengdu: Southwest Jiaotong University, 2006. (In Chinese) 赵荣明, 成都城市边缘区乡村聚落规划设计面临的问题与对策研究[D],成都:西南交通大学硕士论文, 2006.

[6] Wang Jun, Yu Li, Luo Ming, Zhai Gang. Review on Progress in Land Consolidation [J]. Zhengzhou: Areal Research and Development, 2003, 04. (In Chinese) 王军, 余莉, 罗明, 翟刚. 土地整理研究综述 [J], 郑州:地域研究与开发, 2003.4.

An urban healing agenda for reform in Bahrain: where the dweller falls into the urban gap and the sailing boat hits the skyscraper

F. Al Khalifa
Department of Landscape, Sheffield University, UK

Abstract

The change of the Arabian Gulf cities due to the sudden development in wealth after the unearthing of oil has been a subject of curiosity and concern for many years. This paper is based on a completed master's study which investigated the effects of the discovery of oil on the urban identity of Bahrain, by examining the relationship between the old and the new in the urban fabric. The thrust of the study further focused on exploring the role of two governmental institutions, the Ministry of Culture and the University of Bahrain, in stimulating this change. Using a qualitative research approach, the study employed a number of different sources of data. The first group, including archival resources, journal and newspaper articles, in addition to the diaries and writings of Englishmen, especially those of the British advisor Sir Charles Belgrave, aimed at investigating the change in the urban fabric of Bahrain since the discovery of oil. The second group, including questionnaires and interviews, aimed at examining the consequences of this change in the work of the two governmental institutions today. The study provides a description of the change in the urban identity of Bahrain, and an understanding of how the effects of this change in shaping the lifestyle and ideologies of people living on the islands today. Some limitations in the practices of the two institutions are highlighted, and recommendations for both the Ministry of Culture and the University of Bahrain are proposed.
Keywords: urban identity, cultural change, cultural heritage, conservation, oil, Bahrain, Urbanism.

WIT Transactions on Ecology and The Environment, Vol 173, © 2013 WIT Press
www.witpress.com, ISSN 1743-3541 (on-line)
doi:10.2495/SDP130201

1 Introduction

The focus within the title of this paper, "Bahrain: where the dweller falls into the urban gap and the sailing boat hits the skyscraper", describes the problem in Bahrain today: the gap that was created after the Industrial Revolution in the urban fabric, causing segregation between the new and the old. In addition, the continued ignorance of the government to the core problem, and the repetition of the same mistakes on a daily basis, is resulting in a further widening of the urban gap. The public in Bahrain today find themselves tangled between the need to preserve the uniqueness and distinctiveness of their traditions and culture, and the urge to follow contemporary norms of modernisation.

The present study was designed to determine the effect of the discovery of oil on the urban identity of Bahrain, through a thorough investigation of the situation before and after the Industrial Revolution. It further aimed to explore the political, socio-cultural and economic mechanisms behind the on-going degradation in the relationship between the past and the present in Bahrain today by means of evaluating the role of key governmental institutions in Bahrain and their role in the continuation of the effects of the Industrial Revolution.

The aim of this research was to assess the different factors that have shaped the urban fabric of Bahrain throughout the last eighty years following the discovery of oil, to highlight the conflicts and disharmonies caused by this change in the urban identity, and to explore its effects in shaping the lifestyle and ideologies of people living on the island today.

2 The context: this is Bahrain

The research revolves around Bahrain (officially known as the Kingdom of Bahrain), a country in the Middle East with a total area of roughly 270 square kilometres [1]. This is less than one fifth the area of Greater London (1572 square metres) [2]. The country is an archipelago consisting of a large island

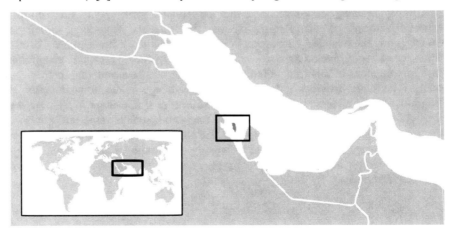

Figure 1:   Bahrain's location.

surrounded by a set of 33 smaller islands, some of which are connected to the mainland through bridges, while others are still only accessible by boat.

Saudi Arabia is connected to Bahrain by the King Fahad Causeway from the west. The state of Qatar is to the southeast of the country across the Gulf of Bahrain [3]. Bahrain's location in the Arabian/Persian Gulf played a big role in shaping its history. Due to its intermediate location between the Western and Indian sub-continents, it has been a transit point and gateway to the Arabian Gulf. This explains why it has always been subject to political and economic demands.

The culture of Bahrain is generally characterised as a Middle Eastern-Arabian Gulf culture (Khaleeji; meaning: associated with the Arab states of the Arabian Gulf). Although the main religion on the island is Islam, Bahrain is however known for its tolerance to other faiths and practices [4]. Consequently, there are many types of religious buildings, including mosques, ma'tams, churches, and temples. Arabic is the main language; however, English is widely used in most official, commercial and educational institutions, and as a second language by the general public.

Bahrain is a constitutional monarchy headed by the King, Sheikh Hamad bin Isa Al Khalifa [5]. It has a very open culture in comparison to many countries in the Arab world. There is a general respect towards women's rights; furthermore, the country gained the status of being the most prolific book publisher in the Arab world in 2005 [6].

3   Bahrain: from desert to development

Cities around the world witnessed vivid changes in their structure, form, and demographics following the Industrial Revolution. The anatomy of this transformation has been investigated by many scholars and researchers who are keen to learn about the transition of the world's cities from organic and traditional to modern, industrial, and functional urban forms. Furthermore, problems such as pollution, global warming, and the social and cultural degradation of cities and regions are collective consequences of the industrial boom which hit most of the world's cities and have been subject to extensive research, exploration and investigation ever since [11, 12].

Bahrain is one of the countries hit by the Industrial Revolution after the discovery of oil. The major challenge in Bahrain's case, as in many Gulf countries, was that it skipped a huge amount of natural and gradual development between the desert life existing before the discovery of oil in 1931 [13] and the Industrial Revolution afterwards, which was the extreme opposite. There was a huge jump into complete modernization in a relatively short period of time.

> Prince Faisal: "*No Arab loves the desert. We love water and green trees. There is nothing in the desert and no man needs nothing. Or is it that you think we are something you can play with, because we are a little people? A silly people, greedy, barbarous and cruel? What do you*

know, lieutenant? In the Arab city of Cordova, there were two miles of public lighting in the streets when London was a village" [14]. (Spoken by Alec Guinness, in the film, Lawrence of Arabia.)

Figure 2: Historic aerial photograph of Muharraq in the 1960s (left), aerial view of Northern Bahrain (Manama) 1977 (upper right), aerial view of Northern Bahrain (Manama) 2007 (lower right) [7–9].

Figure 3: Skyline of Manama, as seen from the sea, 2011 [10].

Although the resources for reform and development were available, the local residents of Bahrain were not ready for such an extreme transformation, and did not have the expertise or capabilities needed at that time for such an alteration. Consequently, a lot of expatriates were employed to lead some of the major urban development and planning projects in Bahrain. This resulted in the creation of urban forms and spaces which are completely alien to the context, caused by foreigners' lack of understanding of local traditions and the local identity of Bahrain. An urban gap was created as a consequence, detaching the modern from the traditional.

The change in urban identity is a phenomenon that has materialized in Bahrain during the last eighty years. Today, the magnitudes of this phenomenon are evident in the economic and environmental, but more importantly, in the social and cultural aspects of citizens' lives in Bahrain.

In 2007, the Bahraini government established criteria for its sustainable development, hoping to reverse some of the devastating consequences of the discovery of oil; the criteria were summarized in a plan to be implemented by the year 2030 [15].

Although the country progressed rapidly in ensuring economic sustainability, unfortunately things have not changed for the better in terms of social, cultural or environmental sustainability. For instance, economic reclamation projects are still taking over most of Bahrain's shoreline, destroying some important natural habitats, marine life, and cutting off public access to the coast [16, 17].

The Bahraini authorities seem to have become completely occupied by their new plans to provide state-of-the-art infrastructure services, housing opportunities for the underprivileged, and good conditions for investment to ensure economic sustainability and growth. However, this obsessive focus on the economy has resulted in matters of equal importance being neglected in the long term, further widening the urban gap created earlier by the extreme transformation led by foreigners in Bahrain. It is obvious today that there is segregation between the historical urban fabric and the newly-developed contemporary urbanization taking place mostly on the seashore.

The urban gap that was created after the discovery of oil and the subsequent change in the urban identity of Bahrain is today being maintained by an on-going disregard of the core problem. It is also obvious that the implementation of a fully-rounded sustainable regeneration strategy is vital for healing the gap in Bahrain's urbanism in a way that will restore its indigenous identity and revive its historic urban fabric.

4   Methodology

The following research questions were addressed in this study: How did the unearthing of oil affect the urban identity of Bahrain, both physically and socially? And what is the role of the government today in stimulating or preventing change in the urban identity?

The question of the effect of the discovery of oil on the urban identity focuses mainly on 'how and why' rather than 'how much' or 'how many'; therefore, this research was best explored through a qualitative approach. The purpose of this research was to implement a historical analysis of the major events and factors that shaped the urban identity of Bahrain before and after the unearthing of oil, followed by a case study examination of two governmental institutions in Bahrain today and their role in affecting the urban identity and the continuation of the phenomenon in question.

This research has been approached along four main lines of investigation. The argument was founded via a literature review that draws extensively from the concepts in question and the context in which these concepts are applied in the focus of this research. This argument was then followed by a critical examination of the writings and diaries of Orientalists and Englishmen, especially Belgrave's diaries, and the translation of those diaries by a number of Bahrainis. I then selected case studies to examine the conflicts between the cultural and economic models of today, and explored the political, socio-cultural and economic mechanisms behind the continuity of degradation in the relationship between the past and the present in Bahrain. Finally, questionnaires and interviews were used to understand the current situation with regards to the role of the Ministry of Culture and the University of Bahrain in the continuation of the problem. 32 responses from the questionnaires were analysed and categorised into different themes; from those themes, five participants were selected to be interviewed using an interview schedule.

5 Urban identity in the relevant context: definition of terms

"Identity" is a term that is used in a wide range of disciplines [18]. In the field of social sciences and particularly in social psychology, the term generally describes one's notion and manifestation of individuality or group affiliations [19]. In Webster's Ninth New Collegiate dictionary (1983), it is defined as "the distinguishing character or condition of a person or a thing" [20].

Although the term has been given a great deal of attention, there is much less agreement in the literature on how the bond between places and people should be measured and defined [21]. Place attachment, place identity, sense of place, and place dependence are all terms that describe people's bonds with places. Lynch (1981) defines identity in relation to places as "the extent to which a person can recognize or recall a place as being distinct from other places" [22].

Of the many concepts used to describe people's associations with places, two are assumed to predict people's strength of affiliation with the history of the place: place attachment and place identity [21]. Place attachment comprises three main components: behavioural, cognitive and affective [23, 24]; however, it is most frequently measured by its emotional elements [21]. As this study is focused on the built environment, the concept of place attachment will consequently not be the focus of this research.

Within the context of the Arab world, in her paper about the crises of identity in the contemporary Arab city, Sherine Aly [25] defines the term "identity" as "the foundation to place attachments and sense of belonging, it is a reflection of people's traditions, culture, aspirations, needs, and their future" [25]. Within her definition of identity, she states that it is a prerequisite to achieving place attachment.

Place identity, on the other hand, is a concept that is more connected with the material environment and is further away from the notion of subjectivity [26]. The word "identity" in this concept refers to two things: sameness (continuity) and distinctiveness (uniqueness) [21]. Place identity is also linked to the Latin term "genius loci", which is used extensively in landscape architecture to describe the character or spirit of a place [27].

The identity of places is therefore a feature that is not easily reducible or separable from the physical qualities of a place. It is not a constantly changing quality, and nor should it be considered constant. It is a quality that brings a sense of belonging and attachment; it connects people together. It is a dominant quality that overcomes the economic deficiency and physical decline of places [25]. Identity cannot be found, nor can it be fabricated; rather, it is an authentic process that links us to previous civilizations and nations through culture, beliefs, and traditions [28]. It is this definition of identity that is more relevant to the scope of this research, one which considers the place and physical environment as a precondition to its existence.

Now that the term "identity" has been well-defined in relation to the physical environment, it is vital to specify the nature and characteristics of that environment by directing the research to focus on one category of "spaces". This research aims to investigate the "identity" of "urban" spaces in Bahrain.

An urban area is generally characterized by a greater inhabitant density. Cities, towns and conurbations are considered as urban areas, while villages and rural areas are not [29]. Despite the general understanding of the term, different nations define the term "urban" in various ways. What is considered an urban area in some countries might not be considered so in other countries [30]. Thus, the United Nations Statistics division defined the term "urban" in the 2005 demographic yearbook for every country according to its own national definition. An urban area in Bahrain is defined using the definition of "urban" by the United Nations as "communes or villages of 2500 or more inhabitants" [31].

The "identity" of an "urban" place can now be defined as the reflection of the traditions, culture and ambitions of all the local people living in an urban area. It expresses their relevance to each other and the coming generation's (sameness: continuity) and on the other hand their uniqueness and distinctiveness from others. Although the urban space is usually understood and read through its material environment rather than the sensual, it is however the sensual environment which enables us to build memories and emotions, and create bonds with places [25].

To further properly understand the term from a historical perspective, one must note that there are theories which hypothesise how urban identities are created, most of which agree that it is created through a complex collaboration between social, built and natural components. For that reason, in trying to understand and define the urban identity of a place from a historical perspective it is essential to understand all the factors that have led to its formation, including the three components mentioned earlier, and not only the historically significant buildings in that place [20, 25].

It is vital also to understand that there are other theories which carry differing associations, but are very much connected with this term. Social identity and cultural identity are directly linked to urban identity and are preconditions for it. The first describes the belonging to a precise category of ethnic group, a certain professional group, religion, nationality, or any bond that connects people together without the constraint of a place, while the second is more constrained by physical space and concentrates on social systems and assemblies rather than the individual's connection with others [32].

This definition of the terms in question and their associated concepts situates this research in its context and sets a framework that excludes other terms which are beyond the scope of this study.

6 Findings and discussion

The urban fabric of Bahrain is a physical representation of the community's beliefs and ideologies. Therefore, the change in Bahrain's urban identity after the Industrial Revolution was only a consequence of the change in society itself; its altering political system, and people's lifestyles and interests, and sources of the economy were all mirrored in the physical environment in which the society was situated.

When the community was mainly dependant on agriculture and the sea as the main source of the economy, when the social structure of the community was dominated by tribal affiliations, and the only materials for building were limestone, palm tree branches, mangroves and mud, this was reflected in the urban fabric of Bahrain, and its general identity and character echoed the socio-cultural, economic and physical constraints of the society and its environment. Houses competed to be built around the coastline, palm tree farms or sweet water resources. The roads were narrow, perpendicular to the sea and used to divide tribal zones. Houses were mainly a maximum of one or two storeys high, built to respect the human scale and to adapt to the environment.

However, when black gold was discovered, things changed; the sandy narrow alleys were widened and asphalted, the houses competed to be built away from each other in urban sprawls, links with the seashore were interrupted by three-lane motorways, and land reclamation further extended the distance between the original urban fabric and the sea. Harbours were filled with gigantic skyscrapers, palm tree farms were replaced by alien structures, and sweet water resources were abundant for the treated seawater. Therefore, in general, it seems that although the discovery of oil had amazing benefits for the economy of the country, it resulted in a change in Bahrain's urban identity and the loss of its unique character.

This change was not only the result of the sudden development in economic circumstances but also because of the isolation of the Gulf in general and Bahrain in particular by the British Empire after the discovery of oil. This isolation had devastating effects on the community, the government, and the cultural heritage of the country. The effects are evident today in the practices of governmental institutions, especially those responsible for the country's cultural heritage and the national legacy of previous civilisations.

One of the more significant findings to emerge from this study is that the government in Bahrain is today stimulating this change in the urban identity. This was evident in the analysed work of two institutions, the Ministry of Culture and the University of Bahrain:

1. The Ministry of Culture, through:
   - The deficiency of the framework in which the Ministry performs, which takes shape in the unsuitable and outdated law that guards Bahrain's cultural heritage and the loose implementation of the regulations in its articles.
   - The lack of a proper conservation system in Bahrain.
   - The absence of public participation in the heritage protection process.
   - The shortage in the promotion of cultural heritage caused by the insufficient collaboration between the Ministry of Culture and the Information Authority.
   - The placement of the "Al Waqf" system and its associated properties under a different guardian body which lacks the expertise and the proficiency required to deal with historic buildings.
2. The University of Bahrain, through:
   - The deficiency of the current architecture curriculum that materialises in the lack of topics covering the significance of the country's cultural heritage and the importance of its preservation at both the national and international level.
   - The lack of specialisation in conservation and conservation or cultural-led regeneration.
   - The unskillfulness of graduates from the Department of Architecture in the fields of conservation and protection of heritage, and their inappropriateness to feed into the Ministry of Culture.

Taken together, these results suggest that the urban identity of Bahrain has been changing for the last eighty years since the discovery of oil, and it is still transforming very rapidly at the expense of the unique character it used to possess, due to the deficiencies of governmental institutions.

Although the urban fabric still has some traces of previous civilisations and the normative urban form that existed before the Industrial Revolution, it however no longer has a clear identity of what it is. It seems that Bahrain is in the process of modernisation, but at the same time, it struggles to keep some aspects of the traditional. The country is finding its way into a new identity and is exploring the possibilities to settle into a new character which reflects both the significance of its history and the importance of its future.

The results of this research support the idea that there needs to be more collaboration between the governmental institutions that are responsible, either directly or indirectly, for the protection and promotion of the country's cultural heritage, in order to slow the pace of change and control the alteration and destruction of the remaining important heritage.

One possible implication of this is the possibility for the Ministry of Culture to have its own department within the Information Authority (previously ministry of information and culture), despite the recent separation of the two bodies. This will minimise the efforts needed for collaboration between the two organisations and will assist in the promotion of the country's cultural heritage and the advertisement of the Ministry's programmes and activities.

7 Recommendations

The findings of this study suggest several courses of action for both institutions, the Ministry of Culture and the University of Bahrain:

1. Recommendations for the Ministry of Culture:
   - To have a proper conservation system that will ensure the protection of Bahrain's cultural heritage and its physical, social and economic sustainability in the future.
   - To refine the law regarding the protection of Bahrain's cultural heritage according to the recommendations set out in the previous chapters.
   - To collaborate with the University of Bahrain by assigning some real projects and developing programmes and activities for students of architecture to learn the conservation practice through the proficiency of the conservation team at the Ministry.
   - To consider including "Waqf" properties under the umbrella of the Ministry of Culture, or at least through the collaboration with the Ministry of Justice, Islamic Affairs and Endowments.

2. Recommendations to the University of Bahrain:
   - To repair the deficiency in the current curriculum of architecture, by enhancing the existing module which tackles the indigenous architecture of Bahrain, and include within its syllabus the national and international importance of the country's cultural heritage.
   - To offer more often the elective module specialising in the conservation of historic buildings.
   - To consider in the future having a postgraduate-level programme specialising in the conservation of historic buildings and/or conservation/cultural-led urban regeneration.
   - To collaborate with the Ministry of Culture and try to educate a number of local proficient graduates to feed into the Ministry of Culture and work on the cultural heritage of the country.

8 Conclusion

The findings of this research add substantially to our understanding of the current urban identity of Bahrain, by comprehending the factors that shaped its transformation up until it reached its current condition. Furthermore, it grasps the importance of the Ministry of Culture and the University of Bahrain in stimulating or preventing change in the urban identity of Bahrain.

This research has thrown up many questions which are in need of further investigation; some of these will be fully addressed in a PhD thesis which is currently being carried out. The PhD study will cover the overall sustainability of the urban fabric of Bahrain, including the socio-cultural, economic and environmental aspects. Hence, the findings discussed in this paper will feed into one central part of the PhD study, which aims to study the use of the existing heritage and the respect of the urban identity of the country in the regeneration process, to ensure the continuity of the culture, character, and uniqueness of Bahrain cities throughout future urban renewal projects.

Considerably more work will need to be done to draft a proper listing system that suits the context of Bahrain and the community in which this system will be applied. Future research should therefore concentrate on a new law for the protection of the country's cultural heritage.

It would be interesting to compare the traditional "Waqf" Islamic endowment system with the modern western conservation system, in an attempt to draft principles for a conservation practice which is more appropriate for application in the Arab-Islamic region today, instead of the adaptation of other nations' practices and systems.

More importantly, what is now needed is a cross-organisational study involving collaboration between different governmental institutions and the formation of joint projects and programmes to safeguard Bahrain's cultural heritage and spread awareness among the public of its importance.

References

[1] Gugger, H., *Bahrain lessons*, Laboratoire de la production d'architecture, 2010.

[2] Wikipedia, *Greater London*, http://en.wikipedia.org/wiki/Greater_London.

[3] Wikipedia, *Bahrain*, http://en.wikipedia.org/wiki/Bahrain.

[4] Ministry of Foreign Affairs, *Ambassador Houda Nonoo highlights religious freedom in Bahrain*, Bahrain, http://www.mofa.gov.bh/Default.aspx?tabid=7824andlanguage=en-USandItemId=1549.

[5] Bassiouni, M. C., Report of the Bahrain Independent Commission of *Inquiry*. Bahrain Independent Commission of Inquiry, 2011.

[6] Toumi, H., Bahrain tops publishing sector among Arab states. Gulf News: Al Nisr Publishing, 2006.

[7] Ministry of Culture, Pearling: testimony of an island economy, 2010.

[8] Ministry of Culture, *Aerial View of Manama 1977*, 2011.

[9] Ministry of Culture, *Aerial View of Manama 2007*, 2011.

[10] Bahrain Economic Development Board, *Skyline of Manama*, 2011.

[11] Sexton, T., The Impact of the Industrial Revolution on Urban Life, http://voices.yahoo.com/the-impact-industrial-revolution-urban-life-1806379.html.

[12] LeGates, R. T. and Stout, F., *The City Reader*, Fifth Edition. New York: Routledge, 2011.

[13] Oxford Business Group, *The Report: Bahrain*, 2009.

[14] Lean, D., *Lawrence of Arabia* (written by Robert Bolt and Michael Wilson), Horizon Pictures, 1962.

[15] Skidmore, O. and M., Bahrain National Planning Development Strategy *2030*, Bahrain Economic Development Board, 2007.

[16] Ministry of Culture, RECLAIM: Kingdom of Bahrain National *Participation in Venice Biennale 2010*, Manama, 2010.

[17] Al Ansari, F., *Public Open Space on the Transforming Urban Waterfronts of Bahrain: The Case of Manama City*, University of Newcastle, 2009.
[18] Baris, M. E., Uckac, L., and Uslu, A., Exploring public perception of urban identity: The case of Ankara. *African Journal of Agricultural Research*, **4(8)**, pp. 724-735, 2009.
[19] Wikipedia, *Identity (social science)*, http://en.wikipedia.org/wiki/Identity_(social_science).
[20] Oktay, D., The quest for urban identity in the changing context of the city. *Cities*, **19(4)**, pp. 261–271, 2002.
[21] Lewicka, M., Place attachment, place identity, and place memory: Restoring the forgotten city past. *Journal of Environmental Psychology*, **28(3)**, pp. 209–231, 2008.
[22] Lynch, K., *A Theory of Good City Form*. MIT Press: Cambridge, 1981.
[23] Jorgensen, B. S. and Stedman, R. C., Sense of place as an attitude: Lakeshore owners' attitudes toward their properties. *Journal of Environmental Psychology*, **21(3)**, pp. 233–248, 2001.
[24] Kyle, G. T., Mowen, A. J., and Tarrant, M., Linking place preferences with place meaning: An examination of the relationship between place motivation and place attachment. *Journal of Environmental Psychology*, **24(4)**, pp. 439–454, 2004.
[25] Aly, S. S. A., Modernization and regionalism: Approaches for sustainable revival of local urban identity, *2011 International Conference on Green Buildings and Sustainable Cities*, **21**, pp. 503–512, 2011.
[26] Dixon, J. and Durrheim, K., Dislocating identity: Desegregation and the transformation of place. *Journal of Environmental Psychology*, 24(4) pp. 455–473, 2004.
[27] Wikipedia, *Genius loci*, http://en.wikipedia.org/wiki/Genius_loci#Art_and_architecture.
[28] Abel, C., Architecture and Identity: Towards a Global Eco-culture. Architectural Press: Oxford, 1996.
[29] Wikipedia, *Urban area*, http://en.wikipedia.org/wiki/Urban_area.
[30] United Nations, Table 6: Urban and total population by sex: 1996–2005, *Demographic Yearbook*, 2005.
[31] United Nations, Definition of urban, *Demographic Yearbook*, 2005.
[32] Twigger-Ross, C. and Uzzel, D. L. Place and identity processes. *Journal of Environmental Psychology*, **16(3)**, pp. 205–220, 1996.

Section 6
Sustainability and the built environment

Pathways to an oil-constrained future: analogies with climate change mitigation and adaptation

R. J. Brewster
*Institute of Sustainable Development and Architecture,
Bond University, Australia*

Abstract

The global production of oil is predicted to have reached a peak in the first decade of this century and will gradually decline, while demand outstrips the discovery and exploitation of new oil sources. This paper investigates issues of adapting urban development to an oil-constrained future, exploring the analogy between oil depletion and climate change. These issues are two of the global wicked problems this century; however, oil depletion is likely to have greater certainty in its predicted impacts. The terminology of climate change mitigation and adaptation is modified to assess its application to oil depletion actions, referring to recent policy research by Hirsch *et al* on oil supply mitigation as a case study. The categorisation of the proposed administrative measures and physical options is analysed using a non-metric ordinal scale, to indicate how closely they align with the proposed mitigation and adaptation definitions. It is concluded that while there is some blurring between the categories (in a similar way to global warming actions); the modified terminology is a useful way to categorise and analyse oil depletion actions. Current oil strategies are geared to mitigation actions, but adaptive measures will become much more important in the longer term future as oil supply becomes constrained.
Keywords: climate change adaptation, climate change mitigation, global problem, oil depletion, Peak Oil, sustainable urban development.

1 Introduction

The future changed dramatically in 2008; the price of oil spiked to US \$147 a barrel prior to the world plunging into a multifaceted financial crisis [1]. The

WIT Transactions on Ecology and The Environment, Vol 173, © 2013 WIT Press
www.witpress.com, ISSN 1743-3541 (on-line)
doi:10.2495/SDP130211

price of oil collapsed to less than US$40, and recovered to around US$100 a barrel by late 2012; but the global financial crisis lingered. A consensus of views was that the era of cheap oil may end in this decade, as demonstrated by the Association for the Study of Peak Oil and Gas [2], International Energy Agency (IEA) [3] and others (e.g. [4, 5]). It was a time of national reflection on Australian future directions for growth and development [6]. International United Nations-led forums continue ineffectual debates about climate change action and the role of renewable energy to replace oil in mitigating global warming impacts [7, 8]. The worldwide production of conventional oil will decline while demand outstrips the discovery and exploitation of new oil sources.

The imminence of global Peak Oil prompted a PhD investigation by the author into the relationship between oil dependency and urban residential development in the Australian context. Part of the investigation was presented by the author [9] to the Wessex Institute of Technology 2011 sixth conference on sustainable development and planning. This paper presents a second part of the research on adapting to the oil-constrained future, drawing on the analogy between oil depletion and the terminology of climate change mitigation and adaptation.

2   Oil depletion and climate change

One of the well-reported and commonly known consequences of oil combustion in all its forms is resultant carbon dioxide (CO_2) and other greenhouse gas emissions that contribute to global warming and climate change. This section addresses the relationship between oil consumption and climate change, particularly in the Australian policy context, and draws on recent reports that are relevant to the author's research.

2.1 Oil consumption and climate change relationship

The Intergovernmental Panel on Climate Change (IPCC) [10] estimates that oil contributed a 34.6 per cent share of all energy sources in the total global primary energy supply of 492 Exajoules in 2008. The IPCC 2007 report [11] highlights the seriousness of climate change and the imperative to reduce global CO_2 production to limit average global temperature rise to 2°C. However, the IPCC Assessment Report No 5 due in 2013 is expected to revise predictions such that a range of 3–6°C by 2100 will be the more likely scenario, with more drastic consequences for the planet. Climate change is widely regarded as a key global problem. Global problems are not just important problems, or problems that affect many people. Rather they are those problems that affect the whole of the planet, and potentially all of the people who live on it, on a scale and in a manner that are both unsustainable and profoundly inequitable [12].

The 2008 Garnaut Climate Change Review [13] makes recommendations for urgent action to reduce carbon emissions. The report is an excellent primer on climate change and includes the issues of energy security within that context. The review recognises transport, land-use and buildings are major contributors of greenhouse gas emissions, and that cities are major centres for energy demand, requiring large quantities of energy in both construction and operation. Implementation of climate change mitigation planning principles should embrace broader sustainable development principles and energy transition to a low carbon economy. This should include consideration of energy supply infrastructure, embodied energy and operational energy demand from buildings, and urban infrastructure. Cities should achieve the form, density and spatial pattern of urban development and associated infrastructure that reduce greenhouse emissions. However, the review does not examine in any detail the issues associated with Peak Oil and future oil depletion, particularly in relation to transport and urban development patterns. A 2011 review of the report [14] takes into account findings of recent climate change research and global conferences, and relevant considerations of the global financial crisis. The update accepts the International Energy Agency forecasts of only a slight decrease in global oil supply from 31.5% to 28.5% to 2030. It also concedes that changes in fuel mix rely on gradual replacement of infrastructure and fleet, which is problematic with a long lead time [14: p. 24]. In contrast, an earlier 2006 study by Droege [15: pp. 60–61] makes a stronger link between climate change and the post-Peak Oil scenario, advocating that preparing cities and regions to:

'strengthen regional and urban economic and energy autonomy, are the most sensible strategies to prepare for both Peak Oil and climate change ... Of these two, Peak Oil poses decidedly more imminent risks to cities and human settlement and, some argue, may well serve to help mitigate climate change, albeit in economically disastrous ways.'

The complexities of the economic, social and environmental consequences of oil depletion extend well beyond the context of urban development noted in the Garnaut review into every facet of modern society and technology. Newman and Jennings [16: p. 37] contend that current trends in urban development are not sustainable under these circumstances:

'The two problems are clearly linked – if cities try to move from oil to 'dirty fuels' like oil shale, tar sands, or coal to liquids, this will be much worse in greenhouse terms. Saving oil on the other hand will be a major contributor to reducing greenhouse [effects].'

Oil dependency and efforts to maintain global oil supply are also emerging global problems. Hence the interlinked issues of oil supply depletion and climate change are arguably two of the key global problems of this century [4, 5]. However, oil depletion is likely to have greater certainty in its predicted impacts, and is more of an immediate threat to the economy and people's lives than climate change [17].

The Australian Senate Inquiry into the nation's future oil supply and alternative transport fuels [18] was released during the period of rapidly rising oil prices, but prior to the global financial crisis. The report was prompted by the question of 'Peak Oil' and made a detailed study into the peaking of global oil supply and the demand implications for Australia. The Peak Oil timing uncertainty, demand inelasticity causing high volatility in prices, calls for prudent action to reduce oil dependency and mitigate greenhouse emissions. Alternative fuels have energy (and environmental) cost and emissions penalties [18: p. xii]. These views are echoed in a similar study: *Queensland's Vulnerability to Rising Oil Prices Taskforce Report* [19]; and *Oil Vulnerability Strategy/Action Plan for Queensland research paper* by Waller [20]. The Waller paper overviews a range of critical issues and poses broad principles for mitigation strategies. One of the key messages is that the Queensland economy is protected by its large coal, coal seam gas and natural gas resource endowments, which 'provide a natural hedge against the oil price outlook' [20: p. 10]. The author's view is that this 'soft' message overlooks the obvious reliance on future clean coal technology to lower CO_2 gas emissions. It also seeks to perpetuate the exploitation of fossil fuels.

The Waller paper also goes soft on the household petrol price rise impacts, even though it acknowledges the vulnerability of low density outer suburban living. It suggests adverse equity impacts may need some offsetting policy measures. In contrast, the modelling of the road transport impacts warrants 'a major response in terms of reduced oil-based liquid fuel use, delivered primarily via sharply increased fuel efficiency and fuel switching' [20: p. 6]. Of course fuel switching is not simply choosing a different pump at the service station, without wholesale vehicle modification to gas (LPG/LNG/CNG), or hybrid battery/plug-in electric energy sources, complemented by the new fuel distribution system. The magnitude of the fuel demand in Queensland is such that 'total transport usage is projected to increase by 50% by 2030, from some 7,300ML to over 11,000ML' [20: p. 23] set out in Figure 7 in the report and reproduced at Figure 1.

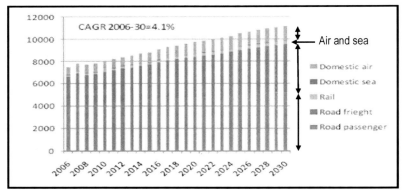

Figure 1:   Queensland's transport oil demand, 2006–30 (million litres) [20].

2.2 Global warming impacts

In relation to the built environment, the global warming impacts are evenly spread across a large number of building materials. Steel, bricks, concrete and aluminium are the largest contributors because of the embodied energy inputs to the production of these materials. The dominant contributor to global warming is CO_2; the only other significant contributor being methane emissions from landfill of organic materials, principally wood.

The estimate by the Australian Greenhouse Office (AGO) and RMIT[21] of greenhouse emissions from building construction at 14 % is broadly in line with other studies which have found the direct energy used on site to assemble the building is approximately 5-13% of total embodied energy [22: p. 2]. The AGO estimates that 'oil will make up approximately 32% of energy use in building materials and construction (two-thirds of this is direct energy use in construction) [21: p. 39]. Natural gas is projected to be 22% of energy in building materials by 2055. Oil and gas together are projected to account for some 120 PJ (54%) of total building energy demand'.

The effort to transfer to alternative energy sources for power generation is indicated in a US National Petroleum Council (NPC) [23] presentation on energy futures. It includes a comparison of actions to mitigate the equivalent of one Gigaton per annum of carbon generation, shown at Figure 2 [23: slide 30]. The examples represent a huge effort (currently all depending on the oil economy) needed in developing and in many developing countries, if a global response is to restrict average temperature rise to 2° in the most optimistic IPCC scenarios.

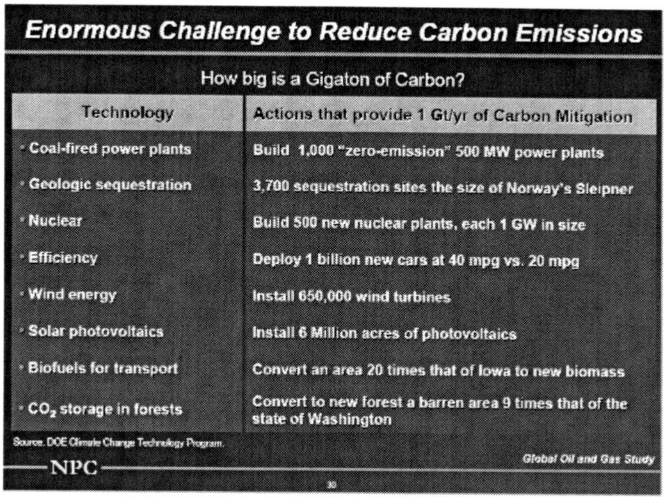

Enormous Challenge to Reduce Carbon Emissions

How big is a Gigaton of Carbon?

Technology	Actions that provide 1 Gt/yr of Carbon Mitigation
Coal-fired power plants	Build 1,000 "zero-emission" 500 MW power plants
Geologic sequestration	3,700 sequestration sites the size of Norway's Sleipner
Nuclear	Build 500 new nuclear plants, each 1 GW in size
Efficiency	Deploy 1 billion new cars at 40 mpg vs. 20 mpg
Wind energy	Install 650,000 wind turbines
Solar photovoltaics	Install 6 Million acres of photovoltaics
Biofuels for transport	Convert an area 20 times that of Iowa to new biomass
CO_2 storage in forests	Convert to new forest a barren area 9 times that of the state of Washington

Source: DOE Climate Change Technology Program.

NPC
Global Oil and Gas Study

Figure 2:   US National Petroleum Council 2008: carbon offset comparisons [23].

3 Oil and global warming mitigation and adaptation analogy

3.1 Mitigation and adaptation terminology

The terminology used in climate change research and policy makes a distinction between mitigation and adaptation and is fairly well understood (e.g. [3, 11, 13]). This terminology is also loosely used in literature and policies dealing with oil depletion, mainly as *mitigation* strategies. This can be confusing because actions to mitigate oil depletion are applied both to conserving supply and finding alternatives. However, the author considers the terminology is a reasonable analogy to analyse Peak Oil response actions, but needs to be modified for oil.

Terms for climate change are defined by the IPCC [11: p. 871] as:

Mitigation	Actions that reduce the impact of human activity on the sources of greenhouse gases or enhance their sinks, aimed at reducing the extent of global warming.
Adaptation	The process of adjustment to climate changes that will occur despite efforts to reduce greenhouse gas emissions. Adaptation planning actions can adjust natural or human systems in response to climatic stimuli or their effects, which moderates harm or exploits beneficial opportunities. These actions will contribute to increasing resilience of human settlements to climate change.
Adaptive Capacity	The ability of social, economic, environmental, institutional and the political systems to adjust to change, moderate potential damage, take advantage of opportunities, and cope with the consequences.
Resilience	The ability of a social or ecological system to absorb disturbances while retaining the same basic infrastructure and ways of functioning, the capacity for self-organisation and the capacity to adapt to stress and change [24].

There is also a category of dual-purpose actions that have aspects of both mitigation and adaptation; or they are complex and difficult to allocate. Transformation of these terms to apply to future oil supply constraints in the context of urban development could be defined in the following proposed terms:

Oil demand mitigation:

Conserving oil supply and reducing price vulnerability

Actions that reduce the impact of land development and building construction activities on global oil demand, aimed at prolonging oilfield production and reducing the extent of vulnerability in oil supply and pricing.

Oil supply adaptation:

Urban development less dependent on oil supply and adaptive living to increase resilience

The process of adjustment to globally reducing oil supply that will occur despite efforts to reduce oil demand. Adaptive actions adjust land development and building construction activities in response to oil supply shortages or their secondary effects, which moderates the extent of supply vulnerability and increases resilience. It also includes lifestyle change to adaptive living.

Adaptive capacity:

Adjusting systems to be resilient to decreasing oil supply and higher pricing structure

The ability of social, economic, environmental, political, and institutional systems to adjust to change in oil supply and pricing vulnerability, moderate potential damage, take advantage of opportunities, and cope with the consequences of reducing oil supply. These actions will contribute to increasing resilience of human settlements to oil supply vulnerability and depletion.

3.2 Mitigation or adaptation actions?

If an oil-related material can be produced, or an oil-related process can be undertaken, in a more fuel/energy efficient way, the action becomes one of mitigating the vulnerability. If a suitable substitute material or alternative process is available, the action is more one of adapting to the vulnerability. As in climate change actions, however, these notional distinctions become blurred in relation to oil vulnerability; because actions to mitigate (e.g. use less oil) can also be applied to adaptation (e.g. adopt the use of alternatives). This is compared to climate change, where an increase in greenhouse gas emissions can result from several unrelated causes and lead to a range of multivariate consequences. These effects range from global warming and more extreme weather events to sea level rise and ocean acidity [11]. Some effects may be both beneficial and adverse, such as the geographic shift in temperate climatic zones. However, there is not a similar body of research and policy in relation to oil policy that deals separately with mitigation and adaptation strategies in a consistent analytical manner.

A search of the literature in 2010 failed to reveal any research comparing oil and climate change mitigation and adaptation. Fortunately a book released at the 2010 World Oil Conference in Washington DC provides a case study. It follows a 2007 report on Peak Oil implications and the same authors Hirsch *et al.* [25] address oil *mitigation* issues in two ways–administrative measures and physical options. The primary objective is to address the need that 'an uninterrupted supply of moderately priced oil is essential to world economic wellbeing, let alone growth' [25: p. 84]. The thrust of this strategy appears to attempt to mitigate depletion to maintain a business as usual approach to the use of oil in the American context. The investigation into the 'impending world energy mess' is summarised in three aspects [25: p. 231]:

a. The impending decline of world oil production, which the world has yet to fully comprehend, let alone prepare for;

b. The intoxication with renewable energy, which is incapable of providing the world with large amounts of liquid fuels or electric power at costs comparable to petroleum alternatives;

c. Climate change, the consideration of which has overshadowed a multitude of energy decisions, in spite of the fact that there are large questions in the science.

The authors conclude that even if all the suggested oil mitigation measures were implemented quickly, 'oil shortages will almost certainly grow more rapidly than our best mitigation efforts, and this implies significant world shortages before our mitigation efforts catch up and surpass world oil production declines' [25: p. 233]. This conclusion implies that liquid fuel supply will somehow match future demand–albeit on a reduced scale–from biomass, oil shales, tar sands, gas-to-liquid and algae sources [25: pp. 145–172]. The authors envisage transport fuels would be complemented by the conversion to natural gas and electrification of vehicles; and clean coal, gas and nuclear power generation, supplemented by solar and wind power. They take a pessimistic view about 'the concept of renewable energy with its promise of eternal energy for nature' [25: p. 234]. as being incapable of satisfying the overall energy needs of USA.

Hence no specific distinction is made between oil *mitigation* and *adaptation* measures. In a personal communication at the 2010 World Oil Conference, the lead author Robert Hirsch [26] reinforced this view by not holding an opinion about any relevance of a separation of these aspects and tended to combine the two terms. The author considers that a closer examination is warranted to determine if some of the suggested 'mitigation' options are more aligned to 'adaptation' as described in the above proposed definitions, despite the lack of semantic separation. Table 1 below uses the Hirsch program administrative measures and physical options–with a non-metric ordinal scale–to indicate how closely they align with the mitigation and adaptation definitions proposed above. Categorisation is based on the author's climate change and Peak Oil research. The table demonstrates that most (9 out of 16) Hirsch proposed mitigation measures could also have varying relevance to adaptation measures.

Administrative measures: these cover 'options that can be implemented by individuals, organizations and governments, either voluntarily of via mandates'. They include rationing of oil supplies, car-pooling and tele-commuting [25: p. 85].

Physical mitigation measures: these include deployment of more fuel efficient vehicles; more reliance on heavy oil and oil sands, gas to liquids, coal to liquids, and enhanced oil recovery technology [25: p. 111]. A range of options are discussed for alternative fuels, electric vehicles and stationary power generation.

The author considers Options such as telecommuting, plug-in electric vehicles, hydrogen fuel cells, solar and wind power to be adaptive strategies to live with less oil supply. Other options such as plug-in hybrid electric vehicles and natural gas (both for transport and stationary power) are slightly more aligned to mitigation. This is because they are both exploiting a finite fossil fuel to maintain a business as usual approach to transport and motorised machinery. Rationing of oil supplies is important to both aspects. The other relevant measures are more aligned to mitigating oil demand to conserve future supply.

Hirsch *et al* note that 'performing a meaningful analysis of the best-case mitigation of world oil production decline is the selection of the most important variables, while making reasonable assumptions on other important factors'. They acknowledge that analysis is hampered by the 'multitude of complexities and unknowns' surrounding oil production decline, but postulate a 'worldwide crash program' of *mitigation* that would start instantaneously from a business as usual situation [25: p. 109]. The Hirsch program assumes all countries would act with equitable goodwill, which the authors caution is unlikely as oil exporting nations will withhold supplies to suit national objectives, including their own longer term resource needs. This underlying caution supports the author's view that the act of mitigating oil demand at the local level may actually cause an economic disadvantage, while allowing a business as usual approach elsewhere, at both intra- and inter-national scales. Hence an *adaptation* program is likely to have fewer adverse impacts.

Table 1: Comparison of Hirsch proposed measures with the author's proposed mitigation–adaptation definitions on a non-metric ordinal scale.

Mitigation options: proposed by Hirsch *et al* [25]	Descriptive definitions: proposed by Roger Brewster	
	Mitigation action	Adaptation action
Administrative measures:		
Pricing and allocation controls for rationing of oil supplies	XX	XX
Car-pooling	XX	X
Telecommuting	XX	XXX
Physical measures:		
More fuel efficient vehicles including: - hybrid electric vehicles - plug-in hybrid electric vehicles - plug-in electric vehicles	XXX XXX XXX	X XX XXX
More reliance on heavy oil and oil sands	XX°	–
Enhanced oil recovery	XXX	–
Coal to liquids	XXX	–
Alternative transport fuel options: - Natural gas - Gas from shale and coal seams - Biofuels - Hydrogen fuel cells	XXX XXX° XXX° XX	XX X° X° XXX
Solar power generation	XXX	XXX
Wind power generation	XXX	XXX
Nuclear power generation – (Using Thorium cycle only)	XXX (subject to waste disposal issues)	XXX (subject to waste disposal issues)

Key: – not relevant to adaptive actions for transport. **X** Relevant. **XX** Highly relevant. **XXX** Close fit to proposed definitions. °Not preferred due to environmental impacts.

3.3 Discussion

The analogy between oil depletion and climate change actions suggests that the proposed set of definitions could (simplistically) be applied to categorise oil depletion measures. As noted above, while the categorisation has a subjective aspect that is open to debate, it is based on the author's climate change professional policy experience and on Peak Oil research. The table indicates that the 'XXX' rated measures are considered by the author to most closely fit the proposed definitions in relation to the nominated policy actions or strategies. Interestingly, however, the mitigation 'XXX' actions are a much closer fit for 11 of the 16 in the list. Adaptation actions are almost evenly spread: 'XX' plus 'XXX' actions making up only half the total. There is also a close commonality in relevance between nine of the 16 mitigation and adaptation actions. The above analysis shows that mitigation actions dominate. It also appears to support a view that a notional separation is blurred by cross-cutting measures, as actions to mitigate (conserve oil supply) can also apply to adaptation (using alternatives).

It should be noted that the Hirsch study focuses on transport, and although it is pervasive throughout the economy, the study does not consider the broader aspects of planning and developing the built environment. If these and other social elements were added to the list, the range of adaptive actions would increase to include: inner city living in compact urban form; transit oriented development; behavioural change to a public and active transport focus; alternative and lower embodied energy building materials and construction processes. Renewable energy sources would feature more prominently, with local distribution grids. In the longer term future adaptive measures–including those in table 1–will become much more important as the inevitability of oil supply constraint becomes real. This is also analogous to climate change actions, which have transitioned from mitigation to adaptation as the reality of overshooting the 2°C temperature rise appears to be inevitable. It is considered that the modified mitigation and adaptation terminology is a useful way to categorise and analyse oil depletion actions, but in a flexible application of the model.

An adaptive strategy is likely to pose fewer adverse external threats to the national economy. Such a view is in keeping with the notion of oil depletion being a global wicked problem [12]. Future petroleum depletion (including oil and gas) is considered to have most of the characteristics to identify it a global wicked problem. This makes the resolution of the issues at all scales of urban development and levels of government (and internationally) an intractable proposition. Hence there will be economic winners and losers in the post-Peak Oil scenario, which will gradually impact on the economic performance of cities, and could jeopardise the sustainability of future urban development. This rather gloomy scenario is supported by most of the cited commentators and makes an urgent transition to adaptive measures all the more important [1, 4, 5, 15, 16]. Such adaptive measures must adjust in ways that contribute to increasing resilience of human settlements to oil supply vulnerability and depletion:

- changes in oil supply and pricing vulnerability;
- moderating potential damage;

- taking advantage of opportunities;
- coping with consequences of reducing supply in an oil-constrained future.

4 Conclusion

The analogy between oil depletion and climate change actions is tested by applying a modified set of mitigation and adaptation definitions to a case study to categorise oil depletion strategies. The author considers that the modified terminology is a useful way to categorise and analyse oil depletion actions, but in a flexible application of the model. The analysis of the case study shows that mitigation actions dominate the strategies. It also appears to support a view that a notional separation is blurred by cross-cutting measures, as actions to mitigate depletion (conserve oil supply) can also apply to adaptation (using alternatives).

Using the analogy of mitigation and adaptation aligns Peak Oil research with the widely accepted terminology in climate change research and policy making. It is concluded that the proposed modified mitigation and adaptation terminology is a useful way to categorise and think about oil depletion actions. The definitions warrant further peer review to gain acceptance. While the case study strategies are geared to mitigation actions, adaptive measures will become more important in the longer term future as oil supply becomes constrained.

References

[1] Rubin, J., Why Your World is About to Get a Whole Lot Smaller: oil and the end of globalization, Random House, New York, 2009.

[2] Association for the Study of Peak Oil and Gas (ASPO), Newsletter No 97 January 2009. Online. http://aspoireland.org/newsletter/

[3] International Energy Agency (IEA), *World Energy Outlook 2010*, International Energy Agency and Organisation for Economic Cooperation and Development, Paris, 2010.

[4] Heinberg, R., Peak Everything: waking up to the century of decline in Earth's resources, Clairview Books, London, 2007.

[5] Newman, P. Beatley, T. and Boyer, H., *Resilient Cities: responding to peak oil and climate change,* Island Press, Washington, D.C., pp. 6–21, 2009.

[6] Australian Government, *Our cities: the challenge of change*, Major Cities Unit, Department of Infrastructure and Transport, Canberra, 2010.

[7] United Nations, Department of Economic and Social Affairs (UN/DESA), *World Economic and Social Survey 2009: Promoting Development, Saving the Planet*, United Nations, New York. Online. www.un.org/en /development /desa/news/policy/wess-2009.shtml, 2009.

[8] United Nations Framework Convention on Climate Change (UNFCCC), Conference of the Parties (COP 18) 26 November –7 December, 2012.

[9] Brewster, R.J., Significance of global oil depletion to urban residential development, in *Sustainability Today,WIT Transactions on Ecology and The Environment, Vol 167*ed. C.A. Brebbia, WIT Press, Southampton, ISSN 1743-3541, pp. 151–163, 2011.

[10] Intergovernmental Panel on Climate Change (IPCC), *Special Report on Renewable Energy Sources and Climate Change Mitigation: Summary for Policymakers*, Technical Support Unit Working Group III, Potsdam Institute for Climate Impact Research (PIK). Online. www.ipcc.ch/publications_and_data/publications_and_data_reports.shtml# SRREN. p. 10, 2011.

[11] Intergovernmental Panel on Climate Change (IPCC), Climate Change 2007: Synthesis report. Contribution of Working Groups I, II and III to the Fourth Assessment Report of the Intergovernmental Panel on Climate Change, Core Writing Team, R.K. Pachauri and A. Reisinger (eds), IPCC, Geneva. 2007.

[12] Tanter, R., What are global problems?, Nautilus Institute for Security and Sustainability, RMIT, Melbourne. Online. www.nautilus.org/gps/intro/, 2008.

[13] Garnaut, R., *Garnaut Climate Change Review Final Report*, Cambridge University Press, Melbourne. Online. www.garnautreview.org.au, 2008.

[14] Garnaut, R., The Garnaut review2011: Australia in the response to climate change, Cambridge University Press, Melbourne, p. 24, 2011.

[15] Droege, P., The Renewable City: a comprehensive guide to an urban revolution, Wiley-Academy, Chichester, pp. 60–61, 2006.

[16] Newman, P. and Jennings, I., *Cities as Sustainable Ecosystems: principles and practices,* Island Press, Washington, DC; London, p.37, 2008.

[17] UK Industry Taskforce of Peak Oil and Energy Security, *The Oil Crunch: Securing the UK's energy future.* Online. www.arup.com/_assets/_download/4D6FF5E5-19BB-316E-408B503DFB26ADDB.pdf, 2008.

[18] Australian Senate, *Inquiry into Australia's future oil supply and alternative transport fuels: Final Report*, Australian Senate Standing Committee on Rural and Regional Affairs and Transport, Canberra, pp. xii-xiii, 2007.

[19] Queensland Parliament, Queensland's Vulnerability to Rising Oil Prices – Taskforce Report, Queensland Government, Brisbane, 2007.

[20] Waller, M., Oil Vulnerability Strategy/Action Plan for Queensland: research paper, Heuris Partners Ltd, Brisbane, pp. 6–24, 2008.

[21] RMIT University & Australia. Dept. of the Environment and Heritage and the Arts, *Scoping Study to Investigate Measures for Improving the Environmental Sustainability of Building Materials*, Australian Greenhouse Office, Canberra. Online. http://nla.gov.au/nla.arc-85449, p.39, 2006.

[22] Crowther, P., Design for Disassembly to Recover Embodied Energy. In Szokolay, Steven S. (Ed.) *The 16th International Conference on Passive and Low Energy Architecture*, 22-24 September 1999, Melbourne. Online. http://eprints.qut.edu.au/2846/,1999.

[23] National Petroleum Council (NPC) 2008 Hard Truths–Facing the Hard Truths about Energy: update presentation, Washington. Online. www.npchardtruthsreport.org/presentations08.php, Slide 30, 2008.

[24] Australia, Climate Change Risks to Australia's Coast: A First Pass National Assessment, Australian Dept. of Climate Change, Canberra, 2009.

[25] Hirsch, R. L., Bezdek, R. H. and Wendling, R.M., *The Impending World Energy Mess: what it is and what it means to you*, Apogee Prime, Canada, 2010.

[26] Hirsch, R.L. Personal communication, 8 October 2010, Senior Energy Advisor, Management Information Services, Inc., Washington D.C.

Environmental sustainability agenda: Metropolitan Area of Mexicali, Baja California, Mexico

R. Rojas-Caldelas, C. Peña-Salmon, E. Corona-Zambrano,
A. Arias-Vallejo & O. Leyva-Camacho
Faculty of Architecture and Design,
Autonomous University of Baja California, Mexico

Abstract

Human settlements worldwide have experienced environmental problems as a result of population growth, an increase in productive activities and low financial capacity of municipalities to provide adequate infrastructure and public services. At the local level, problems of water, soil and air pollution, as well as, land use changes have arisen due to the expansion of urban agglomerations. Regionally, there have been negative impacts on watersheds, ecosystems and biodiversity. Globally, the world is experiencing climate change, the reduction of the ozone layer and the increase of natural disasters. The situation has posed a challenge in terms of urban and regional planning, especially for metropolitan areas and medium-sized cities. The purpose of this study is to present an alternative to integrate environmental sustainability into metropolitan planning in Mexico, specifically applied to the Metropolitan Area of Mexicali, Baja California. Therefore the Environmental Sustainability Agenda has focused on three objectives: first, identifying the weaknesses of the existing environmental and human settlements legal framework; second, developing an environmental assessment and; third, designing policies, strategies and indicators to implement institutional monitoring of environmental programmes. The results were obtained by conducting surveys, regional community workshops, and reviewing previous research. Lastly, this study concludes with six sectoral programs: water, air, solid wastes, green areas, soils and physical pollution and six transversal

WIT Transactions on Ecology and The Environment, Vol 173, © 2013 WIT Press
www.witpress.com, ISSN 1743-3541 (on-line)
doi:10.2495/SDP130221

programs that have effects on environmental education, health, climate change, environmental management and the legal framework.

Keywords: environmental planning, environmental agenda, metropolitan planning, sustainable development.

1   Introduction

Environmental impacts occur at the local, regional, and global scale. From recent global environmental summits, it has emerged that these impacts need to be addressed at their corresponding scale. At the local scale, the impacts include the following: population growth has exceeded the capacity of governments to provide local infrastructure and equipment; urban expansion has resulted in the loss of high quality agricultural land, forests and ecosystems have degraded due to water, soil, and air pollution , the increase of private vehicles, material banks have been exploited by the continued demand of construction materials, the concentration of chemical risk areas, as well as the import of food and other supplies to sustain people's domestic consumption. The regional impacts are related to watershed management, ecosystem protection and conservation, and energy source usage. Global impacts consist of climate change, air emissions, ozone depletion, and increases in natural disasters [1, 2]. The problems pointed out above represent a challenge for the field of planning human settlements, primarily in cases of large metropolitan areas and medium cities.

Facing such problems has required a number of efforts over nearly forty years that have improved environmental management. Legal frameworks, both general and specific, have been implemented to regulate environmental quality. This has occurred in both developing and developed countries. New analytical instruments, environmental evaluation methodologies, and prospecting and statistical measures have been developed as product of scientific and technological advancements. Finally, arrangements and agreements have been made between countries for environmental conservation or for commercial purposes, where environmental protection has become important.

Under the above context both Mexico and particularly the state of Baja California, have tried to respond to the protection of the environment in different ways. First, in 1988, a federal legal framework was put in place. In 1992, the state of Baja California implemented an additional legal framework. Both the federal and state frameworks were complementary to existing human settlement legislation. Second, policies and programmes resulting from the various National Development Plans have been developed since the nineties. Third, international agreements between Mexico and the USA have focused on the protection of the environment in the border area. Some of these agreements have been in place since 1982; others are more recent, such as NAFTA. Therefore, the purpose of this study is to integrate environmental and sustainability aspects into the planning of metropolitan areas in Mexico and to specifically focus on issues involving the Mexican-American border. This is referred to as the Environmental Sustainability Agenda for the Metropolitan Area of Mexicali, Baja California.

2   Methodology

The methodology focuses on the elaboration of the environmental assessment, on one hand we worked on the review of documentary sources that had two types of contributions: on one side, the assessment of the legal framing, another about institutional policies and other instruments for environmental planning and human settlements; on another side, to provide a quantitative overview of the environmental problems of the metropolitan area of Mexicali municipality that included the following topics: water, energy, air, soil and land use, municipal and hazardous solid waste, green space and ecological conservation and risks. On the other hand, in the realization of the environmental assessment for the municipality regions that formed the metropolitan area of Mexicali through the review of participants of different committees from the community that make up the Committee for Development Planning for the Mexicali Municipality (COPLADEMM, for its acronym in Spanish) including representatives of farms, ranches, health, education, tourism, parents associations, businesses, communal land delegates, environmental groups, potable water committee, committee of neighbors and city officials [3].

To perform this community planning exercise sessions were organized through COPLADEMM conducted between September and November 2011. In the first case the assessment of the city of Mexicali was made in COPLADEMM headquarters. The second session was held in the South Valley subregion called Guadalupe Victoria to where members of the various committees of the municipal offices that integrate this area attended. The third was held in the town of Ciudad Morelos, and was attended by community representatives of various administrative sectors in this area.

As result of this second phase two types of information were obtained: on one hand the survey applied to actors from the community regarding issues contained in the environmental agenda. On the other, there were the results of the internal discussion among the participants of the relevant issues to be addressed regionally in the metropolitan area. The environmental information along to the previously mentioned will provide an integrated and complementary assessment vision. Information that will be added to the legal framework. The material generated will serve as input for the design of policies and for the list of indicators.

3   Environmental assessment of the metropolitan zone of Mexicali

3.1 Socio-economic-evolution of the metropolitan zone

The municipality of Mexicali is located in the State of Baja California, Mexico; it is bordered to the north by the Imperial County of California in the United States of America, and east bounded by the Colorado River, state line between Baja California and Sonora. Mexicali sits on a large delta plain shared by two large agricultural valleys: Mexicali (Mexico) and Imperial (USA) both were created, since last century, as a huge irrigation area oriented to export products.

The delta is crossed by numerous seismic faults that are part of the San Andres system, which makes this a highly seismic zone and at the same time, becomes in a rich area in geothermal resources, resulting from tectonic activity and the presence of aquifers that support power generation for the region. Mexicali is located in an arid area, a condition that makes water a scarce resource in both surface and underground; the Colorado River is the only permanent source of supply for Mexicali and other cities in the state, which is regulated since 1944 by the international Mexico-US treaty [4].

The climatic conditions of the region, characterized by extreme dry warm climate, have constrained the development of certain types of crops for agricultural and livestock production, hence the latter activity has less participation in the economy, primarily engaged in the production of meat and milk. Another activity is the extraction of sand, gravel and clay, to support the production of building materials for the manufacture of concrete and block walls, materials that supply both the domestic and international markets.

There are also, regional fresh and salt water bodies, where fishing and aquaculture is accomplished. The Mexicali valley has an extensive network of canals and some lakes from where some species are extracted or cultivated such as: bass, striped, channel catfish, blue catfish, tiger catfish, crappie, carp, bluegill and tilapia. While in the coastal area of the Sea of Cortez in San Felipe there are caught species like mullet, shrimp, shark, sardines and algae [5].

Tourist activities are mainly developed on one hand, in major cities of Mexicali and Algodones, oriented to business, industry, trade and health services and; on the other, focused to recreation in the port of San Felipe, associated to beaches, hunting, ecological, fishing and off-road racing. As places of attraction we can find; San Felipe, Laguna Salada, Guadalupe Canyon, Rio Hardy, The Valley of the Giants and Punta Estrella.

The metropolitan area of Mexicali had its beginning with the settlement of the city in 1903 and from that date to the present has 936.826 inhabitants in the metropolitan area [6]. The development process in the early days of the town was marked by national and international events that have influenced the development of the main economic activities and human settlement in the region. The whole development along time have had produced environmental impacts as a result of continuous population immigration to the border, large development projects: waterworks for agriculture , industry and human settlements, roads and communications infrastructure, changes in land use, an increase in urban and rural settlements and services that have demanded the use of natural resources such as water, energy, building materials, food processing, manufacturing, provision of goods and services and finally the disposal of wastes, resulting in air, soil and water pollution.

The economic development of the region from 1903 to 1950 was based on the primary sector, situation that has been reversed in the 1960s with the federal promotion of industrialization in the northern border of Mexico throughout The

"Maquiladora" programme (assembly industries), industrialization that has been widened until the late eighties.

By the nineties, the economy of Mexicali had been based on three productive sectors: agriculture, maintaining its presence in the local economy; industry, consisting on small and medium size industries export-oriented, but nearly without industrial networks at the regional level and; commerce and services supported in a regional market. In the same period there was a positive growth in the trade and services activities and a cumulative knowledge that have had impacted in a qualitative transformation in the production sector [7].

The last period going from 2000 up to 2012, a period characterized by two global financial crises in 2001 and 2007, they have had an impact on the US economy and therefore on the Mexican economy, due to the dependence for trade in the border area of the northern Mexico. Recent financial crises have affected almost all sectors of the economy, because the previous crises have had impacted the production sector [8]. The instability caused by financial crises have also affected the manufacturing sector and particularly the tertiary sector in 2007 in which the growth was diminished in the real state sector, as well as it was slowed the construction of condominiums and residences oriented to US tourists over coastal areas in San Felipe.

To counter act the crisis, federal government have encouraged the construction sector, with the purpose in mind to reduce the nationwide housing deficit by means of a massive program to stimulate the economy in medium and large cities. Such projects have had two types of effects: a positive one consisted of strengthening metropolitan areas and; a negative one, that has derived to urban sprawl problems within the city-regions. Consequently, in 2005, the national system of cities in Mexico was reclassified from 37 metropolitan areas to 54 metropolitan areas in 2005 [9], under this project was created the Mexicali Metropolitan Area. Such policy has demanded the proposal of new environmental planning tools applied to the regulation of human settlements, like the Environmental Sustainability Agenda for Metropolitan Areas. The development of this agenda for Mexicali, was economically supported by the Ministry of Environmental Protection of Baja California and conducted by the Autonomous University of Baja California.

There has been a bi-national environmental effort between US-Mexico since 1982 known as the agreement of La Paz, that has tried to influence on the prevention, mitigation and enhancement of environmental quality in the border area of northern Mexico through agreements and programs. As an example is The Border Program XXI in the nineties, which had been a result of environmental agreements of the North American Free Trade Agreement (NAFTA), which have had as a main goal the sustainability of the border and to establish initiatives that would lead to the protection and enhancement of environment to safeguard public health and the natural areas of the region. This program has dealt with issues like natural resources, environmental information, environmental health, air and water quality, solid and hazardous waste, enforcement of the law, pollution prevention, as well as emergency or contingency prevention, all these issues are still active in the Border 2012 Program [10].

During the last decade there has been tremendous pressure on the use and quality of natural resources, such as water supply for human settlements in Mexicali and other state cities such as Tecate and Tijuana. The construction sector has demanded the exploitation of large number of sand and gravel and other construction materials, to satisfy the explosive housing growth. The expansion of urban areas had required the conversion of arable land to urban land use and the consequent transfer of water rights to non-agricultural uses; in the same situation is the demand of electric power generation to meet the growing demand of industrial and residential sector as well as for exports. All of these issues have contributed to increase the levels of air, water pollution and solid waste generation.

Current problems of pollution and ecosystem deprivation in the metropolitan area of Mexicali are consequence of the economic, social and environmental dynamics of the border region over more than 100 years. Whose trends are complex, due to their multiple worldwide networks with other cities and regions to sustain its development.

3.2 Environmental problems and priorities

There are similarities between the statistical information and the perception of people on main environmental problems and priorities in terms of a metropolitan agenda as a result of the literature review and from community actors. The following section presents the environmental assessment of the metropolitan area, based on key issues derived from people's perception from different regions, raised through community workshops in 2011, and later from the assessment of legal and-regulatory framework [3].

a. City of Mexicali – air pollution is located in the first place of environmental problems, caused by emissions of private and public transport, electric power generation, industry, unpaved streets, and those from natural sources. The second largest problem, are urban solid wastes, given its continued growth in per capita generation, combined with illegal dumping on property lots, roads and drains within and outside city limits; moreover transfer centers are insufficient. Third, regarding water quality, it needs to improve safe water programmes in rural areas of Mexicali Valley and San Felipe, as it is required to increase the capacity of wastewater treatment. Fourth, industrial activity and of certain services demand storage and transportation of hazardous waste, representing a latent risk in the city. Fifth, the inappropriate amount of green areas that is required according to the national and international standards. Sixth, regarding environmental plans, the city lacks of these documents to provide adequate handling and management of the environment. Finally, visual pollution, as a result of numerous street advertising signs, street garbage disposal, graffiti and many abandoned buildings.

b. North Valley – in this area environmental problems are the result of farming and ranching, extraction and production of handmade bricks that affect air quality, soil and water pollution. Tourism and recreation activities around the Algodones area, have deteriorated natural landscapes due to all terrain transit of vehicles on dune areas contributing to air pollution. As well as in the rest of Mexicali Valley there is the practice of illegal disposal of waste and rubbish over roads and air pollution due to agricultural fields' fumigation. This zone has an area of wetlands, which were fed by water leaks that have been dried due to concrete-lined of All American Canal and excessive groundwater extraction to which this zone is subject for domestic use and irrigation.

c. South Valley – this area is crucial in the provision of goods and services to a wide productive area and small towns. Environmental problems are attached to air and water pollution by agro-chemicals, agricultural fumigation, agricultural fields and domestic waste burnings, besides the transit of vehicles through unpaved roads and streets. Moreover there is illegal disposal of waste and rubbish in drains and roads, as well as household waste disposal on open areas. The lack of sewage systems in small towns, treatment plants and the leaking of agricultural drains have negative direct environmental impacts over surface and groundwater bodies in the valley and the Colorado delta. South valley has been severely affected by the expansion of Cerro Prieto geothermal field, which has increased soils salinity and air and water pollution. The location of the water treatment plant Arenitas have contributed to odor generation and the industrial corridor Ejido Puebla with air and noise pollution.

In the case of San Felipe coastal subregion, the most severe problem is the availability of water, a scarce resource that has been usually over exploited for domestic use and tourism. Recently another aquifer, through Las Tinajas area, has been exploited by mining activities. Added to this is the problem of the disposal of municipal solid waste in San Felipe area, having its critical periods during vacation and holidays seasons due to massive influx of tourists. The presence of tourists affects ecological zones as the estuary, beaches, dunes and hills due to motorized off-road vehicles generating dust clouds, affecting native vegetation and causing soil erosion. Moreover there are illegal settlements located in areas subject to flooding. The northern part of this subregion belongs to buffer zone of the Biosphere Reserve of the Upper Gulf of California, which has land use restrictions.

Priorities were set as a result of literature review and community workshops, Air quality was at the top, followed by solid wastes and water quality and its infrastructure facilities. The three of them were associated with population health problems, such as respiratory and gastrointestinal diseases, allergies and, skin and eyes affections. At another level of priority was placed the topic of urban green areas, as a need of urban public spaces that fulfill social and ecological functions that contribute to environmental improvement. Another topic was environmental education, as a driving force to modify consumption patterns and obedience of laws. Finally, although physical contamination (odors, noise, light and visual pollution) was set in the last place, it contributes to achieve quality of life and livable towns.

3.3 Legal and normative assessment

The legal framework is mainly updated until 2010 and 2011 and it is integrated by 77 agreements that have been decreed from 2002 up to 2010 dealing with environmental matters: water, biodiversity, pollution, energy, solid and hazardous wastes. However, from the total of 19 environmental policy instruments that should have been implemented from the legal framework, they have only been created 12 and from them, just 4 have been updated, however there are still missing 7 planning instruments to be developed.

The missing instruments are: Touristic Land Use Management Plan of the State of Baja California; Municipal Environmental Protection Programme; State Air Quality Management Programme; Local Prevention and Integrated Solid Waste and Special Wastes Management programmes; State Emissions Inventory and Transfer of Pollution Emissions to the Atmosphere; Municipal Residual Water Discharges and Disposal of Debris and State Management of Special Wastes; the State Environmental Journal and; the State Prevention and Control of Lighting Pollution. Meanwhile the four outdated programmes are: Roads and Transport Master Plan 2005; State Programme of Fisheries and Aquaculture 2003–2007; State Ecological Land Use Programme 2005 and Municipal Ecological Land Use Programme 2000.

The Urban Development legal framework consists of 17 urban development plans, programmes and directives in the municipality of Mexicali and 6 of them have not been updated: Urban Development Plan of San Felipe, Regional Urban, Touristic, and Ecological Development Plan of the Coastal Corridor of San Felipe-Puertecitos and the Master Plan of Transit and Transport of Mexicali, the Municipal Ecological Land Use Programme, Urban Development Plan of Los Algodones, Urban Development Directives of Coahuila Station, and also are still missing 4 programmes to be submitted to approval by municipal authorities.

4 Environmental policies and programmes for the Metropolitan Zone

4.1 Environmental topics

In this section it is presented two types of policies; some focused to the solution of key topics of the agenda and others to deal with transversal subjects that must be integrated into each environmental topic.

Policies for key topics, will be oriented, to the prevention, reduction and remediation of pollution by different types of sources, such as air, water and soil pollution; meanwhile the others will aim to strengthen the relationship between urban green areas and natural resources for its sustainable use in the metropolitan area.

    a. Prevention and reduction of pollution

This policy is focussed to the prevention, reduction and remediation of pollution, including the introduction, expansion and/or improvement of water and sanitation systems in human settlements, such as strengthening the infrastructure for solid waste management and special handling at the metropolitan level. In the case of physical pollution, it will be mandatory to strengthen environmental regulation, monitoring and supervision of emission sources for odors and noise. Finally, there are also integrated policies to promote and encourage the establishment of companies promoting clean and environmental certifications of existing productive activities, construction and tourism. This policy has raised four programs: air quality, environmental infrastructure, pollution control and physical environmental information systems.

    b.   Rehabilitation and restoration of sites

This policy will promote the restoration of polluted, abandoned or spoiled areas by productive activities by any previous use, located within or outside urban areas, through remediation and improvement techniques to support new land uses. It also integrates economic recuperation of production activities oriented to new environmental and market conditions.

This policy will consider productive agricultural areas that have been affected by water and soil pollution, natural disasters, inappropriate disposal of hazardous or special handling waste, abandoned sand and gravel pits that have not implemented remedial measurements and sites that have been used for the disposal of urban solid wastes.

    c.   Conservation of natural resources and biodiversity

This policy will reinforce the relationship that should exist between urban green areas and available natural resources for the metropolitan area, in order to achieve a sustainable use of them to preserve ecological and environmental functions, through the development of research and technological development. Conservation of natural resources will include; water management, minerals, landforms, soils, alternative energy sources and biodiversity in the natural, productive and urban area. Similarly it will boost conservation in three areas: one, the interrelationship that should exist between the management of natural areas, agricultural and urban green areas (green corridors); two, it will promote the cinegetic exploitation of biodiversity under sustainable resource management practices and, three, it will strengthen the cultural relationship with landscape through conservation and regulation of archaeological, historical and cultural sites in the urban, natural and regional productive areas.

4.2 Transverse topics

These policies will be oriented to incorporate actions that are crossways to the problems referred previously on key topics, such as environmental culture and education, environmental health, climate change, environmental assessment and legal and normative framework.

    a.   Development of an environmental culture

This policy will have the aim to carry on environmental education in order to achieve cultural changes in consumption patterns, healthy practices, sustainable use and management of natural resources and the promotion of sustainable built environment. It will also incorporate official and informal environmental education and instruction programmes open to the public, service providers and authorities, where the education sector plays an important role for the change.

b. Health enhancement

This policy will be focused on the improvement of human health within metropolitan area, throughout actions oriented to reinforce preventive health programs; the development and improvement of water and sanitation systems and the creation of a database to monitoring progress.

c. Mitigation and adaptation to climate change

Policies to mitigate and adapt to climate change are linked to natural and human processes, like urbanization and industrialization taken place at metropolitan areas. Hence policies will be dealing with the above key topics of the environmental agenda and the making of a strategic climate change programme.

These policies would be guided to build urban resilience systems as is established by World Bank, which over the time can be adapted in several directions: long term social and economic evaluation of provision of environmental services and risk; urban infrastructure strengthening; poverty reduction; urban risk reduction; civil protection systems strengthening; strengthening of intergovernmental coordinated work with civil society; implementation of building and urban infrastructure adaptation programmes; protection and management of key ecosystems; creation of educational programs to inform population of climate change, as well as measures of mitigation and adaptation to be taken; and creation of monitoring information systems.

d. Legal and normative framework of environmental management and human settlements

This policy will be oriented to back up the environmental management framework, which will have an impact on different laws and regulations on environment and human settlements. It will be necessary to make institutional arrangements for the management of the metropolitan area. The work to be done demands a jointly effort among government, private sector and organizations from civil societies and their participation during planning and management processes.

As a complementary issue is the implementation of monitoring and the assessment of the metropolitan environmental agenda, which requires the creation of an environmental information system and indicators , to provide the inputs to support authorities in decision-making processes and to inform the public the achievements on environmental performance.

5 Conclusions

The main challenge of this work will be the development and implementation of the proposed programmes. As a recent metropolitan area, will be deemed necessary to make institutional adjustments to carry out the environmental management of the area, since it implies the convergence and concurrence of the three levels of government, different institutions and the association with the private sector and social organizations. The project of the Agenda will demand also changes in the legal and normative framework to ensure their proper implementation. Another key issue is the enhancement of community participation; this will involve the economic support of government to communities to help them to building up local capacities to create their own organizations, to look for funding, for management and monitoring of projects.

References

[1] UNEP, Keeping track of our changing environment: from Rio to Rio+20 (1992-2012), 2011. Online http://www.unep.org/geo/pdfs/Keeping_Track_es.pdf

[2] UNEP, Global Environmental Outlook 5 (GEO 5), full report, 2012. Online http://www.unep.org/geo/pdfs/geo5/GEO5_report_full_en.pdf

[3] Secretary of Environmental Protection of Baja California and Autonomous University of Baja California. Environmental Sustainability Agenda for the Metropolitan Zone Mexicali, Baja California, Thechnical Report, Mexicali, Baja California, 2012.

[4] Rojas, R. Urban Environmental Assessment: A methodological proposal and application to a study case, Mexicali, Baja California, doctoral thesis, National Autonomous University of Mexico, Mexico, D.F., 2000.

[5] COPLADEMM, Plan Municipal de Desarrollo Mexicali 2011-2013. H. XX Ayuntamiento de Mexicali, 2010, Mexicali, Baja California.

[6] INEGI. Population and Housing Census, 2010. Online http://www.censo2010.org.mx/

[7] Estrella, G. y Ranfla, A demography and economy of a capital state, Mexicali, Baja California, *Estudios Fronterizos*, No. 37-38, pp. 9-32, 1996.

[8] Ranfla, A. and Sánchez, G. Current economic evolution of the municipality of Mexicali, eds. D. Piñera & J. Carrillo, Evolution of urban processes in Baja California in the XX Century in Baja California, a hundred years from the Mexican Revolution, 1910-2010, COLEF-UABC, pp. 142-160, 2011.

[9] SEDESOL-CONAPO-INEGI. Delimitation of the metropolitan areas of Mexico, Secretary of Social Development-National Council of Population-National Institute of Statistics and Geography and Informatics, 2005.

[10] Secretaría de Protección al Ambiente y Recursos Naturales y United States Environmental Protection Agency. Frontera 2012: Programa Ambiental México-Estados Unidos Reporte de Indicadores 2005, 2005. Online http://www.epa.gov/border2012/framework/index.html and http://www.epa.gov/border2012/

The economic sustainability in urban planning: the case of La Manga

J. L. Miralles[1] & S. García-Ayllón[2]
[1]Polytechnic University of Valencia, Spain
[2]Polytechnic University of Cartagena, Spain

Abstract

The urbanization process that shapes the present Mediterranean coast started with the mass tourism that encouraged the Centres and Areas of National Tourist Interest law in 1962, as a strategic national investment. 50 years after its implementation, it is necessary to conduct a retrospective analysis of the results, assessing to what extent have the stated goals in the 1960s been met. The evolution of the macroeconomic, political and legal parameters show certain deviations from initial forecasts of many large urban plans carried out in coastal places created from scratch. The case of La Manga del Mar Menor on the Murcia coast – a target for 250,000 holidaymakers – which came from a desert dune in the 1960s, is certainly an example; poorly documented while enlightening, of the results that have been achieved. The study of real social and economic performance as a tourism product against territorial and landscape impacts, the problem of governance in the context of urban planning and the ability of private property to develop its own sustainable projects in the long run has been approached with the detail and objectivity that allows a comprehensive case study contrasted by the facts. All these elements will be distributed to either side of the balance, in order to evaluate the validity of a coastal development model, that after five decades we can now begin to postulate with enough research perspective.
Keywords: urban planning, urban management, tourism development, coastal development.

WIT Transactions on Ecology and The Environment, Vol 173, © 2013 WIT Press
www.witpress.com, ISSN 1743-3541 (on-line)
doi:10.2495/SDP130231

1 Introduction

La Manga del Mar Menor is a dune line over 20 kilometres in length and a width ranging from 500 meters, at the beginning, to 80 meters at the end. La Manga is located between the Mediterranean Sea and the Mar Menor. The Mar Menor is a salty lagoon of over 170 km^2 and drafts uniform 4 or 5 feet deep.

In 1959 the Spanish government is on the brink of default. To obtain foreign credits is forced to implement an economic development plan. This plan provides for the promotion of tourism. La Manga zone's is selected to promote a great project of tourism development.

This case of urban development for holiday resort on the Mediterranean coast is paradigmatic and has been investigated by a PhD thesis [1]. This paper explains the conclusions of this research about the urban development processes since initial master plan until today when there is a big tourist area with capacity for 250,000 visitors. In other paper presented at the *3rd International Conference on Physical Coastal Processes, Management and Engineering* (in press) the authors explain the changes on coastal landscape and marine ecosystems.

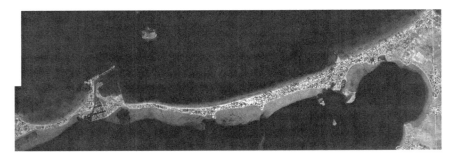

Figure 1:   The Manga of Mar Menor today. Origin: Google Earth.

2 The initial master plan: Bonet plan

In 1950, the Manga of Mar Menor was a long line of sand with two beaches of 20 km on two seas. This place attracted the interest of a visionary promoter in the late 1950s.

In the early 1960s, the Franco Spanish government initiated a policy of foreign exchange earnings through the "enhancement" of the coast. The policy is implemented through the Law National Tourist Interest Centres and Areas (hereafter LCZITN) in 1962. The law allows rapid urbanization in different strategic coastal areas as exception of general planning regulations (Land Act of 1956). The selected areas receive financial aid and state grants. The aim is oriented to create urban infrastructure and resorts of quality for foreign tourism with high purchasing power. La Manga is included in the selected list along with other places like Marbella in Malaga, Son Parc in Baleares, Campoamor and La Zenia in Alacant or Sotogrande in Cadiz [2].

The projects and development works of the tourist areas, with State subsidies, are awarded to the private sector. Often, the management of projects in each area is done by a single developer well connected with the government, for example in the case of José Banús, the developer of Marbella, or Tomas Maestre, the developer of La Manga. Tomás Maestre commissioned the master plan of La Manga to Antoni Bonet, an internationally renowned architect with experience in large projects in South America such as Buenos Aires General Plan or the Plan of Punta Ballena in Uruguay.

Figure 2:   Model of the master plan for La Manga of A Bonet filed in 1963 to Minister Manuel Fraga. Origin: Archive of José Parra.

A. Bonet projects a city born from nothing, designed for a maximum population of 60,000. The city is designed with infrastructure and services oriented to tourism with high purchasing power. The urban design and land consumption, despite the opposition of the developer T. Maestre, following the modernist principles of the Athens Charter of 1933. The sustainability of the proceedings and the reasonable use of space will generate a structured urban fabric that alternates a skyline of high and low density (Figure 2).

This configuration frees maintaining visual quality in environmental quality, zoning enabling integration of endowments, facilities and public spaces, and implements a rational management of urban traffic, all in a difficult space management. Possible seasonality of demand, with peaks in summer and vacant in winter, is mitigated "making" a city with a population stable base of 15,000 and 60,000 summer peaks.

This urban project runs easily by programmed Bonet Plan and strong financial contribution of public subsidies provided by LCZITN. State investment was more than 11,000 million pesetas divided into four lots (Table 1).

Table 1: Approval of public investment in La Manga. Origin: Official State Gazette.

Project	Approved date, Official Gazette	Surface (ha)	Capacity (num. inhab)	Public investment (M pesetas)
La Manga Ranch in Cartagena	12-9-1966	88	16,920	2,200
La Manga Ranch in San Javier	27-1-1969	280	36,400	8,980
Honda Beach (La Manga)	11-2-1967	55	4,500	296
Dos Mares Ranch (La Manga)	25-2-1969	61	1,900	47

Public funding allows T Maestre to create a network of companies. With the sale of plots and buildings for facilities and hotels, T Maestre executes infrastructure works and generates substantial capital gains. The LCZITN allows a large degree of freedom to the authorized project managers. All phases of the master plan are started in just 10 years.

Figure 3: Infrastructure works and buildings in La Manga in the 1960s. Origin: Archive of San Javier.

The elitist environment and economic growth of the 1960s placed at La Manga as an international tourist destination class. Ambitious projects are promoted as casinos, marinas, artificial islands, a beachfront airport and originals architectural proposals.

The architectural quality of the urban proposal attracts wealthy clients and architects that dot the urban space of the most significant works of modernism in the Region of Murcia. The urban plan user stratified into two levels of purchasing power: one mid-level who stay in hotels and high-density residential units of 3 m³/m² and a more exclusive property acquired in single-family parcels minimum size of 600 to 2000 m² with a building on 0.5 m³/m².

3 The crisis of the 1970s: tourist and urban consequences

From 1959 to the economic crisis of 1972 in Spain, the government prioritizes the economic growth. This paradigm is called "developmentalism". The term means to promote at each moment economic development above all else.

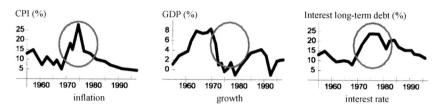

Figure 4: Evolution of the Spanish economy from 1950 to 2000. Origin: official data and authors.

The "developmentalism" of the 1960s is truncated in the middle stage of growth in 1972 by the oil crisis. In Spain, although the crisis takes a little longer to arrive, their consequences are as strong as in the rest of Europe. The GDP fell to negative levels while prices and interest rates reach values of 25% (Figure 4).

In the case of La Manga, the loss of public funding is lethal to the network of companies created by the developer Maestre to develop his macro-project. In addition there is a reduction of revenue by falling sales generated by the crisis. Therefore, the developer must pay his debts to small and medium local contractors through land. So he paid his debts with building plots produced with the urbanization of the 20 km of the dune line.

This is therefore an example of overflow: a macro-project too big that, sooner or later, the promoter cannot continue. So the same developer sows the seed of a process that, years later, will end in a chaotic urban hypertrophy.

In a few years, small and medium local contractors paid with building plots become a little greedy bourgeois estate. Moreover, the arrival of democracy in Spain brings a process of administrative decentralization that gives the urban management to municipalities and autonomous regions. The municipalities are in the process of urban expansion a source of short-term income. Then it generates a new urbanization process, regardless of the initial Bonet plan.

La Manga is then converted, with the complicity of local authorities, in a "Taifa urban kingdom" impossible to govern which initiates a chaotic urbanization (outlawed in many cases). The urban area density increases and gets crowded. Urban gaps are built. The landscape becomes an accumulation of buildings.

Table 2:   Hotel beds and not hotel beds in La Manga until 1988. Origin: López-Morell *et al.* [3].

Year	Not hotel beds	Hotel beds	TOTAL
1965	820	0	820
1966	1.528	217	1.745
1967	3.193	563	3.756
1972	18.228	563	18.791
1973	23.180	1.586	24.766
1977	40.727	1.586	42.313
1978	42.272	2.521	44.793
1984	62.110	2.521	64.631
1985	65.045	2.577	67.622
1988	97.004	2.577	99.576
Percentage	97,4%	2,6%	100%

The first tourist target (with high purchasing power) initiates a difficult cohabitation with a new tourist profile local, less affluent and own a second home cheaply. Finally, the mixture of tourists of different levels is impossible and tourists with high purchasing will be elsewhere.

One indicator of this process is the number of beds and the relationship between hotel beds and not hotel beds (second home) that you can see in Table 2. So in the late 1970s has reached the initial target population of 60,000 beds established in Bonet plan. The target is reached because of the extraordinary growth of second homes. The hotels go to represent 15% of the beds at the end of the 1960s to 2.6% in 1988. So while growth hotel beds stagnate, residential development continues and in 1988 reached a total of 97,004 beds, the 97.4% of total beds.

4   The 1980s and jurisdictional conflicts: the complex urban governance in Spain

In 1978, Spain adopted its new democratic Constitution. Then, the two levels of local and central government are transformed into three levels: local, regional and central. Before 1978, the central government had competence to approve urban laws. And municipalities, with control of the central government, had full competence in planning, urban management and planning discipline. After 1978, the regional administration acquires the competences to approve urban laws and municipalities maintain their competences.

In the initial period of the new constitution, while the new regional administration starts, the stakeholders pressure on municipalities to facilitate land speculation and increased building permits (not always legal). So in coastal areas, administrative decentralization and potential economic development associated to tourism, makes a society that seeks wealth in the short term through capital gains urban. But this causes the development of a low-value tourism model in the long term. In fact, at this time, there was a drop in tourism demand in the area.

In this situation, in 1988, the central government approved a Coastal Act which provides for the protection of a band of 100 meters from the sea-land line (dividing line between the public domain of the sea and land ownership private). This protection directly affects the La Manga strip. Then the Murcia Regional Government approves a regional planning law.

Furthermore, in order to stop the urban chaos of La Manga, the Murcia regional government decided to suspend the processing of planning regulations that replaced Bonet Plan and repealing, retroactively, hundreds of building permits issued by municipalities. This decision creates the outright rejection of the small and medium entrepreneurs and promoters of the construction sector.

Municipalities decide to act on behalf of entrepreneurs and developers and brought before the courts a jurisdiction conflict. They demand that the regional government cannot override their decisions retroactively. We must remember that, in Spain, municipalities can obtain high incomes to urban development.

Finally, municipalities and developers win the case. The court invalidated the retroactive nature of the shares and recognized vested rights as building permits. With this judgment, in La Manga and many other areas of the Spanish coast, consolidates a process of urban overcrowding.

5 Historical analysis of the socio-economic process

Since 1990 there has been overcrowding in many tourist areas of the Mediterranean coast. In these areas there is an urban hypertrophy.

In the case of La Manga, this hypertrophy (currently more than 250,000 beds) leads to an impoverishment of urban development as a tourism product. This statement is justified on three types of indicators: visual, urban and economic.

First, let's talk about the visual effects produced by changing urban model of the late 1970s. The mass of buildings is at the expense of eliminating the alternating low and high density initially projected. This alternation between build and not build zones, allow visual release on both sides. But the mass of buildings along both coastlines has been a claustrophobic effect screen.

On the other hand, the disappearance of the high purchasing power tourist is reflected in dismantling part of the urban fabric of low-density single-family residential. In addition other recreational infrastructure initially project such as the bullring, the airport project and the lakeside city of Veneciola, which are replaced by medium density residential blocks. Besides another buildings such as casinos or hotels, whose construction began, are abandoned despite the continued growth of La Manga. Today they are ghostly form a mass of brick and concrete that remains as a vestige of the past (Figure 5).

Second, there are clear indicators of the process of urban decline in value due to the model change. In particular, the rate of occupation of land or land valuation can observe clearly depletion factors of La Manga as a tourism product (Figures 6 and 7).

Gradual consumption soil accelerates in urban overcrowding period. However, if we look at the indicators separately for the south and north, you can see significant effects.

On one hand, you can see as the great land consumption is concentrated in the years after the term of Bonet plan. Consequently, the south is completely saturated and overcrowding produce the subsequent fall in construction activity.

Figure 5:   Construction (about 1970) and abandonment a part of Casino Dos Mares. Origin: Archive VECOS promoter and photo authors.

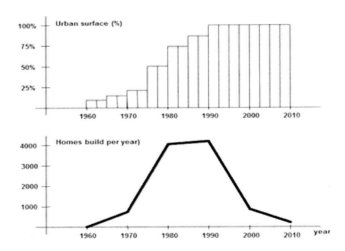

Figure 6:   Evolution of artificial surface and build construction in south zone of La Manga. Origin: the authors.

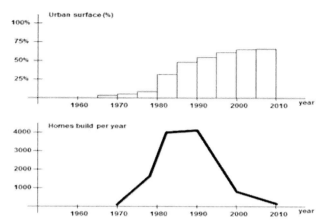

Figure 7:   Evolution of artificial surface and build construction in the north zone of La Manga. Origin: the authors.

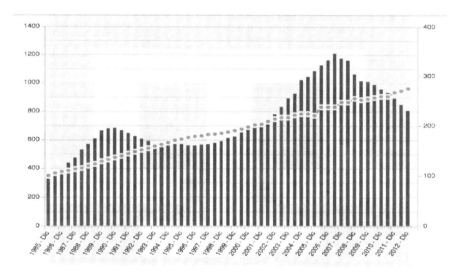

Figure 8:   Evolution in Spain of average real price of houses (Euros/m², left) and increased accumulation of CPI (%, right). Origin: Sociedad de Tasación [6].

But in the north, the construction curve is shifted in time. In fact the development works in La Manga were performed sequentially starting from the south and moving north. You can see as in the northern maintaining the concentration of construction activity in the 1980s and early 1990s. However, in the late 1990s, although the urban surface was only 60% (versus 100% in the South), the construction activity was paralyzed.

That is, the brand of La Manga as a tourism product is no longer attractive and demand for new residential tourist construction disappears.

The fact is indicative of a loss of land value, which happens to be a product with a high value (speculative value based on expectations) to be a product with low market demand and therefore of little value. These events are repeated in many other parts of the Spanish Mediterranean coast [4].

So we have an economic indicators for describe the process. Looking at (Figure 8) the evolution of the average selling price of homes and the evolution of the Consumer Price Index (CPI), one can identify speculative behavior of the housing market because of price increases (in the order of 12% per year on expansive period) are well above the CPI increase (of around 3% per year) [5].

Additionally you can see (Figure 9) the evolution of the number of dwellings completed each year in Spain and its Mediterranean coast.

In both indicators you can see a valley in the early 1990s which corresponds to the 1991–1996 crisis period, strong growth in the 1997–2007 period that corresponds to the "boom" real estate and a sharp decline since 2007 which corresponds with the period of the current crisis.

This effect is heightened on the Mediterranean coast which usually finds over 40% of homes built each year.

The collapse in the value of housing in the Spanish Mediterranean coast occurs since 2007. But in the case of La Manga this effect is attenuated, not better resistance to the crisis, but because the impairment as real estate asset was already anticipated in the previous decade by the above reasons.

The case of La Manga raises two key issues. The returns, income and foreign exchange earned by tourism justify the investments made during the 1960s and 1970s?

And again, if we consider social variables such as employment generation, increased local wealth, generation of local production network; is the investment justified?

The answers are not clear. In fact many urban developments on the Spanish Mediterranean coast have generated strong environmental, social and economic impacts [8].

At La Manga, the change of urban model and the urban overcrowding certainly have produced a complex unsustainable. The large residential growth (four times higher than forecast in the Bonet plan) was performed without executing, the same time, the infrastructures and facilities that tourist need or want. This has caused the flight of visitors with high purchasing power that are contributing the most revenue.

Using the methodology of the evaluation of the planning cost to future [9] is seen as an excessive turnover of the urban project as a tourism product, not produce higher profits or economic or social.

Evolutions of the average daily expenditure per tourist (Figure 10) confirm the hypothesis, in case of La Manga, of diminishing returns and depletion of the life cycle of urban development as a tourism product. So, at this moment, it is very complicated to return the situation and change the model for increased income in the area.

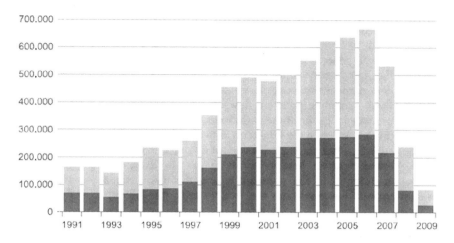

Figure 9: Number of houses finished each year in Spain and the Spanish Mediterranean coast. Origin: National Statistics Institute of Spain [7].

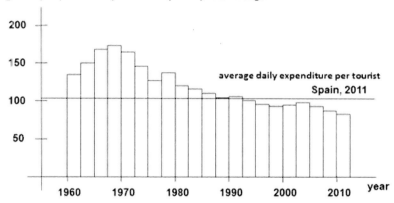

Figure 10: Average daily expenditure per tourist in La Manga (Euros) vs average in Spain in 2011. Origin: the authors.

6 Conclusions

According to the analysis of the case of La Manga, we can draw the following conclusions:

-   From the point of view of governance, the accumulation of power in local government and the excessive freedom of action of private property are not beneficial to sustainable urban development tourism or development to long run. The particular pressures on decision making generate planning policies with short-term visions.

- From a planning point of view, deregulation or lack of control of urban growth process leads to overcrowding. This overcrowding produces in the long term degradation of space and loss of quality of the environment and tourism services.
- From economic point of view, the process of urban overcrowding can produces a profit in the short term, but finally produces a loss of urban product value in the long term with declining revenue.

The case of La Manga is a representative sample to draw general conclusions for the entire Spanish Mediterranean coast. However, it represents a very instructive example of the negative effects that can have a poorly managed tourism project. It demonstrates the need for reflection and urban analysis, social and economic about coast macro-projects to assess their consequences. This need for diagnostic parameters for long-term evaluation is especially imperative now when back in Spain are proposed as potential solutions to the current crisis, the promotion of new macro-projects on the Mediterranean coast as Valdevaqueros in Cadiz, Marina d'Or Golf in Castellón, Mirador on Mallorca Es Trenc or Marina Cope in Murcia.

References

[1] García-Ayllón S. En los procesos de urbanización del mediterráneo: el caso La Manga. PhD thesis, Polytechnic University of Valencia (Spain), 2012 (in process for defence).
[2] Galiana L. and Barrado D. Los centros de interés turístico nacional y el despegue del turismo de masas en España. *Investigaciones Geográficas,* **39**, pp. 73-93, 2006.
[3] López-Morell, M.A., Pedreño Cánovas, A. and Baños Páez, P. Génesis y trayectorias del desarrollo turístico del entorno del Mar Menor. *VIII Congreso de la AEHE.* A Coruña University: A Coruña, 2005.
[4] Rullán Salamanca, O. La regulación del crecimiento urbanístico en el litoral mediterráneo español. *Revista Ciudad y Territorio,* **168**, 2011.
[5] Miralles i Garcia, J.L. Real estate crisis and sustainability in Spain. *Proc of the Sustainable Development and Planning V,* eds. C.A. Brebbia and E. Beriatos, WIT Press: Southampton, pp. 123-133, 2011.
[6] ST – Sociedad de Tasación, www.st-tasacion.es/es/informacion-mercado/ evolucion-precios-vivienda-nueva.html
[7] National Statistics Institute of Spain, www.ine.es/inebmenu/mnu_ construc.htm
[8] Miralles i Garcia, J.L., Díaz Aguirre, S. and Altur Grau, V.J. Environmental impact on the Mediterranean Spanish coast produced by the latest process of urban development. *WIT Transactions on Ecology and The Environment,* Vol 155, WIT Press: Southampton, pp. 379-389, 2012.
[9] Steinitz, C. *Environmental Planning for Communities.* Technology Transfer and Support Division, Office of Research and Development, United States Environmental Protection Agency: Cincinnati, Ohio, 2000.

Influence of trees on the air temperature in outdoor spaces according to planting parameters: the case of the city of Aix-en-Provence in France

L. Rodriguez Potes[1,2], S. Hanrot[3], M. A. Dabat[1] & J. L. Izard[1]
[1]Laboratory ABC, Architecture School of Marseille, France
[2]French Environment and Energy Management Agency (ADEME), France
[3]Research Department, Architecture School of Marseille, France

Abstract

This study is part of a doctoral thesis on the thermal environment in urban green areas in a Mediterranean climate. The purpose of this paper is to demonstrate how urban spaces are subjected to the thermal influences of planting trees. It is based on the air temperature measurements in summer in several streets with trees in Aix-en Provence city in France. The results reveal the effects of trees in cooling the air temperature, according to planting parameters: the foliage percentage, the tree coverage coefficient, the planting distance and the street orientation. The conclusions show that street orientation seems to be more important on the air temperature than the foliage percentage itself, the planting distance and the tree coverage. The contribution of the foliage percentage is insignificant in east-west streets (E-W) (The difference between the street without trees and the street with tree is 0.2°C) and the role of tree coverage coefficient is not certain in this orientation. The results of this study could be used to quantify thermal comfort in outdoor spaces including urban trees and their impact on energy consumption.
Keywords: urban trees, urban microclimate, air temperature.

WIT Transactions on Ecology and The Environment, Vol 173, © 2013 WIT Press
www.witpress.com, ISSN 1743-3541 (on-line)
doi:10.2495/SDP130251

1 Introduction

Urban design requires not only a theoretical knowledge of the climatic conditions and the impact of landscape elements on microclimate, but also the application of this knowledge to create microclimates that are comfortable for people and minimize the use of energy in buildings. To achieve these objectives, the trees are inevitable natural means: they can cool the hot air through evapotranspiration, provide shade on the floor and walls during the summer and control the wind speed. Similarly, cooling the air temperature through the trees is an effective way to reduce significantly the cooling energy consumptions [1]. Finally, the trees can use to filter pollutants, to act on noise reduction, like a sound barrier, to prevent soil erosion and to regenerate the air [2].

There is a growing interest from researchers and the public in topics associated with the microclimate role of urban trees and their contribution to the quality of life in cities. However, it seems that just a little part of research is taken into account in the development of design tools that integrate and organize urban vegetation in time and space.

2 Methodology

2.1 Presentation of the site

The city of this study is Aix-en-Provence, located near the Mediterranean coast in Provence, France, at latitude 43°31'52" north and longitude 5°27'14" east. The climate is characterized by exceptional sunshine of 2800 hours per year, an mean annual air temperature of 13°C, a relative air humidity mean of 55%, an aerology (mistral) attenuated by the surrounding mountains and a rainfall of 500mm per year. The city center is compact; it includes contemporary buildings dating from the 17th to the 19th century with a commercial and residential occupancy. The choice of the city is justified by its size (itinerary of reasonable length), the presence of a wide variety of urban forms and tree alignment in a very short distance as well the presence of a weather station near the city center, which is ideal for this study.

Six streets in the city center, four with trees and two without trees, was chosen for the case study. This opens our study to a wide range of circulation spaces such as streets, avenues and boulevards. The selection of the case study is therefore based on an analysis of the green spaces in the city of Aix-en-Provence.

2.2 Hypothesis

The effects of trees on the thermal conditions in outdoor spaces during the summer are related to the street orientation, the planting parameters (the coverage of the crown and separations between trees and buildings) and the percentage of foliage. These three parameters are used to characterize and to analyze the results.

2.2.1 Hypothesis 1: orientation of the street

Tree effects can change according to street orientation: blocking sunlight or windbreaks, etc. There are three streets orientations in our study: north-south (NS), east-west (EW) and north-east/south-west (NE-SW).

2.2.2 Hypothesis 2: planting parameters

The distance of planting trees in relation to buildings (tree distance) and the size of the crown (tree coverage) can change the thermal conditions. The tree coverage is the zone occupied by the crown under the street.

- The tree distance Da to the center of the roadway is related to the width W of the street and expressed by the coefficient Da/W. So, when Da/W is closer to 1, the trees are near the buildings, when Da/W is closer to 0, the trees are in the axis of the roadway.
- The diameter of the crown $2da$ is reported to W and expressed by the coefficient $2da/W$, this is the tree coverage coefficient. So, when $2da/W$ is closer to 1, the trees fill the sky, when $2da/W$ is 0, there are not trees.

The intersection of these parameters gives three cases of planting trees that it we found on our study site (fig. 1).

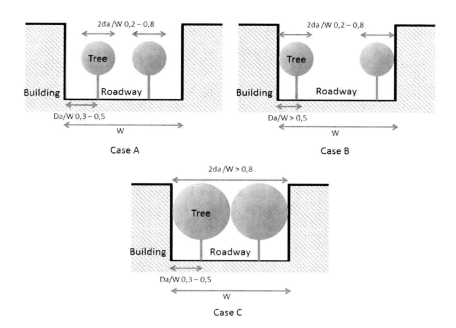

Figure 1:   Planting parameters for every case.

- Case A: trees separated from the building and low tree coverage coefficient: Da/W 0.3 - 0.5; $2da/W$ 0.2 - 0.8.
- Case B: trees near the buildings and low tree coverage coefficient: $Da/W>$ 0.5, $2da/W$ 0.2 - 0.8.
- Case C: trees near the buildings and high tree coverage coefficient: Da/W 0.3 - 0.5; $2da/W>$ 0.8.

2.2.3 Hypothesis 3: percentage of foliage (% F)

The foliage of the trees can cool the air by evapotranspiration and by the shadow on the floor and walls during the summer, reducing the radiation and control the speed of the wind. In this study, the percentage of foliage is related to the LAD (leaf area index). It indicates the total leaf area and determines the degree of light transmission and radiation. It has been calculated from the exploitation of "fish eye" pictures using the method to estimate the "Sky View Factor" (fig. 2). We define a low percentage of foliage <45%, a high percentage of foliage >55% and a mean percentage of foliage between 45% and 55%.

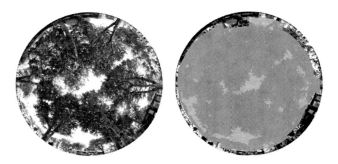

Figure 2:   "Fish eye" pictures to estimate the percentage of foliage.

2.3 Description of the experimental measurement itinerary

For practical reasons of operability of the itinerary, we chose streets closest to each other: Victor Hugo Boulevard (NE-SW), Victor Hugo Boulevard (N-S), Cours Mirabeau (E-W), Cours Sextius (NE-SW), Giuseppe Verdi Avenue (E-W) and Joseph Villevielle Avenue (NE-SW) (fig. 3).

Measurements of air temperature, relative humidity and wind speed were made 9 September 2011. These measurements were taken every three hours (6h to 20h) at specific points in the streets, under the foliage, and a height of 1.5 meters above the ground with the multifunction device TESTO 452. A Mini Testo 175-H2 logger was placed at a reference point (R) close to the others points, 1.5 m above the ground in the shade to save data on the air temperature and air humidity every six minutes. The day was sunny with clear sky with a mean air temperature of 21.4°C, a relative air humidity of 59.4%, a wind speed of 0.58 m/s. The trees identified in the streets were the Platane (*Platanus X acerifolia*) and the *Micocoulier (Celtis australis)*.

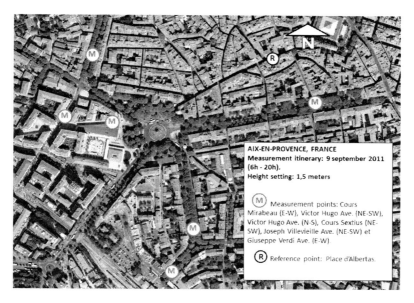

Figure 3: Measurement itinerary [3].

3 Results

The analysis of the results is based on the geometric mean air temperature (TAir°C). The table ranks the mean air temperature from the highest to the lowest and shows the parameters values (table 1).

Table 1: Air temperature and parameters values for every street.

Street	TAir (°C)	Orientation	Foliage (%f)	Distance (Da)	Tree coverage (2da)
Victor Hugo Blvd.	25.9	N-S	53.8	0.4	0.7
Cours Mirabeau	26.2	E-W	43.5	0.4	0.5
Giuseppe Verdi Ave.	26.4	E-W	0.0	0.0	0.0
Victor Hugo Blvd.	26.8	NE-SW	42.5	0.5	0.9
Cours Sextius	26.9	NE-SW	49.7	0.6	0.8
Joseph Villevielle Ave.	26.9	NE-SW	0.0	0.0	0.0

a) North-south (N-S) streets: among all streets, Victor Hugo Blvd. has the highest percentage of foliage (53.8%), a mean tree coverage coefficient (0.7) compared to others and it is the farthest of buildings (0.4). It has the lowest temperature 25.9°C, it is the coolest of all the streets and it has the best combination of parameters.

b) East-west (E-W) streets: the Cours Mirabeau has a percentage of foliage of 43.5%, a tree coverage of 0.5 and a tree distance from the building of 0.4 (farthest of buildings), even it has a light reduction of the air temperature (26.2°C), two tenths below the Giuseppe Verdi Ave.(26.4°C) without trees.

c) North-east/south-west (NE-SW) streets: the Cours Sextius (26.9°C) is in the average in terms of foliage 49.7%, a tree coverage coefficient of 0.8 and a tree distance close to buildings (0.6). The Victor Hugo Blvd. (26.8°C) has a lowest percentage of foliage of 42.5%, a tree coverage coefficient a little higher of 0.9 and a distance tree of 0.6. The Joseph Villevieille Ave. has an air temperature of 26.9°C while it has no trees (0%) and even the Cours Sextius has an air temperature of 26.9°C and a percentage of foliage of 49.7%: they are the hottest NE-SW streets. The orientation and the temperature are almost constant, even the tree coverage and the foliage does not seem to influence the temperature of the air.

d) The comparison between the Victor Hugo Blvd. (N-S orientation, 53.8% of foliage, distance 0.4 and tree coverage 0.7) and the Cours Mirabeau (E-W orientation, 43.5% of foliage, distance 0.4 and cover 0.5) shows that the Victor Hugo Blvd. has a strong tree coverage coefficient and the Cours Mirabeau has an mean value, that means, a difference of 0.2. The distances are the same and there is a gap of foliage density of 10.3%. The parameter combination in these two streets allows it to gain only 0.3°C. The comparison between the Victor Hugo Blvd. N-S and the NE-SW streets, shows temperature differences between 0.9°C to 1°C, whether trees or not. Between the E-W streets and NE-SW streets there are differences in temperature of 0.4°C to 0.7°C.

4 Discussion

The Victor Hugo Blvd. (N-S) has all the settings for it. It has the best planting parameters and a north-south orientation. This combination gives a difference of 1°C compared to the highest temperature (NE-SW orientation). However, we cannot say exactly what is the weight of the orientation and the weight of these settings in the N-S orientation, if that penalizes or improves the thermal conditions. That means that we cannot say in the comparison that the lower air temperature value in the north-south street orientation is due to parameters of trees, it could be related to the orientation but it may be related to the combination of parameters planting.

Three facts arise: either the vegetation does not play a significant role in the temperature of the air, so the difference is mainly due to the orientation. Or improvement of the temperature is only due to the parameters of planting. Or, trees distance, combined with the orientation, reduces the air temperature. This would imply that a north-south street without trees could not have this lower temperature. However, without a north-south street in our study, a definitive conclusion is not possible.

In cases oriented east-west, the combination of parameters seems not to be very important because the street with trees and without trees have almost the same air temperature. So, this means that whatever the way we combine the planting parameters between them, there is not much impact on the temperature, in our cases the street orientation has a more strong impact. Maybe, if they have the highest values of parameters, it may have had a greater difference, for example, if we have more than 53.8% of foliage, a tree coverage of 0.9 with the minimum distance of 0.4, we may have lower air temperatures.

In the NE-SW street, it is difficult to estimate the weight of each parameter in the air temperature value. The combination of all these factors gives almost the same air temperature value, therefore, the combination of distance, percentage of foliage and tree coverage, do not seem to be effective when the street is oriented NE-SW. For example, the three NE-SW streets have a percentage of foliage from 0% to 49.7%, this is a very substantial difference, but it seems that it does not play a positive role.

It is also observed by comparing all the cases that have a mean percentage of foliage with a high tree coverage coefficient, this is equal to a compensation or balance between both. But the optimization of these parameters is reduced by the proximity to the buildings. However, if the planting distance from the buildings is reduced and at the same time it is combined with a good tree coverage and a relatively low percentage of foliage, there is a balance or compensation. That means that the proximity of trees to the buildings may be a factor penalizing.

A higher planting distance from the buildings, as well as a greater tree coverage, whether or not combined, has a positive effect because the air temperature is lower even if the percentage of foliage is lower. But when the trees are very close to the buildings and the tree cover is smaller, that becomes a negative factor, because the air temperature rises even if there are a high percentage of foliage. But we do not know what is the weight in improving the temperature of these factors. It is still unclear, but it may still award that the distance plays an important role in the air temperature. The street orientation seems to be more important than the vegetation itself, but nevertheless, some parameters are having some effect on the temperature of the air, such as the distance from the buildings and the tree coverage coefficient.

5 Conclusion

The analysis of the parameters related to trees and urban planning showed relationships between the way the trees are planted in the city and the thermal condition of these spaces. The orientation, the distances from the buildings and the tree coverage have influences on the air temperature.

Based on the analysis results, we can emphasize these facts:

1. The parameters of the vegetation do not play an important role in the air temperature of the NE-SW street.
2. The tree planting combined with N-S orientation allows a low air temperature, which itself could not have had this performance.
3. Depending on the street orientation, the percentage of foliage may be more or less effective.
4. The proximity of the tree to the buildings plays an important role: A high distance of the trees from the building reduces the air temperature. A low distance of the trees form the building increases the air temperature.
5. The streets orientation, the tree distance and the tree coverage combined or not can compensate a low percentage of foliage and improve a thermal performance.
6. In terms of orientation, E-W streets have better thermal performance than NE-SW. An E-W street, even without trees, is more favorable than a NE-SW street with trees.
7. If the vegetation improves thermal conditions, the street orientation improves too and the combination of both improves greatly.

It is not only the trees that contribute to changing the thermal conditions, but also the urban forms, including street orientation. This is why we get better results if a true compromise occurs between the form of construction of our cities and the environment

References

[1] Akbari et al. *Peak power and cooling energy savings of shade trees*. Akbari, H., Kurn, D.M., Bretz, S.E., Hanford, J.W, Energy and Buildings, 25, 139–148, 1997.
[2] Panagopoulos. *Using microclimatic landscape design to create thermal comfort and energy efficiency*, Actas da 1ª Conferência sobre Edifícios Eficientes, Universidade do Algarve, 25 de Janeiro, 2008.
[3] Aix-en-Provence map taken 11th February 2012 from http://www.bing.com /maps/?FORM=Z9LH3.

A new paradigm of urban development: envisioning sustainable futures in Qatar

Hatem Galal A. Ibrahim
Department of Architecture and Urban Planning,
College of Engineering, Qatar University, Qatar (on leave from:
Department of Architecture in Mataria, Helwan University, Egypt)

Abstract

In the past few years and as a result of the dramatic increase in national income that has accompanied the development of the oil industry, Qatar has undergone immense changes in its social, economic and physical environments. In less than half a century, the country has been transformed from a nomadic and subsistence farming economy into a modern urban/industrial society with a per capita income that is considered one of the highest worldwide. As a result, the demographics of the society have become more global and contemporary and international values and attitudes have impacted the existing cultural and architectural patterns. Qatari architectural trends have become increasingly contemporary and completely detached from the traditional ones that reflect the country's identity. Doha, the capital, has recently witnessed the resurgence of the discourse on Islam as a cultural identity. Qatar's attractiveness today is generated from its modernized architectural patterns and styles that balance traditionism and modernism. Many of the newly designed buildings are strictly reproducing the Qatari traditional elements and styles.

This paper focuses on understanding the relationship between culture and identity in Qatar. Traditional places where major festivals and cultural social activities take place, within the social and urban fabric of culturally diverse cities. The paper investigates this idea as an approach of maintaining the principles of traditional Qatari architecture while taking advantage of the introduced modern technology. The paper also calls for integrating the identity of the place within the contemporary urban environment of old cities.
Keywords: Qatari architecture language, contemporary architecture, sustainable development, urban environment, cultural identity.

WIT Transactions on Ecology and The Environment, Vol 173, © 2013 WIT Press
www.witpress.com, ISSN 1743-3541 (on-line)
doi:10.2495/SDP130241

1 Introduction

Traditional architecture is being recognised as the true bastion of rationality. There is nothing superfluous in traditional architecture. The solutions proposed are the result of centuries of empiricism. At the same time, its relationship with its setting is more appropriate, as it is the source of life for all those living in it. The setting is carefully preserved and transformed with extreme sensitivity, never forgetting that it will have to be passed on to future generations.

In the past, when the building envelope was the main element man used to protect himself from a harsh climate, he had to depend on passive energy and natural resources, such as sun, wind and earth. Passive energy involves the use of natural energy sources for environmental, healthy and economical reasons in our buildings. Traditional architecture, in the Arab world, represents a living witness for the suitability of this architecture to the local environment, which incorporated the essence of sustainable architecture.

Adham [1] states that the Architecture of Qatar is exemplified by its capital city Doha, which has changed significantly from a small town with no more than 20,000 inhabitants in the early 1950s to a global city and a regional economic hub with more than 1.7 million inhabitants in 2010 [2]. Doha's rapid pace of urbanization is depicted in Figure 1 below, which clearly shows the significant expansion of its built agglomeration over the past 65 years, from approximately 1.3 square kilometers in the late 1940s to over 200 square kilometers in 2010 [2, 3].

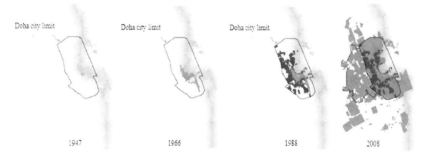

Figure 1:   Doha's urban growth 1947–2008.

The contemporary architecture of Qatar is a result of a range of contemporary urban dynamics that are inextricably linked to complex and interconnected forces and processes of economic transformation, cultural restructuring, and globalization. These dynamics involve all the key components of urban systems-human, natural, and built that significantly differ from the dynamics and processes that governed urban growth patterns of Doha during the second half of the 20th century.

Until the early 1990s, Doha's urban growth patterns progressed at a relatively slow rate through state-funded infrastructure, services, and housing projects. The slow rate of urban development was widely attributed to the country's relatively unstable labor market [3]. The references attribute this instability to the country's oil-based economy in which the hiring of construction and expatriate workers correlated with the country's fluctuating oil revenues [1, 4].

Since the late 1990s, Doha's urban growth has been progressing at a much faster rate, which is attributed to a transition from oil-based toward a competitive and more complex globalized economy [5]. This transition, despite the strong dependence of government's spending on oil revenues, has made Qatar's rapid growth the fastest in the world during the 2000s. The transition resulted in substantial domestic investment in infrastructure and promoted diversification in the country's labor market, including employment in entrepreneurship, education and event tourism sectors [2, 6]. As a result, Doha begun to emerge as a global center for media, education, culture and finance through huge investments and several initiatives such as the Al Jazeera Channel, the Doha Economic Zone, the Education City, Qatar Foundation for Education, Science and Community Development and the "Pearl Island" reclamation project. This was accompanied by a construction boom that erected skyscrapers, sport facilities, shopping malls, gated communities and iconic museums and libraries.

As a result of the dramatic increase in national income that has accompanied the development of the oil industry, Qatar has undergone immense changes in its social, economic and physical environments. In less than half a century, the country has been transformed from a nomadic and subsistence farming economy into a modern urban/industrial society with per capita income that is considered one of the highest worldwide. As a result, the demographics of the society have become more global and contemporary and international values and attitudes have impacted the existing cultural and architectural patterns. Qatari architectural trends have become increasingly contemporary and completely detached from the traditional ones that reflect the country's identity. Doha, the capital, has recently witnessed the resurgence of the discourse on Islam as a cultural identity. Sincerely at times, but opportunistically at others, many architects got engaged in the design of various historicist styles to satisfy the growing demand for a contemporary Islamic architecture. The modern and post modern Qatari architecture have gone their way disregarding tradition and as a result, the Qatari cultural Architectural traditional identity has been erased. Qatar's attractiveness today is generated from its modernized architectural patterns and styles that balance tradition-ism and modernism. Many of the newly designed buildings are strictly reproducing the Qatari traditional elements and styles as shown in Figure 2 [7].

Figure 2:   Modern buildings designed on Qatari traditional architectural patterns.

2   Scope of work

In Qatar, contemporary western architecture becomes significant with a fast growth compared to the traditional trends, and the country has been transformed into a modern progressive urban with per capital incomes that are considered one of the highest incomes worldwide. The contemporary architecture have impacted the urban development and directed to be detached from the Qatari architecture language. Significant distracts in Doha bear witness to the struggle between culture, history and place making culminating in the question of a Qatari national identity. This concludes the first theoretical part of a running research project funded by Qatar National Research Fund – QNRF (http://www.qnrf.org). It develops the idea of developing indicators for unifying the Qatari architecture language and the contemporary architecture. A detailed theoretical study, are carried out to emphasize the architectural traditional elements that reflect the culture identity. This process is a part of presenting an introductory framework for unifying the Qatari architecture language in the urban contemporary environment with the support of city image and urban identity. The developed framework can facilitate urban identity for the groups associated with definite urban environments and play an important role in the formation, change, and reproduction of the identity of the place.

The next phase of the project is still on process and to be published in future. The second phase aims at applying the developed framework based on the developed framework for assessing Qatari architecture language in three contemporary case studies in Qatar.

3   Contemporary architecture: the case of Qatar

Today's awareness is about the environment and minimizing the use of energy. Subsequently today's architecture concerns the changes in the atmosphere and how to protect it. The trend wasn't negotiated in old architecture. This is because of using local building materials and trend that meet the environment. The buildings at this time are to build for last without harming the nature. An example is shown in Figure 3; Um Salal Mohammed fort, which is located in Qatar and was built using limestone as a local material.

Since Qatar has become an open country to the whole world, it has been affected by the changes in architecture. The huge development in Qatar a few

Figure 3:   Um Salal Mohammed fort in Qatar.

years ago increased the flow of people with different cultures and life styles. This variety of cultures in addition to the open market and globalization affect the style of architecture in Qatar. It becomes more open and accepts other cultures and had been expressed the latest building's technology. As a result, Qatar begun to emerge as a global center for media, education, culture and finance through huge investments and several initiatives such as the Al Jazeera Channel, the Doha Economic Zone, the Education City, Science and Community Development. A construction boom that erected skyscrapers, sport facilities, gated communities and iconic museums.

Therefore, the architecture in Qatar nowadays is a mix of European, Asian, Islamic, Arabian and local trends so that Qatar architecture image becomes difficult to be recognized (Figure 4).

Figure 4:   Contemporary architecture in Qatar – globalization trend.

However in the other direction, other traditional buildings are stringing the identity of the country (Figure 5). This direction goes with what Qatar Vision 2030 is about: Preserving Qatar's national heritage and enhance Arab and Islamic values and identity. Preserving its identity in all aspect and architecture is one of the major aspects of the vision. Qatar Vision seeks also to meet sustainability requirements and to be reflected in the contemporary architecture; keep the identity; use sustainable technology and materials and accordingly lead to good contemporary architecture [8].

Figure 5:   Traditional architecture in Qatar.

4   Qatari traditional architecture language

In this part, the significant traditional elements of Qatari architecture are to be identified. The aim of this part is to assess the contemporary architecture in Qatar in terms of integrating these elements. This is to be analyzed as an approach for applying the developed framework in the second phase of the UREP project (Qatari architecture language – case studies analysis).

4.1 Materials and building elements

The traditional architecture in Qatar has its distinguished style that reflects the real taste of the people, who built the houses and of those who lived in them. The people of the region are governed by certain inherited social traditions. People are also bound by the prevailing environmental conditions, as regard to the building material that suit the climate. The building material and the climate are the main two factors that direct the way and decide the style of the building elements. The Qatari traditional *architecture* features is clear from the combination between the traditional materials and the different building elements as follows:

4.1.1 The wooden beam
The palm trunks and 'Danshall' wood stems are used to make bridges in the old traditional houses. The wooden bridges as shown in Figure 6 were made on top of the doors and window opining. They were also used to join the corners of the walls of the room. The use of the materials described above can be clearly seen with the very simple crossed pattern of bamboo canes directly on top of the mangrove pole beams supporting the roof.

Figure 6:   The use of wooden beams in the ceiling bridges (the Danshall).

4.1.2 The traditional Qatari wall
Ordinary natural mud is usually used while putting courses of strong and solid stone walls. The walls of the building are covered from inside and outside with mud, either by only mud or mixed with plants such as grass or hay to prevent cracks due to desiccation, rain water, wind and other atmospheric elements. The process of spoiling and disfiguring will continue as long as the remaining parts of the walls are left without maintenance and reinforcement (Figure 7).

Figure 7:   Some examples of mud wall in traditional Qatari architecture.

4.1.3 The wind tower
The wind tower was used in the past as a ventilation system that catches the air and distributed to the different spaces of the buildings. Wind tower was designed for use in dense urban situations where there was a need to draw air down into

the courtyard houses. The wind towers were constructed on a square plan and contained a cruciform device on the internal diagonals which allowed air to funnel down into a space at the bottom of the tower (Figure 8).

Figure 8:   The idea and examples of wind tower in Qatari traditional buildings.

4.1.4 Ornamental elements

There are two main ornamental elements, which was used in traditional Qatari buildings during the centuries.

4.1.4.1   Wall alcoves or recess

They are horizontal wall cuttings made of carol bricks "fouroush" quarried from the sea shore. It was an economic and easy way and used for making wall opening for light and ventilation (wall air tower – wall badjair) (Figure 9).

Figure 9:   Alcoves and recess in traditional Qatari architecture.

4.1.4.2   Parapet and terraces

All types of traditional buildings in Qatar were characterized by the presence of varied balconies on the tops of minarets, upper rooms and towers. These upper terraces were often compatible terraces with the kind and pattern of the building in Qatar which shows that such traditional architecture is completely characterized by these terraces (Figure 10).

Figure 10:   Parapet and terraces pattern in Qatari traditional architecture.

4.1.5 The openings

The opening in Qatari traditional architecture consists of two building elements: the wooden doors and the windows. The significant details include the following.

4.1.5.1 The wooden door

Doors design and construction varied with time, cost and area, particularly in their rural or urban styles although. As would be expected, the wooden door is popular in Qatari traditional buildings. The best type of wood used for making doors is the sago palm wood. It is famous for its wooden door that carries plant-like and geometrical decoration. The design of doors and their doorways differed all over the Qatar peninsula dependent upon where their manufacture or craftsmen originated. In the construction over the door there are two more details. There is the standard ventilation solution above the door where the opening is protected by wrought iron bars set in the teak frame (Figure 11).

Figure 11:   Some typical examples of Qatari traditional door.

4.1.5.2 The windows

The windows were rectangular recesses. They were one and half meters high, one meter width and 45 cm thick (it was almost the same thickness of the wall). All round the window from the outside, there was a wooden frame with a horizontal wooden board in the middle. This horizontal board divided the frame into two equal rectangles; one on the top and one below. Through the frame and the horizontal board there were some iron bars. The rows of windows in an old ruined building are typical in their size and positioning of those in many of the old buildings, particularly *majaalis* which are usually characterized by the open character of their walls (Figure 12).

Figure 12:   Traditional Qatari windows.

4.2 Landscape components and activities

Landscape elements draw the traditional sense in the spaces includes: lighting, signage, benches, and other amenities. They emphasis the traditional elements of architecture creating an essence of the old Qatari era; new features and sophisticated lighting systems are also developed to provide illumination (Figure 13) show Souk Waqif as a significant traditional example [7].

Figure 13:   Souk Waqif: furniture, lighting and signage system.

4.3 Function and activities:

The existing of traditional activities such as galleries, workshops, art events and concert are also affecting the traditional value in the place. This is including art shops and exhibition rooms, souvenirs and restaurants serving a traditional cuisine.

5   Establishing traditional architecture values- tabulation and analysis procedures

The purpose of this part is to develop a check list of the indicators/parameters based on traditional architecture for integrating the Qatari architecture language in the urban contemporary environment with the support of city image and urban identity. Based on the previous theoretical study of Qatari architectural traditional elements, establishing architecture parameters that can be used in assessing the unifying of Qatari language with the contemporary architecture is to be established.

A framework is developed, taking into account the concluded elements/ parameters that affect the Qatari traditional value and based on the previous theoretical study. The traditional values are classified into three main parts: the building components, the function/ activities and landscape components as shown in Figure 14.

Building elements are providing as a guide to developers. They clearly identify the architectural elements and design features which reflect the Qatari architecture. The incorporation of these architectural elements and design features into the contemporary developments make a positive contribution to the unique character of the local architecture in Qatar.

Landscape components are a second parameter, which gives a lasting and often a sense of traditional and of the quality of development. Landscaping provides visual appeal and environmental comfort. It improves both the appearance and value of property and instills confidence and pride in the neighbourhoods. Landscape design involves a variety of elements that include both soft and hard surfaces, water, screening, fencing and lighting. Soft surfaces refer to live planting including trees, shrubs, grass and ground cover. Hard surfaces refer to non-live elements such as paved areas, stone, screening and edges. The integration of traditional landscape with a contemporary architecture is very effective in reflecting the sense of place and the identity of the country.

There is a relationship between activities and identity and in particular how activities can be used to promote the identity of the country. Traditional Qatari activities include horse racing, camel racing, and falconry is strengthen the sense of the place and reflects a fourth dimension of the identity of the place.

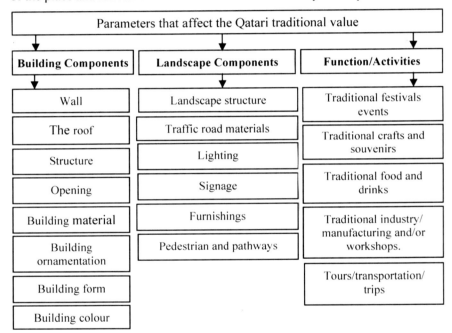

Figure 14:   Parameters for Qatari traditional architecture.

6   Future work

A detailed review of the contemporary architecture in Qatar is to be carried out. This review demonstrates where 'Traditional Criteria' are available in the chosen application (traditional responsive contemporary trend). A questionnaire will be designed based on the produced values in Figure 14. The questionnaire is to be distributed to the experts and professionals in addition to the stockholders to measure the responses on the elements that reflect traditional responsive contemporary architecture. Three selected contemporary case studies in Doha are to be carried out for three significant different contemporary trends neighbourhoods: Al- Dafna, Souq Waqif, Pearl Qatar urban areas (Figure 15).

a) Al- Dafna Area   b) Souq Waqif   c) Pearl Qatar

Figure 15:   Three selected case studies: Dafna, Souq Waqif and Pearl Qatar
               areas.

The limitation of the implemented framework and the outcome of the research
are to be discussed. The results of the case studies demonstrate what was learned
and what was gained in understanding the Qatari contemporary language. It
might be advised to implement a scoring system of framework variables in kind
of recommended interactive tools such as an agent, which enables local
authorities, investors, and architects to have a conclusion concern the rank of
unifying the Qatari architecture language and the contemporary architecture in
Qatar.

7 Conclusion

Traditional architecture is a significant trend for fortifying the cultural identity.
One of the main reasons for the attractiveness of Qatar is its ability to balance
between the Qatari and the modern language in the contemporary architecture.
    Many of Qatar's heritage buildings are magnificent in the sense that they
were traditionally designed strictly according to the Qatari architecture trend. In
recent years, Qatari urban has come to encompass a greater variety of western
architectural styles. Some buildings are entirely distinctive and local in their
character and many other buildings are the product of direct western
architectural.
    This paper presents indicators based on traditional architecture for integrating
the Qatari architecture language in the urban contemporary environment with the
support of city image and urban identity. These indicators are to be developed by
exploring the specific characteristics of the contemporary architecture. The
developed of the Qatari traditional elements based on a theoretical study is
concluded.
    The developed Qatari traditional elements are intended to cover key issues
dealing with traditional architectural. This aims to adapting the past with the
present and having a concluded image of the future. The traditional values are
classified into three main parts: the building components, the function/activities
and landscape components.
    The future work is to be conducted by a technical review from decision
makers and experts in the field, whom are well-versed and respected in the
subject. The purpose of this stage is to review the implemented framework that

can unify the Qatari architecture language and the contemporary architecture. It is also providing an evidence for the effectiveness of the established variables. This stage is allowing the necessary development and verification of the developed indicators.

Acknowledgment

This paper was made possible by an UREP award [UREP 11 - 019 - 5 - 004] from the Qatar National Research Fund (a member of The Qatar Foundation). The statements made herein are solely the responsibility of the author.

References

[1]   Adham, K., Rediscovering the Island: Doha's Urbanity from Pearls to Spectacle (Chapter 9). *Tradition, Modernity and Urban Development*, ed. Y. El-Sheshtawy, pp. 218–257, 2008.

[2]   QGSDP, Qatar National Development Strategy 2011~2016: *Towards Qatar National Vision 2030*, General Secretariat for Development Planning, 2011.

[3]   Al-Buainain, F., Urbanisation in Qatar: A study of the Residential and Commercial Land Development in Doha City 1970–1997 Dissertation, University of Salford, 1999.

[4]   Al-Kuwari, M. K., *The Development of Doha and a Future Urban Strategy for Qatar*, University College of Swansea, Wales, 1992.

[5]   Alraouf, A.A., 2010, A New Paradigm in Knowledge-based Urban Development: From Knowledge to Creativity Economy, Qatar Urbanity Transformed. *Proc. of the 3rd Knowledge Cities World Summit*, eds. T. Yigitcanlar, P. Yates and K. Kunzmann, Melbourne, Australia: World Capital Institute, pp. 1273–1285, 2010.

[6]   The World Bank – WB, *Turning Qatar into a Competitive Knowledge-Based Economy: Knowledge Economy Assessment of Qatar*, Doha, Qatar: The World Bank – Report to Qatar Planning Council, 2007.

[7]   Ibrahim, H. and Khalil, R., Rooting Old Souk in the Contemporary Urbanism of Qatar, Spaces Flows: An International Journal of Urban and ExtraUrban Studies, 2(1), pp. 69–85, 2012.

[8]   Qatar National Vision 2030, General Secretariat for Development Planning (GSDP), Virginia Commonwealth University in Qatar – Center for Research in Design, 2008.

New Urbanism and sense of community in new Egyptian settlements: case study – El Sherouq city, Egypt

S. Shafik & S. El Bayar
Arab Academy for Science and Technology and Maritime Transport, Department of Architectural Engineering and Environmental Design, Alexandria, Egypt

Abstract

In the past, each street and alley had a story to tell, each having its own flavor. Different neighborhoods reflected the cultures and beliefs of different people. Due to industrialization, the rise of car dependence, and technological advancement, cities and towns' edges and centers have faded away because of urban sprawl. New communities have emerged far away from the heart of the city. These new communities lack identity, sense of community and suffer problems such as social exclusion. New Urbanism emerged as a reaction to undo and avoid the negative impacts of urban sprawl. This research aims to check which New Urbanism principles are already applied and which can be applied to Panorama El Sherouq neighborhood in El Sherouq City, Egypt. The scope of this paper will focus on the relationship between New Urbanism principles and sense of community. It highlights New Urbanism principles and clarifies sense of community in an analytical example. Finally, this research aims to evaluate the sense of community in Panorama El Sherouq and to achieve a set of recommendations to apply New Urbanism principles to enhance sense of community.
Keywords: New Urbanism, sense of community, neotraditionalism.

1 Introduction

In old Egyptian neighborhoods, people were attached to their neighborhood as they built up memories of growing up, memories of their ancestors that once lived there, and memories of warm neighbors that looked for one another.

Neighborhoods play a big role in shaping one's identity and sense of community. A well planned neighborhood allows people to bond together.

Due to industrialization, the urban population increased according to the census of Egypt in various years [1]. Peasants immigrated from the rural to the urban in search of better job opportunities. Cities and towns' edges and centers faded away with the urban sprawl. The cities identity and historical background are erased by new unplanned developments. Moreover, people focus on their own competing fast paced life, that they become isolated from one another. Thus, sense of community started to fade away.

Achieving urban sustainability is a major obstacle to many cities and towns because of the growing urban sprawl. New Urbanism emerged as a reaction to undo and avoid the negative impacts of urban sprawl. The main objective of New Urbanism is the promotion of sense of community [2]. Along with sense of community, there were other social goals like social equity and common good. Questions arose whether or not New Urbanism is actually capable of promoting sense of community in new settlements and whether or not New Urbanism principles could be adopted in New Egyptian settlements.

2 Definition of New Urbanism

New Urbanism or neotraditionalism is a western movement emerged in the nineteenth century as a reaction to the unplanned urban sprawl. New urbanism is identified as an umbrella term for design tenets of Traditional Neighborhood Development (TND) and Transit Oriented Development (TOD) [2]. TND principles are inspired from the urban form used in centuries before the invention of automobiles. In addition, TOD is dense development of housing and commercial units taking into consideration transportation connections [3].

New Urbanism principles is concerned with walkable, connected, mixed-use and diverse neighborhoods. It supports the traditional neighborhood structure and the quality of architecture and urban design. Other principles include: mixed housing, increased density, narrow streets, and discernible neighborhood center [4].

3 New Urbanism Movement

Founded in 1993, a group of architects formed the Congress of New Urbanism (CNU) seeking to create principles based on their previous works to create better performing neighborhoods. CNU held many congresses to demonstrate goals and principles of New Urbanism. Their goal is to reform the public policy to support the restoration of existing urban centers and towns within metropolitan regions, the reconfiguration of sprawling suburbs, taking into consideration the natural environment, and preservation of the built heritage. According to the CNU, public policy should be formed to support diverse uses and population in neighborhoods, communities should be designed for pedestrian, transit, and automobiles. Not only that, but communities should embrace public spaces and civic institutions. Moreover, urban space should be shaped by architecture and landscape that reflect local history, climate, ecology, and building practice [5].

In 2000, the CNU outlined the principles in the *Charter of New Urbanism*. The charter includes principles to guide public policy development practice, urban planning, and design. The principles are distributed into three scales: The region: Metropolis, city, and town; the neighborhood, the district, and the corridor; the block, the street, and the building [5].

4 Definition of sense of community

Based on Joseph R Gusfield, the term community covers two aspects: the territorial and geographical part of the community like neighborhood, town, and city. The second aspect is relational which is related to the quality of human relationships. Gusfield stated that the two aspects are interdependent to sense of community [6]. On the other hand, Durkheim stated that community develops around interests and skills more than environment [7].

The most widely accepted definition to date for sense of community by David W. MacMillan and David M. Chavis is "a feeling that members have of belonging, a feeling that members matter to one another and to the group, and a shared faith that members' needs will be met through their commitment to be together" [8]. The definition includes four elements: membership, influence, integration and fulfillment of needs, and shared emotional connection. The correlated four elements make up the definition of sense of community.

Based on Chavis and MacMillan [8] membership is feeling of belonging or personal relatedness among residents. It is bounded by language, dress, and rituals. Boundaries are created among people in fear of rejection for being different. Membership grants emotional safety, sense of belonging, identification, feeling of acceptance, and the willingness to sacrifice for a group of members. Another membership attribute is personal investment. Members of a community have a common symbol system identified by a logo, landmark, or an architectural style. Nonetheless, members are attracted to a community in which they feel that they are influential.

Chavis and MacMillan [8] stated that influence is a sense of mattering of making a difference to a group and group mattering to its member. Research proves that one can influence others taking into consideration needs, values, and opinions of other members. People feel they have influence through leadership role even if it was indirect. Group cohesiveness is determined by community influence and conformity. However, group may lay pressures on members for conformity causing into negative outcomes in the community. A balanced community is where members don't give up their own choices for conformity and yet be accepted by the other contradicting members. In addition, participation leads to greater "ownership of the community, greater satisfaction, and greater cohesion between members". Moreover, influence of a member on the community and the influence of the community on a member function parallel to each other to achieve community cohesiveness.

Another key element of sense community according to Chavis and MacMillan [8] is integration and fulfillment of needs or in other words reinforcement. A community should be able to fit different members together so that they meet other member's needs while meeting their own. Community should reward members through status of membership, success of the community and competence of other members to reinforce sense of community. Individuals are attracted to communities that offer them the most. Apart from the survival needs, there are the shared values where a community is able to organize and prioritize its need to be fulfilled through activities. Individuals with shared values, beliefs, priorities, and needs form cohesive communities.

As for the emotional connection, Chavis and MacMillan [8] stated that individuals that share history strengthen the community. Contact hypothesis states that the more members of the community interact, the more likely they are close and the more positive the quality of interaction, the stronger the bond between members is. Not only had that, but sharing important events bring people closer together. Events shouldn't be ambiguous and left unresolved, closure to events impacts cohesiveness. Moreover, personal investment among members enhances community cohesiveness. Additionally, honoring members for positive impacts create emotional connections between different members. Another attribute enhancing the emotional connection is the spiritual bond found in many religious communities.

Other researchers such as Buckner describe sense of community as "the sense of belongingness, fellowship, "we-ness", identity, etc., experienced in the context of functional (group) or geographically based collective" [9]. Another definition by Glynn identified sense of community's main elements as homogeneity, interdependence, shared responsibility, face-to-face relationships, and common goals [10]. Later on, Joranko stated the importance of connection, belonging, support, safety, empowerment, and participation to sense of community [11]. Talen stated that there are other elements that impact sense of community such as homogeneity, income, gender, and education [2].

Based on the previous discussion, Table 1 shows that some elements mentioned by Buckner, Glynn, and Joranko are similar to each other and can fall under the four elements proposed by MacMillan and Chavis. In addition, there are other points introduced by them that are not included in the four elements by MacMillan and Chavis.

Based on MacMillan's and Chavis definition and theories of sense of community, a Chavis, Hogge, McMillan and Wandersman [12] developed Sense of Community Index (SCI) to measure sense of community. It was criticized on the limited variability of its true or false response. Later on, a research of immigrant integration in a Western State provided a Sense of Community Index version 2 (SCI-2) which covered all elements of sense of community using a Likert like scale. In this paper, SCI-2 will be implemented to evaluate the degree of sense of community in Panorama El Sherouq.

Table 1:   Sense of community elements and their attributes.

Sense of community elements	Attributes
Membership:	• Emotional Safety • Boundaries • Sense of Belonging • Identification • Personal Investment • Common Symbol System • Feeling of Acceptance • Sacrifice • Identity
Influence:	• Influence of an individual on a community • Leadership • Influence of community on individual • Conformity • Participation • Empowerment • Shared Responsibility

Integration and Fulfillment of Needs:	• Rewarding Members:
	  • Status of members
	  • Success of the community
	  • Competence
	• Shared values, needs and priorities
	• Meeting others needs while meeting your own
	• Support
	• Safety
	• Interdependence
	• Connection
	• Common Goals

Shared Emotional Connection:	• Shared History • Interaction & Quality of Interaction • Events Closure • Shared Important Events • Investment • Honoring Members • Spiritual Bond • Fellowship • Face to Face relationships
Demographic features:	• Homogeneity • Age • Gender • Education

5   New Urbanism and sense of community

New Urbanists claim that the built environment can foster sense of community.
Table 2 shows the relationship between New Urbanism's Charter and the five
elements of sense of community derived from the previous discussion.

Table 2:   Relationship between New Urbanism's charter and sense of community.

Charter principle	Sense of community
The region: Metropolis, city, and town	
The physical organization of the region should be supported by a framework of transportation alternatives. Transit, pedestrian, and bicycle systems should maximize access and mobility throughout the region while reducing dependence upon the automobile.	Shared Emotional Connection: interaction, face to face relationships Integration and fulfillment of Needs: connection, meeting other needs while meeting your own
The neighborhood, the district, and the corridor	
The neighborhood, the district, and the corridor are the essential elements of development and redevelopment in the metropolis. They form identifiable areas that encourage citizens to take responsibility for their maintenance and evolution.	Membership: personal investment Influence: participation, shared responsibility
Neighborhoods should be compact, pedestrian friendly, and mixed-use. Districts generally emphasize a special single use, and should follow the principles of neighborhood design when possible. Corridors are regional connectors of neighborhoods and districts; they range from boulevards and rail lines to rivers and parkways.	Integration and Fulfillment of Needs: shared needs, connection Shared Emotional Connection: interaction, face to face relationships
Many activities of daily living should occur within walking distance, allowing independence to those who do not drive especially the elderly and the young. Interconnected networks of streets should be designed to encourage walking, reduce the number and length of automobile trips, and conserve energy.	Shared Emotional Connection: interaction, face to face relationships Integration and Fulfillment of Needs: interdependence, needs connection
Transit corridors, when properly planned and coordinated, can help organize metropolitan structure and revitalize urban centers. In contrast, highway corridors should not displace investment from existing centers.	Shared Emotional Connection: interaction, face to face relationships Integration and Fulfillment of Needs: connection
Appropriate building densities and land uses should be within walking distance of transit stops, permitting public transit to become a viable alternative to the automobile.	Shared Emotional Connection: interaction, face to face relationships Integration and Fulfillment of Needs: connection
Concentrations of civic, institutional, and commercial activity should be embedded in neighborhoods and districts, not isolated in remote, single-use complexes. Schools should be sized and located to enable children to walk or bicycle to them.	Integration and Fulfillments of needs: reinforcement of needs
A range of parks, from tot-lots and village greens to ballfields and community gardens, should be distributed within neighborhoods. Conservation areas and open lands should be used to define and connect different neighbor- hoods and districts.	Shared emotional Connection: interaction, face to face relationships Integration and Fulfillment of Needs: connection
The block, the street, and the building	
Streets and squares should be safe, comfort- able, and interesting to the pedestrian. Properly configured, they encourage walking and enable neighbors to know each other and protect their communities.	Integration and Fulfillment of Needs: connection, safety Influence: participation

Table 2:   (Continued).

Charter principle	Sense of community
Civic buildings and public gathering places require important sites to reinforce community identity and the culture of democracy. They deserve distinctive form, because their role is different from that of other buildings and places that constitute the fabric of the city.	<u>Membership</u>: common symbol system, identity <u>Influence</u>: empowerment
Preservation and renewal of historic buildings, districts, and landscapes affirm the continuity and evolution of urban society.	<u>Membership</u>: common symbol system, identity

6 Analytical example: Kentlands and Orchard Village

Kim Joongsub [13] made a comparative case study between two suburbs Kentlands and Orchard Village; both suburbs lie in Gaithersburg, USA. Kentland is 352 acre development designed in 1988 by Andres Duany and Elizabeth Plater-Zyberk (among the co-founders of New Urbanism). Kentlands is planned for around 1,800 residential units and around 800,000 square feet of retail and office space. It includes mix of housing types, retail, office, civic uses within the community; and diverse high dense neighborhoods configured in narrow grid streets. There are a few cul-de-sacs and a network of alleys, small land lots with narrow setbacks and traditional architecture elements. Garages face alleys rather than streets. Public open spaces cover an area of 100 acres that include tot lots, common greens, lakes, and parks. Each neighborhood has a central common green and the design respects local topography and landscape.

Similar to Kentlands, Orchard Village is a suburban community with similar average single family home prices to Kentlands. The average household income, age of development, and housing types are also similar to those of Kentlands. Unlike Kentlands, Orchard Village has curvilinear streets and lots of cul-de-sacs. Similar housing types lie on large land lots and lacks retail facilities. In addition, it doesn't include common central greens, landmark, and doesn't reflect traditional architecture. Orchard Village has fewer sidewalks than Kentlands, bigger setbacks, and lower housing density [13].

Figure 1:   Kentlands [13].   Figure 2:   Orchard Village [13].

Joongsub [13] performed a survey that covers four points: pedestrianism, community attachment, social interaction, and community identity. Pedestrianism and social interaction fall under the shared emotional connection because it promotes face to face relationships. Community identity and community attachment fall under membership.

Respondents to the survey [13] stated that they find Kentlands as convenient, fun, and pleasant to explore. On the other hand, respondents from Orchard Village stated the lack of sidewalks discouraged walking. In addition, Kentlands' respondents referred to it as home and they don't plan to move elsewhere. They also mentioned the traditional architecture style and traditional town planning strengthened community identity. Respondents from Orchard Village did not complain nor showed strong bonding to it. Moving on to the social interaction, Kentlands supports sense of community which is facilitated by the physical environment. There were many positive responses about social interaction from Kentlands with a few negative responses coming from apartments and condominiums residents as they felt physically isolated from the rest of the community. Orchard Village respondents also expressed satisfaction with the level of social interaction but many wished for a stronger social interaction like the one at Kentlands. The lack of tot lots, the unfit clubhouse size, and lack of participation in community activities marked a weakness in Orchard Village. However, cul-de-sacs facilitated social interaction on an intimate scale but not beyond its boundaries. As for the community identity, Kentlands residents expressed that they had a strong physical character and identity which makes them proud of the environment they live in. Respondents of Orchard Village pointed out many positive aspects about it but none described it as attractive or distinctive. This comparison reveals the high degree of sense of community enjoyed by Kentland's residents due to the built environment that follow New Urbanism principles [13].

7 Case study: El Sherouq city, Egypt

El-Sherouq City lies on the outskirts of Cairo, Egypt. It is 35 km away from the center of Cairo and covers an area of 12,454 acres. Initially, it was built to provide residence away from the crowded city and stay connected through a network of highways. This factor contributed to the use of private cars as the main transportation which led to the isolation of Sherouq City's residents. Among Cairenes, Sherouq City is known as "Madinet el Ashbah" which means the city of ghosts. Panorama El Sherouq neighborhood lies on the western part of El Sherouq City was chosen to evaluate its sense of community according SCI-2. The neighborhood is composed of similar four story buildings with different sized apartments. Panorama Mall lies in the corner of the neighborhood and includes a supermarket, a bank, hypermarket, and miscellaneous stores. Buildings are configured around parks and streets are lined with trees.

Although Panorama El Sherouq has potentials of a mall within a quarter of a kilometer, which is considered a walkable distance based on Cairo's rough weather, it lacks many elements that can promote a stronger sense of community.

Figure 3: Buildings approach in Panorama El Sherouq. (Source: www.dyarna.com.)

Figure 4: Panorama Mall. (Source: www.aswaqalex.com/.)

The Panorama Mall is underdeveloped and many stores did not open yet. On top of that, the neighborhood lacks gathering places such as squares and on street cafeterias, and limited mixed-use. Although it includes pocket parks, individuals don't visit it often due to the lack of activities there. Members of Panorama El Sherouq travel back to Cairo on weekends to go to recreational areas such as the movies or a nice restaurant. They depend on their own cars because of the lack of public transportation. All the buildings are similar in form. Members feel safe walking in the streets because of the security and enjoy the quiet atmosphere.

A SCI-2 questionnaire was distributed to members of Panorama El Sherouq. The questionnaire included 24 questions. Every 6 questions cover one of the four elements of sense of community. Respondents had a variety of answers to choose from starting from not at all, somewhat, most of the times, and completely. For the 24 questions:

Not at All = 0, Somewhat = 1, Mostly = 2, Completely = 3

Total Sense of Community Index = Sum of Q1 to Q24

The first element, membership, scored an average of 13 points out of 18. The factors with the least points were emotional safety and identification as shown in Figure 5. Respondents stated that they can barely recognize their neighbors and that many found it hard to trust other community members.

The influence factors with the lowest average points are the presence of good leaders in the community, whether the community can influence members and whether members can influence their community. These results are illustrated in Figure 6. Influence scored an average of 11 out of 18. Many members complained that no one pays attention to the community problems.

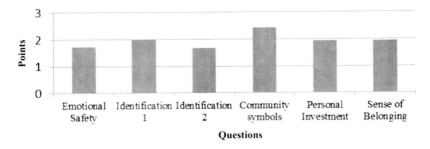

Figure 5: Membership.

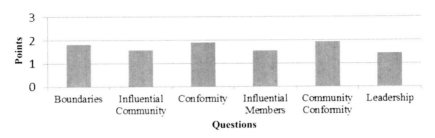

Figure 6: Influence.

The element integration and fulfillment of needs is illustrated in Figure 7. It scored an average of 11 out of 18 points. During the questionnaire, respondents claimed that the daily basic needs such as food and drinks are available in Panorama Mall. However, they still needed to go back to Cairo on weekends to hang out with their friends and families in gathering spaces such as the mall, cafes, and restaurants.

Figure 8 shows the different factors that are linked to shared emotional connection. The lowest issues are members spending time together and caring for each other. It scored an average of 13 out of 18 points. Members claimed that the neighborhood lacks viable gathering spaces.

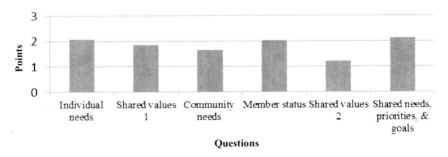

Figure 7: Integration and fulfillment of needs.

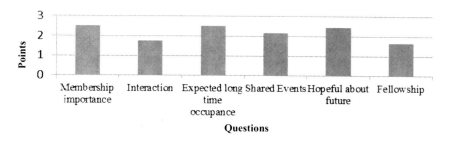

Figure 8:   Shared emotional connection.

The average Sense of Community Index for Panorama El Sherouq is 48 out of 72. Panorama El Sherouq weaknesses lie in the lack of public transportation and viable gathering spaces. These weaknesses diluted the rich face to face social interaction. In order to enhance the sense of community in Panorama El Sherouq, the physical design of the built environment needs to be enhanced as well to be able to foster rich face to face social interaction. This could be reached through gathering spaces like parks robust with activities for kids, teenagers, and adults. In addition, public transportation needs to be integrated within El Sherouq City to connect different neighbourhoods within El Sherouq City with each other and connect it to Cairo as well. However, there are factors other than the physical design that play a role in sense of community like age, expected tenure, gender, education, and homogeneity.

8 Conclusion

The built environment may not directly impact sense of community but it can encourage other attributes that can enhance it. New Urbanism includes many of these attributes in their design principles. This is proved in Kentlands community, where the New Urbanism principles impacted sense of community. This shows that there is a link between the built environment of the community and the psychological sense of community. However, there are other contributors such as the demographics and sharing important events such as disasters that can bring members closer together.

In order to enhance the sense of community in new Egyptian settlements, the configuration of buildings should foster social activities that allow rich face to face social interaction. The design of the neighborhood should be walkable, mixed use and include gathering spaces such as parks. These design principles are embedded within New Urbanism.

Further research can be carried out on what extent does traditional neighborhood design principles embedded within New Urbanism impact sense of community. Further research may be investigated on measuring and evaluating sense of community in other new Egyptian settlements. Sense of community is a major key issue in sustainability. For this reason practitioners should consider the relationship between sense of community and the built environment.

References

[1] Sims, D., *Urban Slums Report: The Case of Cairo*, Egypt, Cairo, 2003.
[2] Talen, E., Sense of community and neighborhood form: An assessment of the social doctrine of new urbanism, *Urban Studies*, 36(8), pp. 1361-1379, 1999.
[3] Port, A., *Application of Selected New Urbanist Principles To Residential Infill Developments in Mature Suburbs of Greater Boston*, Massachussetts, 2004.
[4] Duany, A. & Plater-Zyberk, E., *Towns and Town-Making Principles*, New York: Rizzoli, 1991.
[5] Congress of the New Urbanism, Charter of the New Urbanism. http://www.cnu.org/.
[6] Gusfield, J. R. , *The community: A critical response*, New York: Harper Colophon, 1975.
[7] Durkheim, E., *The division of labor in society*, New York: Free Press of Glencoe, 1964.
[8] Chavis, D. M. & MacMillan, D. W., Sense of Community: A Definition and Theory. *Journal of Community and Psychology*, 14(1), pp. 6-23, 1986.
[9] Buckner, J., The Development of an Instrument to Measure Neighbourhood Cohesion. *American Journal of Community Psychology*, 16(6), pp. 771-791, 1988.
[10] Glynn, T. J., Psychological Sense of Community: Measurement and Application. *Human Relations*, 34(7), pp. 789-818, 1981.
[11] Joranko, D., *The Sense of Community on a Racially Integrated Residential Block in Lansing, Michigan*, https://www.msu.edu.
[12] Community Science, Community Science Publications, www.communityscience.com.
[13] Joongsub, K., Creating Community: Does the Kentlands Live up to Its Goals? *Places Journal*, 13(2), pp. 48-55, 2000.

Green, brown or grey:
green roofs as 'sustainable' infrastructure

J. Rogers
RMIT University, Australia

Abstract

Green roofs, along with vertical gardens are increasingly seen as the symbol Sassi (*Strategies for Sustainable Architecture* 2006) or epithet Weiler and Scholz-Barth (*Green Roof Systems: A Guide to the Planning, Design, and Construction of Landscapes over Structure* 2009) of 'green' and 'sustainable cities' because of the ecosystem services that they provide Beatley (*Green Cities of Europe: Global Lessons on Green Urbanism* 2012). The list of benefits attributed to green roofs is broad and widely shared. They include reduction in the heat island effect, noise reduction, energy conservation, amenity, replacement of lost green space where 'the footprint of a building is replaced with a green roof, with no net loss of green open space or habitat' Hopkins and Goodwin (*Living Architecture: Green Roofs and Walls* 2011), increased property values, storm water management along with what has been described as 'green relief' in highly dense cities. Green roofs it is further claimed to 'transform cities from urban grey to urban green' (Weiler and Scholz-Barth, 2009) while at the same time mitigating the effects of climate change.
  The paper is based on an evaluation of five green roofs in the city of Melbourne, Australia that analyzes to what extent these projects meet the claimed sustainability benefits. It poses the question are green roofs simply 'green' branding or does their construction provide tangible 'sustainability' outcomes and if so what and for whom.
Keywords: sustainability, sustainable cities, green roofs, brown roofs, public space, access and equity.

WIT Transactions on Ecology and The Environment, Vol 173, © 2013 WIT Press
www.witpress.com, ISSN 1743-3541 (on-line)
doi:10.2495/SDP130271

1 Introduction

Green Roofs, along with vertical gardens are increasingly seen as the symbol (Sassi [1]) or epithet (Weiler and Scholz-Barth [2]) of 'green' and 'sustainable cities' because of the ecosystem services that they provide (Beatley [3]). They are also often seen as the antidote to the impacts of the compact, dense city: a spatial layout that is well established in sustainable city discourse. This paper poses the question are green roofs simply 'green' branding or does their construction provide tangible 'sustainability' outcomes and if so how have they been, and how could they be measured across the three poles of sustainability – environmental, economic and social? In the literature there is an overriding emphasis on defining green roofs in terms of colour – green, brown or grey –that works to silence the critic – because, after all, who would choose grey?

The paper begins with an exploration of how the terms 'green' and sustainable' are deployed in discussions about the benefits of green roofs internationally because the meaning of these terms is far from being self-evident. It then turns to a discussion of what could be considered the 'darker' less 'friendly' side of the case for green roofs where green roofs are seen as a replacement for other 'green spaces' in cities or as Davis [5] puts it the 'architectural privatization' of democratic public space, and considers some of the implications of this within a sustainability framework. The paper concludes with a brief case study of five green roofs in the city of Melbourne. The discussion forms part of a larger study that evaluated the projects according to sustainability criteria drawn from existing literature on the benefits of green roofs. The focus in this paper is principally on access and design intent. While there is some evidence of reduction in energy use and storm water flows in the rooftops studied the social benefits are limited to those who currently occupy the buildings.

Before beginning however it is important to consider the question what is a green roof? Discussions about what they are – or put more simply – what is 'green' about green roofs – suffer from being muddled, muddied, vague and often contradictory.

2 What is a green roof?

Along with green walls, rain gardens, street trees and permeable paving, green roofs are part of an emerging global discourse around greener cities. 'Green roof' is an umbrella terms used to describe a number of systems for green rooftops of buildings. The list of benefits attributed to green roofs is broad and widely shared. They include reduction in the heat island effect, noise reduction, energy conservation, amenity, replacement of lost green space, where 'the footprint of a building is replaced with a green roof, with no net loss of green open space or habitat' (Hopkins and Goodwin [4]) increased property values, storm water management along with what has been described as 'green relief' in highly dense cities. Green roofs, it is further claimed, 'transform cities from urban grey to urban green' (Weiler and Scholz-Barth [2]) while at the same time mitigating the effects of climate change.

Green roofs can be either extensive or intensive, depending on the load bearing potential of the building, depth of soil, maintenance required, access and the aims of the project. Extensive green roofs it has been argued present a:

> ...tremendous opportunity to retrofit and green existing structures in cities, thereby realizing multiple benefits of green roofs, including: reduced runoff and flood management; reducing energy demands in heating and cooling houses; improving the longevity and replacement costs of roofs; and benefiting city climate all while also providing for aesthetics and wildlife benefits in downtown areas. The latter includes ground nesting birds and various types of bees that feed on the nectar of blooming plants' (Tourbier [6]).

Pioneered in Germany extensive green roofs were made possible by the development of geofabrics and lightweight soils. Plants are essential elements in the functioning of green roofs because they intercept and delay rainfall runoff by holding precipitation in the plant foliage and absorbing water in the root zone causing an eventual reduction in total runoff by 50 percent or greater (Tourbier [6]). An extensive green roof typically has shallow soil (50–150mm), is not irrigated, generally requires little maintenance, have limited plant diversity and limited or no access.   Hardy, drought tolerant, low height plants are required in what is often a dry, hot and windy environment. They may provide green 'views' for occupants of adjacent rooms or buildings (Kwok and Grondzik [7]). Extensive green roofs can be retrofitted to existing buildings with a slope of up to 35 degrees, although roofs with a slope of over 20 degrees require a baffle to prevent soil slump.

An intensive green roof in contrast has deeper soil to support a larger variety of plants. Soil depths vary depending on the planting requirements – from 200–300mm for lawn up to 1.5–1.8 meters for large trees (Kwok and Grondzik [7]). Intensive green roofs provide accessible open space and often include larger plants, food growing areas and trees as well as walkways, water features and irrigation systems. As a result intensive green roofs require high levels of maintenance and greater accessibility.   Because of this difference specifications differ dramatically from extensive green roofs. Intensive green roofs are feasible only on flat roofed buildings and the added weight of soil and water requires a substantial building structure.   They are therefore more costly but are more energy efficient than extensive green roofs and have the capacity for greater storm water retention. To protect plants and occupants in a usually high wind environment intensive green roofs require a windbreak and a railing or wall. Trees should also be anchored against wind. Green roofs tend to be labour-intensive and require fertilization and irrigation (Tourbier [6]). The potentials for retrofitting existing buildings with intensive green roofs are limited.

Use of the terms 'intensive' or 'extensive' to describe green roofs has however been criticized because it is 'terminology' driven rather than use driven and can lead to confusion and inaccuracy in the design documentation and client expectations (Hopper [8]). The problem with the use of blanket terms, according to Weiler and Scholz-Barth [2] is that

> ...neither clearly reflects the system's expected purpose or use nor adequately conveys design or maintenance requirements. Furthermore, a terminology-driven, rather than use-driven, approach to the design and construction of green roofs can lead to additional confusion and inaccuracy in design, documentation, and client expectations.

What the authors are referring to is that rather than being simply 'green', green roofs serve a range of different purposes depending on design and client intent. What is significant here is the way in which the term 'green' dominates discussions around rooftop plantings and as a result assumptions are made about the benefits of all green roofs.

3 Green or brown?

In the literature the term intensive is often used to describe roof top gardens that are distinguished by alternative terms including 'Eco roofs', 'living roofs', nature roofs, 'brown' or biodiversity roofs, spontaneous green roofs, edible buildings, landscape over structure, elevated landscapes, cool roofs and blue roofs, and somewhat disparagingly 'sedum roofs' because of the dominance of sedum species in the construction of green roofs internationally. What all of these distinctions are alluding to is of course the purpose or intent of green roof construction in the first place because not all of them necessarily tick all of the sustainability, or even environmental 'boxes' in the same way. The distinctions reflect a broader debate within green roof discourse about whether all green roofs are, or should be 'green'. For instance, for Gedge [9], living roofs should reflect local places and so 'decisions shouldn't be made on the basis of horticulture but in relation to nature and the environment'. Such roofs may not be 'green', but are seen as a 'replacement for natural habitat'. Building on the work of Stephan Brenneisen in Switzerland in the 1990's, Gedge campaigned for the creation of biodiversity roofs in London for the black redstart and other wildlife as an alternative to the 'uniform swards of sedum' Grant [10]. Biodiversity roofs are topographically varied, include habitat features such as logs and are typically planted with wildflowers.

Within the Australian context Hopkins and Goodwin [4] coin the term 'bushtop' in an attempt to distinguish green roofs in the Australian context from other international examples. They define bushtop somewhat whimsically as referring to:

> ...the Australian bush or natural landscape that holds historic iconic status in the Australian psyche. Given that the great majority of the population lives in cities and are relatively isolated from the bush, the authors' concept of the bushtop is to transpose a little piece of the bush onto the tops of city buildings to help reconnect people with their cultural and environmental heritage. The difference between a bushtop landscape and a rooftop garden is that the bushtop is the integration of natural systems, plant communities, animals, birds and insects

interacting with each other to survive and operate as an ecosystem, whereas a rooftop garden is an ornamental horticultural display.

For these authors 'green' denotes an urban aesthetic that is not necessarily in keeping with the indigenous Australian landscape. This is more than just a matter of words and exchanging words. "Green' as metaphor denotes an urban aesthetic that reinforces a particular globalized way of seeing and thinking about what an urban landscape should 'look' like. In doing so, other 'brown' spaces are excluded from being worthy of consideration or value.

4   Green or grey?

Green roofs more generally are seen as an effort to 'green' the 'grey' landscape of cities in a period of rapid urbanization. Their importance has particular synergies in Australia, one of the most urbanized countries in the world with over 80% of the population living in urban areas in 2007. This figure is set to increase more rapidly in the coming decades. By 2050, Australia, New Zealand and Northern America are all expected to be over 90 per cent urban; a figure that is higher than anywhere else in the world (United Nations [11]). Therefore, managing the effects of urbanisation is considered to be one of the most urgent practical challenges of sustainability. Global sustainability is increasingly an issue of urban sustainability (Bugliarello [12]). Within this context the need for green roofs goes hand in hand with arguments to increase the density of cities globally as a way of mitigating the impact of urbanization and reducing urban 'sprawl'. However, one needs to ask why the focus on the 'greenness' of green roofs? The construction of green roofs is also closely connected to other key terms in the sustainability lexicon including liveability and resilience. 'Green' as a leitmotif or symbol for green roof raises a whole series of questions about what a green roof actually is and does. Does 'green' in fact denote 'sustainability'? Green as a descriptor overlooks the harshness of conditions on a rooftop in a temperate climate. Should plant selection always be based on 'greenness'? What is the connection between sustainability and green? And how relevant is the use of the term 'green' particularly in the Australian context? As Latz [13] has argued:

> The topic of green roofs is closely connected to 'ecological correctness', and is part of the indemnification vocabulary of sins committed in bad conscious like landscape consumption and the displacement of nature.

What Latz is suggesting is that much of the rhetoric around green roofs is about language-in-use. Contained within the rhetoric is a future vision of what a city should look like. In this future 'green', 'liveable', resilient dense city public open space on the horizontal plane is at a premium and so, as the argument goes, elevating that space onto walls and rooftops of buildings will allow for increased densities to create a system of 3 dimensional green spaces in cities, without the loss of open space. In a simple rendition of the dominant sustainable city storyline Hopkins and Goodwin [4] express the benefits of green roofs as follows:

This new urban form features higher densities, reduced private vehicle travel distances, promotion of public transport and reduction of the 'suburban sprawl'. This means that cities are becoming denser and the space between the built form is coming under pressure from competing activities, resulting in less open and green space in the public realm. One of the tools available to the urban designer or landscape architect for creating more open space and natural environment, as well as accommodating the other competing pressures for space, is to use the surfaces of the built form – the walls and rooftops of the buildings – to create a new open space using living walls and green roofs.

The unspoken question in all of this is of course, access. Defined as Landscape over structure or the integration of landscape and architecture green roofs are often seen as a replacement for 'green' space at ground level, a claim that is often couched in terms of adding to green spaces in cities. However, who lives or works in the buildings above the ground and who can occupy the space needs careful consideration. Or put another way if green spaces at ground level are replaced by elevated green space what are the socio-political consequences of this move?

Beyond questions around the 'social' sustainability of green roofs however, questions have also been raised about the economic sustainability of green roofs. As an example a 2006 study focusing on mitigation of New York's hear island effect (Rozenzweig *et al.* [14]) examined the impact of urban forestry, living (green) roofs and light roofs on the near surface temperatures and the heat island effect. The study developed nine mitigation scenarios within 6 case study areas in the city and evaluated each of the scenarios in terms of temperature reduction and cost effectiveness. Each of the scenarios was based on a combination of three key strategies – street plantings or urban forestry, green roofs or light roofs and while the study found that each of these strategies had an effect of temperature the study recommended that a '...combined strategy that maximizes the amount of vegetation in New York City by planting trees along streets and in open spaces, as well as by building living (or green) roofs (i.e. ecological infrastructure), offers more potential cooling than any individual strategy'. There were two significant determinants for this finding. Firstly, while land availability for street planting was considered a constraint for urban forestry, the cost of green roofs as compared to street plantings was considerable. The study found that implementation costs ranged from $199 million for open space planting to $5,855 million for living roofs. Significantly, the study noted that:

> Of the three heat island mitigation strategies considered in this study, urban forestry, and particularly planting and kerbside street trees, contributes additional non-energy benefits such as fostering environmental equity in poorer neighbourhoods that tend to have hotter temperatures and fewer street trees, and bringing cooling benefits to areas where people live and work [14].

Within the Australian context, Williams *et al.* [15] have identified perceived cost as a significant barrier to adoption of green roofs and the development of incentive schemes. They point out that the dominant form of green roof in

Australia currently is intensive involving higher maintenance costs and a lack of demonstration projects to inspire confidence. Other barriers identified by the authors include lack of an established green roof industry, lack of scientific data for evaluation, minimal inclusion in green star rating schemes and planning policies, plant selection, availability of substrate components and mixes, lack of Australian standards and guidelines, lack of experience and knowledge and questions around the use of potable water for irrigation. Despite these barriers to adoption the authors note that there is increasing interest in establishing green roofs in Australia.

5 Green roofs in Melbourne

The city of Melbourne is the capital city of Victoria, Australia. Green roofs in the city are a somewhat recent phenomenon when considered within the international context. Early examples include the Freshwater Place residential tower in Melbourne (2002) with its Level 10 rooftop Half Acre Garden and Melbourne City Council's CH2 building (2006) – Australia's first 6-star Green Star Design commercial office. More recent examples include the Pixel building and The Venny a Children's Community Centre in Holland Park, Kensington with a 200sqm, extensive green roof. The Venny roof was developed as part of a 2-year research project with the University of Melbourne to gather information about green roofs in a Melbourne context. Since 2008, Melbourne City Council and influential business groups have become active promoting the benefits of green roofs. Growing Up: The Blueprint to Green Roof Melbourne" is one such program being run by the Committee for Melbourne and the city of Melbourne hosts Canopy – Melbourne's Green Roof Forum a quarterly discussion forum supported by Green Roofs Australia and Weblow a commercial mulching firm. The following discussion is based on a brief case study of five green roofs in the city of Melbourne that is part of a larger study that evaluated these projects using sustainability criteria (Table 1). Each of the five projects was evaluated against the key criteria with a focus on what evidence was available to establish the claim. Data was gathered using site visits and interviews. The discussion here focuses specifically on two key aspects of the evaluation concerned with design intent and access after proving a brief overview of key specification for the projects in Tables 2–5.

While two of the projects, CH2 and the Pixel building share a similar intent the remaining three are quite different. In three of the green rooftops (CH2, the Venny and the Pixel building) plant health is periodically monitored by University of Melbourne researchers. One of the rooftops (Freshwater Place) required high levels of resource input and maintenance. All of the rooftops have limited access. In fact, each of the site visits access involved a complex process of appointments, tours and security. In the case of the Venny, the inclusion of the rooftop reflected the values of the place with no access to the rooftop other than for maintenance. In four of the five sites there were varying degrees of recreational space for occupants with no access for others. Visual access came from above. While for each of the sites there is some, often anecdotal, evidence of reduction in energy use and storm water flows the social benefits of green roofs are largely confined to existing occupants and again anecdotally include increased productivity and amenity. As a result claims to social sustainability remain tenuous.

In addition with the exception of the Hassell rooftop the other 4 rooftops were new constructions. This seems to reflect findings of a 2009 study in Melbourne by Wilkinson and Reed [16] that posed the question – Why are there not more green roofs on buildings in our city centre? The study analyzed 526 buildings in Melbourne CBD and found that 'a very small proportion of CBD stock in Melbourne is found to be suited. These buildings are most likely to be low secondary locations, ungraded or B grade buildings, privately owned, concrete framed and not overshadowed by adjoining Of the 526 buildings analysed 78 appeared to be suitable for green roof technology but given the type of buildings for most of these 78 buildings a retrofit seemed unlikely. The authors concluded that 'greater potential for green roof retrofit exists in the suburbs or regional towns where lower rise buildings may reduce the amount of overshadowing found in city centres (Wilkinson and Reed [16]).

Table 1:   Sustainability criteria.

1.	Environmental
a.	Reduce heat island effect (reduce radiated heat from buildings)
b.	Noise Reduction
c.	Increase biodiversity: -plants -invertebrates -birds -mammals
d.	Reduce storm water run-off contributing to:- - water quality -flood mitigation/ reduced run-off
e. Improve air quality	
2.	**Economic**
a.	Reduce energy use in building -Heating -Cooling
b.	Increase roof longevity
c.	Increase worker productivity
d.	Increase property values
e.	Job creation
3.	**Social**
a.	Increase recreational use of space
b.	Green relief
c.	Increase food production in city
d.	Increased amenity
e.	Worker health

Table 2:   The Venny, Kensington.

Location	JJ Holland Park, Kensington
Type	Extensive, New construction, module based
Access	Limited
Area	Lower Roof Area total: 108m^2 East Zone: 14.6m^2 West Zone: 63m^2 South Zone: 30.5m^2
Pitch	Minimal gradient (1:100)
Input/resources	Minimal
Design Intent	A communal backyard that provides facilities and programs for disadvantaged young people in the Kensington area. The Green roof is understood to reflect, even symbolize, the broader sustainability agenda adopted at the centre.

Table 3:   Freshwater Place.

Location	Queensbridge Square, Melbourne. The green roof is built on top of a 9 story car park.
Type	Intensive, new construction, in situ.
Access	Residents and guests of residents only
Area	1650m^2 or half an acre
Pitch	Minimal gradient (1:100)
Input/resources	The green roof is irrigated using water from a water storage tank underneath. A wind break wall has been built as the roof suffers from high wind exposure from the south.
Design Intent	Constructed as an elevated landscaped garden as part of residential lifestyle facilities on level 10 – including a pool, sauna, gym, barbeque area, sauna and home theatre. There are 540 apartments in the Freshwater Place tower. Recently a small vegetable garden has been planted in crate boxes on a small balcony on the west façade.

Table 4:   The Pixel building.

Location	Cnr Bouverie and Queensbury street, Melbourne.
Type	Extensive, new construction, extensive, modular and in situ.
Access	Building is currently vacant. Future access for office workers and guests.
Area	840m^2
Pitch	Minimal (1:100)
Input/resources	Regular weeding and monitoring of plant health. Maintenance by Melbourne University, Burnley.
Design Intent	To achieve a 6 star Green building award and to create recreational space for building occupants.

Table 5:   CH2: Council House.

Location	Little Collins st, Melbourne.
Type	Extensive and Intensive. New Construction, module based.
Access	Council staff and staff guests only. Online tours available.
Area	–
Pitch	minimal
Input/resources	Irrigation
Design Intent	Visual amenity, human comfort, research, part of 6 star green building rating.

Table 6:   Hassell rooftop.

Location	61 Little Collins st, Melbourne.
Type	Extensive, Retrofit, minimal planting.
Access	Minimal. Staff and staff guests.
Area	small
Pitch	Minimal gradient (1:100)
Input/resources	Minimal, hand watering of smart pots.
Design Intent	A recreational space for staff. An event space.

6   Conclusion

What this brief survey begins to suggest is that despite the list of well-accepted and often-repeated benefits of green roofs, none of the rooftops surveyed met all of the sustainability claims that circulate in academic literature and the popular media. There is also a lack of data that supports the claims made by green roof enthusiasts and most of the data that does exist is derived from small 'test' plots rather than built projects and this is particularly true in the Australian context. As a result, reliable predictions of performance are 'difficult' (Snodgrass and McIntyre [17]).

What all of this suggests is that the design intent of any given green roof project should be at the forefront of sustainability claims.   And while some 'green' roofs may indeed be green and others brown; rather than relying on generalized claims about the benefits, design intent needs to be stated from the outset.   Otherwise discussions will remain terminology-driven rather than use-driven [2] and all green roof projects run the risk of being labelled as simply green branding.   In addition without careful attention to questions of access the contribution that green roofs will make to 'sustainability' for ALL residents of a city is not guaranteed.

References

[1]   Sassi, P. *Strategies for Sustainable Architecture* Taylor and Francis: Oxon, 2006.

[2]   Weiler, S. and Scholz-Barth, K. *Green Roof Systems: A Guide to the Planning, Design, and Construction of Landscapes over Structure* John Wiley and Sons Inc: Hoboken, New Jersey, 2009.

[3]   Beatley, T. *Green Cities of Europe: Global Lessons on Green Urbanism* Island Press: Washington DC, 2012.

[4]   Hopkins, G and Goodwin, C. *Living Architecture: Green Roofs and Walls* CSIRO Publishing: Collingwood, Australia, 2011.

[5]   Davis, M. Fortress Los Angeles: the Militarisation of Urban Space (Chapter 1) *Variations on a Theme Park: The New American City and the End of Public Space* ed. M. Sorkin. Hill and Wang: New York, pp 154-180, 1992.

[6] Tourbier, J.T. Green Roofs, urban vegetation and urban runoff (chapter 44) *The Routledge Handbook of Urban Ecology* eds. I. Douglas, D. Goode, M. C. Houck and R. Wang Routledge: Oxon pp. 572-582, 2011.

[7] Kwok A.C. and Grondzik, W.T. *The Green Studio Handbook: Environmental Strategies for Schematic Design*, Second Edition, Elsevier: M.A. and Oxford. 2011.

[8] Hopper, L.J. *Landscape Architectural Graphic Standards: Student Edition* John Wiley and Sons: New Jersey, 2007.

[9] Gedge, D. Sustainable Entrepreneur, *Green Futures Magazine*, 9th October, 2006 http://www.forumforthefuture.org/greenfutures/articles/sustainable-entrepreneur-0

[10] Grant, G *Ecosystem Services Come to Town: Greening Cities by Working with Nature* John Wiley and Sons: UK, 2012.

[11] United Nations Department of Economic and Social Affairs *World Urbanization Prospects The 2007 Revision* United Nations: New York, 2008. http://www.un.org/esa/population/publications/wup2007/2007WUP_Highlights_web.pdf

[12] Bugliarello, G. 2006 Urban Sustainability: Dilemmas, Challenges and Paradigms' *Technology in Society* Vol. 28, pp. 19–26.

[13] Latz, P. Introduction *Green Roof-A Case Study: Michael Van Valkeenburgh Associates' Design for the Headquarters of the American Society of Landscape Architects* ed. Christian Werthmann, Princeton Architectural Press: New York, pp 14-15, 2007.

[14] Rozenzweig, C. Solecki, W.D. and Slosberg, R.B. Mitigating New York City's Heat Island with Urban Forestry, Living Roofs, and Light Surfaces: New York City Regional Heat Island Initiative: Final Report 2006 http://www.fs.fed.us/ccrc/topics/urbanforests/docs/NYSERDA_heat_island.pdf

[15] Williams, N.S.G, Rayner, J.P and Raynor, K.J. Green roofs for a wide brown land: Opportunities and barriers for rooftop greening in Australia. *Urban Forestry and Urban Greening* **9,** pp. 245-251, 2010.

[16] Wilkinson, S. J. and Reed, R. Green roof retrofit potential in the central business district, *Property Management, 27* (5), pp.284 – 301 2009.

[17] Snodgrass, E. C. and McIntyre, L. *The Green Roof Manual: A Professional Guide to Design, Installation, and Maintenance,* Timber Press: Portland, Oregon, 2010.

Hive minds: distributed intelligence within the biomimetic studio

S. Barry
Manchester School of Architecture, Manchester, UK

Abstract

Biomimetic design finds its muse in the natural world, more pertinently from the processes, anatomy, and function of site-specific flora and fauna. Maintaining a critical role in the development of a sustainable and environmentally responsible society, it relates to the dynamic between climate and living organisms, seeking to work with rather than against the external environment, promising to yield new means by which built environment research and design professionals may respond to and interact with their environment. At Manchester School of Architecture, innovation within biomimetic design studio culture has led to the incorporation of design strategies, which examine the properties of living systems in order to extrapolate desirable attributes from them and subsequently synthesise new responses. Employing research by design methodologies, students learn from the evolution of natural systems, incorporating these findings in their design work, emphasising ways of thinking and designing that brings architecture into a process of environmental and biological focus. As such, the methodology employed raises the prospect of closer integration of form and function, promising to yield new means by which students may respond to and interact with their own environment. This paper advocates the proposition and utilisation of the biomimetic model with regard to architectural education and building design. The development of which may prove more than a hypothetical metaphor, but a new biomimetic design paradigm, a model for holistic, sustainable urban design, an ecologically synergistic, generative architecture of an energy positive and progressive tomorrow.
Keywords: biomimetics, process-based ecotonic architecture, biomimetic sustainability, architectural education.

WIT Transactions on Ecology and The Environment, Vol 173, © 2013 WIT Press
www.witpress.com, ISSN 1743-3541 (on-line)
doi:10.2495/SDP130281

1 Introduction

The conceptual apparatus of architecture has always given a central role to the relationship between mankind and nature, the shapes of living organisms having been adapted for architectural use [1]. The material practice of architecture is at the beginning of a substantial reconfiguration in which the convergent fields of biology, structures, engineering and computation has ignited a previously unexplored evolutionary process. Natural systems provide a new conceptual model for biomimetic design experiments, exploring the architectural interrelationship between site specificity, organism, efficiency and community proposing biomimetic solutions to the future urban built environment.

Biomimetic design maintains a critical role in the development of a sustainable and environmentally responsible society. It relates to the dynamic between climate and living organisms, seeking to work with rather than against the external environment. It raises the prospect of a closer integration of form and function, promising to yield new means by which built environment research and design professionals may respond to and interact with their environment, and the design potential and responsibility of designing within it.

1.1 The biomimetic model

Biomimetic architecture concerns itself with climate (or perception of climate) as a major contextual generator, and with benign environments using minimal energy as its target. Drawing first inspiration from Gibson who describes ecology as a fit between niche and occupier [2], we reinterpret place through notions of ecology, evolution and environmental forces. This proposes an advancement from Norberg-Schultz's [3] theories of space, place, space and character, and environmental forces (climatic, social and perceptive) to complete the grammar of architecture. By applying process based natural analogy, mediation is achieved between the architecture of ecological time and times disembodiment, a by-product of the postmodern condition.

The M. Arch Atellier QED (qoud erat demonstrandum), at Manchester School of Architecture has developed its studio culture as a prototype pedagogical hive mind. Two holistic models of natural systems, organism and community are applied to architecture in order to determine the formation of an environmental ethic. To create an autonomous architecture it is necessary to have a model that is both ecologically and ethically sound; the single idea of an organism is not so. Here individual buildings must be seen as part of an archi-ecosystem, isolatory vacuums both natural and intellectual are biocidic.

1.1.1 Biomimetic architecture at MSA

Bioclimatic analysis and design delivers a built form that enables oscillations around and between a given set of environmental parameters: maintaining bioclimatic homeostasis. The exchange of climatic information and energy functions over time, displaying attributes of growth viewed by Thompson [4] to always be a 'function of time', so that growth and metamorphosis be considered as events in time and space.   Strategic and tactical approaches regarding successful form and function are informed by a thorough understanding of appropriate site analysis. A climatically derived form simultaneously signs and interprets place whilst maintaining a gradated continuum between inside and out. Appropriate signing of place clearly acknowledges the already demonstrable effect the climate has upon it. For this purpose, building intelligence is both passive and reactive, mitigating the effects of a dynamic external environment upon internal conditions whilst harnessing their energy so as to maintain optimum internal environment.

Through this analysis biomimetic design challenges the notions of `sustainability` and how contemporary ideologies may be translated into living systems with a future, rather than future living systems. Allowing the development of broad areas of research that promote holistic rather than exclusive architectural models for sustainable design, that merge an astute selection of observed properties with sophisticated artificial technologies and thus inform their subsequent hybrid development.

1.1.2 Biomimetics: aesthetics versus process

Recently, process based biomimetics; a concept closer in fidelity to the ecology of life has emerged generating a new architectural polemic within the QED research unit at MSA.

Bios, life is not an aesthetic, it is a process. Empty replication in architecture delivers a superficial pastiche of "the natural". Ultimately redundant, this artificial offspring of the ego is not the natural progeny of interpreting site or place. No amount of aesthetic camouflage will alter the fact that architectural interventions remain just that; they cannot be appropriated into an aesthetic chimera. Rather its form should interpret honestly the processes and circumstances in which it exists as a climatic modifier within its (urban) ecosystem.

The study of process in intrinsically context based, one cannot be studied without each other. The studio instead seeks to produce ecologists of built form; Archi-ecologists who through research demonstrate an understanding of the processes involved in nature, seeking to emulate how they work rather than simply how they look. Through understanding ecological processes we can extrapolate these into architectural situations.

2   Hive mind: ecotonic autopoesis

It is an autopoetic assumption that the boundaries of an organism are not defined according to physical boundaries such as skins but are extended along its sensory and functional inputs and outputs [5]. Architecturally inclusive and yet clearly linked to resource flows across the site and through the building. Systems constantly seek to actively distinguish themselves from their environment in an attempt to preserve their distinctness and maintain their identity. It is a complex landscape in which fragments may retain their identity and yet meld, through negotiation and chance, into a new form of continuity [6]. Boundary maintenance is a crucial part of the self-preservation of all systems, which can be understood as self-reverentially enclosed life-worlds populated respectively by friends and enemies. Such systems are latent with relevant potentials, both for threats to members of such systems, as well as for possible sources of 'energy' and 'nourishment' able to sustain and evolve new arrangements [7].

2.1 Alpine cliff climber

For example, symmetrical schismogenesis occurs when two or more conditions reinforce each other within given situation and encourage exponential growth in one direction [8], generating an architectural ecotone, tectonic intervention. Complementary schismogenesis occurs when 'mutually promoting' actions are essentially dissimilar but mutually appropriate [9]; a concept tested in Alpine Cliff Climber (Figure 1), which aims to provide a direct link between two Alpine resorts in one smooth flow creating a parasitic symbiosis. The tower is primarily a cliff scraper with the majority of the building mass climbing the great cliff heights of the fragmenting urban barrier.

Figure 1:   Alpine Cliff Climber, T. Bedford, MSA BArch.

Investigation into the growth patterns of climbing plants opened a basis for mimicry in regards to their helical formation and tendril growths used to scale vertical faces. The organic building shape evolved through light studies, creating the optimal shape to collect the maximum available solar gain for energy generation at the site. To take advantage of the location's wind conditions a single large helical turbine is integrated into the top of the tower to generate energy.

The bio construction combined with growth formation of climbing plants is what allows the climbing plant to minimise material usage and to maximise strength and growth height. The tower's internal and external structures mimic the natural helical formation creating maximum strength and stability within an organic shaped cliff scraper. Rock face ties mimicking natures tendrils, reach out from the tower's primary structural cores connecting them to existing natural cracks and faults within the cliff face using adapted rock climbing techniques. This combination allows the tower to freely twist and bend without compromising structural stability.

Ecotones have been described by Holland et al. [10] as 'zones of transition between adjacent ecological systems, having a set of characteristics uniquely defined by space and time scales and by the strength of interactions between adjacent ecological systems', as such they are dynamic entities with both a spatial and temporal property [11]. As such Alpine Cliff Climber creates the desired direct link to provide efficient movement between the two alpine resorts, whilst also providing an effective transition zone or ecotone (Figure 6), a dynamic intervention to an otherwise fragmenting urban barrier.

2.2 ParaSITE/ecotone

The study of process in intrinsically context based, one cannot be studied without each other. Process based biomimetics seeks to produce ecologists of built form; Archi-ecologists who through research demonstrate an understanding of the processes involved in nature, seeking to emulate how they work rather than simply how they look, challenging notions of environmental complexity, structural formation and habitation (Figure 2).

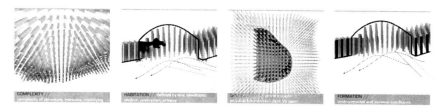

Figure 2:   Urban cave/speleogenic skin, C. Loucaides MSA BArch.

Through understanding ecological processes we can extrapolate these into architectural situations. This concept has been explored through a 'parasitic' site analysis conducted on areas undergoing urban regeneration in Manchester.
ParaSITE extrapolates a viral analogy identifying areas in need of parasitic regeneration. The biomimetic approach to this project identified Manchester as a healthy organism with a well developed *"circulatory"* network system. Some parts of this organism are thriving and some are disintegrating or undergoing change. The suggestion is to introduce a beneficial parasitic urban remediation process that would catalyse this process of change according to the needs of these areas. Considering the social and cultural needs of this site, one of the parasites introduced was responsible for developing a three-dimensional mesh of networks, thus increasing circulation and furthering the growth of other parasites.
This project formed a complete amalgamation of both site research and environmental factors (Figure 3), forming a site-specific masterplan. The three-dimensional mesh of networks generated through ParaSITE analysis defined where the spaces, paths, bridges, and access points would be located in the final development. The network is defined by extending the surrounding roads/paths on the site plan, the wind patterns, sun altitude and longitude at different times of day and season and water movement.

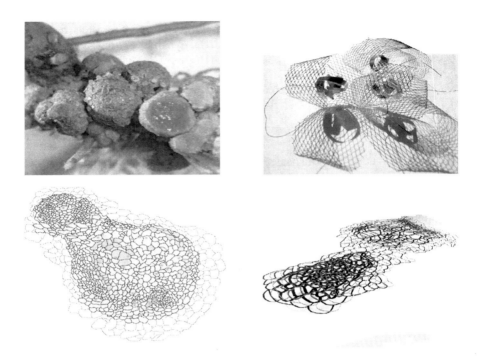

Figure 3:   Development pattern of parasite characteristics; the parasite, conceptual form, growth/life pattern, architectural translation and architectural use. ParaSITE, Mayfield, Manchester, C. Loucaides MSA BArch.

Problems identified through the theoretical site research defined which life characteristics were required in order to overcome and solve them. Four parasitic organisms (living on or with a host for mutual benefit) were chosen. One of the parasites was responsible for de-composing/recycling, the other for fixing or controlling, the other for zoning and defining location of spaces, and finally the fourth for generating a "root" network system used for movement. Form and function of the spaces was a mixture of all the above characteristics; a traditionally biomimetic response, the way that nature would solve the problem. Whilst this remains a theoretical investigation, it has evolved to become a scalar ecotone; a zone of transition between adjacent ecological systems, having a set of characteristics uniquely defined by space and time scales and by the strength of the interactions between adjacent ecological systems.

2.3 Ecotonal development

Ecotones are edges [12], transitional areas [13] or boundaries [14–16] and are typically characterised in ecological research as areas displaying a high rate of change compared to that of adjacent areas [17]. This high rate of change is reflected in the ecotone dynamics and the fluxes between neighbouring ecological systems, affecting the structure at macro, meso and micro scales within these systems [18–20]. As such they occupy zones of transition, transformative spaces that are capable of adaptation and change.

As biological organisms we live our lives within spatio-temporal zones bounded by natural and artificial extensive boundaries; within zones extended by time and space, limited and marked by a borderline. However, there are latent zones which we also inhabit, ecotonic zones of intensity, for example those found in zones of temperature which define different ecosystems (from hot jungles to cold tundra). These zones are not bounded by spatio-temporal frontiers but by intensive borderlines, critical points of temperature, pressure, gravity, tension, density and connectivity. They are the points that define abrupt transitions in the state of the creatures, which inhabit those zones; and form the basis of the research into the potential ecotonal development and site remediation of the Siberian biomine.

2.3.1 Siberian biomine

The Siberian biomine (Figure 4) is concerned with exhibiting the plight of Norlisk, Siberia, one of the most polluted cities in the world, by demonstrating its inherent ecological similarities to Putorana, a UNESCO World Heritage Site of unquestionable natural beauty, and restoring the level of ecological health that equals its neighbour. The scheme is based upon complete remediation of the site, positively redeveloping its entire landscape ecology over a phased 200 year period. The current mining industry will be completely revolutionised through branding new sustainable and ecological mining processes; bioleaching. In time this will completely eradicate the existing mining methods employed by the metallurgy plants in Norilsk. Consequently, the interpretation centre becomes perpetually refreshed through different media over time, evolving technologically in sync with the changes of the landscape in which it sits.

Figure 4:   Siberian biomine, Norlisk, Siberia, R. Barker, L. Griggs, R. Vigelskas, J. Tan, MSA BArch.

In the initial phase of the scheme visitors encounter a series of spaces designed to relate a comparative juxtaposition between Norilsk and the Putorana Plateau. As the industrial mining process gradually evolves and is replaced by the new bioleaching mining system, the visitor experience exhibits the changes to the entire city's infrastructure and habitat through an augmented reality within its exhibition suite.

3 Conclusion

The research by design case studies discussed in this paper demonstrate the possibilities of understanding natural processes and examining architecture through biological analogy. Para-biotic investigations conducted at Manchester School of Architecture propose that we should no longer regard buildings as truly living or as machines for living in, rather as a process based biotic architecture that supports life and living systems whilst exhibiting, but not possessing the attributes of life. The development and design of ecotonal and parasitic research may prove to be more than a hypothetical metaphor; instead they encompass the possibility of a new design paradigm, a model for holistic, sustainable urban design, an ecologically synergistic, generative architecture of an energy positive and progressive tomorrow.

Acknowledgements

The author wishes to acknowledge the following students whose BArch research projects are showcased in this paper: Robert Barker, Tom Bedford, Lindsay Griggs, Costas Loucaides, Reece Vigelskas and Jason Tan.

References

[1] Portoghesi, P., *Nature and Architecture*, trans. Young, Erika, Skira Editore, Milan, 2000.
[2] Gibson, J. J., *The Ecological Approach to Visual Perception*, Houghton Mifflin, Boston, 1979.
[3] Norberg-Schultz, C., *Genius Loci – Towards a Phenomenology of Architecture*, Rizzoli International Publications, New York, 1979.
[4] Thompson, D., *On Growth and Form*, Cambridge University Press, Cambridge, 1992.
[5] Hight, C., *'Subject boundaries negotiations – aka: getting' jiggy in da oikos'*, Steel, B., ed., *Negotiate my boundary – mass customisation and responsive environments (+RAMTV)*, AA Publications, London, 2002, pp. 17.
[6] Woods, L., *'Inside the Borderline'*, *"Borderline"*, Research Institute for Experimental Architecture, Europa, Springer-Verlag, Vienna, 1998, pp. 32.
[7] Schumacher, P., *'autopoesis > definitions'*, AADRL design studio brief 01, Steele, B., ed., *Negotiate my boundary – mass customisation and*

responsive environments (+RAMTV), AA Publications, London, 2002), pp. 20.

[8] Hight, C., Schumacher, P., *'Living prototypes for the autopoetic metropolis'*, AADRL design studio brief 03, Steele, B., ed., *Negotiate my boundary – mass customisation and responsive environments (+RAMTV)*, AA Publications, London, 2002, p. 26.

[9] Bateson, G., *"Steps to an Ecology of Mind: Collected Essays in Anthropology, Psychiatry, Evolution and Epistemology"*, Chicago University Press, Chicago, 2000.

[10] Holland, M. M., Risser, P. G., Naiman, R. J., *"Ecotones: the Role of Landscape Boundaries in the Management and Restoration of Changing Environments"*, Chapman and Hall, New York, 1991, pp. 142.

[11] Hufkens, K., Ceulemans, R., Scheunders, P., *'Estimating the ecotone width in patchy ecotones using a sigmoid wave approach'*, *"Ecological Informatics 3"*, 2008, pp. 97.

[12] Orlóci, L., Orlóci, M., *'Edge detection in vegetation: Jornada revisited'*, *"Journal of Vegetation Science 1"*, 1990, pp. 311-324.

[13] Peters, D., Gosz, J., Pockman, W., Small, E., Parmenter, R., Collins, S., Muldavin, E., *'Integrating Path and Boundary Dynamics to Understand and Predict Biotic Transitions at Multiple Scales'*, *"Landscape Ecology 21"*, 2006, pp. 19-33.

[14] Kent, M., Gill, W. J., Weaver, R. E., Armitage, R. P., *'Landscape and plant community boundaries in biogeography'*, *"Progress in Physical Geography 21"*, 1997, pp. 315-353.

[15] Fortin, M. J., Olsen, R. J., Iverson, L., Hunsaker, C., Edwards, G., Levine, D., Butera, K., Klemas, V., *'Issues related to the detection of boundaries'*, *"Landscape Ecology 15"*, (2000), pp. 453-466.

[16] Fagan, W. F., Fortin, M. J., Soykan, C., *'Integrating edge detection and dynamic modelling in the quantitative analysis of ecological boundaries'*, *Bioscience 53*, 2003, pp. 730-738.

[17] Risser, P. G., *'The status of science examining ecotones'*, *"Bioscience 45"*, 1995, pp. 318-325.

[18] Naiman, R. J., Décamps, H., *"The Ecology and Management of Aquatic-Terrestrial Ecotones"*, Parthenon Publishing Group, Paris, 1990, pp. 316.

[19] Cadenasso, M. L., Pickett, S. T. A., Weathers, K. C., Jones, C. G., *'A framework for a theory of ecological boundaries'*, *"Bioscience 53"*, 2003, pp. 750-758.

[20] Saunders, S. C., Chen, J., Drummer, T. D., Crow, T. R., *'Modelling temperature gradients across edges over time in managed landscape'*, *"Forest Ecology and Management 117"*, 1999, pp. 17-31.

Student preference for alternative modes of transport at the University of Pretoria, South Africa

J. L. du Toit
Department of Town and Regional Planning,
University of Pretoria, South Africa

Abstract

The University of Pretoria is the largest contact university in South Africa with more than 45,000 contact students. A significant increase in students over the last decade has contributed to severe parking shortages on and around the main campus. Consequently, the University has been considering four alternative modes of transport to reduce car usage, including (1) pedestrian routes, (2) bicycle routes, (3) a hop-on/hop-off campus bus, and (4) park-and-ride. A campus-wide voluntary online survey was conducted to determine students' preference for each mode, including a fifth one – a fare-free bus. The latter is based on 'Unlimited Access', a concept that has been successfully implemented at numerous universities in the US, whereby the university pays the transit agency for student ridership. A total of 755 students responded to the survey while responses were weighted to represent the actual student population. The survey showed the fare-free bus to be most preferred, even for car-users, suggesting that the University should rather, or at least also, consider an intervention similar to Unlimited Access. The paper examines possible reasons why the fare-free bus was most preferred, and argues the importance of consulting best-practice and student preference surveys in campus planning interventions.
Keywords: alternative modes of transport, unlimited access, fare-free transit, campus planning, preference surveys.

WIT Transactions on Ecology and The Environment, Vol 173, © 2013 WIT Press
www.witpress.com, ISSN 1743-3541 (on-line)
doi:10.2495/SDP130291

1 Introduction

Universities present unique transportation challenges due to high parking demand and travel patterns that do not necessarily correspond with typical peak flows. Transportation on campuses has therefore been covered in numerous studies, particularly with regard to students as the largest stakeholder group on campus. While some focus on planning aspects (e.g., see Balsas [1]), many cite Ajzen's [2] Theory of Planned Behaviour and appear to focus on behavioural aspects, such as travelling intensions (e.g., see Kerr *et al.* [3]), commuting habits (e.g., see Shannon *et al.* [4]), and preference for alternative modes of transport (e.g., see Zhou [5]). An alternative mode that appears to be quite popular in the US is fare-free transit, based on a concept known as 'Unlimited Access'.

'Unlimited Access' involves an arrangement whereby a university pays a local transit agency an annual lump sum based on expected student or staff ridership. The university typically utilises funds it would otherwise have spent on providing and maintaining parking facilities. Students or staff can then use fare-free transit on selected routes around the campus by simply presenting or swiping their university ID cards. Unlimited Access has been successfully implemented at numerous universities in the US under various names, such as UPass, ClassPass and SuperTicket, with only one programme failure reported so far. Some of the advantages for the university include reduced parking demand and better recruitment and retaining of students, while the transit agency is able to increase ridership and revenue and improve its overall service. For students the potential benefits include increased mobility and affordability to attend university, as well as fairness – the university subsidises *all* students, not just those with a car by providing parking below market rates (Brown *et al.* [6]; Brown *et al.* [7]; Zolnik [8]).

This paper focuses the preference of students at the University of Pretoria, South Africa, for alternative modes of transport, including a mode such as fare-free transit, or a 'fare-free bus' as it was termed in this study. The University urgently needs campus planning interventions that could bring about greater modal change among students, while the study reported here is intended to help inform such interventions.

2 Background and research aim

The University of Pretoria is probably the most comprehensive university in South Africa with nine faculties and a business school. Currently the University has more than 600 buildings spread over approximately 1 200ha of land across six campuses (University of Pretoria [9]). The main campus, which is the focus of this study, is located in the suburb of Hatfield east of central Pretoria, the administrative and R&D capital of South Africa. Although the campus grew incrementally over time, it has long since comprised a kind of superblock that is completely fenced off from surrounding neighbourhoods with controlled access all around. Public roads that used to cut across campus have been closed off over the last two decades and integrated into the campus' built fabric. Consequently, most students who travel to campus by car have to find kerbside parking outside the perimeter fencing of the campus, much to their frustration with ad hoc fines or having to tip self-appointed 'car guards' to reduce the threat of car theft. Although the University recently constructed a multi-storey paid-parking facility on campus, a significant increase in students over the last decade has contributed to severe parking shortages on and around campus. According to the University's Bureau for Institutional Research and Planning, the total number of contact students increased from about 28,000 in the year 2000 to about 44,000 in 2010. Total headcount currently stands at over 45,000, making the University of Pretoria by far the largest contact university in the country. Moreover, the University's Strategic Plan projects an estimated total enrolment of 55,000 students by the year 2025 (University of Pretoria [10]). This further increase, coupled with a growing middle class that would include car-owning students, highlights the importance of planning for alternative modes of transport to-and-from the main campus.

The University's Facilities Management Department has indeed been considering four alternative modes of transport to reduce car usage, including (1) pedestrian routes, (2) bicycle routes, (3) a hop-on/hop-off campus bus, and (4) park-and-ride. Although some attention has been paid to pedestrian and bicycle routes as part of campus planning, these are certainly not yet identifiable nor have they been planned or implemented as fully integrated modes to extend beyond the campus. The 'hop-on/hop-off campus bus' was also merely an idea at the time of the study, and refers to a bus that would operate a circular route on campus. Only the park-and-ride had been implemented at the time of the study, which involves busses that operate between the main campus and the university sports-grounds, including one of the smaller satellite campuses where there is a surplus of parking.

The aim of this study was to examine students' preference for these four alternative modes of transport given the urgency of the parking problem and, hence, assess the possible impact these four modes may have on reducing car usage. However, the research team felt it necessary to also test the concept of 'Unlimited Access', which was conceptualised and described as a 'fare-free bus' for the purpose of this study. From a planning perspective, and given the particular context at the University of Pretoria, the research team hypothesised that a fare-free bus, if based on an arrangement similar to Unlimited Access, will probably be preferred to the four modes currently considered by the University. If this was the case, it would suggest that Unlimited Access, or fare-free transit, may actually be more effective in reducing car usage on and around the campus.

3   Research design and methods

A campus-wide voluntary online survey was conducted on the University's student portal during the second half of 2010. A questionnaire was designed that would first capture information on students' travel behaviour to-and-from the main campus, including current place of residence while studying, and current mode of transport to-and-from the main campus. The questionnaire then provided a brief description of each of the five alternative modes, followed by 10 four-point Likert-scales that required students to rate the likelihood of using each mode to travel to-and-from the main campus *both* in addition to and instead of their current mode (i.e., two scales times five different modes), with '1' denoting 'never', '2' – 'occasionally', '3' – 'regularly' and '4' – 'always'. An open-ended question was also provided following the rating of each mode asking students what they thought the University could do to increase their use of that particular mode. After ethical clearance was obtained from the Faculty, the University's division for Education Innovation developed a web-based version of the questionnaire for piloting. The pilot revealed no serious problems and the questionnaire went live on the student portal together with a cover note explaining the purpose of the survey and an informed consent that students had to tick to access the questionnaire.

Within about a month a total of 755 students responded after which the survey was closed following a noticeable decline in responses. Data were imported into SPSS (Statistical Package for the Social Sciences) for analysis. The University's Bureau for Institutional Research and Planning then provided a student headcount for the year disaggregated into strata based on sex, race, and level of study (under- vs. postgraduate). Because each of the 755 responses were logged with a student number, it was possible to allocate each response to a stratum and calculate weights in SPSS for each stratum based on a particular stratum's response rate. Thus, each response within a particular stratum was weighted during data analysis to account for unequal response rates across strata, thereby representing the student population more accurately in terms of sex, race and level of study. All figures in subsequent tables are therefore weighted figures.

4 Findings

Findings are presented in terms of students' (1) current mode of transport to-and-from the main campus, (2) preference ratings for alternative modes *in addition to* current modes, and (3) preference ratings for alternative modes *instead of* current modes. Table 1 shows a percentage breakdown of current mode of transport to-and-from the main campus ranked in order of the most to least used mode in terms of combined percentages. Students could have indicated multiple modes of transport, while results are disaggregated by place of residence while studying.

Table 1 shows that more than half (about 55% or 34,000 in total) of all trips generated to-and-from the main campus involve individual private car trips, making it by far the dominant mode of transport. If being dropped off and lift clubs/car pools are included here, the reliance on private car to travel to campus is even higher. These levels of private car usage can be considered very high for a student population in a developing country, yet it merely reflects a country known for high levels of car-dependence coupled with bad public transport. Formal public transport, notably bus and train, make up only 6.5% of all trips, while mini-bus taxis, an informal industry servicing former Black townships mostly, make up about 4%. Train usage may have increased since 2011 with the opening of the *Gautrain*, a passenger rail system linking Johannesburg with Pretoria and terminating in Hatfield near the main campus. Although walking comprised the second biggest mode (about 16%), a large portion of it does not necessarily involve walking between home and campus, but between home or campus and public transport stops.

Table 1:   Current mode of transport to-and-from the main campus.

Current mode of transport to-and-from the main campus	Place of residence while studying					
	Within a 5km radius from the main campus		Outside a 5km radius from the main campus		Combined	
	Count	%	Count	%	Count	%
Private car	11,357	37.7	22,453	71.1	33,811	54.8
Walking	9,322	30.9	679	2.2	10,002	16.2
Dropped off	1,302	4.3	2,091	6.6	3,393	5.5
Bus	1,933	6.4	1,344	4.3	3,276	5.3
Park-and-ride	2,260	7.5	638	2.0	2,898	4.7
Mini-bus taxi	1,455	4.8	1,073	3.4	2,528	4.1
Lift club/car pool	552	1.8	1,767	5.6	2,319	3.8
Bicycle	1,170	3.9	321	1.0	1,491	2.4
Motorcycle/scooter	538	1.8	753	2.4	1,291	2.1
Train	260	0.9	461	1.5	721	1.2
Total	**30,149**	**100.0**	**31,580**	**100.0**	**61,729**	**100.0**

Note: The total combined count of 61 729 is necessarily higher than the approximate total of 45,000 students due to some students using multiple modes of transport.

What is critical, however, is that more than 11,000 students use a private car, but reside within a 5km radius from the main campus, an area that would include all the University residences, the high-density suburbs of Sunnyside and Arcadia, and most student communes. Yet, these students can probably be expected to show higher levels of public transport use, including of lift clubs/car pools, and lighter forms of travel such as bicycles, motorcycles and scooters. However, while a mere 4% of trips by these students comprise bicycles, a larger proportion of trips by students who reside *outside* a 5km radius comprise motorcycles and scooters (2.4%), as opposed to trips by those who reside *inside* a 5km radius (1.8%). The necessity and likewise potential to reduce car usage, especially among students who reside within a 5km radius from the main campus, is clearly evident. It is in this regard that student preference for alternative modes of transport, especially within a 5km radius from the main campus, becomes important.

Table 2 shows mean preference ratings for alternative modes of transport *in addition to* current modes by students who reside within a 5km radius from the main campus, disaggregated by car-users vs. non car-users. The different modes are ranked in order of most to least preferred in terms of the highest to lowest combined mean. Since a four-point Likert-scale was used ranging from 1–4, ratings lower than 2.5 denote relative low levels of preference, while ratings higher than 2.5 denote relative high levels of preference.

Clearly, students preferred to use a fare-free bus in addition to their current mode of transport more than any other alternative mode (combined mean = 3.1), although the standard deviation (1.5) suggests quite a variation in responses. Thus, students tended to prefer to use a fare-free bus either 'never' or 'always' in

Table 2:   Preference ratings for alternative modes of transport *in addition to* current modes.

Alternative modes of transport	Students who reside within a 5km radius from the main campus: car-users vs. non car-users						t-Test
	Car-users		Non car-users		Combined		
	Mean	Std. Dev.	Mean	Std. Dev.	Mean	Std. Dev.	*p*-value
Fare-free bus	3.1	1.4	3.1	1.6	3.1	1.5	.99
Pedestrian routes	2.5	1.1	3.5	1.3	2.9	1.3	*.00
Hop-on/hop-off campus bus	2.6	1.4	2.7	1.4	2.6	1.4	.82
Park-and-ride	2.3	1.3	2.1	1.2	2.2	1.3	.25
Bicycle routes	1.7	1.1	1.7	1.3	1.7	1.2	.68

Note: *Significant at the .05 level. (Equal variances assumed.)

addition to their current mode. Only two other modes yielded relatively high levels of preference, i.e., pedestrian routes and a hop-on/hop-of campus bus, while two modes yielded relatively low levels of preference, i.e., park-and-ride and bicycle routes, the latter being the least preferred. Inconvenience, car-oriented road networks, and concerns over safety – both in terms of crime and accidents, are likely to deter students from cycling, including the possibility of bicycle theft and facing intolerant drivers (e.g., see Balsas [1]).

There were no statistically significant differences between the preference ratings of car-users vs. non car-users, except for pedestrian routes, which appeared to be preferred much more by non car-users (*p* = .00). While non-car users preferred pedestrian routes more than any other mode, car-users, interestingly, preferred a fare-free bus more than any other mode, even above park-and-ride, which is actually intended for car-users. Considering the estimated 11,000 students who live within a 5km radius from the main campus and use a car to travel to-and-from campus, what is of critical interest here is that a fare-free bus may therefore help to significantly reduce car usage more so than any other mode, in so far as students would be willing to use such a mode in addition to their current mode. Table 3 similarly shows mean preference ratings for alternative modes of transport *instead of* current modes.

When asked about the extent to which students would use any of the five alternative modes instead of their current mode, the same order of preference emerged, with a fare-free bus again emerging as the most preferred mode overall (mean rating = 3.1) and bicycle routes as the least preferred (mean rating = 1.6). Both car-users and non-car users again expressed the same level of preference for a fare-free bus (mean ratings = 3.1), while non car-users' preference for pedestrian routes dropped from a rating of 3.5 (in addition to current mode) to 3.1 (instead of current mode). Thus, non car-users now also prefer a fare-free bus more so than any other mode apart from pedestrian routes.

Table 3 therefore reiterates the finding above that a fare-free bus may help to significantly reduce car usage, this time in so far as students would be willing to

Table 3:   Preference ratings for alternative modes of transport *instead of* current modes.

Alternative modes of transport	Students who reside within a 5km radius from the main campus: car-users vs. non car-users						t-Test
	Car-users		Non car-users		Combined		
	Mean	Std. Dev.	Mean	Std. Dev.	Mean	Std. Dev.	*p*-value
Fare-free bus	3.1	1.5	3.1	1.6	3.1	1.6	.98
Pedestrian routes	2.1	1.2	3.1	1.5	2.6	1.4	*.00
Hop-on/hop-off campus bus	2.4	1.3	2.7	1.5	2.5	1.4	*.02
Park-and-ride	2.2	1.4	2.2	1.3	2.2	1.3	.61
Bicycle routes	1.6	1.1	1.6	1.1	1.6	1.1	.98
Note: *Significant at the .05 level. (Equal variances assumed.)							

use such a mode instead of their current mode. Again, preference ratings for a fare-free bus between car-users vs. non car-users were not statistically significant (p = .98), meaning that a fare-free bus system may be targeted at both car-users and non car-users to increase ridership. The fact that car-users in a 5km radius from the main campus in both instances showed relatively low preference for park-and-ride, suggests that students would rather struggle to find parking as close as possible to where they have to be if they are going to use their cars, or else substitute their cars for another mechanised form of transport, like a fare-free bus, that might as well save them the difficulty of finding parking or changing modes at a park-and-ride facility.

While the benefits of a fare-free bus system for non car-users may be evident, the reasons why even car-users opted for this mode more than any other require further examination. A Chi-squared Automatic Interaction Detection (CHAID) was used to test which independent (predictor) variable had the strongest interaction with car-users' preference ratings for a fare-free bus within a 5km radius from the main campus, both in addition to and instead of their current mode. Independent variables that were tested included (1) sex, (2) race, (3) level of study (i.e., under- vs. postgraduate), and (4) type of study (i.e., full- vs. part time). Preference ratings were recoded into nominal variables denoting 'never', 'occasionally/regularly', or 'always'. Statistical significance was calculated at the .05 level, while weights were scaled down to n = 755 to avoid inflated chi-square values.

In terms of the preference for a fare-free bus *in addition* to current mode, 'race' emerged as the strongest predictor, with a significantly larger percentage of Black students (including Coloured and Indian students) (about 58%) indicating that they would always use a fare-free bus as opposed to the percentage of White students (about 17%), while a significantly larger percentage of White students (about 62%) indicated that they would use it occasionally/regularly as opposed to the percentage of Black students (about 42%) (χ^2 (1, N = 152) = 29.535, p = .00). Consequently, no Black student indicated that they would never use it whereas about 21% of White students did though. Similarly, in terms of the preference for a fare-free bus *instead of* current mode, again, a significantly larger percentage of Black students (about 63%) indicated that they would always use a fare-free bus as opposed to the percentage of White students (about 21%), while a significantly larger percentage of White students (about 56%) indicated that they would use it occasionally/regularly as opposed to the percentage of Black students (about 32%) (χ^2 (1, N = 152) = 23.134, p = .00).

Black students, many of whom are likely to be more familiar with public transport compared to their White counterparts, seem willing to exchange a costly car for a fare-free bus whilst being a student, whereas White students appear to be more attached to their cars, opting to use a fare-free bus occasionally or regularly, but not necessarily always. While parking shortages around campus may cause White students to realise the benefits of being car-free at times, being without a car *per se* is not likely to be an option if one can afford a car anyway, since having a car is convenient or even necessary in a country where public transport is otherwise still very bad. Responses to open-ended questions also suggest that students were less eager to share a fare-free bus with the public, citing 'crime and grime' as reasons. However, considering current demographic shifts at South African universities, the proportion of Black students at the University of Pretoria is likely to increase over time, which would probably lead to an even greater demand in future for a system such as Unlimited Access, thereby making such as system even more feasible than it current appears. Another reason why students preferred a fare-free bus more than any other alternative mode, apart from it being free, may include perceptions that it would be more convenient and safer than walking or cycling. Further research is necessary to confirm such possible reasons.

5 Conclusion

This paper focused on students' preference for alternative modes of transport, including (1) pedestrian routes, (2) bicycle routes, (3) a hop-on/hop-of campus bus, (4) park-and-ride and (5) a fare-free bus – the latter based on the concept of 'Unlimited Access'. Although the University are currently considering the first four only, a fare-free bus was most preferred, even by car-users, while bicycle routes were least preferred. This suggests that the University should rather, or at least also, consider an intervention similar to Unlimited Access to significantly reduce car usage and parking shortages on and around its main campus. The study thus highlighted the importance of preference surveys and consulting best practice in campus planning interventions. Although South African campuses face unique challenges, campus planners in South Africa can gain useful ideas from countries with similar car-oriented cities and cultures, especially in the US and Australia. Unlimited Access does however require a partnership with a local transit agency. In this case it would be the City of Tshwane Metropolitan Municipality, although the municipality's bus service is currently in dire straits. This presents a challenge for the University should it consider Unlimited Access, although such a partnership may actually help to improve the municipal bus service.

References

[1]   Balsas, C.J.L., Sustainable transport planning on college campuses. *Transport Policy*, **10**, pp. 35–49, 2003.
[2]   Ajzen, I., The theory of planned behaviour. *Organizational Behavior and Human Decision Process*, **50**, pp. 179–211, 1991.
[3]   Kerr, A., Lennon, A. and Watson, B., The call of the road: factors predicting students' car travelling intentions and behaviour. Transportation, **37**, pp. 1–13, 2010.
[4]   Shannon, T., Giles-Corti, B., Pikora, T., Bulsara, M., Shilton, T. and Bull, F., Active commuting in a university setting: Assessing commuting habits and potential for modal change. *Transport Policy*, **13**, pp. 240–253, 2006.
[5]   Zhou, J., Sustainable commute in a car-dominant city: Factors affecting alternative mode choices among university students. *Transportation Research Part A*, **46**, pp. 1013–1029, 2012.
[6]   Brown, J., Hess, D.B. and Shoup, D., Unlimited Access. *Transportation*, **28**, pp. 233–267, 2001.
[7]   Brown, J., Hess, D.B. and Shoup, D., Fare-free public transit at universities: An evaluation. *Journal of Planning Education and Research*, **23**, pp. 69–82, 2003.
[8]   Zolnik, E.J., Cost attribution in unlimited access transit programmes: Case study on the UConn Prepaid Fare Program failure. *The Professional Geographer*, **59(3)**, pp. 365–377, 2007.
[9]   University of Pretoria, UP at a glance, http://web.up.ac.za/sitefiles/file/publications/2012/afr/UP_at_a_glance(afr).pdf
[10] University of Pretoria, Strategic plan: The vision, mission and plan of the University for 2025, http://web.up.ac.za/sitefiles/file/publications/2012/afr/strategiese_plan_2012.pdf

Sustainability paradigm: perspective of the small retailers

D. Sams, E. Scarboro, J. Parker & I. Mayoylov
Georgia College & State University, Marketing Department, USA

Abstract

The preponderance of academic research examines sustainable behaviour of large US retailers, while research of small retailers in the United States (US) who make a significant contribution to the US economy and collectively have a major impact the natural environment has garnered little attention. Therefore, this study fills a gap in the literature by examining key business decisions as to environment, ecology, and economy. As a key member of the value chain, small retailer in the United States' attitudes toward the built environment, stakeholder pressures, and green marketing decisions are examined. This exploratory study provides important development steps in creating validated measures including the built environment, environmental assessment, economic decision, and supplier/distributor decision behaviours.
Keywords: small retailers, built environment, scale development, triple bottom line, environment, economic, ecology.

1 Introduction

The 21st Century arrived with many of the same environmental concerns and debates that have been around for decades; however, in the United States (US) consumers entered the 21st Century more environmentally informed than ever before. Thanks to advances in technology, increasing numbers of US citizens have access to a greater quantity and quality of information about their impact on the environment. Information as to diseases borne out of environmental contaminates (e.g., Asthma and Mesothelioma) and various products' (e.g., tin) links to environmental degradation are no longer invisible to the consuming public (WebMD Inc. [1]). The voice of the environmentally conscience as well as economically concerned citizens in the United States grows continually (Ottman *et al.* [2]). Coupled with consumers' demand for change, increasing costs of natural resources and demand of many resources exceeding supply the

 WIT Transactions on Ecology and The Environment, Vol 173, © 2013 WIT Press
www.witpress.com, ISSN 1743-3541 (on-line)
doi:10.2495/SDP130301

business focus as to the environmental concerns of the past are today's business problems that can no longer ignore (Hirshberg [3]).

From a holistic and integrated perspective, it is realized that the behavior of businesses (large or small) has great potential to harm or improve the natural environment and while impacting the world economy. Humans are not passive units of production and in the natural environment humans are co-creative insiders. Claims made in the late 20th Century that preservation of the ecology and the natural environment are economically sound business decisions requires addressing in earnest to garner profitability for all parties including the eco system. Previous research shows that "saving the planet" is a winning proposition for companies as well as the environment (Hirshberg [3]). According to Mintel/Environmental Business International Inc. [4], in spite of the recession, by 2011 more than 29% of respondents from an online survey of 2000 respondents over the age of 18 from across the continuous United States reported that they are purchasing more environmentally friendly products in spite of the costs (SC Johnson [5]).

The retail industry has grown globally with retail revenues above $14.4 trillion in 2008 up 3% from 2003 to 2007 and expected growth to $20 trillion by 2020 (Euromonitor [6]). Discerning retailers, to be truly green (economically and environmentally), are holistically addressing the 3Es (ecology, environment, and economy) and not taking a Newtonian view of the 3Es as mutually exclusive. Thus, it is more than merely selling *green* products; retailers must also make *green* decisions for the betterment of society and their business.

Best known for their greenness are the big-box US retailers such as Wal-Mart. Nevertheless, the small US retailers account for 40% of all retail sales and provide jobs for around eight million people (approximately 55% of all jobs and 66% of new jobs since the 1970s) managements' collective decisions as to environmental sustainability have a significant impact on the 3Es. Almost 95% of all retailers have only one store outlet in the US and thus small retailers make up most of the retailing industry (Independent Retailer [7]). There are multiple retail footprints (1,067,984 in 2010) on US soil of which 1,041,996 (97.6%) are the footprints of many small retailers (<100 employees) (SBA.gov [8]) and thus their collective impact on the built environment warrants research into the attitudes and behaviors of small retailer.

To create a sense of clarity, the built environment and its scope must be operationalized in order to understand the level of impact on the built environment possible from multiple small retail establishments. The built environment includes *land use patterns, transportation systems, and design features that together provide opportunities for travel and physical activity* (Transportation Research Board Institute of Medicine of the National Academies [9]). The current study focuses on the creation of scales to measure the small retailers' attitudes and behavioral choices within the design aspect of the built environment. More specifically, the scales are designed to examine the attitudes towards toward decisions that impact the 3Es including economic, promotional choices, natural resource behaviors, and value chain relationship decisions.

Further, scales have been created to measure the impact of stakeholders on the small retailers' decisions as to engaging in activities that influence the 3Es. Stakeholder pressure on US retailers (e.g., special interest groups, customers, consumers, community members) to conduct their business in an environmentally sustainable manner and to offer environmentally friendly products continues to increase. Because of their size and numbers, retailers have been marked by their impact on the environment and have come under government regulations, pressure from the media and consumers to demonstrate that they care about the environment. According to a 2008 survey for the National Retail Federations seventy-two percent of retailers surveyed admitted that customer demand is the number one reason for change over other stakeholder pressure (National Retail Federation [10]). Consumers for decades have demonstrated the desire to align themselves, even piggyback on the goodness of others (Zinkhan and Carlson [11]). Therefore, a significant economic benefit for the *green utopian* company (i.e., all members of the supply chain addressing the 3Es at the same level) is to strategically address the expectations of a *greening* society to gain a unique competitive advantage through implementation of best practices in environmental and fiscal sustainability that is difficult and arduous for competitors to replicate (Kotler and Keller [12]). Therefore, the scales designed to measure the propositions in this study of small retailers' perceptions of the needed level of response (e.g., stocking and marketing of sustainable products, and alignment with likeminded value chain members) to stakeholders' pressure for environmentally responsible behavior were created. When addressing a changing retail environment, retailers' choices impact the design aspect of the built environment (such as location – traffic to and within the retail facility, egress and ingress, parking; store atmospherics; and materials handling – transportation, and resource lifecycle).

Some retailers have been recognized for their role as environmentally responsible citizens thus creating a differential competitive advantage (i.e., offering consumers something unique and valuable other than lower prices than competitors) (e.g., Wal-Mart 2007) over their less environmentally conscientious competitors (Smith [13]). For example, in 2007, the Chief Executive Officer of Wal-Mart put the world's largest retail on a path toward sustainability and by 2009 his successor recognize the need to go beyond the walls of Wal-Mart and to reach across Wal-Mart's suppliers around the world (Allen *et al.* [14]). Much of this change may be a result of the negative publicity Wal-Mart received over the years in many Michael Moore's productions and popular press.

With the 3Es as the company's focus, success involves significant efforts in aligning with like-minded, self-regulating value chain members in order to create and maintain satisfaction, loyalty, and trust (Phillips *et al.* [15]). Further, decisions within the value chain such as product liability, material usage and resource choices, lifecycle considerations, and eco-efficiency are aligned among members. From a profitability viewpoint with the demand chain in mind, sustainability decisions are weighed against standards, costs, and resource availability for product conceptualization, product development, and supply chain and manufacturing process decisions. Taking this integrative approach necessitates tying short-term behavior decisions to long-term corporate profitability and environmental sustainability.

With the 3Es as the company's focus, success involves significant efforts in aligning with like-minded, self-regulating value chain members in order to create and maintain satisfaction, loyalty, and trust (Phillips *et al.* [15]). Further, decisions within the value chain such as product liability, material usage and resource choices, lifecycle considerations, and eco-efficiency are aligned among members. From a profitability viewpoint with the demand chain in mind, sustainability decisions are weighed against standards, costs, and resource availability for product conceptualization, product development, and supply chain and manufacturing process decisions. Taking this integrative approach necessitates tying short-term behavior decisions to long-term corporate profitability and environmental sustainability. The current study takes a holistic approach to examine attitudes of the small retailers toward environmentally sustainable value chain (Closs *et al.* [16]). This study creates scales to measure demand chain decisions made by small retailers.

In spite of the upward trend in environmentally conscious consumers, the US population is one of the most skeptical in the world as to environmental issues such as pollution (GFK Group [17]). That very consumers' skepticism derived from inadequate or incorrect information as to what are truly environmentally sustainable products, green companies, and the green product's true benefits has resulted in the terminology *green washing*. Green washing is perceived as manufacturers, retailers, marketers, and other profit making organizations feigning green to make a profit (Green Eco Communities [18]). *Green washing* risks the continued depletion of vital resources to the points of scarcity or obsolescence. Thus, marketing's role in the *greening* of the United States' product markets has been a two-edged sword. By providing the consuming public with information about the benefits of *green* products or of the value chain members' (i.e., demand and supply chain) *green* behavior it has been productive in moving consumers up in the green spectrum where more and more consumers are making personal efforts to be *green*; however, abusive behavior (e.g., false claims) has made believability of claims questionable (Grant [19]). Deceptive *green* advertising (i.e., intentional act or state of mind of the agent) and/or misleading advertising (i.e., lack of intention of deceiving) have are equally confusing to the consumer and thus consumers' desire to engage in goodness of deeds is often overshadowed by skepticism fostered by *green washing* along with assignment of responsibility to the speaker (advertiser/retailer) (Attas [20]). It is the assignment of blame that can be costly to the retailer. It is also unfortunate that green washing has caused consumers to hold ambivalent attitudes (i.e., simultaneously holding positive and negative evaluations) toward products labeled as *green* or *environmentally friendly* fearing that the products may be inferior products of low quality even though they help save the planet (Chang [21]). Consumers may see these products as less effective, or one that requires more in terms of the amount used or effort expended, and/or costs more than non-green products and as a product that is likely being marketed as a *green* product in order to make a sale (Stafford [22]).

When marketers tout products as *true green* that are only a pale shade of green, if that, it also harms environmental efforts by creating skepticism and doubt that leads to poor purchasing decision which potentially affects the green retailer and his or her future environmental decisions. When retailers utilizing deceptive marketing tactics, products wrapped in *green* rhetoric and/or claims of one's greenness the deceptive behavior negatively impact the 3Es for all stakeholders. Consumers' skepticism cannot be changed without truth in advertising that clearly reveals the product's quality, green features, and value chain members' green processes from start to finish. However, advertising budgets are typically less than 5% of gross sales of retailers; thus, are limited necessitating using a well-planned strategic marketing campaign (SBA.gov [8]) that alone without clearly visible holistic environmentally sustainable behaviors on the part of the small retailer may truly be a waste of marketing dollars and do more harm. See the appendices for scale items that measure advertising decisions made by small retailers. Arguably, a holistic approach conceptually assumes internal processes are sustainable. Thus, this study examines the attitudes and behaviors of the US small retailer toward both internal sustainability practices (i.e., environmental assessments, economic and *green* marketing decisions) and sustainable decisions behavior based on external pressures (e.g., built environment and value chain) as they influence the 3Es.

2 Theoretical foundation, relevant literature and propositions

Small retailers with a limited advertising budget may have difficulty overcoming consumer ambivalent attitudes toward their greenness unless they strategically market using a holistic approach to environmental sustainability that includes alignment with likeminded value chain members. Whenever possible, the retailer must take a holistic approach to sustainability including aligning with suppliers and distributors who also keep future generations' needs in mind in all phase of the business. The built environment is impacted the act of extraction of raw materials, manufacturing, and product handling (e.g. fuel efficient transportation, limit distance traveled by materials, limit resources needed to process the raw materials, construction materials for containers used in transport must be sustainable, etc.), as well as sales of final products. Successful retailing of green products means managements' embracing a cradle-to-cradle mentality for which long and short-term sustainable decisions cycle continuously through feedback loops of knowledge acquisition, process development through production /product improvements.

The triple bottom line is the notion of corporate accountability and reporting the value of an organization based on the concept of integrated economic, environmental, and social activities (Savitz and Weber [23]). The 3Es – economic (economy) – profitability; environmental (environment) – air quality, water quality, energy usage, waste produced; and social (economy, ecology and environmental) – impact of retailers' sustainable decisions on the community as described by Hirshberg [3] in his 2008 book Stirring It Up: How to Make Money and Save the World adapt well to the triple bottom line concept.

For an organization to succeed over the long run, it must be financially sound and take steps to minimize negative environmental and ecological impacts while behaving in a manner that conforms to societal norms. Adopting the stewardship principle (i.e., an obligation of management to see all stakeholders benefit from a company's actions) by voluntarily engaging in sustainability efforts wherever possible address the 3Es satisfying the criteria for the triple bottom-line (Elkington [24]). Overall, there is little academic research on the interface between sustainability defined by the triple bottom line and small retailers. Therefore, based on existing literature.

P_1:   The majority of small retailers do not actively engage in activities that support a triple bottom line.

The question as to level of influence of the environmentally sustainable behavior of retailers' influence on consumers' purchasing behavior have been addressed to some extent by researching large retailers (e.g., Wal-Mart), leaving small retailers' behaviors within the built environment virtually unknown (Allen et al. [14]). Understanding the behavior of the small retailer is paramount when viewing the retail industry holistically as the small retailers collectively hold the most potential for the largest physical footprint in their industry (SBA.gov [25]). Nevertheless, opportunities to gain ecological and environmental sustainability may not resonate with a small retailer whose ownership believes in the single (economic) bottom line only. The single bottom line philosophy may be true for small retailers, at least in the first five years of business, because of the need to financially survive the first five years in business. In the US, 50% of small businesses (e.g., retailers) go out of business (Longley [26]).

P_2:   The majority of small retailers in business less than five years believe that only the big retailers can afford to be environmentally sustainable.

Many companies recognize the threat of public pressure and/or the cost of government regulations; and, make strategic changes wherever possible. Research has shown that big retailers have taken action to demonstrate their commitment to the green movement. A growing number of consumers want to feel, to varying degrees that the choices they make ultimately matter (Ottman et al. [2]). Companies have responded to this need by developing, producing, and marketing more environmentally friendly products. In big box stores (e.g., Wal-Mart) and pharmacies and on nearly every aisle in many retail establishments in the US there are products with claims of being green, natural, or sustainable. In every product category from baby supplies to vitamins to business-to-business there are more green products than ever before (Lewis et al. [27]). However, unethical corporate behavior such as misrepresentation or deceptive practices by marketers as to levels of environmental sustainability of products or processes are cogs in the wheel of sustainability that impede forward momentum of the drive toward green utopian consumption. In the areas of advertising and promotion resides the greatest possibility for green sheening to harm the movement toward a sustainable planet and environmentally sustainable companies' profitability. Sadly, green washing has washed over consumers through bombardments with faux green images creating more uncertainty than answers (Green Eco Communities [18]). If retailers believe consumers' perceptions are jaded because of bad marketing behavior, then retailers with limited advertising budgets may avoid spending money on ads making environmental sustainability claims. Due to the lack of research as to small retailers' sustainability behaviors, the following is hypothesized on research surrounding small retailers' business behaviors:

P_3:   Management of small retailers react to pressure from various stakeholder groups to be environmentally sustainable.

 Retailers play a pivotal role in the supply chain as the direct link to the consumer. Retailers in the US today have the ability to dictate to suppliers their own environmental requirements for the products that go onto their shelves or selecting suppliers that act in environmentally sustainable ways (Lewis *et al.* [27]). Yet, the cost to check and re-check supply chain members' behaviors may seem financially prohibitive and inevitably must be passed on to the consumer. Choosing the right supply chain members and developing a level of trust between members is important as carefully managing supply chain members may be too costly for small retailers. Value chain best practices required careful choices of chain member partnerships, building relationships with chain members, and developing trust across the entire chain. With the 3Es as the company's focus, success involves significant efforts in aligning with like-minded, self-regulating value chain members in order to create and maintain satisfaction, loyalty, and trust (Phillips *et al.* [15]). However, academic research is silent as to whether the small retailer has the power or resources to dictate to their suppliers; therefore, the following is proposed based on an academic study in 2012 by Jay Hamister that found that moderate levels of supply chain management were reported by the small retailers in study. This is an indicator that small retailers are for the most part not truly engaged in making supply chain decisions and are depending on availability not ability of supply chain providers (Hamister [28]).

P_4:   Management of small retailers in the US does not believe they have the power to dictate environmentally sustainable behaviors from their suppliers.

 Companies striving for a green utopian state, develop environmental policies for operating company facilities, and set green standards for the company and their supply chain partners. Taking this integrative approach necessitates tying short-term behavior decisions to long-term corporate profitability and environmental sustainability in an end-to-end approach (Closs *et al.* [16]). For the retailers this may be all but impossible; however, efforts to be sustainable and sell a number of environmentally sustainable products are possible for many retailers.

 The concept of sustainability for modern living must consider issues within and without buildings for which design is one element (Gray and Jasuja [29]). Design taken together with location of the establishment has an impact on transportation to and from supply chain members and consumers; thus, has a great impact on sustainability that one retailer sets a chain of sustainable options in place for the betterment of society as a whole. Therefore, even a small retailer who may feel overwhelmingly an inability to create any significant impact on the environment due to their small size and limited resources, in fact, can make a significant impact. In order to be able to market authentic 'green' many companies are striving to increase their "triple bottom line" in this age of accountability with stakeholders not just stockholders by capturing the essence of sustainability through the measuring of the impact of their organization's overall environmental footprint on the world (Savitz and Weber [23]). Certifications as to sustainability are commonplace in the US. As to third party certifications as to environmental sustainability, these certifications help reduce consumer confusion and add value to the brand by aligning with legitimate and widely recognized third party certification companies (International Institute for Sustainable Development [30]). However, many companies self-regulate through the use of environmental management systems (EMS) to manage both strategic and operational decisions as to environmental integration and accountability (Sarkis and Sroufe [31]). Self-regulation may be the only viable option for small retailers due to costs involved with third party certifications. Third party costs vary in direct costs for small businesses depending on the type of certification but typically are thousands of dollars; however, the larger portion comes from indirect costs such as consultancy fees (CTDA [32]). In the sustainability movement, self-regulation has developed, but is limited to a few specific industries (e.g. chemical industry, nuclear power, international maritime) (Lennox [33]). As well, many of the self-regulating industry organization are not well-structure and appear to add little to no value to a company who gains the certification, mostly because the standards are not well-established and/or recognized; but also because the costs are higher than many organization can afford and because the consuming public does not recognize many of these organization as legitimate. However, Green Seal, located in Washington, DC, is an organization based on scientific research (i.e., sustainability product life cycle assessment) in the formulation of standards. Green Seal has been in business for 20 years and writing sustainability standards for 18 years. According to Dr Baldwin of Green Seal, the standards application within many industries has moved incrementally upward in demand only in the last five years. In industries such as professional cleaning products and building products, the industry demand for sustainability (e.g., US Green Building Council and state legisled purchasing regulations) has pulled sustainability compliance to forefront (Baldwin [34]). Therefore, scales were designed to measure the following proposition.

P_5: The majority of small retailers periodically measure their own level of sustainability, as external agencies are perceived to be too costly.

3 Methodology

3.1 Scale development

In order to accurately measure the concepts proposed in this study, a survey instrument was created for purification with a small sample of business owners. The researchers carefully developed questions relevant to each of the constructs in the study based on expert judges in the field. The descriptive survey consists of 36 quantitative questions. No demographic information is included as all respondents are identified as meeting the criteria of this study as being a small retailer (independently owned retailers with <100 employees).

The survey was designed as a subjective self-report instrument developed specifically for the retail industry that may, however, reflect response bias unless steps are taken such as guarantee of anonymity are implemented. The use of self-report scales is theoretically sound, because many of the decisions to engage in environmentally sustainable behavior are psychological in nature and involve attitudes and emotions known only to the person surveyed (Spector and Jex [35]). All purified measures must demonstrated good internal consistency with Cronbach's alpha statistics of > .70 (Hair *et al.* [36]). Validity (e.g. content, criterion, discriminant, convergent) must be examined.

3.1.1 Attitude toward the triple bottom line scale
The proposed attitude scale is a multidimensional (i.e., ecology, environment and economic) seven-point Likert scale consisting of nine items. Higher (lower) scores represent higher (lower) strength of the retailers' attitude toward the triple bottom line. See appendices for scale items.

3.1.2 Perceptions of retailers' ability to be environmentally sustainable scale
This scale is operationally defined as a unidimensional construct that measures the retailers' perception of their ability to financially afford to engage in environmentally sustainable behavior. This is a seven-point Likert scale consisting of four items. Higher (lower) scores represent higher (lower) levels of perceived ability of the small retailer to financially engage in environmentally sustainable behavior.

3.1.3 Perception of stakeholder pressure scale
This scale is operationally defined as a unidimensional construct that measures small retailers' perception of the need to respond stakeholder pressures as to environmental decisions internal to the retail establishment. This scale is a seven-point Likert scale containing nine (9) items. Higher (lower) scores represent higher (lower) levels of perceived influence of stakeholder pressure on retailers' environmental decisions.

3.1.4 Supplier/distribution decision behavior scale
Supplier/distributor decision behavior is operationally defined as one's ability to influence decisions surrounding supply chain member behavior. This unidimensional measure is a seven-point, Likert scale containing six (6) items. Higher (lower) scores represent higher (lower) levels of perceived ability to influence decisions surrounding supply chain members.

3.1.5 Environmental assessment behavior scale
This scale is operationally defined as engagement in environmental assessment directly related to the retail establishment. This unidimensional measure is a

seven-point, Likert scale containing three (3) items. Higher (lower) scores represent higher (lower) levels of perceived impact on the built environmental by small retailers' sustainability decisions to engage in environmental assessments.

3.2 Other relevant variables

As a check to the legitimacy of the answers to the survey, participants are asked to report their most expensive utility bill as well as the average cost in summer and winter. In the State of Georgia, were this study will be conducted, summer rates are nearly twice as much for electricity as they are in the winter months. As well, the cost of electricity is typically greater for most retailers than other utilities as lights are on and heating and/or air conditioning for extended periods of time.

3.3 Validity

Content validity demonstrates the adequacy with which the measures assess the domain of interest. In designing the scales for this study, the constructs were presented to expert judges in the field to determine content validity. Other forms of validity will be examined after data collection. The research team is in the process of collecting data to pilot test (100+ respondents) the survey instrument for validity and reliability. The pilot test will be used to inform the propositions in the study prior to determining directionality of hypothesized relationships. An exploratory factor analysis, scale reliability, and validity check will be implemented prior to administering the study across a large sample.

4 Conclusions

In the absence of exiting scales, this study describes the process of scale development for the propositions in this paper. These scales are designed specifically to measure the propositions in this study. These scales will be tested for validity and reliability on a small sample prior to implementing the full study.

References

[1] WebMD, Inc., Asthma. Online. http://www.emedicinehealth.com
[2] Ottman, J.A., Stafford, E.R., and Hartman, C.L., Avoiding green marketing myopia. Environment, (June), pp. 22-36. 2008.
[3] Hirshberg, G. Stirring it up: how to make money and save the world. Hyperion Books: New York. 2008.
[4] Mintel Environmental Business International Inc., U.S. consumers still willing to pay more for green products. Environmental Leader LLC, (March). Online. http://www.environmentalleader.com
[5] SC Johnson, The environment: public attitudes and individual behavior – a twenty-year evolution. Online. https://www.scjohnson.com.

[6] Euromonitor, Recent trends in U.S. services trade: 2010 annual report. June (4163), Online. http://www.usitc.gov

[7] Independent Retailer, Rebirth of small retailers. Online. http://independentretailer.com.

[8] SBA.gov, 2010 county business patterns comparison. Online. http://www.sba.gov.

[9] Transportation Research Board Institute of Medicine of National Academy, Does the built environment influence physical activity? examining the evidence. Online. http://onlinepubs.trb.org, p. XII.

[10] National Retail Federation. What can green do for you: gaining strategic advantage in retail via environmentally sound practices. Online. http://www.nrf.com

[11] Zinkhan, G.M. and Carlson, L., Green advertising and the reluctant consumer. Journal of Advertising, 24(2), pp. 1-6. 1995.

[12] Kotler, P. and Keller, K.L., Marketing management. 14th ed., Prentice Hall: Boston. 2009.

[13] Smith, A.D., Making the case for the competitive advantage of corporate social responsibility. Business Strategy Series, 8(3), pp. 186-195. 2007.

[14] Allen, M., Walker, K.L., and Brady, R., Sustainability discourse within a supply chain relationship: Mapping convergence and divergence. Journal of Business Communication, 49(3), pp. 210-236, 2012.

[15] Phillips, J.M., Liu, B.S., and Costello, T.G., A balance theory perspective of triadic supply chain relationships. Journal of Marketing Theory and Practice, 6(4), pp. 78-91. 1998.

[16] Closs, D.J., Speier, C., and Meacham, N. (2011) Sustainability to support end-to-end value chains: the role of supply chain management. Journal of the Academy of Marketing Science, 39, pp. 101-116. 2011.

[17] GFK Group, North America, USA: American consumers lead the world in environmental skepticism. Online. http://www.gfk.com

[18] Green Eco Communities, What is greenwashing. Online. http://www.greenecocommunities.com. 2009.

[19] Grant, J., Green marketing. Strategic Directions, 24(6), pp. 25-27. 2008.

[20] Attas, D., What's wrong with 'deceptive' advertising? Journal of Business Ethics, 21(1), pp. 49-59. 1999.

[21] Chang, C., Feeling ambivalent about going green. Journal of Advertising, 40(4), pp. 19-31. 2011.

[22] Stafford, E., Energy efficiency and the new green marketing. Environment, 45(3), p. 12.

[23] Savitz, A. and Weber, K., The triple bottom line. Jossey-Bass: CA. 2006.

[24] Elkington, J., Cannibals with Forks: The triple bottom line of 21st century business, John Wiley and Sons: Hoboken. 1998.

[25] SBA.gov, What is SBA's definition of a small business concern. Online. http://www.sba.gov

[26] Longley, R., Why small businesses fail: SBA. Online. http://usgovinfo.about.com

[27] Lewis, L.E., Schmidt, K. and Duvall, M.N., Retailer sustainability and the supply chain. Natural Resources and Environment, 24(4), pp. 18-22. 2011.

[28] Hamister, J. W., Supply chain management practices in small retailers. International Journal of Retail and Distribution Management, 40(6), pp. 427-450. 2012.

[29] Gray, C. and Jasuja, M., Built environment: PeBBu domain 4. International Council for Research and Innovation in Building and Construction – Development Foundation, Final Report. pp. 4-79. 2005.

[30] International Institute for Sustainable Development. The ISO 14020 series. Online. http://www.iisd.org

[31] Sarkis, J. and Sroufe, R., Strategic Sustainability: The State of the art corporate environmental management systems. Greenleaf Publishing, (Sum), pp. 5-9. 2005.

[32] CTDA, Green building certifications and standards, Online. https://www.ctdahome.org

[33] Lennox, M.J. The prospects for industry self-regulation of environmental externalities, in making global self-regulation effective. N. Woods ed., Oxford University Press, UK. 2006.

[34] Baldwin, C., Personal telephone interview. Green Seal, Washington DC (Mar), 2011.

[35] Spector P. and Jex, S., Development of four self-report measures of job stress and strain: interpersonal conflict at work scale, organizational constraints scale, quantitative workload inventory, and physical symptoms inventory. Journal of Occupational Health Psychology, 3(4), pp. 356-367. 1998.

[36] Hair J.F., Anderson, R.E., Tatham, R.L. and Black, W.C., Multivariate data analysis, 5th ed. Upper Saddle River: Prentice-Hall, Inc. 1998.

Section 7
Sustainable tourism

Spatial and environmental preconditions for the establishment of nautical tourism ports

M, Kovačić[1], S. Favro[2] & M. Perišić[3]
[1]Faculty of Maritime Studies, University of Rijeka, Croatia
[2]Adriatic Expert, Split, Croatia
[3]Plovput, d.o.o. Split, Croatia

Abstract

This paper analyses the spatial and environmental characteristics of the Croatian Adriatic from the aspect of nautical tourism development. Analysis of the characteristics important for nautical tourism development will deal with the most attractive locations on the Croatian Adriatic, and it will recommend and suggest further development of all the elements of nautical tourism together with its complementary activities – nautical economy.

The trends observed in nautical tourism in the more developed Mediterranean tourist countries may be expected or are already present in Croatia as well. That experience facilitates the design of the development direction for Croatia. Namely, geographical, historical and the surrounding specific features of the Croatian coast, the mentality of the local inhabitants, the level of economic development which includes the development of communal, traffic and social infrastructure, etc., imposes to the planners certain limitations which were not present in those countries, or were not of the same shape and extent.

The authors analyse spatial possibilities in the function of nautical tourism development. They analyse legal features and suggest solutions that support development of nautical tourism that respects the area and its acceptance and other possibilities.

Keywords: nautical tourism port, development, special planning, environmental precondition, protection.

WIT Transactions on Ecology and The Environment, Vol 173, © 2013 WIT Press
www.witpress.com, ISSN 1743-3541 (on-line)
doi:10.2495/SDP130311

1 Introduction

Among Mediterranean countries, Croatia has all the conditions for the development of nautical tourism and has comparative advantages in relation to the majority of other countries, which refers to better indebtedness of the coast and islands, a greater number of well positioned and sheltered ports, more favourable positioning in relation to emitting the nautical tourism market, better preserved nature and cleaner seas.

The variety of relief forms, bays, island and islets, is one of the most attractive elements of nautical tourism navigation. The indented coast offers interesting cruising and has good shelters. The Adriatic Sea is a deeply drawn bay of the Mediterranean Sea, stretching in the direction northwest-southeast. The coastline of the Croatian Adriatic is 6,278 km long, of which 1,880 km refers to the coast, and 4,398 km to the islands. The indentedness coefficient of 11.10 places Croatia in the second position, after Greece

2 Defining the issue

Even though the Croatian littoral area represents one integral whole, there are several regions with specific geological, morphological, climatic, and social characteristics that are part of larger functional macro regions. They are [8]:

- Northern Croatian Littoral;
- Central Adriatic;
- Southern Croatian Littoral.

Istria and Kvarnerski Zaljev Bay are at the utmost northern part of the Croatian coast that is deeply drawn in the European land mass. Therefore, that area has the best connections with the European countries where the tourists come from. That connection is established mainly through sea ports in Pula and Rijeka, airports in Pula and on Krk island, and through a road network that is, because of being close to the Austrian and Italian borders, easily connected to European networks. Učka tunnel and road modernization (the so called, "Istrian Y") make this region even closer to the tourist market and even more promising in tourism development. There are two sub regions with specific geographical characteristics in this area:

- Istria, which extends from Piranski zaljev Bay to Kamenjak Cape;
- Kvarner which includes the eastern Istrian coast, Opatija Riviera and Rijeka coastal area, Vinodol and Crikvenica Riviera, foothills of Velebit, and islands in Kvarnerski Zaljev Bay (Cres, Lošinj, Krk, Rab, and smaller islands).

According to the research, 45% of the total water surface that nautical ports cover belongs to the Northern Croatian Littoral, 39% to the Central Adriatic, and the remaining 39% to the Southern Croatian Littoral. Intensive development of nautical tourism has caused a noticeable pressure on the environment. However, there are no data on how much funds have been invested in that period on the protection of the environment endangered by nautical tourism and on the safety of vessels because values have been ignored.

2.1 Statistical data of previous development

The beginnings of nautical tourism on the Croatian coast date between the two World Wars when boaters were using the services of the existing ports on land and on the islands. It was only late in the 1960s and early in the 1970s that the plans for building ports exclusively for nautical tourism occurred. The first period of construction of marinas lasted from 1975 to 1984, and in that period 19 marinas with 4,466 sea berths were built on the Croatian coast of the Adriatic. Individual developmental initiatives on a small number of locations were characteristic for that period, while the system of the nautical tourist offer still did not exist. The second period of construction of marinas was marked by planned development, due to the establishment of the "Adriatic Club Yugoslavia" in 1983, later renamed ACI [1]. Consequently, 20 more marinas with 5,814 sea berths were built between 1984 and 1990, so there were 39 marinas with 10,280 sea berths up to the 1990s. The interval from 1993 up to this day is marked by the privatization of marinas and the developmental interests of their new owners.

In 2008, the total number of nautical ports was 97, out of which 58 were marinas. The number of nautical ports increased for 31% from 2002–2008, which shows a fast development of Croatian nautical tourism. According to the statistical data of the Croatian Bureau of Statistics [4] from 2009 there were 98 ports of nautical tourism on the Croatian coast. As much as 58 of them are marinas. In those 58 marinas (out of which 10 are land/dry berth) there are 21,491 berths at disposal to boaters on a water surface area of $3.293,558$ m^2. Apart from ports of nautical tourism, there are also more than 800 ports, little ports, and bays evenly distributed along the land and island coastline.

In one year, i.e. in 2010, the number of ports of nautical tourism increased by 2 marinas (there were 60 marinas out of which 10 were land/dry berths) and there were 65 berths (16,913 berths recorded in 2010) at disposal to boaters on a water surface area of $3.313,110$ m^2 [4].

In the Croatian tourist industry, nautical tourism makes only about 8% of the total number of arrivals or 2% of the total number of overnights. Nevertheless, it has a more dynamic growth rate than stationary tourism. One of the reasons for that is the Croatian favourable geographical position in relation to European countries where nautical tourists come from. Most nautical tourists come to Croatia from Western Europe. Therefore, German, Austrian, and Italian boaters account for 70% to 80% of the nautical business in Croatia, while domestic and Slovenian boaters account for 10% to 12%.

The final analysis of nautical tourism in the Republic of Croatia has been carried out, according to statistical data of the Croatian Bureau of Statistics, from 2011. In 2011, the statistical survey covered 98 nautical ports on the Croatian coast, as follows: 61 marinas (of which 11 were land marinas) and 37 other nautical ports. The total water surface area was $3.295.891$ m^2 and there were 17,059 moorings. On 31st December 2011, there were 14,286 vessels permanently moored in nautical ports, which was 1.0% less than on 31st December 2010. Out of the total number of stationed vessels, 85.5% used water moorings, while 14.5% used land moorings. The profit from nautical tourism grows every year in the whole area of the Republic of Croatia. From 2004 to 2010 the profit increased by 257.272 kn. In 2009, the profit from tourism was 6.5 billion Euros while the profit from nautical ports was approximately 75 million Euros (out of which 405, 6 million kuna was achieved from berth renting). The total profit of nautical tourism in 2009 was approximately 700 million kunas which was more than 10% of the total Croatian income from tourism. The profit from nautical ports, cruising and charters was also included in that total profit. According to data of the Croatian Bureau of Statistics, the total income realised in 98 nautical ports in 2011 amounted to 600.2 million Kuna, out of which 439.4 million Kuna (73.2%) was realised through the renting of moorings. Compared to 2010, the total profit increased by 4.5%, while the income gained through renting of moorings increased by 0.8%.

Among Adriatic counties the highest income received from nautical ports (almost 140 million kunas) was by the County of Šibenik-Knin. Primorsko-goranska County had an income of 94,85 million kunas or 8.5% higher in relation to 2010.

3 Research methodology

The following section of this study gives an overview of the main spatial and environmental features of individual counties and of legal regulations important for the establishment of the nautical tourism system in Croatia.

3.1 Spatial plans as a factor of sustainable development of nautical tourism

Spatial planning is a precondition for achieving a better distribution of economic functions in space, protection and enhancement of natural and man-created values, and an optimal distribution of facilities intended for some activities, including nautical tourism [20].

The scientific approach to spatial planning in nautical tourism is necessary because it is an economic activity that requires coastal and marine space as an important precondition for business and development. Of all nautical ports, marinas require a lot of top quality coastal area so the planning of their location in the space has a special significance. What attract boater's attention the most are landscape and historic urban cores, so the biggest trend in the construction of marinas is in those areas. This represents a constant threat to disrupt or even completely devaluate such areas. Experts in different fields are included in solving these issues. Available natural resources are analytically and quality viewed through the analysis of specificity in content and economy in investments. The analysis that has been carried out for the purpose of this study has indicated the need to consider new locations for nautical infrastructure, and revision of previously planned locations. From the standpoint of environmental protection, tourist demand for nautical and tourist capacities in an area have to be satisfied, and at the same time protect and preserve the area.

Based on the Spatial Plan of Republic of Croatia made in 1989, and the strategy of spatial planning, pursuant to the Spatial Planning Act [19] the criteria about exploiting the space were defined:

- capacity of nautical centres for commercial berths shall be limited to a maximum 1,000 berths, and a minimum 200 berths,
- determining the number of berths of nautical ports through the purpose of the aquatorium, while ports of nautical tourism with less than 100 berths will be considered as ports in international exclusive nautical centres in which boaters require excellent quality services.

In plans for the development of nautical ports in some counties (Primorsko-goranska County, Istria County, and later other counties) in Croatia, restrictions regarding marinas' capacities for commercial berths have been established. A maximum of 1,000 berths and a minimum of 200 berths have been determined. The limitations were not determined for communal berths and sports associations, or sports boat harbours. For certain tourist accommodation capacities smaller landing places with up to 100 berths should be determined (hotel boat harbours), which will not be considered as nautical centres. Future capacities of nautical ports weren't specifically considered then by the County's master plan. The Spatial Planning Act [19] determines, for physical plans at all levels, the obligation to define the organisation, protection, exploitation and purpose of the space, respecting social and economic, natural, cultural and historical and countryside values, and other elements important for the development and protection of the environment included in the plan. Modification and amendments made to this Act in July 2004 have special importance for the protection and planning of coastal sea area. Aimed at the protection of coastal sea and purposeful, sustainable and economically efficient exploitation, this document defines the protected coastal areas (ZOP) which includes all islands, 1,000m of coastal belt and 300m of sea belt. The amended document determines that the Physical Planning Act is of special importance for the Republic of Croatia and that all plans within the area shall be brought upon the obtained approval of the Ministry of Environmental Protection, Spatial Planning and Construction. Pursuant to the stated Act and Amendments, construction shall not be permitted if the urban plan has not been accepted, except for the infrastructure objects beyond the construction areas.

A Decree about the management and protection of the protected coastal sea [18], determines that:

"no construction can be planned in ZOP, including single and several buildings for anchoring, if the location of anchorage has not been published in the official navigational publications."

According to this Decree, an anchorage is a specially marked water area possibly equipped with adequate equipment for safe anchoring of vessels. In the protected coastal area (ZOP) out of the construction area it is not allowed to plan nautical tourism ports nor plan or perform the levelling of the coast. The number of berth places in one or more berths in a tourist unit cannot exceed 20% of the total accommodation capacity of the unit, but not above 400 berth places. According to this Decree a berth in a nautical tourism port is a place for a vessel of standard length of 12m, and a vessel equals 3-bed accommodation capacity. It should be noted that the number of berths in a marina is dimensioned according to a 12 m long yacht, which length is taken as a measurement standard berth for planning and making projects of berths in a marina. The number of berths of an existing nautical tourism port cannot be increased if such increase has not been planned by the county physical plan. The nautical tourism port is planned to be built in villages and detached construction areas for catering and tourist purposes with a maximum of 400 berth places. Various facilities may be planned in nautical tourism ports, like catering, trade, services and sports facilities. Due to a mandatory adjustment of spatial planning of coastal counties with this Regulation, counties' plans regarding nautical ports have been changed and coordinated.

The adopted Physical Planning and Construction Act [14], later referred to as the Act, Article 51 defines restrictions of interventions in the protected coastal sea (ZOP):

(1) no construction can be planned in ZOP, including issuing a location permit or a decision regarding construction conditions for construction purposes for:
- Berths and nautical ports, and levelling the coast or the sea out of the construction area,
- anchoring, if the location of anchorage has not been published in the official navigational publications.

In Article 52 of the Act it is defined "Planning of catering, tourism and sport purposes" for:
- The number of berth places in one or more berths in a tourist unit cannot exceed 20% of the total accommodation capacity.

The nautical tourism port in the construction area of village and detached construction areas outside villages can be expanded by the spatial plan of a county and new ones can be planned with the water surface of 10 ha maximum. Various facilities may be planned in nautical tourism ports, like catering, trade, services and sports and recreational facilities. Furthermore, in Article 71 of the Act, in the part that defines the content of county spatial plan it is specified:

(1) County spatial plan particularly defines:

- acceptable usage of areas for recreation,

(3) Areas for other purposes outside villages are also defined in the County spatial plan (location, type, the biggest capacity and type) as well as guidelines for determining detached construction areas, and purpose for:

- nautical tourism ports,

- sport purposes,

- areas for aquaculture and fisheries infrastructure."

It is well known that marinas, in general, are constructed in direct contact with areas of significant tourist accommodation and recreational capacities, or within the harbour basins near large urban centres [8]. Marina also must have a possibility to expand in the immediate surrounding area, but not at the expense of beaches and other maritime and recreational facilities, or protected parts of nature. To determine the spatial coverage of some nautical ports, in order to determine a uniform standard, the term "berth for vessels" should be defined. A berth in a nautical tourism port is a place for a vessel of standard length of 12m, and a vessel equals one accommodation capacity of apartment type, or a 3-bed accommodation capacity.

It requires an area of 112.5 m^2 for berths in the sea, and 90.0 m^2 for dry/land berths, or the total area per berth of 101.2 m^2 (land and water surface). Consequently, the water surface for a nautical port for 400 vessels should be at least 45 ,000 m^2, i.e. 4.5 ha, not including the piers' area and other constructions in the sea. The number of yachts per hectare of aquatorium should not be under 50 or over 120 yachts. To accept the same number of vessels on the land (dry berth), an area of 36 000 m^2, i.e. 3.6 ha, is needed.

For Croatian conditions, it is recommended that 2/3 of berths are situated in the sea, and that for 1/3 of the vessels are provided places on the land. The support to such statement is, above all, the advantages of dry berths:

- conservation of natural advantages;
- rational use of available surfaces;
- greater security of vessels;
- a continuous availability to vessels;
- lower price of equipment and accommodation of vessels;
- use of the coast and water surface for more appropriate purposes.

The issue of determining a *minimum capacity* of marinas is significant because the minimum capacity defines the border of which an efficient use of communal, technical and sanitary facilities and equipment depend. On the other hand, an optimum capacity indicates a limit which should not be exceeded because of economic, functional and ecological reasons. The number of objects in nautical ports and their capacity reflects an optimal functionality level – conditions in which the local infrastructure is able to meet the needs. Selective forms of tourism, such as nautical tourism, are the most acceptable forms of tourism due to their compatibility with natural features and possibilities that contribute to the optimal use of touristic features of the market.

3.2 Spatial and environmental features

According to expert opinion, Croatian nautical tourism is at its turning point. In order to attain high efficiency and a continuous and balanced development, the strategy, partial managing of subjects and objects of nautical tourism has to be harmonised with specific features and requirements of the local community for the purpose of sustainable development. The Croatian Government decided to order a study of the development of the nautical tourism of Croatia from a scientific experts' team headed by the Hydrographic Institute of the Republic of Croatia [16].

The vision of nautical tourism in the Republic of Croatia is to be the regional leader in nautical tourism and act so through optimal exploitation of the complete capacities and comparative advantages, trying to establish the balance between the overall atmosphere of the stay and maximum protection of the environment.

The mission of the system of nautical tourism is to ensure the quality service to each boater in order to satisfy all their needs in accordance with the policy of preserving the physical and landscape values of the coast, for the purpose of social and economic prosperity of the locations and areas where the activity is performed.

When selecting the location, the most important criteria should be a protected position and physical and ecological acceptability (multi-criteria analysis of the location's natural characteristics). Before planning the construction it is necessary to conduct comprehensive hydrologic, oceanographic and meteorological research and specify the possible negative consequences for the living world of the area.

Obtained data would determine the potential of a particular area for development of nautical tourism capacities considering geographical, maritime, ecological, social and economic characteristics of the location [13]. Wide presentation of obtained data to local communities, holders of preliminary initiative for development of particular nautical structure (marina, port) would be accompanied by the acceptance of general government's orientation as a holder of nautical tourism development.

The development of nautical tourism in Croatia has to provide quality services to each boater in order to satisfy all their needs in accordance with the policy of preserving the physical and landscape values of the coast, for the purpose of social and economic prosperity of the locations and areas where the activity is performed.

Conclusions of the study of the development of nautical tourism in Croatia predict the development of about 15,000 berths in the next 10 years by the development of new marinas, dry marinas and coastal and insular nautical ports and moorings.

3.3 Selecting the location of nautical destination: acceptance capacity of the location

Further development of reception capacities of nautical tourism (marinas, nautical ports and dry marinas) should be connected with the existing tourist destinations on the coast that already have infrastructure and partly disrupted environment [10]. When choosing locations for the development of new marinas, priority should be given to the areas that are already devastated, such as abandoned industrial and military structures. In the existing marinas, it is necessary to carry out a qualitative restructure of the capacities together with the advancement of the quality of services, in order to make the marinas qualified to satisfy the needs of a modern boater. In the analysis of the existing offer of nautical capacities, areas for marinas near airports and important traffic routes should be defined, especially in the south of the Croatian coast with the world famous tourist destination – Dubrovnik that lacks in receptive nautical capacities.

An important role in sustainable development of nautical tourism in Croatia should have the existing town and tourist ports on islands [7]. Their modernization contributes to that area's humanization, and in this way they can be included in the nautical supply of Croatia. Those ports are very picturesque by themselves, because they fully reflect the identity of Istria, Kvarner, and Dalmatian coastal towns that – besides being natural – also have tourist attractiveness. It is necessary to provide safe berths, electricity and water supply, toilets and waste disposal. Boaters don't usually stay too long in these ports; only for the purpose of supplying or in the case of bad weather. Tourist towns are an important element of tourist supply, therefore revitalization and modernization of their ports is very important, as well as their adaptation to meet the standards of modern nautical demand.

In strategic development, it is essential to determine specific infrastructural and logistic requirements of marinas as well as the needs and expectations of their guests [9]. When choosing a location for the construction of a marina it is important to choose the ones that are less attractive for other forms of selective tourism, and the one that meet the needs of constructing a marina or port for boaters. One of the key factors in decision making regarding the construction or expansion of marinas and ports, as well as other nearby facilities, is the preservation of the environment and its maximum protection. The development has to be within the limits of the sustainability of capacities [12, 17]. The trends on the Mediterranean that indicate an increase in the length of vessels should be taken into account as well as the growing demand for nautical destinations. According to many authors [2, 3], the socio-economic effects of marinas are reflected in recovering locations and they stimulate the development of the environment.

4 Results and recommendations

In analysing existing trends of development of the nautical economy and nautical tourism with complementary activities on the Mediterranean, it is visible that the Northern Adriatic has to develop models of adjustments and implementation of successful trends from the surrounding area.

In fact, the vicinity and accessibility of the Northern Adriatic as a comparative advantage has dropped to second place in comparison with the nautical and more attractive Dalmatian sea due to the development of transport connections of the Central Adriatic and Southern Croatian Littoral with leading European markets (highway; low cost airlines).

The result was a drop in demand for an annual berth, as well as reduced transit in this area. Monitoring leading nautical destinations of the Mediterranean that have substituted their lack of natural attractiveness of the sea intended for cruising with specially developed complementary activities and with connections with other selective forms of tourism, the need to adapt and implement the existing models to revive the nautical tourism traffic is obvious. A possibility for a better presentation of local, cultural, artistic, gastronomic, sport and entertainment offer through organisation of thematic cruising (individual, fleet, racing) raises by making interconnections of all entities of nautical tourism with the county and local tourist boards. With better organisation of communal moorings and anchorages, and their interaction with major nautical and economic entities, marinas will provide a synergic economic effect on the entire area, and, which is more important, it will raise the general attractiveness of the sea in the Primorsko-goranska County. An appropriate and attractive service will be provided by such an approach in order to prolong the stay of vessels on permanent berth in County marinas before sailing towards Dalmatian waters during seasonal summer cruises. It will boost sailors' arrivals on weekend sailing trips during the early and late season.

Attractive facilities and interesting events can provide an appropriate relaxing entertainment atmosphere to weekend boaters, sometimes even without the need to sail from the main marina if the feeling that the owner of the vessel feels at home is achieved. This can be achieved by encouraging the development of indigenous activities and catering services during the season on the harbour shore – the waterfront. In this way, the attractiveness of a certain locality in touristic offer would be raised, and until now, little known coastal and island places would become even more attractive in the field of nautical tourism.

Special attention should be paid to the organisation of moorings for mega yachts with all necessary infrastructural demands, as well as the type and level of services that this type of clientele seeks. Construction of berths for mega yachts (3–5) should be envisaged for all coastal and island marinas that would have the potential to attract the wealthiest segment of the market in nautical demand, that has been in a constant exponential rise on the Mediterranean in the last decade by presenting its attractiveness in an appropriate professional way (Croatian Tourist Board).

Based on conclusions from the Study, the most attractive locations for receiving the exclusive type of boaters on their own or chartered vessels – mega yachts have been recognized. On those locations it is necessary to ensure berths meet the needs for infrastructure, an excellent offer of products and services, and ensure high quality accommodation on the coast if needed. For the best clients of this type of tourism, the excellent tourist offer should be ensured [15].

Despite the financial crisis, seen from the aspect of the production of mega yachts, that segment still shows growth, while in the maritime business, demand still exceeds supply. Benchmark analyses that have been carried out have shown that successful mega yacht marinas are mainly focused on the quality of basic service delivery (anchoring, food and drink delivery, technical services, etc.) and their personalisation and not on the choice of comfort. However, it has been proven that the combination of doing business between the marina and real estates and commercial tourism (hotel, wellness, shopping) is almost mandatory. Today, five ACI marinas located on the Northern Adriatic have been qualified for admission to accept mega yachts: Umag up to 40 m in length, Rovinj up to 60 m, Pula up to 25 m, Cres up to 50 m and Opatija up to 40 m in length. The term yacht for personal use should be defined. In Croatian practice it is defined as a vessel on which a simultaneous presence of more than 12 passengers is not possible and which is primarily used for leisure, sport and recreation. Nautical ports Split and Dubrovnik can accept mega yachts of up to 60 meters in length while the marina in Korčula can accept a vessel up to 40 meters in length. The number of such berths in Croatia is insufficient so owners take their mega yachts to competitive countries, such as, Monte Negro, Italy and Greece. Two locations on the Southern Adriatic (Split and Dubrovnik) are still being considered to construct or, in the existing marinas, to expand the area (water surface) to accept mega yachts. It should be emphasized that it is desirable that locations where mega marinas would be constructed are near mainland airports, and that is why these two cities have been chosen.

A special segment of nautical tourism is traditional cruising sailboats. The Croatian fleet today has about 300 boats for several days' cruising and daily excursions with food preparation. Wanting to attract clients from Western Europe that have better purchasing power, most of the ship owners repair and reconstruct their boats during the winter break in order the improve the quality of their service. In careful selection of interesting locations on the coast, it is necessary to choose ports that could, with the help of the government, be renovated to accept cruising boats. After organizing such system of ports for traditional sailboats that would be equipped with appropriate infrastructure, the system for organizing cruising and berth reservation would be established.

5 Conclusion

A systematic approach to further development means different organization of nautical tourist supply in order to avoid business moves that could have a devastating effect on natural surroundings. Therefore, complete developmental problems should be based on taking into consideration high ecological standards in nautical tourism and optimal consumption of Croatian *natural capital*. Every marina – existing or the ones that will be built – should be approached in a differentiated manner. In the development of the approach it is necessary to take into consideration other elements apart from micro location, such as: urbanization of wider marina micro location, hydro meteorological characteristics of the area where the marina is situated, and its distance from the nearest nautical corridors, etc. By taking into consideration the complexity of those and other variables, new standards in nautical tourism of the Republic of Croatia will be set that appropriately determine the mission and vision of future development.

Through the further development of Croatian nautical economy, economic and social prosperity of the regions where it is organised will be ensured. Exploiting comparative advantages, such as the Adriatic Mecca should transform the nautical tourism system into a "boaters' paradise in the middle of Europe" which will offer adventure and the feeling of safety and uniqueness.

References

[1]   Adriatic Croatia International Club, ACI Marinas.
[2]   Bizzarri C., La Foresta D., *Yachting and pleasure crafts in relation to local development and expansion: Marina di Stabia case study*, 2nd International Conference on Physical Coastal Processes, Management and Engineering, Coastal Processes, Naples, Italy, WIT Transactions on Ecology and the Environment, Volume 149, 2011, 53-61.
[3]   Cooper, W., *Yachts and Yachting, Being a Treatise on Building, Sparing, Canvassing, Sailing and the general Management of Yachts.* Memphis, Tennessee, USA. General Books, 2010.
[4]   Croatian Bureau of Statistics of Croatia www.dzs.hr
[5]   Environment Protection Act, "Official Gazette" 82/94, 128/99.
[6]   Favro, S. & Kovačić, M., *Physical plans in managing sea and coastal area*, 25th International Conference on Organizational Science Development, „Change management", pp. 1049-1058, Portorož, Slovenia, 2006.
[7]   Favro, S., Kovačić, M., Gržetić, Z., *Towards sustainable yachting in Croatian traditional island ports,* Environmental Engineering and Management Journal, 9(6), p. 787-794, 2010.
[8]   Favro, S., Kovačić, M., *Nautical tourism and nautical tourism ports, Spatial features of the Croatian Adriatic, Selecting locations for nautical tourism ports,* Split: Branch of Matica hrvatska, 2010.
[9]   Gračan D., Strategic Thinking in Developing Nautical Tourism in Croatia, Faculty of Tourism and Hospitality Management, University of Rijeka, Croatia, Tourism and Hospitality Management, Vol. 12, No. 1, 111-117, 2006.
[10]   Group of authors: New Trends Towards Mediterranean Tourism Sustainability, chapter Kovačić, M: *Sustainable development of nautical tourism in Croatia*, Hospitality, Tourism and Marketing Studies, Nova Science Publishers, Inc. Hauppauge NY 11788-3619, USA, 2012.
[11]   Johnson, L., Clean marinas, clean boat bottoms and nontoxic antifouling strategies. http://www.icomia.com/library/introduction.asp 2005.
[12]   Klarić, Z., Determining carrying capacity in the Mediterranean, and its impact on understanding sustainable tourism development In: *Towards sustainable tourism development in Croatia. Proceedings International conference* pp. 17-32, Zagreb: Institute for Tourism, Zagreb, 1994.
[13]   Kovačić, M., Luković T., *Spatial characteristics of planning and construction of nautical tourism ports,* GEOADRIA, 12(2), 131-147, 2007.
[14]   Law on Spatial Planning and Construction, Official Gazette 76/07, 38/09, 55/11, 90/11.
[15]   Luck M., Nautical Tourism: Concepts and Issues, Cognizant Communication Corporation, New York, USA, 2007.
[16]   Ministry of Sea, Traffic and Infrastructure, Ministry of Tourism, 2009-2019 Development strategy of nautical tourism in the Republic of Croatia. Zagreb: Ministry of the Sea, Transport and Infrastructure, Ministry of Tourism, 2008.

[17] Orams, M., Marine Tourism: Development, Impacts and Management. London, UK. Routledge, 1999.
[18] Regulation on Management and Protection of Coastal Marine Areas, Official Gazette 128/04.
[19] Spatial Planning Act, Official Gazette 30/94, 68/98, 61/00, 32/02, 100/04)
[20] Šimunović, I., *Planning or the Right on the Future*, Marjan tisak, Split, 2005.

Rottnest Island, Indian Ocean: moving towards sustainability

P. Amaranti, R. Mau & J. Tedesco
Rottnest Island Authority, Western Australia

Abstract

Rottnest Island is a nature reserve which lies in the Indian Ocean, approximately 18 kilometres west of the city of Perth, Western Australia. The special attributes of a holiday settlement with no private land ownership or private vehicles, based around heritage buildings in a significant conservation reserve, make Rottnest Island unique in the region. The Island which is managed on behalf of the Western Australian government by the Rottnest Island Authority is mostly self-funded and operates primarily on the revenue received from visitors from fees and charges for holiday accommodation and recreational services. Funding is also received from business leases, a State Government annual contribution and through grants and sponsorship. Financial business modelling has demonstrated that the RIA's commercial operations are financially profitable and sustainable. However significant costs are associated with conserving Rottnest Island's natural and cultural heritage assets, maintaining essential infrastructure and meeting government administrative requirements. Rottnest Island's utilities and infrastructure requires significant capital injections. The associated costs cannot be met in the short-term. The RIA needs to balance the need to maintain visitor affordability with generating sufficient revenue and funding to protect and maintain the Island's environment and heritage values and assets at an acceptable level. The Authority is committed to finding a solution to achieve environmental, social and economic sustainability.
Keywords: Rottnest Island, sustainability, financial, environment, social, heritage, commercial operations, conservation, carrying capacity, climate change.

1 Introduction

1.1 Context and significance

Rottnest Island is a marine and terrestrial protected area that lies in the Indian Ocean, approximately 20 kilometres west of the capital city of Perth, Western Australia (Figure 1).

Figure 1:   Location of Rottnest Island, Western Australia.

The Island is 11 kilometres long and up to 4.5 kilometres at its widest point with a land area of 1900 hectares surrounded by 3800 hectares of marine reserve. The Mediterranean climate, scenic natural environment, biodiversity and turquoise waters in 63 sheltered beaches and 20 bays make Rottnest Island a favourite holiday destination.   The Island also has cultural and spiritual significance for Aboriginal communities across the State.

Rottnest Island welcomes an estimated 500,000 visitors each year, including accommodated guests, day-trippers and people staying on private boats. Visitors reach the Island by ferry (30 or 45 minutes depending on departure ports), private boat or light aircraft (15 minute flight). The majority of visitors are Western Australians (60%), with the balance of Interstate (20%) and International (20%) visitors.

Rottnest Island's significance lies in its environment, including terrestrial, lake and marine ecosystems, and in its rich and diverse cultural heritage. The terrestrial landscape has great intrinsic beauty and unusually high landscape diversity. The marine environment has high habitat diversity that supports a range of temperate and tropical species.

The Island's cultural and social heritage results from a history spanning Aboriginal, maritime (from as early as 1610), colonial, European, military and recreational use. The special attributes of a holiday settlement with no private land ownership or private vehicles, based around heritage buildings in a significant conservation reserve, make Rottnest Island unique in the region.

1.2 Managing Rottnest Island

Rottnest Island is managed by the Rottnest Island Authority under the WA *Rottnest Island Authority Act 1987* (RIA Act). The Minister for Tourism is responsible for administering the Act on behalf of the Western Australian State Government. The control and management of the Island is vested in the Rottnest Island Authority (the Authority) which consists of a chairman and five other members appointed by the Governor on the nomination of the Minister for Tourism. Members are selected according to their relevant experience. The Authority is supported by a government agency (RIA) which oversees the daily operation of the Island with a core staff of just over 100.

The Rottnest Island Authority was established for the purpose of enabling it to:

a) *provide and operate recreational and holiday facilities on the Island;*
b) *protect the flora and fauna of the Island; and*
c) *maintain and protect the natural environment and the man-made resources of the Island and, to the extent that the Authority's resources allow, repair its natural environment.*

The operations undertaken to perform these functions are complex and include provision of holiday accommodation and facilities, school education programs, interpretation and tours; supplying utilities for water, power, gas, wastewater and waste management; provision of public transport, roads and paths, boating facilities and an airport; and managing the A-class reserve (terrestrial and marine) and heritage assets.

The RIA does not deliver all the services on the Island alone. Partners include:

- the Rottnest Island Business Community (RIBC) – independent businesses that operate a variety of recreational, accommodation, dining, wellbeing and retail services under lease from the RIA;
- volunteer organisations which contribute to visitors' enjoyment, provide information, assist with enhancing and conserving the Island, and help to raise funds;
- facilities and maintenance contractors who manage the Island's utilities and provide cleaning, delivery and maintenance services across the Island; and
- government departments such as the Police, Rescue and Emergency Services, Fisheries, Marine Safety, Department of Health and Department of Education which provide staff, training and other support functions.

1.3 Financial challenges

The RIA Act requires the Authority to *"perform its functions in such manner as to ensure that, taking one year with another, its revenue is at least sufficient to meet its expenditure.'* The RIA operates primarily on the revenue received from visitors in the form of admission fees and charges for holiday accommodation and recreational services (mooring fees, bike and recreational activity hire, bus tours). Funding is also received from business leases, a State Government annual contribution for both capital expenditure and environmental management, and through grants and sponsorship. The RIA is able to outsource provision of some services to reduce costs and risks while maintaining responsibility. The RIA currently has a revenue base of $34 million per annum.

Financial business modelling has demonstrated that the RIA's commercial operations, including accommodation, bike hire and moorings, are financially profitable and sustainable. However significant costs are associated with conserving Rottnest Island's natural and cultural heritage assets, maintaining essential infrastructure and meeting government administrative requirements. Rottnest Island's utilities and infrastructure require significant capital injections to maintain adequate supply.

Some sections of the community have asked the RIA to maintain affordability by keeping fees and charges down. However this needs to be balanced with generating sufficient revenue and funding to maintain the Island's environment and heritage values and assets at an acceptable level. This will be another major challenge facing the RIA over the coming years, especially in the uncertain climate of the global economic situation.

2 Strategic directions and management

The RIA's has a vision for Rottnest Island to be "a model of ethical tourism based on financial, environmental and social sustainability". This vision is underpinned by a desired outcome that "Rottnest Island visitors enjoy recreational and holiday experiences in healthy natural and cultural environments".

Under the RIA Act, the direction for RIA management of the Island is established in a five-year plan which sets out guiding principles, policy statements, major initiatives and a summary of operations. The guiding principles and policy statements make clear the policy framework that will govern all decisions in the life of a plan. The current management plan came into effect in July 2009 and remains in place until 2014 (RIMP).

Detailed planning and delivery of the RIMP is underpinned by:

- the guiding principles and policy statements in the RIMP;
- market research to understand visitor trends, demographics and expectations so that the Island experience meets the needs of visitors while retaining a focus on sustainability and protecting the environment; and
- the principles of ethical tourism and recreation.

Holiday and recreation services for visitors are offered in conjunction with commercial operators. Ferry, barge and air services, accommodation providers, shops, restaurants and recreation businesses provide essential elements of the visitor experience. The RIA strongly supports the commercial sustainability of private business on Rottnest Island as part of ensuring a sustainable future. Planning and delivery is undertaken in consultation with key stakeholders.

2.1 Ethical tourism and recreation

Ethical tourism is a responsible approach that reduces social and environmental impacts. For example holiday makers can put pressure on fragile environments, often inadvertently destroying what they came to see, and depleting resources at the expense of local people. Ethical tourism means doing everything possible to ensure that when people go on holiday their impact on the local environment, culture and people is positive rather than negative [1].

An increasing number of visitors are interested in ecotourism [2]. Many are seeking 'ethical' destinations where they can be assured that their experience is based on conservation and sustainable management. Many travellers also want to leave as small a footprint as possible when they visit Western Australia, particularly in national parks [3]. For the RIA, ethical tourism means that all visitors are attracted to Rottnest Island to enjoy the environment in a safe, friendly and relaxed culture, knowing that the Island is well managed on sustainable principles. It also means that visitors play their part in caring for the Island environment and leave with a deeper appreciation and understanding of its natural and cultural heritage values.

2.2 Financial sustainability

The RIA has a corporate objective to acquire and manage its financial and other resources to become financially sustainable. Financial sustainability is defined as generating enough income (from all sources provided in the Act) to enable the RIA to fund operating and asset replacement expenditures. It does not include a commercial rate of return for the whole agency, but commercial rates of return may be required from certain operations. It also excludes the purchase of additional significant capital items.

The RIA has made significant advances towards financial sustainability over the past five years and in 2007-08 reported its first positive financial result followed by a profit in 2008-09. The RIA continues to face a challenging fiscal environment with an objective to maintain profitability and increase its revenue base to invest back into the island.

Key factors for the RIA in meeting its financial sustainability target are:
- The RIA acts in a 'business-like' manner to perform financially like a private business whilst providing several non-commercial functions for the benefit of the Western Australian community. The costs for these services cannot be fully recovered e.g. environmental and cultural heritage management.

 WIT Transactions on Ecology and The Environment, Vol 173, © 2013 WIT Press
www.witpress.com, ISSN 1743-3541 (on-line)

- The RIA operates as a State Government agency. While the RIA has some flexibility regarding its operations within its own legislation, for example an inferred power to employ and purchase, other State legislation and Government policy often inhibit the RIA from exercising such flexibilities.
- While the RIA is 'asset rich' in the form of holiday accommodation units, utilities and other infrastructure, it has cash-flow challenges that need to be addressed to maintain its viability. In the past, limited net cash revenue has resulted in the RIA not having adequate finances to maintain its facilities and other infrastructure to the required standards.

2.2.1 Moving forward

The RIA aims to become financially sustainable by generating sufficient cash-based funding to enable it to operate as required by the Act. The intention is to acquire and manage financial and other related resources such as staff and assets to become commercially sustainable. This will include achieving additional funding through review of fees and charges as well as raising revenue through offering new recreational and other services.

The RIA will seek to fund specific projects through grants, private partnerships, commercial sponsorship and raising loans for revenue generating projects. Cost savings can be achieved through a variety of activities including reprioritizing expenditure, efficiency improvements, reducing levels of servicing and introducing new technologies. Initiatives presented in this RIMP are limited to those that can be funded at this time. The RIA will measure success in moving in the direction of being financially sustainable by reference to the profit and loss statement and cash-flow statements.

2.3 Environmental and social sustainability

The Corporate objective is for Rottnest Island's natural environment and cultural heritage to be conserved and enhanced as models of sustainability within Australia. The RIA and its partners are working towards basing all operations on sustainable principles, practices and technologies to the extent that this is commercially achievable.

The RIA has applied the commonly accepted definition of sustainability being *'development which meets the needs of the present without compromising the ability of future generations to meet their own needs'* [4]. Public consultation indicated that sustainability received strong support from RIA staff and stakeholders. There was a desire for the RIA to show leadership in becoming a benchmark for sustainable recreation and for the Island to be a showpiece for demonstrating environmental sustainability.

2.3.1 Sustainable visitor capacity

Visitation at Rottnest Island is highly seasonal. Visitor numbers peak over summer and in all school holidays, when accommodation is at saturation point, putting pressure on some popular locations around the Island. Sustainable visitor capacity refers to the type and amount of visitor use a particular site can support over a given period without compromising its environmental, cultural and social values including the visitors' recreational experience [5].

Visitor capacity and related approaches based on limits of acceptable change, visitor impact management and 'tourism optimization management' have been used in Australia and overseas as a basis for conservation of natural and cultural heritage while providing high quality recreation experiences [6–11].

The RIA funded the development and application of a new visitor management tool at Rottnest Island – the sustainable visitor capacity (SVC) framework [12]. The SVC framework was employed to assess current visitation levels and impacts in selected areas around the island, including several sites characterised by fragile ecosystems and large numbers of visitors. The methodology proved valuable in providing an estimate of sustainable visitor capacity that took into account environmental impacts, visitor satisfaction, service capacity, socio-cultural impacts and management strategies.

The visitor capacity research provided input into management controls to ensure all sites were managed sustainably. The research also provided an informed basis for recreational planning in the marine and terrestrial environment leading to the development of a Recreational Opportunity Spectrum, influencing node design for a Coastal Walk Trail, general service delivery (e.g. tours), visitor education, event planning and coastal management.

2.3.2 Conservation action planning

Conservation Action Planning (CAP) is a relatively simple, straightforward and proven approach for planning, implementing and measuring success for conservation projects [13]. The RIA has developed a Conservation Action Plan as part of the RIMP. The CAP process is an international recognized open source standard for conservation planning. It provides a comprehensive methodology for biodiversity conservation management that established biodiversity indicators for the RIA's Environmental Management System and annual performance-reporting framework. The CAP project team, with assistance from various external advisors and stakeholders, identified conservation targets and their threats, developed indicators to assess their viability and devised various strategies and measures to ensure the long term sustainability of the Island's terrestrial environmental values. Together, these represent a testable hypothesis of conservation success that forms the basis of an "adaptive" approach to conservation management.

2.3.3 Sustainability accreditation

In 2010, the RIA implemented an internationally recognised organization wide sustainability program. The RIA subscribed to the EarthCheck Sustainability Accreditation Scheme – a leading global benchmarking program for travel and tourism, designed to help and encourage the industry to make and benefit from cost savings and worthwhile improvements in key sustainability performance areas [14].

The RIA fulfilled the EarthCheck benchmarking requirements for the accommodation, vehicle and community areas, focusing on energy, water, waste, paper, cleaning and pesticides. In 2011, the RIA achieved 'Bronze Certification' and as a result has now established baseline reporting criteria.

The next stage of accreditation is 'Silver which requires a comprehensive environmental risk assessment to be undertaken across all aspects of the operations. Environmental risk profiles were created with suggested treatment plans to mitigate risks and set annual performance targets. The RIA is in the process of finalizing the implementation of an Environmental Management System that meets or exceeds ISO 14001 standards.

Implementing an internationally recognized sustainability program has provided a framework for improving practices and independent assessment of progress Promoting Rottnest Island as a sustainable tourism destination is a critical element of the Island's tourism marketing strategy and fundamental to helping achieve economic sustainability on the Island. Targeted reductions in rates of resource usage (e.g. power, water, gas) and in all forms of waste have the potential to achieve long-term financial savings for the RIA and all other operators on the Island.

2.3.4 Development planning control
The RIA has recently reviewed and subsequently improved its development planning and assessment process that now apply to all internal and external operations undertaken by the RIA, its partners (e.g. Rottnest Island businesses, contractors) and private developers.

Development is limited to the designated Settlement Area, as specified in the Act, unless approved by the Minister or provided for in the RIMP. All developments will be subject to the development assessment and planning controls and will be formally assessed and managed to ensure consistency with the style and scale that is appropriate to Rottnest Island. Assessment will include ensuring compatibility with heritage and sustainability requirements.

Developments that may adversely affect the environment will be progressed in consultation with the Environmental Protection Authority (EPA) to ensure proposals conform to the WA *Environmental Protection Act 1986* or similar legal requirements that may apply during the life of the RIMP. Similarly, any other legally required determinations by third parties will be sought, including for health, heritage and Aboriginal heritage purposes.

Any proposed development that may have a significant impact on the environment, heritage or social aspects of the Island, including potential adverse impact on visitor amenity (e.g. additional traffic and noise) will be subject to public comment. Furthermore, the Minister responsible for the Authority may direct that public comment be sought for any proposed development. Together these measures provide a high level of protection for Rottnest Island from inappropriate development or cumulative impacts of development.

2.3.5 Social sustainability initiatives
Social sustainability initiatives include positioning the Island as an ethical tourism destination, Aboriginal reconciliation and economic opportunities for Aboriginal people, heritage conservation, community education and

interpretation, improving customer service, maintaining a safe and secure environment and volunteer support.

Education and involvement of RIA staff and partners (including contractors, volunteers and the business community) and Island visitors is an important component of developing a sustainability culture on the Island. Interpretation about sustainability initiatives tells visitors how they can help, allowing everyone to play a part in protecting Rottnest Island for future generations.

2.4 Climate change and global factors

Long-term planning is based on consideration of external factors including climate change, global trends including the global economic crisis and fuel prices, and emerging economic, social and environmental issues. Tourism Australia has identified climate change as the top challenge facing the Australian tourism industry in the next 10 years [3].

For Rottnest Island, climate change is most likely to damage features that attract visitors and exacerbate existing management issues including coastal erosion and cliff collapses, fire control and the success of vegetation restoration programs. A priority is to protect the Island's ecosystems to give them the best chance of adapting. Ecological systems are best able to adapt to change if they are healthy and intact. For instance, Rottnest Island's marine sanctuary zones were designated to provide such protection.

The RIA had commissioned a preliminary climate change vulnerability assessment to be undertaken that recommended priorities for further information gathering, research or development of adaptation strategies as a basis for future RIA management decisions [15].

The RIA has identified a suite of 'leading' commercial, market and societal indicators that will provide alerts to possible adverse effects on the Island and the RIA as an organisation. These indicators, for example the level of advance bookings, will be monitored on a quarterly basis to gauge any effects.

The RIA's corporate risk management framework will enable threats to be documented, rated with a risk level and management responsibility identified. Various responses are detailed in the corporate risk database.

3 Summary

The vision for Rottnest Island is it being a model of ethical tourism based on financial, environmental and social sustainability. Challenges to financial sustainability arise from significant costs associated with maintaining essential utilities and infrastructure, and conservation of environmental and heritage values.

Moving towards financial sustainability will include achieving additional funding through fees and charges and raising revenue through offering new services. The RIA will explore opportunities for Public Private Partnerships for delivery of its utility services. Specific projects will be funded through grants, private partnerships, commercial sponsorship and raising loans for revenue generating projects. Cost savings will include reprioritising expenditure.

Environmental and social sustainability will be achieved through implementation of a range of strategies. EarthCheck, a leading international tourism sustainability accreditation program provides the framework for working towards sustainability through a process of independent assessment of progress and benchmarking against other similar operations and best practice standards. Visitor research and the development of a sustainable visitor capacity model underpins planning of recreation facilities and management of popular sites in the Reserve.

The RIA has strengthened its development approval process to ensure that all planned developments are consistently assessed and do not adversely affect the Island's environmental, cultural and social values. The RIA will identify, monitor and respond to external threats and opportunities including climate change to ensure effective forward planning and risk management.

References

[1]   Sustainable Stuff, www.sustainablestuff.co.uk/what-ethicaltourism.html
[2]   Ecotourism Australia, www.ecotourism.org.au
[3]   Tourism Western Australia, *Tourism 2020 Discussion Paper*, 2008.
[4]   Sustainability, www.swinburne.edu.au/ncs/sustainability.htm
[5]   Queensland Parks and Wildlife Service, www.epa.qld.gov.au/parks_and_forests/activities_in_parks_and_forests/tourism_in_protected_areas_in itiative/
[6]   Newsome D, Moore, SA, and Dowling RK, *Natural Area Tourism, ecology, impacts and management*, Channel View Publications, 2002.
[7]   Northcote, J. and Macbeth, J., Conceptualizing yield – sustainable tourism management, *Annals of Tourism Research*, Vol. 33 (1), pp. 199–220, 2006.
[8]   CRC for Sustainable Tourism, www.crctourism.com.au
[9]   Kangaroo Island Tourism Optimisation Model, www.tomm.info/
[10]   United Nations Environment Programme, Priority Actions Programme, *Mediterranean Action Plan: Guidelines for carrying capacity assessment for tourism in Mediterranean coastal areas*, Regional Activity Centre, 2006.
[11]   United Nations Environment Programme, Priority Actions Programme, *Mediterranean Action Plan: Carrying Capacity Assessment for tourism development*, Coastal Area Management Programme Fuka-Matrouh-Egypt, Regional Activity Centre, 1999.
[12]   Northcote, J., Scherrer, P. and Macbeth, J. 'Assessing sustainable visitor capacity for small island destinations: the case of Rottnest Island, Australia'. *International Conference. Sustainable Tourism: Issues, Debates and Challenges*, Anissaras-Hersonissos, Crete, 22–25 April, 2010.
[13]   Conservation Measures Partnership, www.conservationmeasures.org
[14]   EarthCheck, http://www.earthcheck.org
[15]   Coastal Zone Management Pty Ltd., *Rottnest Island Preliminary Climate Change Vulnerability Assessment*. Report for Rottnest Island Authority, 2011.

Marine spatial planning as a tool for promoting sustainable economic development including tourism and recreation in a coastal area: an example from Pärnu Bay, NE Baltic Sea

G. Martin[1], J. Kotta[1], R. Aps[1], M. Kopti[1], K. Martin[2],
L. Remmelgas[2] & M. Kuris[2]
[1]Estonian Marine Institute, University of Tartu, Estonia
[2]Baltic Environmental Forum, Estonia

Abstract

The Baltic Sea is a dynamic economic region where the competition between various uses of the sea (e.g. recreation and tourism, shipping, fishing, wind farms, extraction of mineral resources) is constantly increasing due to the limited marine area. In addition, the sensitive ecosystem of the Baltic Sea and the potential strong impact of climate changes call for an approach that would also ensure the sustainable development of the coastal marine areas in the future. The main objective of spatial planning of marine areas is to balance various interests. Well-advised spatial planning of marine areas enables to create useful synergies in addition to avoiding conflicts and thereby serve as basis for sustainable development of marine areas by taking into account the characteristics of single marine areas or sub-areas. Marine spatial planning is a practical way to make the use of marine areas more rational, to balance the conflict between social, economic activities and the protection of the ecosystem of the sea and to put social and economic objectives into practice in an open and planned manner. An important result of maritime planning is avoidance/minimisation of conflicts between the activities carried out and planned at sea as well as conflicts between the use of the sea and nature. In the current study, we demonstrate how maritime spatial planning enables to balance interests of different economic sectors together with nature conservation in a limited coastal area with high recreational potential in the NE Baltic Sea. Tools and methods developed within the pilot project in the Pärnu Bay area give a good basis for wider implementation of

WIT Transactions on Ecology and The Environment, Vol 173, © 2013 WIT Press
www.witpress.com, ISSN 1743-3541 (on-line)
doi:10.2495/SDP130331

MSP in the Baltic Sea area and provide a good example of possibilities of sustainable development of main economic sectors balanced with environmental issues in the coastal areas.

Keywords: Marine Spatial Planning, sustainable coastal development.

1 Introduction

Intensification of human economic activity in marine areas create potential for conflicts and misuse of limited natural resources. These conflicts escalate especially in the coastal areas where in addition to the economic and nature conservation issues also recreational and aesthetic values of the environment start to play important role. Marine Spatial Planning is a relatively new tool starting to be implemented in many European countries to organise and ensure proper management of marine and coastal resources. There is a lack of good examples of implementation of this approach in the Baltic Sea area and therefore recent series of pilot studies were initiated in the Baltic Sea for developing and testing methodology in different ecological and economic environments. The Pärnu Bay pilot area handled in the current paper is located in the northern part of the Gulf of Riga and encompasses Pärnu Bay and the estuary thereof in the Gulf of Riga, NE Baltic Sea; the land boundary of the area extends from the Matsi Recreation Area in Varbla Rural Municipality to the Latvian border at Ikla. The area is administratively situated in Pärnu County, Varbla, Tõstamaa, Audru, Tahkuranna, Häädemeeste and Kihnu Rural Municipalities and in Pärnu City. The surface of the pilot area is 1990 km²; all influenced by a complex of diverse human use and varied environmental conditions.

The objective of MSP is to determine the general principles for use of the planning area in cooperation with interest groups, having regard to the existing and possible future usage of sea and coast, environmental conditions and requirements of nature conservation. Another objective of the current pilot project was to experimentally implement MSP methodology in the Pärnu Bay pilot area, to find out difficulties, possible gaps in information and methodology and contribute to development of MSP methodology for Estonia.

The necessity of preparing the Pärnu Bay plan is caused by the continuously intensifying use of this particular sea area. The intensity of maritime transport is increasing and new activities have been initiated or are being planned (e.g. introducing areas designated for various water sports, construction of offshore wind farms) that are at times in contradiction with other activities or the objectives of environmental protection. Planning is related to the need to minimise the impacts arising from the use of the sea to the marine environment and ensure sustainable development. A plan of the marine area should help make decisions when planning new activities for the respective marine area and grant a certain degree of assurance for the current users of the sea; their activities have been accounted and shall be considered in the future when new activities are initiated.

The specific objectives of the current project were to:
- ensure protection and preservation of the marine resources of the Pärnu Bay area;
- ensure protection of area of ecological significance;
- promote minimising and resolving conflicts between human activities and protection of the marine environment;
- minimising contradictions between various human activities and propose solutions; and
- preserve/ensure the development of existing activities characteristic for the region (fishing, maritime transport and ports, tourism and "Summer Capital", marine research).

The current paper is based on the materials developed in the framework of the project BaltSeaPlan [1].

2 Environmental setting

2.1 Sea and coastline

The area is a typical for the Gulf of Riga with specific environmental conditions. The salinity of seawater is generally lower in the Gulf of Riga than in the open part of the Baltic Sea, while the concentrations of nutrients are significantly higher. This in turn affects several other environmental parameters such as the transparency of water, which is generally substantially lower in the Pärnu Bay region than in other adjacent marine areas. Pärnu Bay is largely affected by freshwater inflow from the Pärnu River. The high amount of freshwater also brings a substantial amount of organic material that in turn affects the optical properties of the seawater of the region. The seabed topography is typical for the northern part of the Gulf of Riga. The project area is characterised by dominance of shallow coastal waters with maximum depths extending down to merely 15 meters. Seabed deposits in the Pärnu Bay and the open part of the Gulf of Riga generally consist of silt and sand, but there are also extensive areas with boulders and pebbles in the northern part of the project area.

2.2 Other important environmental characteristics

The Gulf of Riga is subject to relatively large annual water temperature fluctuations. From the end of June to the middle of August the temperature of the surface water generally remains above 18°C. The Gulf has some ice cover every winter. Ice usually appears to form in shallow bays in the middle of December. In harsh winters this process is brought forward by about a month and in warm winters is postponed by roughly the same amount of time. Pärnu Bay is the first part of the Gulf of Riga to freeze. The pack ice that is piled up on the shore by strong westerly winds has occasionally even threatened the resort buildings on Pärnu beach. The Gulf is completely frozen during roughly 60% of winters. Estonia's thickest coastal ice – 90 cm, was recorded in the eastern part of the

Gulf of Riga during the extraordinarily cold winter, 1941/1942. In average winters the ice cover melts by the end of April. In warm winters the whole sea is free of ice by March. In some winters there has been ice in Pärnu Bay for up to 6 months.

The largest fluctuations in sea level along the Estonian coast have also been observed in the Gulf of Riga. Strong and prolonged western winds raise the water level in the east, and easterlies lower it. In October 1967 the water level in Pärnu Bay rose 253 cm and in January 2005 275 cm above its average level, respectively. These high sea-levels caused extensive flooding in the town. In December 1959 the level dropped to 120 cm below the average; as a result many shallow bays dried up and the sea receded occasionally hundreds of metres.

2.3 Valuable environmental areas

Owing to low salinity and short geological history of the Baltic Sea area the diversity of the marine biota in the study area is low. Freshwater species generally prevail in the biota [2].

3 Socio-economic setting

The coastal area is quite densely populated. The mean population density in the municipalities bordering with the project area is 38 inhabitants per km² (without Pärnu city 8.8 inhabitants per km²). The marine area chosen as the pilot area is intensively used. Activities with a long-standing tradition that have already been established are shipping (shipping lanes and Port of Pärnu), fishing (use of various types of fishing gear) and recreation and related activities (intensively used recreation and coastal areas in Pärnu Bay). In addition the extensive wind energy parks are planned for the project area. Nature conservation activities that encompass the majority of the described territory can also be viewed as a separate type of human use.

3.1 Existing and planned sea use in the Pärnu area

The existing interests of marine area uses in the Pärnu Bay pilot area may be divided into larger groups: national nature conservation and sustainable use of natural resources (including scientific research and monitoring), non-governmental environmental organisations, ports, shipping and shipping lanes, sea tourism, fishing, recreation. The activities of the natural and legal persons belonging to the mentioned interest groups are regulated by relevant Acts and legislation established on the basis thereof, of which the most important are the following: the Planning Act, Building Act, Ports Act, Maritime Safety Act, Water Act, Fishing Act, Earth's Crust Act, Exclusive Economic Zone Act, Nature Conservation Act, Environmental Monitoring Act, Environmental Supervision Act, Public Information Act.

The interests are expressed according to the procedure and terms and conditions provided in valid legislation and the right to use the natural resources is realised on the basis of actually receivable permits, licences, etc.

Currently granting/receiving the right to use the natural resources of the marine area of the Pärnu Bay pilot area often takes place on the basis of several different Acts. For example, upon encumbering the marine area with construction works, the Law of Property Act (everyone may use a public body of water pursuant to the procedure provided by Acts or established on the basis thereof), Planning Act (county plan for public body of water) and Water Act (the Water Act provides public bodies of water owned by the state (including the territorial sea and inland sea); in order to encumber a body of water with construction works, the superficies licence provided in the Water Act shall conform to the requirements of the respective county plan) shall be relied on. The Water Act and related Acts regulate the construction of construction works that are permanently connected to the shore such as wharfs and jetties, installation of navigational marking (permit for special use of water) and underwater cables (permit by the Government of the Republic, permit for special use of water) and construction of construction works that are not permanently connected to the shore, e.g. wind farms (superficies licence by the Government of the Republic, permit for special use of water).

Applying for a right to use the natural resources for a marine area and granting thereof pursuant to the cases, procedure and terms and conditions provided in the relevant Acts generally eliminates the possibility of a conflict of interests between valid permits and licences. In the event that such a conflict arises for any reason, a mechanism exists to resolve the legal conflict. When characterising the existing situation, it may be said that, based on the valid legislation and the issued permits and licences (with different periods of validity), the marine area of the Pärnu Bay pilot area is already "planned", i.e. divided between the current users in both spatial and time aspects. Further planning/re-planning of the marine area of the Pärnu Bay pilot area is therefore subject to proposals for creating new rights by restricting or amending the existing rights.

The situation can be illustrated by the creation of a new interest group – wind farm developer – on the basis of legislation that determines the procedure and terms and conditions for such creation. Planning a wind farm on the basis of the Fishing Act and the Fishing Rules on a marine area in the Pärnu Bay pilot area prescribed for fishing may serve as an example. In the course of disclosure (Public Information Act) accompanying the marine area plan of the wind farm and the later environmental impact assessment of the plan, the interested parties can reach a solution that satisfies both parties. Upon reaching a compromise (between the wind farm developer and representatives of the fishing industry in this case), further planning of the marine area or amending the existing plan would mean complete or partial limitation of the fishing right in the marine area to be allocated for the wind farm along with making the respective amendments in the Fishing Act and/or the Fishing Rules.

The legally ensured and currently planned human uses of the Pärnu Bay pilot area are indicated in Figure 1.

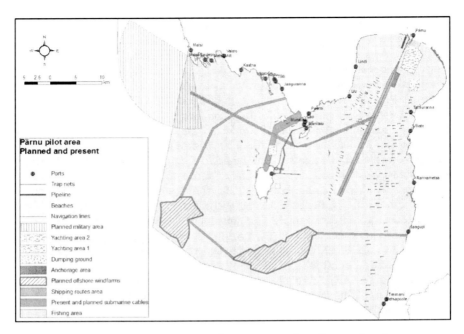

Figure 1:   Planned and present human uses of the Pärnu planning area.

3.2 Tourism and recreation in the Pärnu area

3.2.1 Situation and main issues

Tourism is set to be one of the most important economic sectors for the region promoted by exceptional environmental setting. The length of the coastline of Pärnu County is 242 km, the coastal waters are shallow and among the warmest in Estonia, thus creating favourable conditions for the development of the tourism and recreation industry. Pärnu is annually visited by approximately 500,000 people of whom a third are Estonians and two-thirds are foreigners. The Pärnu County "Sun Circles" that divide the county into four serve as basis for tourism routes: the blue sea region, the land by the sea, the green riverland and the ancient woodland. There were approximately 200 hotels and restaurants in the county in 2009 with 75% of them in the Pärnu urban area. The proportion of companies with activities directly meant for vacationers is about five per cent in the county. Most of the establishments providing accommodation are located in the territories of local governments that are well known as summer resorts, i.e. in Pärnu and in Audru, Tõstamaa, Häädemeeste, Tori and Tahkuranna Rural Municipalities. Many of the holiday villages and camps are located in coastal regions and mostly active during the peak season, i.e. summer.

The tourism sector is characterised by heavy seasonality. 46% of the visitors visited the region in the three summer months in 2009 (including 43% in Pärnu City). As a positive trend, seasonality in general has decreased and the proportion of visitors during summer months only increased again in 2008–2009.

3.2.2 Main forcing factors

The Pärnu County "Sun Circles" that divide the county into four serve as basis for tourism routes: the blue sea region, the land by the sea, the green riverland and the ancient woodland. The location of Pärnu by the sea and the international highway connection of the Via Baltica create good preconditions for movement of vacationers and tourists for moving by sea or vehicle.

3.2.3 Adopted vision and monitored trends

According to the Pärnu County Development Strategy 2030+, the following is mentioned as important issues in terms of development of tourism and recreation:

1. activity of the local population as the largest contributors to regional tourism products in shaping the recreation and tourism cluster;
2. modernisation of the infrastructure that supports the current recreation and tourism;
3. creation of an integral development conception of recreation and tourism for the county and directing the activities to more specific target groups and markets;
4. county-wide development of recreation and tourism products; and
5. better usage of the location of the county between two focal points (Tallinn and Riga) and creation of stronger business and marketing relationships with these centres.

4 Conflict analysis of existing and planned sea uses in the Pärnu area

4.1 General overview

For the described project area in total 12 different uses and 28 combinations of different uses were identified during the stock take process (Figure 2, table 1). In this analysis the area of single use is quite limited and is located mostly in the southernmost and easternmost part of the bay (Figure 3). Major part of the area is recorded as double use – mostly it is combination of fishing and nature protection or fishing and wind farms. In the latter case there is obvious conflict of uses and in case of realisation of the wind farm project the conflict is solved in favour of wind farm developers. In the northern part of the Pärnu Bay the combinations of different sea uses include beach bathing areas, sailing areas, dumping areas and fishing areas. In most cases the other uses are geographically separated creating the conflict only with fishing. Ship routes heading towards Pärnu harbour create zones with multiple uses but in this case there is no conflict between them.

Possible conflicts between sea uses can occur in the area between Kihnu Island and mainland. Here the maximum number of multiple sea uses is recorded (5 uses) from which potentially conflicting are dumping, nature protection and fishing. In this case the conflict should be solved with regulatory mechanisms restricting the activities temporally.

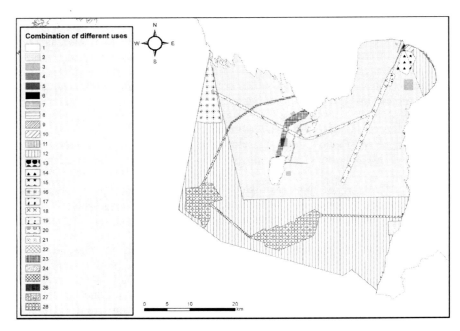

Figure 2:   Combinations of different sea uses in Pärnu pilot MSP area (for explanation of coding see Table 1).

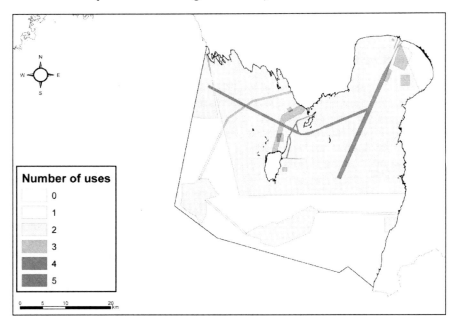

Figure 3:   Spatial distribution of different sea uses in the Pärnu pilot MSP area.

Table 1: Coding of different sea use combinations in the Pärnu planning area.

Code	Ship-route	Beach	Pipeline	Anchoring area	Cables	Dumping area	Nature protection	Fishing	Shipping area	Military	Sailing	Wind farm
1		■					■	■				
2												
3							■					
4			■				■					
5	■						■	■				
6							■					
7	■							■				
8		■										
9							■					
10												
11	■											
12								■				
13		■										
14							■	■			■	
15								■			■	
16								■		■		
17							■					
18	■							■				
19				■								
20	■						■	■				
21	■							■				
22	■							■	■			
23	■				■			■				
24	■							■	■			
25					■							
26					■			■				
27					■							■
28								■				■

4.2 Main conflicts in the pilot area

The main existing conflict in the area occurs between fishing and recreation (water sports). This conflict was alleviated (but still not finally solved) by designating special yachting areas where it is prohibited to hinder or compromise the traffic of vehicles used for water sports (that are marked accordingly) in certain periods. Potential conflicts in case of introduction of new activities include conflicts between nature conservation and other sea uses (the planned military training area, wind farms, also increasing recreation/tourism); conflicts between offshore wind farms and other sea uses (fisheries, shipping, recreation/tourism); conflicts between the planned military training area and fishing, recreation/tourism.

4.3 Methods for dealing with the identified conflicts and solutions

There are obvious conflicts between the need to utilize the marine resources and the need to manage and protect these resources. However, all existing legal human activities in the Pärnu Bay pilot area are regulated by different relevant legal acts in force. In this sense the sea areas concerned are already "planned" which means that sea space is allocated to different kind of sea uses (not to confuse with sea space allocation to different legal entities) according to legal acts in force.

There are many different complex and often overlapping existing human use rights (public access rights, riparian rights, fishing rights, navigation rights, seabed use rights etc.) that are affected by the emerging maritime spatial planning. However, the planning itself needs also to be performed according to the Estonian Planning Act that regulates relations between the state, local governments and other persons in the preparation of plans with aim to ensure conditions which take into account the needs and interests of the widest possible range of members of society for balanced and sustainable spatial development. The strategic environmental assessment resulting from implementation of the planning policy is organised in the cases and pursuant to the procedure provided for in the Estonian Environmental Impact Assessment and Environmental Management System Act (Saunanen and Vaarmari [3]).

All existing human use rights, including the overlapping ones, are allocated and enforced according to the harmonized system of legal acts in force. Therefore, the existing human use activities performed according to issued permits and licenses usually are not in conflict, and if there is any, then there are the legal procedures in force to resolve these conflicts as appropriate.

Introduction of the new kind of human activity (e.g. development of the wind park area) presumes the democratic process of stakeholder participation which takes into account the long-term strategies in and needs for the development of the economic, social, cultural and natural environment.

Method for dealing with the identified conflicts is the consensus building stakeholder meetings as an obligatory element of the maritime planning process. More specifically, the Mutual Learning methodology should be used. Proposed solutions and recommendations are conflict specific.

Based on the analysis of existing sea uses in the pilot area following conclusions and recommendations have been made:

1. The spatial overlapping of the existing fishing and nature protection uses not presumes the conflict by itself. Based on the results of previous scientific studies the fishery is regulated spatially and temporally with the aim to avoid any irreversible impact. If any new scientific facts based concerns would arise then additional fishery restrictions will be introduced and the Fishery Rules will be amended accordingly.

2. The spatial overlapping of fishing area (existing human use) and the wind park area (planned human use) do not necessarily presume the

arising conflict resolution. If the planning process will lead to decision to give the permit for the wind park development in the Pärnu Bay then at that stage it is not clear whether the spatial restriction of existing fishing rights with or no compensation will be imposed or not. If some kind of spatial restriction will be imposed then the Fishing Rules will be amended accordingly. It is proposed to resolve this potential spatial conflict either technically based on the provisions of existing legislation or in a course of negotiations of parties concerned. Considerable opposition of environmentalists (important bird area) and the tourist industry (visual pollution vs. the clean horizon what the industry sells) is expected. Fishery opposition will arise only in the case of potential and expected spatial restrictions of the fishing rights.

3. The spatial overlapping of the multiple but not exclusive human uses beach bathing areas, sailing areas, shipping routes, dumping areas and fishing areas in the northern part of the Pärnu Bay (all are the existing sea uses) do not necessarily cause the conflict of sea uses. All these sea uses, including shipping, dumping and fishing are regulated and enforced in a way that that they are not causing any irreversible impact according to best knowledge we have. However, the whole complex environmental impact will be reassessed if introduction of some new type of human use will be planned or new scientific facts on the possible irreversible harm will be revealed.

5 Recommendations and future steps to implement MSP

According to the Estonian law (Planning Act) MSP is possible but there are still some legal deficits and unclear aspects [4]. Also the human resources and information basis for MSP are weak especially at the municipalities. National maritime policy should facilitate development of maritime spatial planning. The draft National Development Plan "Estonian Maritime Policy" foresees development of an official pilot MSP in 2013 and preparation of MSPs for all counties by 2020. The latter deadline might be too late, considering development in wind energy sector and other plans for use of the Estonian marine area. In the Estonian circumstances the following is important in order to realize the MSP:

- Establishment of proper legal basis for MSP in Estonia (including land-sea planning harmonization, hierarchical planning system, zoning principles in MSP);
- Maritime spatial plans should be developed for the whole Estonian marine area. It is recommended to apply similar principles for spatial planning in marine as well as terrestrial areas, considering thereby the differences arising from different character of sea and land.
- It is advisable to take the existing categories of spatial plans as basis also for planning of marine areas. That means that the general principles of MSP should be set in the national spatial plan (in addition to the territorial sea, the directions can be given also for the EEZ in co-operation with other countries). County level spatial plans should be

elaborated for the whole Estonian marine area and in case of need also general or detailed spatial plans for certain areas.

- MSP documents should be in line with and basis for the permits/licences issued through specific regulations. For example, if the spatial plan foresees sand mining in a certain area then no permits for conflicting uses are given (before the relevant spatial plan must be changed).
- Sea use development should be sustainable and based on eco-system approach. It should follow the goals of the EU Marine Strategy Framework Directive. MSP should be used as an instrument to avoid cumulative effects of the sea use activities on marine biodiversity;

Acknowledgements

The current study was performed in the framework of project BaltSeaPlan Part-financed by the EU (European Regional Development Fund) and with contribution from the Estonian target financed theme SF0180013s08.

References

[1] Martin, G., Aps, R., Kopti, M., Kotta, J., Remmelgas, L., Kuris, M. 2012. Towards a Pilot Maritime Spatial Plan for the Pärnu Bay. BaltSeaPlan report no 13, 53.

[2] Kotta, J., Lauringson, V., Martin, G., Simm, M., Kotta, I., Herkül, K., Ojaveer, H. 2008. Gulf of Riga and Pärnu Bay. Schiewer, U. (Ed.). Ecology of Baltic Coastal waters (217 - 243). Berlin: Springer.

[3] Saunanen, E. and K. Vaarmari. 2010. Maritime spatial planning. Analysis of valid legislation and solutions for amendment thereof. Estonian Environmental Law Centre.

[4] Hendrikson & Ko, 2010. Methodology of maritime spatial planning. http://www.siseministeerium.ee/public/Merealade_planeerimise_metoodika. pdf.

How effective are impact assessment procedures for ecotourism in developing nations? A case study analysis

D. Hernán Valencia Korosi
Australian Centre for Cultural Environmental Research, University of Wollongong, Australia

Abstract

By the late 1980s, *ecotourism* became officially recognised as a sustainable development strategy, and a way to improve the quality of life of marginalised communities. Yet today it is still a field of contested discourses and paradigms, especially in developing countries, where environmental legislation is still often ambiguous and not powerful enough to ensure enforcement of the outcomes of planning and assessment instruments. It has been argued that impact assessment procedures are not only meant to identify potential impacts of a proposed development, but should endorse responsible environmental management practices, and active community involvement in the decision-making process. This study compares the theory and practice behind ecotourism assessment and management of the La Escobilla Turtle Sanctuary and the Xixim Ecolodge through the analysis of initial project impact assessments, semi-structured interviews with representatives of different sectors of Mexican society, and a survey of tour operators. It aims to determine whether or not current Mexican environmental legislation for assessment procedures is providing an adequate framework for the adoption of sustainable tourism practices. It is argued that impact assessment procedures often poorly incorporate social and cultural variables, and hence fail to acknowledge tour operators' management and operation skills, and therefore decrease the quality of impact prediction and monitoring strategies for future ecotourism management.
Keywords: La Escobilla, Xixim Ecolodge, ecotourism, impact assessments, sustainable development, environmental legislation, developing countries.

WIT Transactions on Ecology and The Environment, Vol 173, © 2013 WIT Press
www.witpress.com, ISSN 1743-3541 (on-line)
doi:10.2495/SDP130341

1 Introduction

Today, ecotourism is the fastest growing sector of the tourism industry (Almeyda *et al.* [1]). Tourists around the world are becoming more aware of the footprints and impacts of traditional mass tourism, preferring responsible and sustainable travel experiences (Honey [2]). This trend has led to what different authors have called the "greening of the tourism industry", characterized by the incorporation of terms such as "eco", "sustainable", and "alternative" but with no essential changes from mass tourism practices (Buckley [3]; Farquharson [4]; Fennell and Dowling [5]; Pardo [6]) . Environmental planning and assessment practices have also played a crucial role in the greening process as they have become tools to control the development of proposals that might have potential impacts on the environment, and on the wellbeing of local populations (O'Faircheallaigh [7]) .

   Ecotourism projects are not exempt from procedures requiring the development of Environmental and Social Impact Assessments (EIA and SIA respectively) to demonstrate adequate protection and impact monitoring strategies (García [8]). In Mexico, EIA procedures are mandatory under the 1988 Environmental Protection and Ecological Equilibrium General Law (LGEEPA) that dictates which components and standards should be observed when developing such evaluations (Cámara de Diputados del H. Congreso de la Unión [9]). At the same time, the LGEEPA, in agreement with other legislation, regulates the protection of ecosystem services ensuring that impact assessment procedures are enforced considering all components of the environment/society that could be affected by the development (SEMARNAT [10]). However, this is not necessarily the case in reality, as current EIA procedures are hardly promoting sustainable and responsible practices, and SIA procedures are not enforced by law, leaving a gap in the overall assessment of projects (Becerra [11]; Brito [12]; Juárez [13]; Sangines [14]). Therefore, it is important to understand how the theory and practice behind ecotourism has been addressed, and whether or not Mexican environmental legislation has allowed the adoption of adequate planning and assessment procedures for the implementation of responsible ecotourism practices.

   This paper forms part of a broader PhD project aiming to compare Mexican and Australian environmental and social impact assessment procedures for ecotourism. The study uses several different methods to analyse the effectiveness of EIA/SIA including the study of legislation at a national scale, interviews of government, NGO and academia representatives, and a tour operators' survey. In this paper I identify the issues behind the theory and practice of ecotourism impact assessments focusing on two case studies on the Pacific and Caribbean coasts of Mexico. The La Escobilla Turtle Sanctuary in the coast of Oaxaca while the Xixim Ecolodge is on the coast of Yucatan.

   Both the La Escobilla Turtle Sanctuary and the Xixim Ecolodge have undergone EIA and SIA procedures in the past. However, final reports have shown little scientific and social based knowledge to support current management and impact mitigation strategies. In addition, such procedures have not addressed issues concerning administrative and operation skills of tour operators to enable adequate management. Limited funding and government support, and the deficient application of impact assessment procedures have triggered a series of issues within these two enterprises that threaten their success and need to be resolved appropriately.

2 Methods

2.1 Case studies

Case studies were selected according to their proximity to protected areas or areas of environmental and/or heritage significance. They are located on Mexican coasts, one in the Caribbean coastal town of Celestun, and the other in the Pacific coastal town of La Escobilla. Both have been chosen to compare experiences each ecotourism business had in the understanding of EIA and SIA practices prior, during and after the implementation of their activities, and how this understanding reflects the current management practices each enterprise has adopted for the prevention of potential impacts.

Additionally, during 2010, a 30-question survey was designed for tour operators to understand the efficiency of the planning process before the implementation of the business. The survey consisted of five sections aiming to relate the outcomes of the initial impact planning and assessment process with current management practices. Each section had five questions relating to the general planning, impact planning, community participation, sustainable development and demographic information from each of the tour operators (Table 1).

Table 1:   Survey structure and design.

Section	Description
A. Planning	• Conceptualization and understanding of ecotourism theory and practice • Benefits and constraints of ecotourism enterprises • Government support and funding
B. Impact Planning	• Quality of EIA/SIA procedures • Mitigation and preventive measures • Monitoring strategies
C. Community Participation	• Community involvement in the EIA/SIA decision-making process • Value of local knowledge • Benefits of active participation
D. Sustainable Development	• Sustainability of the business • Benefits of the project for the local environment • Benefits of the project for the local community
E. Demographic information	• Age, origin, level of education, family structure, and transportation behaviours • Aspects of the business that could be improved • Aspects of the survey that could be improved

2.2 Interviews

During 2010 and 2011, in-depth, semi-structured interviews were undertaken in Spanish, with key informants of Mexican society involved in ecotourism planning and management in order to identify and understand, on the one hand, ongoing issues with impact assessment procedures, and on the other hand, to compare the theory and practice behind the implementation of EIA and SIA practices. Key informants were NGO representatives, government officials, and academics with ample experience in the sector (Table 2). An iterative comparative analysis of the interview data was conducted in order to gain in-depth knowledge of the benefits and constraints of the ecotourism industry. A qualitative research approach was appropriate as the group of key informants were interviewed on an individual and personalised basis following the method used by Matysek and Kriwoken [15]. It is important to highlight that names of participants have been kept confidential as part of an ethics agreement.

Table 2:   Interviewees from different sectors of the Mexican society.

Sector	Institution	Department/Office
Government	National Commission for the Development of Indigenous Communities – CDI	• Department of Alternative Tourism within Indigenous Communities
		• Consultation and Planning General Directorate
	Mexico City Natural Resources Secretariat-SMA	• Assessment and Environmental Impact Directorate
	National Commission of Natural Protected Areas – CONANP	• Natural Protected Areas Conservation Program
	Secretary of Environment and Natural Resources – SEMARNAT	• Tourism and Urban Development Directorate
	Tourism Secretariat – SECTUR	• General Director's Office
NGO	Oaxaca's Coast Westland Network Association – RHCO	• Regional Ecotourism Office
Academia	University of the Sea – UMAR	• Resource Institute
		• Industry Institute
	Mexico National Autonomous University – UNAM	• Institute of Ecology
	National Institute of Ecology – INE	• Department of Ecosystem Studies

3 Results

3.1 Case studies

3.1.1 La Escobilla Sanctuary, Santa María Tonameca, Oaxaca, Mexico
La Escobilla Turtle Sanctuary is located 34 km southeast of San Pedro Pochutla and 30 min southwest of Puerto Escondido in the rural coastal town of La Escobilla (Fig. 1B). The town was populated during the 1940s by Indigenous Zapoteco immigrants from el Lagartero, Pochutla, who became illegal egg poachers of the Olive ridley turtle (*Lepidochelys olivacea*) in the 1950s, and

continued for almost 30 years due to the lack of suitable agricultural produces and other subsistence resources. By 1970, the Mexican government introduced a ban to stop the illegal extraction of eggs resulting in a tragic confrontation between the inhabitants and the Navy officers in which a local boy was badly injured. This event triggered a change in the mentality of the local people who now protect the turtles through the ecotourism (Macedo [16]). The Sanctuary is operated by the Sociedad Cooperativa El Santuario de la Tortuga La Escobilla (hereafter, the Cooperative), which is formed by members of four local families. Members of the Cooperative have low education and live in marginalised conditions. They have being working on the ecotourism business since 1997 aiming to run a successful enterprise and adopt sustainable living practices to improve their quality of life and protect the populations of the Olive ridley turtle. Since the formation of the Sanctuary, members of the Cooperative have struggled to operate an enterprise, which was thought to provide better financial opportunities to their members through the promotion of conservation-oriented activities.

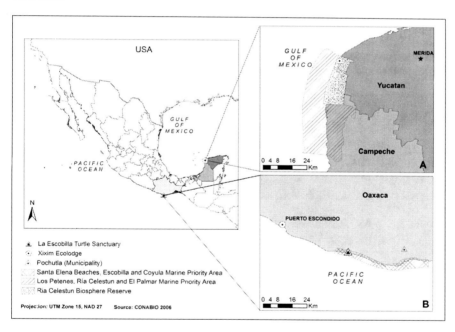

Figure 1:   Location map. A) Xixim Ecolodge within the Ria Celestun Biosphere Reserve and the Los Petenes, Ria Celestun and El Palmar Marine Priority Area. B) La Escobilla Sanctuary within the Santa Elena Beaches, Escobilla and Coyula Marine Priority Area (Source: CONABIO 2006).

Activities such as wildlife watching and guided tours to nesting sites are the most popular within the Sanctuary. Costs of wildlife watching tours to the estuary on a "cayuco" range from $15 to $25 MX pesos for children and adults respectively, and guided tours to the nesting sites are $100 MX pesos per person during the nesting season. In addition, the Cooperative has to pay the National Commission for Protected Areas (CONANP) an access fee of $70 MX pesos per person, which, according to the Sanctuary Manager, represents a loss in the overall profits of the business. Simultaneously, the restaurant (Fig. 2A) provides a great variety of local seafood dishes and Mexican "antojitos" at a reasonable price. Antojitos are tasty local made snacks such as "tacos", "enchiladas", "sopes" and "quesadillas". A conference centre (Fig. 2B) has also been built to serve as a classroom for workshops and other group activities becoming an additional source of income when rented to external parties. Accommodation in rustic cabins (Fig. 2C) is not highly successful even though tariffs are modestly cheap, ranging from $250 to 500 MX pesos for 2 or 3 bed cabins. Camping is not popular, but tents can be hired for $100–140 MX pesos, with an extra $50 MX pesos fee for the camping sites. Additionally, members of the Cooperative work on a daily basis "communal salary" named "tequio", where every member has a designated task, to be fulfilled during the day. Through this system, the overall daily profits are evenly distributed between members. However, profits are not enough to fulfil each member's living needs; hence they are struggling to successfully operate the business. The Sanctuary has also established the use of green technologies with the objective of reducing environmental impacts such as Biodigestors and composting systems.

Figure 2:   A) Restaurant, B) conference centre, and C) rustic cabins (Source: Valencia 2010).

3.1.2 Xixim Ecolodge, Celestun, Yucatán, Mexico

The Xixim Ecolodge (hereafter the Ecolodge) is located 2 km north-east of the port of Celestun in the Yucatan Peninsula enclave within the Ria Celestun Biosphere Reserve (Fig 1A). The Ecolodge is a successful private luxurious business aiming to provide an eco-friendly, educational and relaxing experience to visitors, with additional promotion of interpretative and educational components. The total area of the project comprises 25 ha with only 14,445.25 m² being built. All infrastructures are located 80 m outside of the Zona Federal Marítimo Terrestre (ZOFEMAT), a designated buffer zone where no infrastructure can be built according to the Mexican Coastal Development Regulation. This measure was also planned in order to preserve the coastal dune ecosystem and protect the Ecolodge against hurricanes and other natural disasters. The rest of the 25 ha have been left fairly untouched, and two walking tracks have been built to encourage guests to admire and learn about the local flora and fauna of the surrounding area, and, to a greater extent, to contribute to the conservation of the Biosphere Reserve. Each room at the Ecolodge provides a series of colour printed brochures to be used by guests during their trekking experience and to promote education and interpretation of local biodiversity. Furthermore, a series of green technologies have been introduced to reduce the impact on the environment such as solar heating for swimming pools (Fig. 3A) and a SIRDO system for solid wastes recycling and management (Fig. 3B) among others. However, due to the lack of public electricity services, the Ecolodge uses a diesel generator (Fig. 3C) to power electronic and electrical devices such as refrigerators, water pumps, lighting system, and electronic appliances.

Figure 3:   A) Solar heating systems, B) SIRDO solid waste recycling system, and C) diesel generator (Source: Valencia 2010).

Even though the Ecolodge does not provide ecotouristic services on site, it has numerous business partners which offer and provide services such as wildlife watching, nature safaris or canoeing. Additionally, the Ecolodge has established partnerships with local environmental organizations to promote environmental consciousness and awareness among the local population and other interested groups. According the Ecolodge manager, these partnerships have promoted initiatives like releasing turtles into the ocean, an activity that has become popular among local schools.

Finally, some of the issues determining the number of visitors to the Ecolodge include the quality of the access roads, which are often in bad shape, becoming flooded during the rainy season, worsening the access to the Ecolodge. Resolution of this situation has been tried in consultation with the National Commission for Protected Areas (CONANP) and the Celestun Municipality, but until 2011, such improvements have not been made. The costs of accommodation range from $276–$330 USD in low season (May–November) to $290–$383 USD per day in peak season (December–April).

3.2 Responses from interviewees

Most interviewees agree that ecotourism endeavours are subjected to a series of problems during their implementation depending, on the degree of planning and management skills. On the one hand, EIA/SIA procedures are relatively expensive and intricate, requiring a complex set of skills and sufficient amount of planning and time (representative of the Department of Ecosystem Studies, INE, 2010). However, time and money are not often available resulting in deficient decisions and irresponsible practices (representative of the Consultation and Planning General Directorate, CDI, 2010). At the same time, private enterprises are usually run by educated people with adequate knowledge of the administrative and managerial components of the business, with significant financial resources, and higher education degrees. In addition, these operators have a clear understanding of the environmental components of the enterprise, and have the means to ensure its protection through adequate EIA/SIA and management practices (representative of the General Director's Office, SECTUR, 2011). On the other hand, indigenous and rural community endeavours often struggle to balance the financial and conservation components of the business, resulting in poor implementation of effective protection and impact management strategies, hence increasing the number of impacts within the site (representative of the Department of Alternative Tourism within Indigenous Communities, CDI, 2010). Frequently, these ventures are under pressure to keep operating and usually require a complex set of skills which is often lacking among operators, as they often modify their farming habits to become tour operators within a short period of time (representative of the Natural Protected Areas Conservation Program, CONANP, 2010). Furthermore, the lack of adequate management skills due to poor education and living conditions directly affects the quality and success of the business (representatives of the Resource and Industry Institutes, UMAR, 2010).

In response, impact assessment procedures often fail to capture these issues, as well as the needs and interests of tour operators, paying more attention to legal requirements to gain approval. The result is that other sections of the evaluation are being left unattended (representative of the Regional Ecotourism Office, RHCO, 2010). Another issue is that tour operators are not aware of land uses and ownership conflicts, leading to the implementation of unsuitable infrastructure and activities resulting in unidentified and poorly manageable impacts (representative of the Assessment and Environmental Impact Directorate, SMA, 2010). Finally, tour operators fail to embrace the principles of ecotourism, and their practices more closely resemble like traditional mass tourism. In this sense, tour operators should become aware of the impacts of the activities they promote by adopting more responsible and sustainable practices (representative of the Tourism and Urban Development Directorate, SEMARNAT, 2010, and representative of the Institute of Ecology, UNAM, 2011). Additionally, answers to the survey have provided evidence of the initial planning process, as well as information regarding administrative procedures before the implementation of each project. In regards to Section A, tour operators from the Cooperative were not aware of what ecotourism means and what benefits and constraints could be envisaged from the establishment of such an enterprise. However, respondents agree that some sort of benefit would be obtained from the venture. Surprisingly, owners of the Ecolodge experienced the same problem until appropriate research was undertaken. In regards to the EIA/SIA decision-making process, the Sanctuary and the Ecolodge members described it as a fair and inclusive process where their interests and concerns were acknowledged and reflected within the final report. Not surprisingly, answers to Section B showed little understanding of impact assessment procedures and the likely impacts of ecotourism activities. Section C, on the other hand, showed concerns from tour operators in regards to community involvement in the EIA/SIA process and the importance of acknowledging operator's interests. In Section D, tour operators confidently stated that the business has generated tangible benefits for both the environment and the local community by protecting both turtle nesting sites and the overall habitat of the Olive ridley turtle. On the other hand, the creation of employment which improves the quality of life of local inhabitants, as well as promoting a sense of ownership among participants, has indirectly increased the importance of their work for the benefits of the protected area. Finally, Section E showed interesting facts about participants and the way they behave towards the project. On the one hand, participants of the Sanctuary are of mature age, living close to the project site, and are proactive to engage in practices to increase their management capacities. However, the lack of possible replacements to undertake management, operation and administrations positions within the projects, threatens the permanency of the business in the long run.

4   Discussion

It is clear that several issues are affecting the conceptualisation and hence the implementation of impact assessment procedures for ecotourism according to the analysis of the case studies (Table 3). Firstly, EIA/SIA procedures often failed to analyse tour operator's management and operation skills, in order to acknowledge their financial capabilities to administrate and manage the ecotourism business. Nevertheless, operators have constantly participated in on-site capacity-building workshops to enhance their knowledge of the business. However, a clear understanding of critical principles such as follow-up strategies, and adaptive management schemes is often lacking. It is imperative these issues be resolved if tour operators decide to compete and succeed within the tourism industry. Secondly, private enterprises successfully operate their businesses at an increase level of comfort to provide guests with a luxurious, healthy and relaxing experience. However, they will need to consider not to trespass the boundaries between traditional mass tourism and ecotourism as this will create unforeseeable impacts in the long run. Thirdly, although the extensive use of alternative technologies to minimise the impact on the environment is a suitable option, adequate prevention of potential impacts is not guaranteed, constant monitoring and maintenance of such technologies is required. On the other hand, complex and expensive impact assessment procedures should evolve into procedures that are simpler, cheaper and more holistic. Assessment procedures should ideally include considering operators' needs and interests, and include effective environmental protection measures to ensure the adequate management of natural and cultural resources. Using the Sanctuary as an example, after fifteen years of constant operation, no major improvements to their quality of life have been experienced, and issues with the operation have arisen in spite of the benefits the Cooperative has achieved. In 2011, the Cooperative was heavily fined by Environmental Protection Authority (PROFEPA) after failing to register the EIS on time. Until this legal requirement is amended, activities have been stopped and the continuation of the project is threatened as, according to the Sanctuary Manager, members do not have the means to cover such fines. Finally, in comparison with developed countries, issues often reside in the accuracy and quality of EIA/SIA guidelines as they are still ambiguous and complex procedures are hard to understand by local tour operators.

Table 3:   Positive and negative outcomes from the EIA/SIA procedures within the two case studies.

Cases		EIA procedures	SIA procedures	Ecotourism principles and practices
La Escobilla Turtle Sanctuary	Negative	• Poorly executed • Management does not reflect EIA outcomes • No monitoring, prevention or follow-up measures • Poor scientific base knowledge	• Poor relation with EIA components • No monitoring or follow-up strategies. • Deficient management and operations skills • No financial analysis	• Poorly understood • Hardly financially sustainable
	Positive	• Awareness of the need to protect the environments	• Sense of ownership and protection of local knowledge	• *Ad hoc* education and interpretation strategies
Xixim Ecolodge	Negative	• Sloppy • No monitoring or follow-up • Poor scientific base knowledge • Justification tool	• Poor or lack of information about potential social impacts • No monitoring, prevention or follow-up measures • No SIA	• Ambiguous • No essential changes from mass tourism • Hardly financially sustainable
	Positive	• Awareness of environmental protection • Preventive measures	• Partnerships with other businesses	• Advance education and interpretation strategies

5   Conclusions

The theory and practice of ecotourism, as conceived in the developed world, has not yet been fully accepted or adopted in Mexico, which shows discrepancies between the principles and actual management and operation of ecotourism practices. Perhaps the main reason is that tour operators usually lack appropriate skills to manage and operate such businesses due to the lack of adequate knowledge about the intrinsic relationships that rule the natural world. Socio-economically speaking, ecotourism *per se* is a business and a sustainable development strategy, and as such, it needs to fulfil the operators' financial and living necessities in order for them to continue investing time and money in the operation and maintenance of the venture. If these components of the enterprise are not effectively addressed, potential impacts will continue to arise, diminishing the value of the natural environment and consequently the value of the enterprise. In this way, impact assessment procedures play a fundamental role by identifying adequate pathways towards effectively managing potential impacts. At the same time, Mexican impact assessment standards provide a vague but complex framework for tour operators to address all components of the planning process. Identification, monitoring and follow-up strategies of potential impacts require sound and reliable scientific methodologies in order for tour operators to adequately plan and operate their enterprises. Such methodologies, which are applied by experts, should be communicated in a simple and effective way so that tour operators can understand the implications of their implementation. In this sense, tour operators need to increase their understanding of the theory and practices behind ecotourism, as well as mastering a different set of skills if they wish to become competitive, successful, and sustainable enterprises. At the same time, they will need to become capable of adopting sound conservation strategies in order to preserve the natural and cultural environment. Finally, adequate management of natural resources has become an essential task for tour operators, and requires numerous skills and adequate funding to effectively operate. Therefore, ecotourism businesses need to integrate educational and interpretative components into their advertised activities to make sure guests leave with the appropriate knowledge to share the information with other people, and thus continually promote responsible tourism practices.

Acknowledgements

I would like to thank the Mexican National Council for Science and Technology (CONACyT) for their sponsorship of this project. I would also like to deeply thank my supervisors (Lesley Head and John Morrison) for helping me with the discussion.

References

[1] Almeyda A.M., Broadbent E.N., Wyman M.S. and Durham W.H., Ecotourism impacts in the Nicoya Peninsula, Costa Rica, *International Journal of Tourism Research*, pp. 17, 2010.
[2] Honey M., *Ecotourism and Sustainable Development: Who own Paradise?*, Island Press: Washington, pp. 551, 2008.
[3] Buckley R., A Framework for ecotourism, *Annals of Tourism Research*, **21** (3), pp. 661–669, 1994.
[4] Farquharson M., Ecotourism: A dream diluted-Environmental theory turns commercial ploy, *Business Mexico*, **2 (6)**, pp. 8–11, 1992.
[5] Fennell D.A. and Dowling R.K., Ecotourism Policy and Planning: Stakeholders, Management and Governance (Chapter 17), eds. D.A.

Fennell and R.K. Dowling, *Ecotourism Policy and Planning*, CABI, pp. 331–343, 2003.

[6] Pardo G.L., Políticas públicas y ecoturismo en comunidades indígenas de México, *Teoría y Praxis*, (**5**), pp. 33–50, 2008.

[7] O'Faircheallaigh C., Environmental agreements, EIA follow-up and aboriginal participation in environmental management: The Canadian experience, *Environmental Impact Assessment Review*, (**27**), pp. 319–342, 2007.

[8] García G., Evaluación de Impacto Ambiental, Un Proceso Multidisciplinario, *Derecho Ambiental y Ecología*, (**30**), pp. 45–46, 2009.

[9] Cámara de Diputados del H. Congreso de la Unión, *Ley General del Equilibrio Ecológico y Protección al Ambiente*, Gobierno de los Estados Unidos Mexicanos, Ciudad de México, pp. 107, 2011.

[10] SEMARNAT, *Requisitos y Especificaciones de Sustentabilidad del Ecoturismo: Requirements and Regulations of Sustainability in Ecotourism*, pp. 77, 2006.

[11] Becerra R.E.A., La Evaluación de Impacto Ambiental en México. Situación Actual y Perspectivas Futuras, *Derecho Ambiental y Ecología*, (**30**), pp. 51–53, 2009.

[12] Brito P., La Evaluación de Impacto Ambiental, un instrumento de política ambiental indispensable, pero carente de reglas claras y objetivos en México, *Derecho Ambiental y Ecología*, (**30**), pp. 47–49, 2009.

[13] Juárez J.R., La Evaluación de Impacto Ambiental: La Necesidad de Actualizar este Instrumento a la Luz de Nuevos Modelos, *Derecho Ambiental y Ecología*, (**30**), pp. 55–57, 2009.

[14] Sangines A.G., Política ambiental en México: Génesis, desarrollo y perspectivas, *Boletin ICE Economico*, (**821**), pp. 163-175, 2005.

[15] Matysek K.A. and Kriwoken L.K., The Natural State: Nature-Based Tourism and Ecotourism Accreditation in Tasmania, Australia, *Journal of Quality Assurance in Hospitality and Tourism*, **4 (1/2)**, pp. 129–146, 2003.

[16] Macedo J.A., *De Actor a Sujeto: El Camino al Ecoturismo de la "Cooperativa Santuario de la Tortuga de La Escobilla (ANP)"*, Oaxaca., Universidad Autónoma Metropolitana, Unidad Xochimilco, División de Ciencias Sociales y Humanidades, Tesis de Maestría, UAM, 274, 2010.

Community involvement in the assessment of the importance of sustainable rural tourism indicators for protected areas: the case of the Nevado de Toluca National Park in Mexico

G. González Guerrero, M. E. Valdez Pérez & R. Morales Ibarra
Centro Universitario UAEM Tenancingo,
Universidad Autónoma del Estado de México, México

Abstract

This paper uses objective sustainable tourism indicators in a subjective way to examine the importance that local people attaches to them. The legal rights that local people have over resources in Protected Areas make it not only important but also crucial that communities be involved in monitoring. For this reason it is necessary to know the importance they attach to indicators, which, in turn could be considered as a reflection of the importance they attach to resources. For the research, a revision of available indicators was conducted. Nineteen of these indicators were selected as being applicable to the context of the Nevado de Toluca National Park. Interviews were conducted with the local people in three parts. The first part referred to their perception of the tourism activity in the area, the importance they attached to each of the indicators using a 5-point Likert scale, and their knowledge ability on the subjects of sustainable development or tourism. The second part of the interview consisted of a set of 12 photos they had to order according to the importance they attached to them. These pictures were representative of the resources found in the Nevado Park and the community. The last part of the interview was meant to help characterise the household as regard to their livelihoods. The paper concludes that more work needs to be done with indicators at the community level. Because of the technicalities of indicators, there exists the risk of leaving the local people at bay even though sustainable tourism has called for community involvement. Although

WIT Transactions on Ecology and The Environment, Vol 173, © 2013 WIT Press
www.witpress.com, ISSN 1743-3541 (on-line)
doi:10.2495/SDP130351

interviewees attached importance to the monitoring of resources it is equally important that they understand their possible participation in it.

Keywords: rural tourism, sustainability indicators, community involvement, national parks, Mexico.

1 Introduction

Sustainable tourism emerged in response to growing concerns about the adverse impacts that tourism has resulted in the areas of environmental, social and even economic destinations. This was not the exception in rural areas, however, as mentioned by Wall [1] referring to the tourism that is practiced in areas that are predominantly natural "one might wonder if the average ecotourist puts more pressure on the environment the tourist who practice mass tourism and you may not need to see endangered species in remote locations and whose needs and waste can be more easily planned and managed." However, despite latent adverse impacts, the growth of tourism does not stop. For this reason ways have been sought to lessen the impacts of tourism. Indicators have been seen as a way to monitor the effects of tourism on resources and local communities (World Tourism Organization [2]).

It has been concluded by Mowforth and Munt [3] that "sustainable tourism is only definable in terms context, control and position of those who define it." Based on this premise the same can be concluded about sustainability indicators. Thus the questions arise, who are developing sustainable tourism indicators? What is their context and position? Which stakeholders are involved in the monitoring and use of indicators? While one can argue for the development of indicators by 'experts' in the subject (Miller [4]) the movement toward decentralization, and tourism projects and natural resource management by local communities suggest the need for these communities to be actively involved in decision-making (Simmons [5], Scheyvens [6], Nunan [7]). Accordingly, there is a need to bring communities to the fore in the context of indicators for sustainable tourism (Blackstock *et al.* [8]).

2 Sustainable rural tourism indicators

After three decades sustainable tourism remains at the centre of debates that question its value and utility (Wall [1], Velikova [9], Liu [10]). What is the rationale for developing indicators for a concept that has been described as contradictory, ambiguous and unhelpful? In Miller's words [4], "the indicator development process can help determine the fundamental principles on which to base the concept". In other words, it is possible that through the development of indicators for sustainable tourism the concept itself may be built.

As mentioned (Lawrence [11]), "sustainability indicators can be an important tool to help individuals, institutions, communities and societies to build different and better options for their future." The World Tourism Organization (WTO) designed and compiled in 1996 and then in 2004 a series of indicators for sustainable tourism. The focus of these indicators is on the welfare of host communities, the maintenance of cultural assets, the intensity of use, social impact, waste management, the planning process, critical ecosystems, consumer satisfaction, local content and the load capacity, among others. These documents have been prepared as a guide for those involved in planning and tourism management.

Some countries have developed frameworks according to their context. One example of it was the case of Korea, where the WTO's sustainable indicators were used to monitor the management activities of the Mt. Sorak National Park. The purpose of the study was to evaluate whether the park was being manage in a sustainable way. The findings were expected to assist in a change of the way in which the park was being managed (Kang [12]).

The Association of Caribbean States adapted a set of indicators considering some criteria such as security, identity and culture, child prostitution, employment in tourism, quality of bodies of water, energy consumption index, water consumption index, environmental management and use, efficiency of the solid waste management system, efficiency of the waste water management system, tourist satisfaction, and national and local product consumption index. The purpose was, again, to ensure the achievement of sustainability in the tourism activity (Association of Caribbean States [13]).

Miller [4] used a set of indicators to find out the consumer's point of view on the subject. The purpose was to find out whether or not tourists made decisions about their holidays based on the available information on sustainable practices in the destinations.

More comprehensive studies on indicators have been made in the last decade. For example, Lozano-Oyola *et al.* [14] develop an indicator system for cultural destinations. They propose goal programming to construct composite indicators and provide guidelines to use these tools for planning. However these attempts are aimed at tourism managers and local agents as main users, although they do suggest "a participative approach... to take advantage of local knowledge" (see also Blancas *et al.* [15]; Blancas *et al.* [16]). Choi and Sirakaya [17] use a Delphi technique to arrive at a set of 125 indicators that include the political, social, ecological, economical, technological and cultural dimensions. They state that this set will be used as a starting point to be later adapted to the characteristics of different communities. They also state that in further research they will seek the input of different stakeholder groups including local residents. Tsaur *et al.* [18] although employing the Delphi technique, they apply an integrated perspective by seeking the input of local residents, tourists and resource administrators to evaluate sustainability in an ecotourism destination in Taiwan. This study helps to illustrate that different stakeholders have different priorities. For example experts and resource administrators pointed at the environment as the most important factor in sustainability. Tourists were more concerned with high-quality travel experiences. For the local people their livelihoods were the main factor. Thus, directly or indirectly, these studies show that there is a need for research that puts the local people at the centre of the discussion on sustainability and indicators.

3 Participation of the local people

The need for local people to be involved in the development and use of indicators has been highlighted by authors such as Miller. He mentions, "if indicators of sustainable development and, further, the concepts of sustainable development and sustainable tourism must be accepted and understood by the general public, then they must be relevant to the public" (Miller [4]).

In similar terms, the Brundtland Report states: "the law alone cannot enforce the common interest. It principally needs community knowledge and support, which entails greater public participation in the decisions that affect the environment" (World Commission on Environment and Development [19]). Thus, the importance of involving local communities can be seen from two perspectives. On the one hand involving the local communities may help to avoid possible tension and conflict from viewing outsiders as the sole possessors of knowledge (Chambers [20]). On the other hand there is the fundamental right that communities have to engage in tourism from the point of view that ultimately they will receive not only the benefits but also costs of tourism (Johnson and Snepenger [21], Sharpley and Sharpley [22]).

The case of protected areas is different to other places of tourism activity in that decrees place restrictions on the use of resources which would imply a closer monitoring. The reality, however, is that in developing countries such as Mexico, budgets and personnel for monitoring are insufficient (Anderson and James [23], Gauld [24]). Local communities can thus be seen as suitable to monitor informally as they can closely perceive changes in the state of resources. In the Mexican context locals communities are not only suitable but also the most appropriate because many of these local communities have claims over the resources. As mentioned by Tsaur et al. [18] "residents could act as stewards of natural resources to effectively care for and conserve local resources". However, in order to achieve the active involvement of local communities in monitoring and using indicators, these have to be meaningful for the local people (see also Yates et al. [25]).

4 Study site: the Nevado de Toluca National Park

The setting for this research is the Nevado de Toluca National Park. The park covers 53,988 hectares, of which official documents suggest that approximately 20,000 of these remain forested (CEPANAF et al. [26]). It has four sites that are officially regarded as tourist areas: el Mapa, Dos Caminos, the volcanic Crater and the Deer Park (see Figure 1). El Mapa and Dos Caminos and the Deer Park are part of the Zinacantepec Municipality. In these three tourist areas visitors have picnics, take walks or ride horses. However, only Dos Caminos and the Deer Park have tourism services and infrastructure, with the Deer Park considered being in slightly better condition (CEPANAF et al. [26]). El Mapa and Dos Caminos are closer to Toluca and Mexico City but farther from the main attraction of the Nevado Park: the Crater.

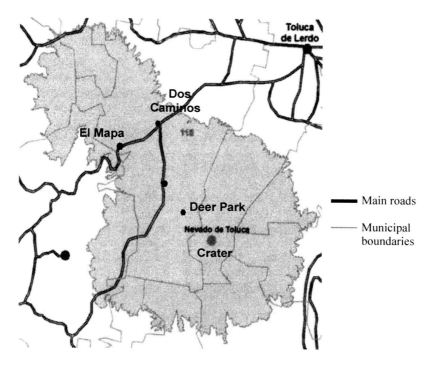

Figure 1:   The Nevado de Toluca National Park and its main tourist areas.

As a National Park, the Federal Government of Mexico has a legal reason to be involved in its management, although some of the latest legal developments have meant that the federal government has delegated some of its responsibilities to the state government. This has given the state government a valid reason (and obligation) to be more actively involved than before. The municipal government's involvement is somewhat less clear, although the state government stakeholders appear to have expectations of its involvement. At the local level there are individual landowners and ejido members with clear group and individual land rights as well as other community members with interests in the park's resources, possibly simply for leisure activities.

The Nevado de Toluca National Park is home to 15 rural communities. The size of the settlements ranges from 2 to 500 houses. The size determines the number and kind of services that can be found in each. Potato and oats are the most common crops grown, although maize can be found in the lowest-lying areas. It is also common to come across herds of cattle or flocks of sheep being herded to grazing areas.

Most of the settlements were formally established in the first part of the 20th century. Before then, what today is known as the Nevado de Toluca National Park was referred to by its *nahuatl* name Chignahuiltecatl (Nine Hills) or Xinantecatl Volcano. Most of its 53988 hectares were then divided amongst three haciendas: *la Gavia, la Huerta* and *Tejalpa,* which were formed after the conquest of Mexico in 1519.

The Nevado Park was constituted by decree in 1936. The decree made it clear that due to the ecological importance of the area, conservation was a priority and this could not be achieved if excessive exploitation (by ejidos or individual owners) prevailed. Owners affected by the decree were given a period of six months to prove their ownership, after which they would receive compensation for their land.

The decree was not fully executed in the Nevado Park; the area was declared a National Park but the individual land owners and ejido members were not compensated and did not leave the area. By the time of the decree most ejidos had already been formed. The Loma Alta ejido (a Zinacantepec ejido inside the Nevado Park), for example, was granted more land in August 1936, seven months after the decree. The decree meant that in the absence of compensation, ejidatarios and individual owners maintained their claims, but as they were inside the National Park heavy restrictions were imposed on the use of resources: The area already being used for agricultural purposes could continue as such, but the rest had to be left as a conservation area. In consequence the Nevado de Toluca National Park was made subject to three kinds of property rules: ejido, individual and federal property.

San Juan de las Huertas (SJH) is one of the communities with claims over the Nevado Park in the form of ejido with 2 170 hectares. Its ejido manages the Deer Park, which is one of the main tourist sites of the Nevado Park. However, while the tourist area (Deer Park) is within the boundaries of the Nevado Park, the community itself is outside it. In practice this means that many ejidatarios and community members may not necessarily be aware of what happens in the tourist area.

From the perspective of the rural/urban dichotomy SJH can be categorised as an urban community. In 1973 its population had already surpassed the size considered rural because of its population size. By 2005 the community already comprised 11,835 inhabitants divided amongst 2562 households, according to the official census (Instituto Nacional de Estadística Geografía e Informática [27]). However, it cannot be said that SJH automatically became urban the year it exceeded 2 500 inhabitants. The process of change has been long and a diversity of factors beyond population size has contributed to it. It is in this setting and in this community that the research was conducted.

4.1 Methodology

For this research the indicators provided by the WTO were reviewed. Of all the indicators proposed by the organization, those that could be applicable to the setting of the Nevado Park were chosen. Nineteen were shortlisted as being the most relevant. Although quantitative in nature, the indicators were used in a qualitative way in order to gain insight into what local people thought was relevant to monitor regarding the available resources and the tourism activity.

Interviews were designed in three parts. The first part referred to their perception of the tourism activity in the area. Interviewees were asked to attach importance to each of the indicators using a 5-point Likert scale. Five points were used for very important and 1 for non-important. This first part of the interview was also used to explore their knowledge ability on the subjects of sustainable development and/or sustainable tourism.

The second part of the interview consisted of a set of 31 photos the interviewees had to arrange in order or importance. These pictures were representative of the resources found in the Nevado Park and the community. But also included pictures meant to represent education, income and family.

The last part of the interview was meant to help characterise the household as regard to their livelihoods. This characterisation included age, maximum education level, occupation, marital status of each household member. It also included the resources that they may own as household (i.e. livestock, land, business, etc.).

The interview was tested with 5 ejidatarios randomly chosen as they arrived to the office of the Ejidal Comisariado (the representative of the ejidatarios). The results from the test showed that for the first part of the interview some indicators had to be re-worded to make them more understandable. The second part of the interview showed that 31 photos were too many. Some of them, the ejidatarios said, were repetitive of resources and were therefore placed consistently on the same level. Therefore, the photos were reviewed to reduce the number to 12. This was done while trying to make sure that the photos of the resources that intended to be represented remained. It was also noticed that some photos were attached different meanings by ejidatarios. For this reason it was thought necessary to specify what the picture meant to represent for the research. This was not to be made known to ejidatarios. However, after they finished arranging the pictures in order of importance they would be asked to explain what each picture represented to them. No changes were made to the third part of the interview because it was meant to help characterise the households and their livelihoods. It was expected that some ejidatarios would perceive the questions as too personal to answer, so they were explained that they did not have to answer if they did not feel comfortable with a particular question.

After these modifications were made to the interview script, a list of ejidatarios was obtained from the Ejidal Comisariado's office. Using a random numbers table, 40 ejidatarios were selected. It was planned to conduct only 22 interviews but an extra 18 names were obtained in case some ejidatarios refused to participate or could not be found.

In addition to these interviews informal conversations were held with various members of the community. Meetings of the ejido were also attended as observant. This allowed examining the dynamics of these meetings and the interaction of ejido members.

It should also be mentioned that although this particular project had duration of one year, research in this area has been conducted for the past 7 years. Therefore, some of the information obtained from this project is analysed in light of information already available.

5 Community involvement in the Nevado de Toluca National Park

5.1 The relation of the local people with the resources

The population of SJH once depended on farming activities but has now diversified or completely shifted to activities within manufacture or services. However, in absolute terms 400 or more households still depend on arable farming and livestock production. Furthermore, not only ejidatarios work in this field but also non-ejidatarios cultivate other people's land, renting it from ejidatarios that do not use it or hiring themselves to work on ejidatarios' land. A small number of ejidatarios also farm livestock. Cattle and sheep are the most common. The livestock are sometimes kept for weeks or months in provisional corrals in the upper area of the Nevado Park, where there is most pasture. People living in the communities in that area are sometimes hired to look after them.

It is also important to consider the people's relations to resources. The population of SJH uses forest resources in various ways. As it is an urban settlement, most households use gas instead of wood as fuel. Yet official figures register that in 2000, 3.28 percent of households still used wood to cook (Instituto Nacional de Estadística Geografía e Informática [28]). Apart from personal consumption, residents of SJH complained of wide illegal exploitation of the forest for profit because the Nevado Park is not appropriately guarded. Nobody appears to know who is responsible for this. Some believe that members of other communities are involved, while others say that the offenders are not from any of the nearby communities but are rich people that can afford to violate the law without major consequences. Other forest resources are also exploited, with the collection of wild fruits, medicinal herbs, fibres and other forest products for consumption and sale. It is also argued that community members, particularly farmers, extract soil illegally to sell to private nurseries (CEPANAF et al. [26]).

There are non-ejidatarios who have a relationship with the natural resources of the ejido based on claims of ownership and pride of possession (González Guerrero [29–31]). Being that the ejido is linked directly with the community some non-ejidatarios believe they have claims of ownership that need to be recognized. This complex relationship that the local people have with the resources shows the relevance of including them in monitoring processes and in the planning and use of indicators.

5.2 The importance of indicators

The indicators were emptied on a table and average numbers were obtained from the results given by interviewees. One of the first things that can be highlighted from the results is that 7 interviewees considered that all 19 indicators were "very important" as they gave an equal mark of 5 to all of them. This shows that, at least for these 7 people, the monitoring processes of the impacts of tourism on the resources and community are extremely important.

It can also be observed that according to the responses, the most important indicator was "increase or decrease of wildlife diversity" with an average of 4.64. Conversely, the least important indicator as per the responses was "adverse social effects" with an average of 3.77. This result seems to be in contrast with a research concluded 2 years ago in the same area. During this research, negative social changes in the community were raised as a main concern of many of the interviewees (see González Guerrero [29]). Back then interviewees argued that young people was acquiring the habit of drinking on street corners in the afternoons, making the community increasingly unsafe. However, this apparent contradiction can be explained by two main points. Firstly, the context given by most of the other indicators may have given the interviewee a sense that indicators regarding conservation and protection of resources were more important. Secondly, as both the tourism activity and the natural resources are outside the immediate geographical area of the community, it may have been difficult to relate them to "adverse social effects" in the community.

Another indicator that had a low average was "national/international organizations involved in development/conservation strategies", with 4.09 points. This is consistent with a generalised view in the ejido that people from outside the community should not become involved in matters of the community or the ejido. This view could also be observed at the ejido meetings. Apart from the conflicts that there were between different ejidatarios, a feeling of mistrust of government institutions was expressed by several participants at the meeting.

However, the interviewees do believe that "the community should be involved in planning and decision making concerning the tourism activity". This indicator ranked 4 in order of importance with 4.41 points. This shows that they want to be involved. It is also a reflection of their view that even though they may accept the involvement of national or international organisations, the community's decision should be above the input of stakeholders external to it.

It is also noteworthy that the indicator "visitors aware of the conservation and preservation of natural resources" ranked 3 in order of importance. Comparatively, the indicator "local people aware of the conservation and preservation of natural resources" ranked 8 in order of importance. This means that while the interviewees consider that the community should be aware of conservation and preservation of resources a greater responsibility is placed on the visitors for this same purpose. This could again be attributed to the fact that the tourist area (the Deer Park) is not in close proximity to the community. From this point of view it can be easier for visitors to be aware of circumstances in the Deer Park than for ejidatarios who are not appointed to watch over it. Additionally, these figures can be interpreted as ejidatarios expecting visitors to act responsibly while visiting the Deer Park.

5.3 The discourse of sustainable development

From the 22 interviewees, 16 had not heard of sustainable development or sustainable tourism and they did not know the meaning of either term. Four mentioned to have heard of it but did not know what it meant. Two had heard about sustainable development. When asked to explain its meaning, both related it to governmental programmes. They said that sustainable development was about subsidies that the government gave to plant trees and prevent fires in the Nevado Park. This view is result of a prevalent discourse on sustainable development in governmental institutions. This discourse is not only reflected in policy documents but it is also part of the official speech of government representatives (see González Guerrero [29]).

6 Conclusions

This study has only been a first approximation to resident attitude towards indicators. It has shown that even though most interviewees did not know the meaning of sustainable development or had even heard about it, they did attach importance to indicators. This shows that monitoring impacts of the tourism activity on resources is important to the local people even though they do not have a name for it. It is thus necessary that sustainable development, indicators, principles, etc. stop being the domain of experts, academics, politicians and international organizations and permeate to the local people.

More research is needed that brings local people to the fore of sustainable development. This requires looking for more creative ways and methodologies that enable bringing the discussion on sustainability and indicators to the local level. This in turn would enable local input into the development and use indicators. Following the movement towards decentralisation this is not only desirable but also a necessity. This is also reflected in the views of the interviewees when they attach more importance to the indicator that shows input from the local people than to the indicator that measures the involvement of national and international stakeholders.

References

[1] Wall, G., Sustainable tourism - unsustainable development (Chapter 3). *Tourism, development and growth. The challenge of sustainability*, eds. S. Wahab and J.J. Pigram, Routledge: London, pp. 33–49, 1997.

[2] World Tourism Organization, *What tourism managers need to know. A practical guide to the development and use of indicators of sustainable tourism,* World tourism Organization: Spain, 1996.

[3] Mowforth, M. and Munt, I., *Tourism and sustainability. New tourism in the third world,* Routledge: London and New York, 2003.

[4] Miller, G., The development of indicators for sustainable tourism: results of a Delphi survey of tourism researchers. *Tourism Management*, **22(4)**, pp. 351–362, 2001.

[5] Simmons, D., Community participation in tourism planning. *Tourism Management*, **15(2)**, pp. 98–108, 1994.

[6] Scheyvens, R., Ecotourism and the empowerment of local communities. *Tourism Management*, **20(2)**, pp. 245–249, 1999.

[7] Nunan, F., Empowerment and institutions: Managing fisheries in Uganda. *World Development*, **34(7)**, pp. 1316–1332, 2006.

[8] Blackstock, K.L., et al., Measuring responsibility: An appraisal of a Scottish National Park's sustainable tourism indicators. *Journal of Sustainable Tourism*, **16(3)**, pp. 276–297, 2008.

[9] Velikova, M.P., How Sustainable is Sustainable Tourism?. *Annals of Tourism Research*, **28(2)**, pp. 496–499, 2001.

[10] Liu, Z., Sustainable Tourism Development: A Critique. *Journal of Sustainable Tourism*, **11(6)**, pp. 459–475, 2003.

[11] Lawrence, G., Getting the future that you want: the role of sustainability indicators. *Community and sustainable development: Participation in the Future*, ed. D. Warburton, Earthscan: London, pp. 68–80, 1998.

[12] Kang, M.H., Monitoring the management of Mt. Sorak National Park utilizing WTO's sustainable tourism indicators. *Journal- Korean Forestry Society*, **12**, 2002.

[13] Association of Caribbean States. Convention establishing the sustainable tourism zone of the Caribbean. Online. http://www.acs-aec.org/Tourism/VII/english/Legalturdoc_eng.htm

[14] Lozano-Oyola, M., et al., Sustainable tourism indicators as planning tools in cultural destinations. *Ecological Indicators*, **18(0)**, pp. 659–675, 2012.

[15] Blancas, F.J., et al., Goal programming synthetic indicators: An application for sustainable tourism in Andalusian coastal counties. *Ecological Economics*, **69(11)**, pp. 2158–2172, 2010.

[16] Blancas, F.J., et al., How to use sustainability indicators for tourism planning: The case of rural tourism in Andalusia (Spain). *Science of The Total Environment*, **412-413**(0), pp. 28–45, 2011.

[17] Choi, H.C. and Sirakaya, E., Sustainability indicators for managing community tourism. *Tourism Management*, **27(6)**, pp. 1274–1289, 2006.

[18] Tsaur, S.-H., Lin, Y.-C., and Lin, J.-H., Evaluating ecotourism sustainability from the integrated perspective of resource, community and tourism. *Tourism Management*, **27(4)**, pp. 640–653, 2006.

[19] World Commission on Environment and Development, *Our common future*, Oxford University Press: Oxford, 1987.

[20] Chambers, R., *Rural development: putting the last first,* Pearson Education Limited: Essex, 1983.

[21] Johnson, J.D. and Snepenger, D.J., Residents' perceptions of tourism development. *Annals of Tourism Research*, **21(3)**, pp. 629–642, 1994.

[22] Sharpley, R. and Sharpley, J., *Rural Tourism: An Introduction.* International Thompson Business Press: London, 1997.

[23] Anderson, T.L. and James, A., Introduction: Parks, politics and property rights. *Parks in peril. People, politics and protected areas*, eds. K. Brandon, K.H. Redford, and S.E. Sanderson, Island Press: Washington, 1998.

[24] Gauld, R., Maintaining centralized control in community-based forestry: Policy construction in the Philippines. *Forests. Nature, people, power*, eds. M. Doornbos, A. Saith, and B. White, Blackwell: Oxford and Malden, p. 223–248, 2000.

[25] Yates, G.E., Stein, T.V., and Wyman, M.S., Factors for collaboration in Florida's tourism resources: Shifting gears from participatory planning to community-based management. *Landscape and Urban Planning*, **97(4)**, pp. 213–220, 2010.

[26] CEPANAF, Biocenosis, and UAEM, *Programa de Manejo del Parque Nacional Nevado de Toluca*. CEPANAF, Biocenosis, and UAEM: Toluca, Undated.

[27] Instituto Nacional de Estadística Geografía e Informática, *II Conteo de Población y Vivienda 2005. Principales resultados por localidad*. INEGI: México, 2006.

[28] Instituto Nacional de Estadística Geografía e Informática, *XII Censo General de Población y Vivienda 2000. Principales resultados por localidad*. INEGI: México, 2000.

[29] González Guerrero, G., *Community organisation for tourism: A Mexican case study*. University of East Anglia: Norwich, 2009.

[30] González Guerrero, G., Questioning the meaning of participation and social equality in sustainable tourism based on the experience of a community-based initiative in Mexico. *Tourism Futures: Creative and Critical Action*, ed. R. T., Ward, Welsh Centre for Tourism Research: Cardiff, 2011.

[31] González Guerrero, G., Local Participation in a Sustainable Ecotourism Initiative: A Collection of Narratives on the Deer Park. *Journal of Tourism*, X(X), pp. 51–71, 2012.

Section 8
Sustainable solutions in emerging countries

Sustainability: the dream of international development projects

M. Dulcey Morán & M. Ferguson
Glyndŵr University London, UK

Abstract

Human development is now seen as a moral imperative for humanity, wherein developed nations assume a moral responsibility to ensure development of the less developed nations. The basis for this imperative includes social-humanitarian, political and economic considerations. However, when success is measured in terms of sustainability, then most human development projects have been abject failures. This study sought to examine the factors that impact on sustainability by analysing the experiences of people who deliver human development projects. Nine people who had worked on one or more of five selected information communication technology (ICT) human development projects, participated in the study. The five projects were initiated and managed by ONGAWA, a Spanish NGO, and implemented in South America and Africa. The study adopted the semi-structured interview format. This approach enabled study participants to freely express their lived experiences of planning and delivering human development projects while at the same time ensuring that the pre-defined research question was addressed. The main finding from the study is that in order to foster sustainability a detailed diagnosis should be carried out. Significantly, the diagnosis should use participatory learning and action (PLA) approaches that mandate involving aid-recipients and active stake holders. However, participants' experiences are that donors and funders often desire rapid implementation and visibility. This is often incompatible with the slow, deliberate pace required by PLA approaches. Since NGOs largely rely on donor funding, they often only poorly or rarely use PLA approaches. The study points to the need for non-governmental organisation involved in development aid and human development projects to formulate strategies to educate donors and

WIT Transactions on Ecology and The Environment, Vol 173, © 2013 WIT Press
www.witpress.com, ISSN 1743-3541 (on-line)
doi:10.2495/SDP130361

funders on the necessity and practical implications of PLA if sustainable human development projects are to be fostered.

Keywords: sustainable development, human development project, participatory learning and action, PLA, non-governmental organisation, NGO, Information communication technology, semi-structured interview.

1 Introduction

Without sustainability, human development projects can lay no claim on being 'development' processes because development entails irreversible progression from impoverishment to enrichment.

1.1 Background

This aligns with the United Nations Development Program (UNDP) Belize [1] definition of human development as:

> *"the process of enlarging people's choices and improving human capabilities (the range of things that they can do or be in life) and freedoms so they can live a long and healthy life, access to education and a decent standard of living, participate in their community and the decisions that affect their lives".*

In the above definition, people's choices may be defined as the range of things that people can do in life. When considering enlarging these choices it is important to be aware of what other choices are available. As a first step, it is worth considering whether the new technologies and modern techniques are better than the previous ones.

However, a significant consideration for human development assistance is the issue of appropriateness, not just for the people who may directly and immediately benefit from the assistance but also for the community where they live. This entails considering three aspects; equity, capability and sustainability.

The answer given by UNDP [2], is that the human development process should be sustainable and equitable and aimed at *"expanding human freedoms for people today and for generations to come"*. When talking about choices, *"the sky is not the limit"*, choices are in fact limited to the rational use of natural resources to an extent that allows marginalised people and future generations to have the same rights to resources. Fig. 1 symbolizes the relation between sustainability and equity. The top-right quadrant represents what development should aim for.

Johansson *et al.* [3] define a process as *"a set of linked activities that take an input and transforms it to create an output"* adding that the transformation *"should add value to the input and create an output that is more useful and effective to the recipient"*. For the human development process, the input is composed of people's choices, human capabilities and freedoms and the output is composed of more choices, improved capabilities and freedoms.

The concept of human development is currently imbedded in the Human Development Index, (HDI), which is based on three components; the Gross

Domestic Product (GPD), literacy rates and life expectancy at birth. The index is a parameter that is calculated relative to the most developed country. However, the HDI is inadequate in 2 respects [4, 5]; Firstly, it excludes soft aspects such as freedom and human rights, a major part of political and social development. Secondly, it is a simple average figure that may not be representative of a population that is not normally distributed.

Equitable but not sustainable	**Human capabilities supported equitably and sustainably**
Unsustainable and inequitable	Sustainable but not equitable

Sustainability

Figure 1:   Sustainable human development [2].

Notwithstanding the above limitations, it is argued that rich countries (those high on the HDI) should have a *"moral obligation"* [6] to foster the development of poorer countries through grants and donations (foreign aid) [7].

However, writers like Moyo [8] have questioned the concept of foreign aid, by asserting that *"aid has been, and continues to be, an unmitigated political, economic and humanitarian disaster for most parts of the developing world"*.

A major criticism of foreign aid is that it creates dependency. Yunus and Jolis [9] explain that foreign aid may be a soft option, putting both the donor and the recipient at ease while not effecting any human development - the recipient communities and governments develop a dependency mentality while donors feel they are helping by giving aid.

Moyo [8] considers that for Africa, foreign aid should be replaced by foreign investment and sustains her words by observing that:

"over the past thirty years, the most aid-dependent countries have exhibited an average annual growth rate of minus 0.2 percent" and that *"between 1970 and 1998, when aid flows to Africa were at their peak, the poverty rate in Africa actually rose from 11 per cent to a staggering 66 per cent"*.

However, Moyo's proposal should be taken with due consideration of mitigating the creation of 'sweat shops', endemic in some Asian countries [10]. Having said this, at a fundamental level, there is now recognition that effective human development should be based on reducing dependency and fostering sustainable independence.

1.2 The context of the study

Since sustainable development requires recipient communities to adopt new approaches, change models such as Hayes' model [11] and Howell's model [12] (depicted in Fig. 2), are possible frameworks for managing development projects.

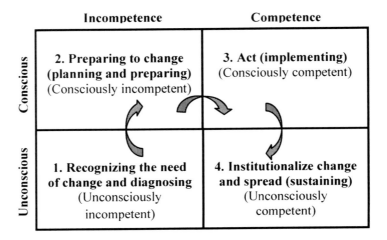

Figure 2:   Relationship between the model of human learning, the change management steps as stages of human development projects' cycle of life (adapted from Howell [12]).

The Food and Agricultural Organisation (FAO) [13] states that:
"international, governmental and non-governmental agencies have realised more and more that the main reason of many unsuccessful human development projects was (and still is) the lack of active, effective and lasting participation of the intended beneficiaries".
It has been reported [14] that human development projects often fail due to a number of reasons, including:

- *"Poor planning and programme formulation*
- *Misallocation of project resources*
- *Rural people's low sense of power*
- *Provision of inappropriate technology*
- *Inadequate promotion*
- *Ineffective training methodologies*
- *Lack of enabling policy"*

It is conceivable that the above problems could be avoided or minimised by understanding, from the outset, what it is that beneficiary communities actually need, expect and can manage. However, this requires their active involvement, not just as passive sources of information but also as protagonists of their own development.

Participatory Learning and Action (PLA) is a family of approaches and methods that enable recipient communities to "*share, enhance and analyse their knowledge of life and conditions*" [15], by way of answering questions about whether it is worth enlarging their capabilities. PLA facilitates the formulation of recipient-centric development plans, a pre-requisite to sustainable development projects.

1.3 Aims

The aim of the study was to determine promoters and inhibitors of PLA.

2 Methodology

This was an explanatory qualitative phenomenological study that sought the lived experiences of people working within ONGAWA, a Spanish NGO that delivers ICT human development projects in Latin America and Africa in order to understand their perceptions of inhibitors and facilitators of implementing participatory approaches when planning and delivering human development projects. ONGAWA was chosen because it uses PLA in some stages of its projects' life cycles. The participative philosophy is evident in ONGAWA's stated model of intervention; "*supply of basic services, capacity building, political advocacy and strengthening active citizenship*" [16].

Primary data for the study derived from semi-structured interviews of a purposive sample of 9 program and project coordinators. The participants were selected because they had or were working on the five active information communications technology (ICT) projects included in the study; although not all of the participants necessarily worked on the same project at the same time. Each interview lasted for about one hour.

The semi-structured questions for the study aligned with the research aim, which was to elicit inhibitors and promoters of participatory processes. Interviews were conducted in Spanish (the first researcher and interviewees' mother tongue). All interviews were recorded and later transcribed and then translated into English by the first researcher to enable triangulation, with the second researcher, during data analysis.

Secondary data for the study came from project reports and information available in the public domain; mainly report archives from the internet.

Bounded segment thematic analysis [17] was chosen for data analysis as it offers access to the original narration.

3 Findings

The main factor promoting the implementation of PLA in ONGAWA's projects is ONGAWA's organisational culture. ONGAWA has a transformational leadership style [11] that encourages and facilitates all its workers to implement, as far as practicable, the participation of aid-recipients and the study participants came across as committed to this philosophy. There is a sense that they learn from each other's and their own experiences; continuously going through the process of abandoning states of *"unconscious incompetence"* [12] and learning how to avoid failure and how to make participation work. Some examples of their learning reveal a form of *"double loop learning"* [11], as they faced errors from the past by exploring possibilities of 'doing things differently' (for example, switching projects from traditional to participatory approaches) or 'doing different things' (for example, by including the *"Human Rights approach"* [18]).

Participants reported that conditions that are often imposed by donors were their main obstacle to implementing PLA. Significantly, this factor is often out of the control of the NGO; that is if the NGO needs to have access to a broad range of funding and grants.

For example, when discussing the trigger for initiating Project 5 one participant made the following admission:

"We pegged the project application to the priorities of 'Spanish Cooperation', specifically we decided to work with health because that was the priority of our main donor" (***Interviewee-9***).

4 A closer examination of 'grant and donor conditions' as the major inhibitor to implementing PLA

'Grant and donor conditions' was identified as the most significant factor impacting on failure or success in implementing PLA when delivering human development projects and is therefore discussed in more detail in this section.

4.1 Donors' desire for 'humanitarian visibility'

Olontuba and Gray [19] analysed the humanitarian aid supply chain, (Fig. 3), and concluded that contrary to conventional business supply chains, NGOs are *"more concerned with relationships with donors than with delivery to recipients"* because they have to convince donors that they are producing results, a concept that is defined as *"humanitarian visibility"* [19]. The implications of the desire for *"humanitarian visibility"* are discussed in sections 4.1.1 to 4.1.3.

Figure 3: A typical humanitarian supply chain (adapted from Oloruntoba and Gray [19]).

4.1.1 Ring-fenced funding or grants

Funding for development is often ring-fenced to 'humanitarian visibility' activities as observed by one interviewee:

*"In many cases, either you have the money in your pocket to identify what you need to do (*meaning funding for diagnostics*) or you are not in* (with a chance to obtain grants)" (***Interviewee-9***).

This leads NGOs to draft development plans without adequate diagnostics leading to poor specifications of development projects as noted in the following observation:

"Sometimes, projects seem to be a solution for recipients' problems but once you start implementing them, you realise that actually they do not address people's needs. That is because sometimes, things have been planned with the intention of meting conditions to get approval of certain grants" (***Interviewee-5***).

However it is not only donors but local officials also often prefer NGO's to avoid local bureaucracy by working as implementation units, instead of working directly from inside institutions and helping to build local capacity:

"We used to be continuously pushed by high and medium-ranking officials because they wanted things done quickly without us 'bothering' local people" (***Interviewee-7***).

The restricted nature of funding is also a major factor for NGOs failing to use PLA as noted in the following statement:

"Generally, there is neither enough economical capacity, nor financial stability to ensure that you can stay working in a place as long as you need to (in order to ensure sustainability)" (***Interviewee-9***).

This is aggravated by the fact that donors often require NGO's to use grants within set time scales as noted in the following comment:

"In some situations like meetings, I used to feel that recipients did not get the point of what we were saying but despite that we had to carry on because the schedule of projects does not allow you to stop" (*Interviewee-7*).

4.1.2 Fostering competition instead of collaboration

The need to complete projects on time means that NGOs working in the same geographical area do not always coordination their activities [20, 21] and sometimes *"poach local qualified staff"* [22] from recipient institutions by offering salaries well above local rates, without caring that this weakens the institutions that they should be strengthening. The following comment is a graphic illustration of this:

"That guy (a medium-ranking official) *who had come from the capital to enforce the improvement of the Health Information System (HIS), was very enthusiast and got involved with our initiative. Nevertheless, after the first year of the project, when things were moving fast, he left the public institution as he got a job with another NGO"* (***Interviewee-7***) (***Project-5***).

4.1.3 Setting objectives unrelated to sustainable development

A concentrate on *"humanitarian visibility"* leads NGOs to set easily achievable objectives in order to demonstrate success. This detracts from specifying indicators consistent with *sustainable human development*, as recognized by one of the interviewees, when talking about project 3:

> "*Our mistake was not to include appropriate objectives' indicators for measuring the quality of results. One example is that although we can say that objectives were achieved, the success in processes of transferring telecommunication networks has not been evident*" (**Interviewee-2**).

This finding is consistent with Birdsall [20] who explains that donors generally do not implement strong systems of evaluation because it could be costly, considering that grants are in the order of billions. The consequences of achieving objectives that do not ensuring sustainability are reflected in following comments regarding different projects:

> "*I wish we had had some more time in order to make sure that everything we had set out to do materialised and became long-lasting*" (**Interviewee-4**) (**Project-1**);

> "*It would have been important to have had a few extra months in order to evaluate how services were performing and how users were evolving*" (**Interviewee-6**) (**Project-2**);

> "*We had the intention of continuing working with the ICT Line after delivering the project because we thought it was important to monitor the telecommunications network and give support to maintenance activities by keeping an eye on the performance of the SPM and to ensure that they keep putting in effect the maintenance plan*" (**Interviewee-8**) (**Project-5**).

4.2 Serving the home economy

There is wide agreement [9, 20–23] that a large percentage of the money that is reported as grants or loans, never reaches the recipients because it never leaves the country of origin; paying contracts for the supply of goods and services. Yunus and Jolis [9] a telling illustration of this:

> "*of the more than 30 USD billion in foreign donor assistance received in the last twenty-six years, 75 per cent never actually reached Bangladesh in the form of cash. Instead, it came as equipment, commodities, supplies, and the cost of consultants, contractors, advisers and experts. Some rich nations use their foreign aid budget to employ their own people and to sell their own goods. The remaining 25 per cent which actually reached Bangladesh in the form of cash went into the hands of a tiny elite of local suppliers, contractors, consultants and experts*"

This inhibits recipient-participation because sourcing supplies and services externally does not develop local capabilities. However, participants in this study noted that they have been allowed to source locally as far as practicable. However, problems of capacity impact on their ability to source locally:

> "*The bidding was stopped twice because there were no candidates meeting all the requirements, including experience in installing telecommunication towers in the jungle*" (**Interviewee-6**) (**Project-2**);

> "*It was when we were looking for suppliers of technologies for our projects in order to make them aware of biddings to ensure that we would receive*

enough bids that we realised that local enterprises might not have the capacity to meet the project's reference terms" (***Interviewee-7***) (***Project-5***).

There appear to be credible and justifiable reasons for using outside sources. However, sourcing this is not a solution; it is in fact an excuse for not building capacities of local suppliers that are also stakeholders since they belong to the community that is expected to be developed.

4.3 Promoting a socio-political agenda

If a project does not recognise the interests of politically powerful local people then it is more likely to fail or be unsustainable, as noted these comments:

"*They* (high-ranking officials) *are able to enumerate the advantages and improvements introduced ...*" (***Interviewee-8***);

"*...if you do not have them, the seminar loses its usefulness and sense*". (***Interviewee-7***);

"*Our big mistake was not to directly involve the regional government from the beginning of the project. There was no political compromise, and there was no way to oblige them*" (***Interviewee-4***) (***Project-1***);

"*In order to roll-out the re-designed processes, it would have been necessary to modify national directives, something that high-ranking officials were not willing to do*". (***Interviewee-4***) (***Project-3***).

Thus it is important for donors to make efforts to create political ownership and "*to respond to proposal of governments (and non-government groups) rather than themselves proposing and shaping programs*" [20]. The following lesson underlines the significance of political ownership:

"*Unlike previous projects, where ONGAWA 'hand-picked', who to work with on a project, for this project an invitation was extended to all regional health directors to present a proposal following which the proposal that met criteria related to local leadership and health indicators was selected*" (***Interviewee-5***) (***Project-1***).

From the foregoing discussion, it can be argued that donor's interests are not always altruistic [24, 25] and that the "*politics of aid*", [23] especially the '*donor's geostrategic interests*" [23] often mean that "*humanitarian visibility*" is valued in preference to *sustainable human development*. This is consistent with the suggestion that foreign aid is an excuse to veil other interests. It is also argued that donors and agencies of certain countries focus their interventions in regions where 'home' registered MNC have a strong presence or interests [26, 27]. For example, Garzón [26] explains that the Spanish Agency for International Development Cooperation's (AECID) geographical priorities [28] seems to coincide with countries where the most important Spanish MNC (including *Telefónica* and *Repsol YPF*) have some kind of interest [29]. That is why some non-profit organisations like *Ecologistas en Acción* [30] and *Cooperación Alternativa y Acción solidaria* [31] question AECID for allocating money to MNC's foundation projects, especially those whose Corporate Social Responsibility (CSR) strategy is not evident; an example of which is the project "*Strengthening of the economic and social endeavours of the communities in the operation zone of Repsol YPF Ecuador in the Ecuadorian Amazon*" executed by

REPSOL YPF Ecuador Foundation funded by AECID with 150.000€ [32]. Grain [27] cites the global agenda for Genetically Modified (GM) agriculture in proposing that the USAID logo "*From the American people*" should be switched to "*For the American Corporations*".

5 Conclusions

Grants conditioned by donor preferences or interests limit the scope for PLA and delivering sustainable development. In many cases when donors impose policies that are in conflict with aid-recipient's policies and values, it is unlikely that NGOs like ONGAWA would get high-ranking officials to engage with the project, and even if the project is implemented there might be issues surrounding its sustainability. Furthermore, in many cases donors want to see quick results. This means that it is often unlikely that they will want to put resources in detailed diagnostics, a pre-requisite for sustainable development but one that may take a long time. It is imperative that NGOs and Donors work together through a process of mutual education in order to ensure well-funded sustainable human development projects.

Acknowledgements

The authors are thankful to Mr Villarroel and staff at ONGAWA, Spain, for facilitating the study and hence the preparation of this paper.

References

[1] United Nations Development Programme (UNDP) Belize. What is Human Development?, ww.undp.org.bz/human-development/what-is-human-development/

[2] United Nations Development Programme (UNDP), *Human Development Report 2011, Sustainability and Equity, a Better Future for All*. Palgrave Macmillan: New York, 2011.

[3] Johansson, H., McHugh, P., Pendlebury, A. and Wheeler, W., *Business Process Reengineering: Breakpoint Strategies for Market Dominance*. John Wiley & Sons: West Sussex, 1993.

[4] Haq, M., *Reflections on Human Development*. Oxford University Press, Inc: New Delhi, 1999.

[5] Ranis, G., Stewart, F. and Samman, E., Human Development: Beyond the HDI. *Centre Discussion Paper No. 916, produced for the Economic Growth Centre of Yale University*. Yale University: New Haven, 2005.

[6] Shleifer, A., Peter Bauer and the Failure of Foreign Aid, *Cato Journal*, 29(3), pp. 379-90, 2009.

[7] Stern, N., Professor Bauer on Development: A review article, *Journal of Development Economics*, 1(1), pp. 191–211, 1974.

[8] Moyo, D., *Dead Aid, Why aid is not working and how there is another way for Africa.* Penguin Books: London, 2010.

[9] Yunus, M. and Jolis, A., *Banker to the poor, the story of the Grameen Bank.* Aurum Press Ltd: London, 1999.

[10] Moran, T., *Beyond Sweatshops: Foreign Direct Investment and Globalization in Developing Countries*, The Bookings Institution: Washington, DC, 2002.

[11] Hayes, J., *The Theory and Practice of Change Management*, 3rd ed. Palgrave Macmillan: London, 2010.

[12] Howell, W, *The empathic communicator.* Wadsworth Publishing Co: Belmont, 1982.

[13] Food and Agriculture Organisation of the United Nations (FAO), *Participatory Development: Guidelines on Beneficiary Participation in Agricultural and Rural Development*, 2nd ed. FAO: Rome, 2003.

[14] Anyaegbunam, C., Mefalopulos, P. and Moetsabi, T., *Participatory Rural Communication Appraisal Starting with the people*, 2nd ed. SADC Centre of Communication for Development Harare and FAO: Rome, 2004.

[15] Chambers, R., The origins and practice of Participatory Rural Appraisal, *World Development*, 22(7), pp. 953-69, 1994.

[16] ONGAWA. Who we are, ongawa.org/wp/?page_id=1479.

[17] Riessman, C., *Narrative Methods for the Human Sciences.* SAGE Publications: London, 2008.

[18] United Nations Population Fund (UNFPA), The Human Rights-Based Approach, www.unfpa.org/rights/approaches.htm

[19] Oloruntoba, R. and Gray, R., Humanitarian aid: an agile supply chain?, *Supply Chain Management: An International Journal*, 11(2), pp. 115-120, 2006.

[20] Birdsall, N., Seven Deadly Sins: Reflections on Donor Failings. *Prepared originally for Conference on Emerging Global Economic Order and Developing Countries (June 28 – July 1 2004).* Economic Association: Bangladesh, 2004.

[21] Easterly, W., Are Aid Agencies Improving?, *Economic Policy*, 22(52), pp. 633-78, 2007.

[22] Knack, S., and Rahman, A., Donor Fragmentation and Bureaucratic Quality in Aid Recipients. *World Bank Policy Research Working Paper 3186*, World Bank: Washington, DC, 2004.

[23] Woods, N., The Shifting Politics of Foreign Aid, *International Affairs (Royal Institute of International Affairs)*, 81(2), pp. 393-409, 2005.

[24] Boschini, A. and Olofsgard, A., Foreign Aid: an Instrument for Fighting Poverty or Communism?, *Paper published by the Social Science Research Network and the World Bank*, The World Bank: Washington, DC, 2002.

[25] Griffin, K., Foreign Aid after the Cold War, *Development and Change*, 22(4), pp. 645-85, 2008.

[26] Garzón, A. La cooperación internacional española (AECID): ¿instrumento para beneficios de los pobres o ganancias de los ricos?, www.rebelion.org/noticia.php?id=142887

[27] Grain. USAID in Africa: 'For the American Corporations'. www.grain.org/es/article/entries/493-usaid-in-africa-for-the-american-corporations

[28] Spanish Agency for International Development Cooperation (AECID). Where we cooperate- Geographical Priorities, www.aecid.es/en/donde-cooperamos/

[29] Chislett, W. Spain's Multinationals: the Dynamic Part of an Ailing Economy (WP). www.realinstitutoelcano.org/wps/portal/rielcano_eng/ Print?WCM_GLOBAL_CONTEXT=/wps/wcm/connect/elcano/Elcano_in/ Zonas_in/DT17-2011#C3

[30] Ecologistas en Acción (2012). No a la financiación de la AECID de la Fundación Repsol-YPF, www.ecologistasenaccion.org/article22559.html.

[31] Cooperación Alternativa y Acción solidaria (2012). La Agencia Española de Cooperación financia la anti-cooperación petrolera en Ecuador: Repsol YPF, www.cooperacionalternativa.org/index.php/home/1-general/171-la-agencia-espanola-de-cooperacion-financia-la-anticooperacion-petrolera-en-ecuador-repsol-ypf

[32] Spain, Boletín Oficial del Estado (BOE). III. Otras disposiciones Ministerio de Asuntos Exteriores y de Cooperación. Resolución de 31 de enero de 2012, de la Presidencia de la Agencia Española de Cooperación Internacional para el Desarrollo, por la que se publican las ayudas de convocatoria abierta y permanente correspondientes al año 2011. www.boe.es/boe/dias/2012/05/14/pdfs/BOE-A-2012-6347.pdf

Demonstrating the importance of criteria and sub-criteria in building assessment methods

R. Banani, M. Vahdati & A. Elmualim
*School of Construction Management and Engineering,
University of Reading, UK*

Abstract

Building assessment methods have become a popular research field since the early 1990s. An international tool which allows the assessment of buildings in all regions, taking into account differences in climates, topographies and cultures does not yet exist. This paper aims to demonstrate the importance of criteria and sub-criteria in developing a new potential building assessment method for Saudi Arabia. Recently, the awareness of sustainability has been increasing in developing countries due to high energy consumption, pollution and high carbon foot print. There is no debate that assessment criteria have an important role to identify the tool's orientation. However, various aspects influence the criteria and sub-criteria of assessment tools such as environment, economic, social and cultural to mention but a few. The author provides an investigation on the most popular and globally used schemes: BREEAM, LEED, Green Star, CASBEE and Estidama in order to identify the effectiveness of the different aspects of the assessment criteria and the impacts of these criteria on the assessment results; that will provide a solid foundation to develop an effective sustainable assessment method for buildings in Saudi Arabia. Initial results of the investigation suggest that each country needs to develop its own assessment method in order to achieve desired results, while focusing upon the indigenous environmental, economic, social and cultural conditions.
Keywords: assessment methods, BREEAM, LEED, Green Star, CASBEE, Estidama, sustainability, sustainable buildings, environment, Saudi Arabia.

1 Introduction

The impact of the construction sector on the environment has been well documented. Since 1990s and upward a great number of rating tools have been developed as suggesting efficient solution to assess the effect of construction on the environment. Recently, a number of assessment methods have been developed in different developing countries such as Malaysia, Jordon and United Arab Emirates (UAE) cater to local conditions and practices [1, 2].This is an evidence of awareness rose about sustainability and its benefits in developing countries.

The most commonly used assessment methods are BREEAM (Building Research Establishment's Environmental Assessment Method), developed in UK in 1990s, and LEED (Leadership in Energy and Environmental Design) developed in the USA in 1998. However, Green Star in Australia, CASBEE (Comprehensive Assessment System for Building Environmental Efficiency) in Japan and Estidama in UAE have subsequently emerged.

A number of environmental factors could prevent the direct use of currently available tools in another country other than its own origin [3, 4]. Some of such factors are (1) Climate context, (2) Geographical Features, (3) Resources consumption, (4) Understanding of building stocks, (5) Government policy and regulation, (6) Understanding of the importance of historical features, (7) Understanding of the cultural value and public awareness. It appears that all these factors vary between regions. Even in one country designing a tool could be a challenge where climate and topography change from one place to another. For example, the research that took place in Jordon by Ali and Al Nsairat [2] concluded that Jordon needs to develop a domestic assessment method considering the differences in its climate and topography.

The Kingdom of Saudi Arabia has witnessed considerable growth since 1973. However, the development of construction sector in the country is influenced by its culture. There has been a notable development in the construction sector in Saudi Arabia. An example of these new developments is King Abdullah City for Atomic and Renewable Energy (KACARE), which is located 30 kilometres from Riyadh with a total Gross Floor Area (GFA) of 22,659,859 square meters. This development includes residential, industrial, commercial, educational, social and cultural areas. The design stage of the development was based on the framework of Sustainable Built Environment Tool (SuBET) to ensure high standards of sustainable urban design.

The application of building assessment tools, therefore, indicates that the awareness of sustainability in Saudi Arabia construction industry has increased recently. However, there is no assessment tool developed which considers the condition of Saudi as a country such as weather, social and culture. Hence, an assessment tool for the efficiency of the application of the concept of sustainability is required.

2   Reviewing environmental assessment methods

2.1 Sustainable buildings rating tools

To guarantee the quality of sustainable construction, a sustainability rating method is required. A report provided by the Pacific Northwest National

Laboratory has defined '*Sustainable building rating systems*' as '*'tools that examine the performance or expected performance of a 'whole building' and translate that examination into an overall assessment that allows for comparison against other buildings*'' [5]. In addition, according to Ding [6], "*As environmental issues become more urgent, more comprehensive building assessment methods are required to assess building performance across a broader range of environmental considerations*"

Different tools have unique characteristics associated with their country of origin which could be considered as a barrier to reaching international status [7]. The characteristic concepts, as proved by Darus *et al.* [1], through applying an international assessment method (*GBTool*) on a Malaysian case, found such a method to be unsuitable for that country as a great number of adjustments would have to be made. Both studies [1, 7] prove that each country should design its own assessment method. Moreover, Reed *et al.* [7] present a useful work for global comparison of sustainable rating tool in order to find an international tool which could be used on a global level.

2.1.1 Environment, economic, cultural and social aspects

There is no doubt that environmental issues have significant importance, but consideration of other aspects of sustainability will deliver successful sustainable assessment tools [8]. Todd *et al.* [9] found that the considerations of economic, social and cultural aspects are responsible for different types of barriers and opportunities that developing countries could face in designing their own domestic rating methods. Whilst a number of studies [5, 8] found that these aspects are required for delivering sustainability successfully. Moreover, Poston *et al.* [10] mentioned that though a number of assessment tools have shifted their emphasis from green to sustainable buildings, there has been criticism of the dominance of environmental criteria at the expense of the social and economic criteria.

Ali and Al Nsairat [2] present economic and cultural aspects, but link their importance with the local context. It is believed that local context determines the importance of economic, social and cultural aspects as a result of their variation from one country to another. For instance, social and cultural aspects in Arabic countries such as Saudi Arabia play an important role in those countries, while economic aspects are the important ones in developed countries. This example is corroborated by Cole [11] who considers the social and economic aspects as important in developing countries with different aspects holding importance in developed countries. Reed *et al.* [7] consider economic, social and cultural aspects as unique characteristics that could prevent a tool take-up. It is noticeable that a number of developing countries have started developing their domestic assessment methods to be suitable with their environment, and economic, social, cultural and historical contexts [9]. An example is the assessment tool Estidama [10] which was developed in the UAE.

2.1.2 Tools criteria

The prime role for the criteria is to achieve an environmental building assessment method goal which "*provides a comprehensive assessment of the*

environmental characteristics of a building" [6]. Systems criteria and its structure have significant effects on the performance evaluation of an assessment method [11]. This is supported by Ali and Al Nsairat [2] who suggests that the system categories define the external boundaries of a tool which is different from one region to another. Therefore, systems criteria are different from one tool to another as a result of continuous development applied to tools criteria to deliver different market, professionals' and owners' aspirations.

3 Existing building environmental assessment tools

3.1 BREEAM

BREEAM has a long track record in the United Kingdom. It is considered as the first green buildings assessment method [6]. The main goal of developing the BREEAM method was to *"Provide authoritative guidance on ways of minimising the adverse effects of buildings on the global and local environments while promoting a healthy and comfortable indoor environment"* [12]. The evaluation of a building takes place in a given time using the BREEAM system, whereby a total score is awarded through adding assessment weighting for each criterion (Table 1). The BREEAM uses a fixed weighting system developed by BRE to provide a means of defining, and ranking the relative impact of environmental issues [13]. Moreover, the different main categories in BREEAM, including the one additional category in BREEAM New Construction 2011, are shown in table 1 [13].

Table 1:   The BREEAM assessment method categories and weightings.

BREEAM categories	Weighting
Management	12%
Health and Wellbeing	15%
Energy	19%
Transport	8%
Water	6%
Materials	12.5%
Waste	7.5%
Land Use and Ecology	10%
Pollution	10%
Total	100%
Innovation (additional)	10%

The additional category incorporated into the new version allows for an extra 10% credit towards the improvement of the building's performance and supports a building being awarded a higher final score.

3.2 LEED

LEED is an environmental assessment system that was designed and developed by the U. S. Green Buildings Council (USGBC), in order to transform the market for green buildings [14]. It is defined as *"a framework for identifying, implementing, and measuring green building and neighbourhood design, construction, operations, and maintenance"* [15]. Currently, LEED is the second worldwide most used building assessment method [16]. However, almost all the studies agree that BREEAM and LEED can be considered as the foundation for most assessment rating tools around the world [7].

To achieve *LEED-NC2009* a building is awarded a total score using a point system for each criterion (Table 2). In fact, the assessment considers all various parameters through different categories which are included in LEED (as shown in Table 2) [15].

Table 2:   The LEED categories and points distribution.

LEED Categories	Possible Points
Sustainable Site	26
Water efficiency	10
Energy and atmosphere	35
Materials and Resources	14
Indoor Environment Quality	15
Total	100
Innovation and design process	6
Regional Priority Credit	4

It can be seen that the LEED categories concentrate on a building's performance relating to environmental sources such as water, energy and materials. As a result, LEED is used not just in the USA, but also in Canada, Spain, China and India [8].

3.3 Green Star

Green Star is an Australian environmental rating system launched in 2003 which was developed by the Green Building Council Australia [17]. The assessment tool was originally developed to accommodate buildings' requirements in hot climates, where cooling systems and solar shading are considered as being of fundamental importance [17]. The council designed the tool to deliver the needs of the environment and the people in their buildings through different purposes: to reduce the impact of buildings on the environment (environmental purpose); to enhance the health and productivity of the buildings' users (humanity purpose) and to achieve cost savings (economic purpose) [17]. Green Star is concerned with delivering sustainability in the building sector in a practical way.

Green Star has a credit points system for each criterion that helps buildings be awarded the rating method assessment (Table 3). The assessment points are awarded by examining a building through various categories. The Australian rating method has various categories that cover most aspects of a building as shown in Table 3 [17].

Table 3:   Green star categories and credit distribution.

Green Star Categories	Possible Points
Management	12
Indoor Environment Quality	27
Energy	29
Transportation	11
Water	12
Materials	25
Land use and Ecology	8
Emission	19
Total	143
Innovation	5

3.4 CASBEE

The Japanese Sustainable Building Consortium (JSBC) is the developer of the environmental assessment method CASBEE that evaluates and rates the environmental performance of buildings. It was launched in 2001 and the first assessment tool for office buildings was completed in 2002. In addition, consideration is given to three main principles in the development of tool to gain maximum environmental benefits which are; (1) Comprehensive assessment throughout the life cycle of the building (2) Assessment of Building Environmental *'Built Environment Quality (Q)'* and *'Built Environmental Lode (L)''* (3) Assessment based on the newly-developed Building Environment Efficiency (BEE) indicator [18].

CASBEE defines *Built Environment Quality (Q) as "Evaluates improvement in living amenity for the building users, within the hypothetical enclosed space (the private property)"; Built Environmental Lode (L) defined as "Evaluates negative aspects of environmental impact which go beyond the hypothetical enclosed space to the outside (the public property)"* [18].

The classifications are awarded through examining a building under different assessment categories that guarantee the application of the concepts of sustainability in the construction. However, CASBEE has different assessment categories from BREEAM, LEED and Green Star. It has two main categories which are (Q) Building Environmental Quality and Performance and (LR) Reduction of Building Environment Loading. The categories involved include: indoor environment (Q), quality of service (Q), outdoor environment on-site (Q), energy (L), resources and materials (L) and off-site environment (L) [18].

Moreover, BEE is considered as a tool indictor and it is an additional process that a building goes through to be awarded the assessment. It could be defined as the following equation calculation:

$$BEE = \frac{Q(\text{Environmental Quality})}{L(EnvironmentalLoad)}$$

It appears that all the categories focus strongly on the environmental issues. It could be said that the tool categories are based on a building's life cycle which plays a key role in the assessment method.

3.5 Estidama

Estidama is the first environmental assessment method developed in the Middle East especially in the Arabian Gulf countries. It means *''Sustainability''* in Arabic and it was developed in 2008 by the Abu Dhabi Urban Planning Council (AUPC) in the UAE. The assessment method has a ratings tool called The Pearl Rating System (PRS) that helps to deliver sustainable development efficiently. The main aim of using PRS is to address the sustainability in a building throughout its entire lifecycle design, construction and operation [19]. In addition, the assessed building can be awarded at least 1 Pearl point which contains a number of required credits for each criterion (Table 4) [19].

Table 4:   Estidama categories and credit distribution.

Estidama categories	Maximum Credit Points
Integrated Development Process	13
Natural System	12
Liveable Buildings	37
Precious Water	43
Resourceful Energy	44
Stewarding Materials	28
Innovation Practice	3
Total	177

4 Tools comparison overview

Table 5 highlights the features that distinguish each assessment tool. According to Ding [6] life cycle assessment is linked with building assessment method. It includes different building phases; design, construction, operation and deconstruction. However, design, construction and operation phases are considered in all potential assessment methods (BREEAM, LEED, Green Star, CASBEE and Estidama) as shown in Table 5. CASBEE is the only tool that considers deconstruction stage. This stage plays an important role in building life cycle [3]. Deconstruction stage is not affected the application of the tool because this stage could be add to a tool while developing it regularly. Further, Ding [6] found that the most impact stage to apply a tool is the design stage and it is included in all rating tools.

4.1 Critical comparison of tools criteria

4.1.1 Energy, water, waste and materials
All assessment method includes an energy category which is a significant criterion (as shown in Tables 1–4). BREEAM and Green Star measure the building Energy performance (BEP) considering the reduction of CO_2 emission whilst LEED emphasises upon the reduction of energy cost. CASBEE and Estidama have a different approach to assess BEP by focusing on the improvement percentage on annual energy consumption.

Water, waste and materials are considered as key categories in all five assessment tools. However, due to limited annual rainfall, hot climate, and the great energy embodied to provide potable water through desalination in the UAE, Estidama is the only tool that considers water conservation as priority criteria (Table 4). Moreover, due to its negative impact on human and environment, both waste water and solid water are addressed in all five schemes efficiently.

Materials are important elements in environmental assessment methods due to their impacts on building users and the environment. Comparatively, BREEAM focuses on material types and LEED, CASBEE and Estidama encourage use of locally manufactured materials. In terms of cost consideration, Estidama and Green star assess materials whilst calculating its cost in relation to building construction.

Table 5:   Primary features of BREEAM, LEED, green star, CASBEE and Estidama.

	BREEAM	LEED	Green Star	CASBEE	Estidama
Developer and Year	the U. K. Building Research Establishment (BRE); 1990	the US Green Buildings Council (USGBC); 1998	Green Building Council Australia (GBCA); 2002	Japan Sustainable Building Consortium (JSBC); 2001	Abu Dhabi Urban Planning Council (UPC); 2008
Building Phases	Design, Construction and Operation	Design, Construction and Operation	Design, Construction and Operation	Design, Construction, Operation and Deconstruction	Design, Construction and Operation
Buildings Types	Offices Housing Healthcare Courts Industrial Units Prisons Retail Schools Multi Residential Schools Neighbourhood	Offices Homes Neighbourhood Development Retail Healthcare Schools	Education Healthcare Industrial Multi-Residential Office Office Interiors Retail Centre	Residential Office Schools Retail Health care Urban development Cities	Offices Retail Multi-Residential School
Scope	New build Refurbishment Existing building	New build Refurbishment Existing building	New build Refurbishment Existing building	New build Refurbishment Existing building	New building Existing building
Categories	Management Health and Wellbeing Energy Transport Water Materials Land Use and Ecology Waste Pollution Innovation (additional)	Sustainable Site Water Efficiency Energy and Atmosphere Materials and Resources Indoor Environment Quality Innovation and Design Process Regional Priority Credits	Management Indoor Environment Quality Energy Transport Water Materials Land Use and Ecology Emissions Innovation	Environmental Quality (Q) Indoor Environment Quality-of-Service Outdoor Environment on site Environmental Load (L) Energy Resources and Materials Off-site Environment. BEE (Building Environmental Efficiency)= Q/L	Integrated Development Process Natural Systems Liveable Buildings Precious Water Resourceful Energy-Stewarding Materials Innovating Practice
Rating	Pass Good Very Good Excellent Outstanding	Certified Silver Gold Platinum	1 – 3 Stars 4 Stars 5 Stars 6 Stars	Poor (c) Slightly Poor(B-) Good(B+) Very Good (A) Superior (S)	1 Pearl 2 Pearl 3 Pearl 4 Pearl 5 Pearl
Update process	Annual	As required	Annual	As required	Not available
Number of certificated Buildings	7,202	2,858	78	80	Not available
International use	Canada, Hong Kong and Netherlands	Emirates, India and Brazil	New Zealand and South Africa	-	-

4.1.2 Indoor environment quality, pollution and management

The quality of indoor environment is considered as key objective in all building assessment methods. All five schemes cover this category with respect to different elements. BREEAM covers materials category giving importance for ventilation and HVAC systems [13]. At the same time LEED covers this category focusing upon *low-emitting materials* criteria [20]. Green Star has emphasised on air condition systems and lighting. Whilst, CASBEE covers indoor environment quality well enough under the sub category of *indoor quality* (Q1) of *Built Environment Quality* category (Q). It also further supports this category by including most of the parameters from *Quality of service* category which is also the sub-category (Q2) of the *Built Environment Quality*. Estidama assesses indoor environment quality with more consideration for materials emission and thermal comfort.

Each tool assesses pollutions category using various methods. BREEAM, Green Star and CASBEE are dedicated the issue as an individual category, whilst LEED and Estidama distribute the themes of pollutions across the scoring process. BREEAM evaluates refrigerant issues beside the number of pollutions such as CO_2 and NOx emissions. Similarly, Green Star addresses the same problems almost like BREEAM.

In contrast, LEED and CASBEE evaluate *Heat island effects* criterion while it is overlooked in BREEAM, Green Star and Estidama [20]. Nevertheless, CASBEE considers local environment of Japan and measures parameters which cannot be found in other assessment methods such as Earthquake Resistance and Restriction of Wind Damage [18]. Whilst, Estidama emphasises on refrigerant issues due to the higher demand of air-condition system.

BREEAM and Green Star consider management as a separate category, whilst LEED, CASBEE and Estidama distribute parameters of management across different assessment categories. Green star focuses on commissioning and environmental management, while CASBEE prioritises planning and management of maintenance. Estidama and LEED explicitly address the management of indoor air quality and materials.

4.1.3 Site, ecology and management

Site and ecology are the most important categories that relate to building environmental effect directly. All five tools cover almost same criteria of land use and ecology. However, each method applies it differently. BREEAM considers the creation of ecology as the most important criterion, whilst under LEED; site selection is a highly important. Green star pays more attention to the ecological value of site, while CASBEE focuses on the local characteristics of the site, townscape and landscape. Estidama focuses more on natural resource management, sustainable land use and creation and restoration of habitat [20]. What is more, the criteria of *Townscape and Landscape*, *Local Characteristics* and *Out-door Amenity* are not given that much importance in BREEAM, LEED and Green Star, however, they are given considerably much importance in CASBEE and Estidama.

4.1.4 Economic and social aspects

Economic aspects contain cost efficiency and quality of services categories. All parameters of cost efficiency are distributed across different assessment categories. BREEAM and Estidama are the only tools which evaluate 'Life cycle costing' parameter under different category. Operation and maintenance costs have been considered in BREEAM, LEED, and Estidama while they are overlooked in Green Star and CASBEE. Indeed, economic issues have been covered in BREEAM, LEED, Green Star and Estidama poorly into their assessment frameworks. Nevertheless, Estidama cover these issues better than the other tools mentioned above.

Quality of service is comprehensively considered only in CASBEE among the five assessment methods. However, BREEAM and Estidama included some criteria in their assessment process such as *durability and protection* and *reliability*. Estidama distinguishes from BREEAM by considering *flexibility and adaptability* and *systems renewability*.

LEED and Green Star, on the other hand, have no criteria that are applicable to this category except system controllability in LEED and flexibility and adaptability in Green Star. Local context of Japan appears in quality of service category in CASBEE in the form of for example earthquake resistance.

Social aspects are in three different categories; innovation, transportation and cultural. BREEAM and LEED both display almost same criteria of innovation [4]. Green Star uses innovation criteria to achieve maximum environmental benefits and fosters the industry's transition to sustainable building [17]. CASBEE has no consideration for innovation criteria due to its evaluation framework.

Estidama has covered innovation category in a unique manner. It achieves the category through embracing it in design with respect to the cultural identity of the region [19]. All five assessment methods covered transportation criteria in their assessment frameworks. However, only BREEAM and Green Star consider transportation as individual category in their assessment frameworks. LEED, CASBEE and Estidama distribute the themes of transportation across the scoring process.

BREEAM considers transportation under *Transport* category whilst distinguishing travel plan, which is related strongly with accessibility of public transport [16]. LEED includes transportation under *Sustainable site* category providing more attention to public transportation access and bicycle facilities. Green Star focuses on car parking provision and cyclist facilities with no attention for community facilities.

CASBEE considers transportation with taking more care for community facilities and bicycle facilities. Estidama has no individual category for transportation, hence it covers same criteria under *Liveable Buildings* category likewise BREEAM. Only CASBEE and Estidama consider culture and tradition significantly while BREEAM, LEED and Green star completely overlook this issue. CASBEE addresses the cultural aspects under '*Outdoor Environment on-Site*' category whilst Estidama deals with it under '*Innovating Practice*' category. Both tools seek to consider environment through cultural and traditional views.

5 Conclusion

This study aims to demonstrate the importance of criteria and sub-criteria in building assessment methods. It is clear that all five assessment tools have common criteria and goal such as energy, water and materials for increase the knowledge about the built environment with decreased impacts of the construction on its users and the environment.

The comparison shows that each tool applies these criteria and have goals based on different aspects; environmental, economic, social and cultural. Indeed, the environmental theme is clearly dominated in all five schemes. However, economic and social aspects have been considered in indirect way through distributed sub-criteria across different assessment categories such as LEED and Green Star. Cultural aspects have been overlooked in the assessment framework consideration such as in BREEAM, LEED and Green Star. Regional environmental circumstances also play an important role in tool's criteria.

Further, the region's policy and regulation are appeared in all assessment methods except Estidama who linked the assessment with international standards. This interface between criteria and region's policy and regulations influenced the implementation of assessment method and results due to their territorial differences. For instance, BREEAM and LEED both included energy category in their assessment framework however, each tool use different energy assessment method as shown in comparison. This provides a significant difference in results [20].

This study has shown that the categories of assessment methods are interrelated to each other and play an important role in identifying the tool orientation and results. Hence, the ultimate goal of delivering sustainability could not be met unless regional preferences are considered in assessment criteria. It is therefore concluded that developing specific tool's criteria considering environment, economic, social and cultural aspects of Saudi Arabia guarantee delivering sustainable buildings in Saudi Arabia successfully.

References

[1] Darus, Z. M., Hashim, N. A., Salleh, E., Haw, L. C., Rashid, A. K. A., and Manan, S. N. A., Development of rating system for sustainable building in Malaysia. *Proc. of Conf. on WSEAS Transactions on Environment and development*, **5(3)**, pp. 206–272, 2009.

[2] Ali, H. and Al Nsairat, S., Developing a green building assessment tool for developing countries – Case of Jordan. *Building and Environment*, **44(5)**, pp. 1053–1064, 2009.

[3] Mao, X., Lu, H. and Li, Q, A Comparison Study of Mainstream Sustainable/Green Building Rating Tools in the World. *Proc. Of Conf. in Management and Service Science*, MASS '09, IEEEE, pp, 1–5, 2009.

[4] Alyami, S. H. and Rezgui, Y., Sustainable building assessment tool development approach. *Sustainable Cities and Society*, **5(0)**, pp, 52–62, 2012.

[5] Fowler, M. and Rauch, M., Sustainable Building Rating Systems Summary. Contract July 2006 for *United States Department of Energy*, pp. 1–55, 2006.

[6] Ding, G., Sustainable construction – The role of environmental assessment tools. *Environmental Management*, **86(3)**, pp. 451–464, 2008.

[7] Reed, R., Bilos, A., Wilkinson, S. and Schulte, K., International comparison of sustainable rating tools. *JOSRE*, **1(1)**, pp. 1–22, 2009.

[8] Haapio, A. and Viitaniemi, P., A critical review of building environmental assessment tools. *Environmental Impact Assessment Review*, **28(7)**, pp. 469–482, 2008.

[9] Todd, J., Crawley, D., Geissler, S. and Lindsey, G., Comparative assessment of environmental performance tools and the role of the Green Building Challenge. *Building Research and Information*, **29(5)**, pp. 324–335, 2001.

[10] Poston, A., Emmanuel, R. and Thomson, C., Developing holistic frameworks for the next generation of sustainability assessment methods for the built environment. *Proc. Of the 26th Annual ARCOM Conference*, Egbu: Leeds, UK, pp. 1487–1496, 2010.

[11] Cole, R., Building environmental assessment methods: redefining intentions and roles. *Building Research and Information*, **33(5)**, pp. 455–467, 2005.

[12] Baldwin, R., Yates, A., Howard, N. and Rao, S., BREEAM 98 for offices: an environmental assessment method for office buildings. *Construction Research Communication Ltd*: London, pp. 1–36, 1998.

[13] Building Research Establishment Ltd (BRE), BREEAM New Construction: Non- Domestic Buildings: Watford, pp. 1–406, 2011.

[14] Sev, A., A comparative analysis of building environmental assessment tools and suggestions for regional adaptations. *Civil Engineering and Environmental Systems*, **28(3)**, pp. 231–245, 2011.

[15] U.S. Green Building Council (USGBC), LEED 2009 for New Construction and Major Renovations Rating System With Alternative Compliance Paths For Projects Outside the U.S: Washington, DC, pp. 1–117, 2009.

[16] Sleeuw, M., A comparison of BREEAM and LEED environmental assessment methods, *Report*, University of East Anglia Estates and Buildings Division: Norwich, pp. 4–11, 2011.

[17] Green Building Council Australia (GBCA). Green Star overview, Online. http://www.gbca.org.au/green-star/green-star-overview.

[18] Japan Sustainable Building Consortium (JSBC). CASBEE, Comprehensive Assessment System for Built Environment Efficiency Technical Manual: Tokyo, pp. 1–307, 2011.

[19] Abu Dhabi Urban Planning Council (AUPC), Pearl Building: Guide for consultant, Estidama, pp. 1–72, 2010.

[20] Kawazu, Y., Shimada, N., Yokoo, N. and Oka, T., Comparison of the assessment results of BREEAM, LEED, GBTool and CASBEE. *Proc. of Int. Conf. on the Sustainable Building (SB05)*: Tokyo, Japan, pp. 1700–1705, 2005.

Infill development as an approach for promoting compactness of urban form

S. S. Aly & Y. A. Attwa
Department of Architecture and Environmental Design,
Arab Academy for Science and Technology and
Maritime Transport, Egypt

Abstract

In the last few decades, urban decay has increased within the city urban fabric; due to the deterioration of the inner city and increase in population. High income citizens abandoned their houses demanding a better quality of life outside the city fabric, leading the old city to be occupied by poorer households or left vacant. Urban decay is linked to suburban sprawl as the economic life is pulled out of the city, instead of a previously developed urban site within the old city fabric. Infill development is the new development of vacant, abandoned, passed over, or underutilized land within built-up areas of existing communities, where infrastructure is already in place. It is a solution to filling gaps in existing communities and playing a critical role in achieving community revitalization, land conservation and alternatives to sprawl development. Taking advantage of existing infrastructure, increasing walkability by contributing safe and attractive pedestrian environment, creating new opportunities for mixed use that recapture the "sense of place" that is largely missing in development projects. Infill development is a solution to enhancing the character, viability and function of the old city. The aim of this research is to articulate the potential and limits of infill development. It focuses on factors that influence decisions to introduce infill development as an approach to smart growth and a solution to urban decay. This is achieved by analyzing international and local examples of infill development to identify the different land use of vacant land in different urban contexts. An analytical comparison is carried on the examples, to achieve broad recommendations for infill development in different urban contexts.
Keywords: infill development, urban sprawl, revitalization, smart growth.

WIT Transactions on Ecology and The Environment, Vol 173, © 2013 WIT Press
www.witpress.com, ISSN 1743-3541 (on-line)
doi:10.2495/SDP130381

1 Introduction

Communities are extending outside the city fabric and beyond the city's edge. The suburbs became attractive to middle and upper class residents. There is an increasing emphasis on developing vacant lands within developed areas and maximizing use of existing public facilities. Urban planning have cured vacant land and urban decay by infill development as a solution to sprawl that will both increase density and revitalize depressed neighborhoods (Faris [1] and Robinson and Cole [2]). Infill development has the potential to have dramatic effects on urban density and urban form. Successful infill development focuses on the existing community fabric, filling gaps in the neighborhood. It is characterized by a healthy mix of uses to support transit and wider variety of services and amenities providing vitality to the communities. Despite the many advantages associated with infill development, there are a number of challenges and barriers prohibit its development. Infill faces political, economical and logistical barriers. The comprehensive infill development is discussed in this paper addressing development impacts, with a focus on integrating new development with existing patterns. It is indented to assist in making more informed decisions when submitting or reviewing site plan or re-zoning vacant lots within the city urban form.

1.1 Problem definition

Due to high population density, communities are extending in patterns outside the city defined edges. Increased infrastructure costs, lengthy commutes and strained public amenities, loss of open space and community health are typically connected with such patterns, destroying existing street systems and distributing the morphology of the open space. Developers bypassing vacant land area for less expensive land beyond the city edges, rather than filling the inner city gaps. According to Downs [3], buildings become neglected when "structures have been converted to higher-density uses than those for which they were designed". Also, as the zoning within that location still remains, the surrounding urban fabric and zoning are very slow to change in response to new demand. Higher income residents demanding a higher quality of life, however social problems and crime arises within the city which has been related to lack of diversity and attributed to sprawl. Brownfield is another cause for city portions losing their viability, obsolescence and its relationship to renovation cost in non-residential buildings. When all the pervious factors occur, they constitute a fracture in the wholeness of the urban form. The great number of sites in this highly damaged condition and their negative impact on the surroundings make their development a matter of great importance (Trancik [10]).

1.2 Urban sprawl and smart growth

Sprawl has been linked to loss of open space, and the exponential increase in new infrastructure costs. Smart growth creates a supportive environment for redirecting a share of regional growth to inner cities. Infill development is a key component of smart growth. The formulation of the US Green Building Council's LEED® building guidelines has created a national standard for developing sustainable communities by encouraging strategies for sustainable site development, including infill development. The new urbanism movement also supported infill development as they stated in the charter of new urbanism that developement pattern should not blur or eradicate the edges of the metropolis (CNU [4]).

1.3 Identifying infill development

Infill development is the new development of vacant, abandoned, passed over, or underutilized land within built-up areas of existing communities, where infrastructure is already in place. The demolition of existing structures and building new structures or the substantial renovation of existing structures, often changing form and function. Infill sites could be divided into vacant lots which often become dumping grounds for waste, posing health and safety hazards, abandoned properties which requires maintenance and demolition costs or brownfields, which are usually lands where old industries, other businesses and warehouses were held.

2 Benefits of infill development

- Enhances the compactness of urban form, as it promotes relatively high density with mixed land uses. It enhance the character and respects historic preservation.
- Increase the efficiency of public transport and urban layout, encouraging walkability, capitalizing on existing infrastructure and minimizes the need for costly new ones thus, providing opportunities for social interaction as well as feeling of safety and belonging.
- Maintain and restores spatial continuity to streetscapes enhancing viability and function of existing communities.
- Introduces compatible uses that complement existing community attributes and needs by increasing the supply of housing types and improving the quality of building stock and revival of city centres.
- Utilizing public facilities to promote the economic health of the city, injecting new life into communities.
- Conserves environmental resources, economic investiment, and social fabric, while reclaiming marginal and abondoned areas.

3 Barriers to infill development

There are different barriers that affect infill development, these barriers include: physical barriers, social barriers, regulatory barriers, economic barriers, infrastructure barriers and the scale of development (Faris [1]).

4 Design principles of a successful infill development

Infill projects should enhance the design and function of the existing community. Infill encompasses many different forms and interpretations. Appearance and function of infill should respect the following common principles:

- **Sociability**
  - **Diversity**: provide a broad range of housing types and price levels to bring people of diverse ages, races, and incomes into daily interaction-strengthening the personal and civic bonds essential to an authentic community (CNU [4]).
  - **Sense of place**: the degree to which settlement can be achieved and mentally differentiated and structured in time and space by residents, the degree of which their mental structure connects with their values and concepts (Lynch [5]).
  - **Public participation:** infill takes place in established communities, input from area residents should be sought, preferably during the infill planning process, and before specific projects are proposed. Gaining the cooperation and trust of the community is critically important
  - **Political support and commitment:** strong political leadership is a necessary component of successful infill development (Faris [1]).
  - **Density:** infill could be developed at a sprawl-like density; however, because of the characteristically high costs of infill land, this type of development will generally occur at higher densities that further smart growth (Ewing [6]).
- **Comfort and image aspects**
  - **Compatibility:** is a largely subjective measure of how well new construction or substantial rehabilitation fits into the existing community structure. Pattern, alignment, size, and shape are the essential elements of compatibility. These elements define the basic relationships between new and old buildings without referencing a specific style of architecture.
  - **The comprehensive plan:** the comprehensive plan should establish a policy basis, goals and objectives for the infill strategy and identify desired characteristics for infill development opportunities.
  - **Zoning regulations:** zoning regulations should support infill and include a clear articulation of intent that reinforces the provisions in the comprehensive plan. There are many zoning options available, including changing an existing zone, or creating a new zone, an overlay zone, or a floating zone. The use of administrative waivers provides a more 'user-friendly' regulatory environment that increases speed and certainty such as: Height, Setback, Bulk, Parking, Area.
  - **Design codes:** the economic health and harmonious evolution of neighborhoods can be improved through graphic urban design codes that serve as predictable guides for change (CNU [4]).
  - **Identity:** while the continuation of existing community character may be a priority in established neighborhood areas, contribution to a desired

future character may be more important than compatibility in areas where change is expected and desired, such as in mixed-use centers.

- **Adaptability**: buildings and developments should be designed to offer variety and flexibility, the need to create developments and buildings with a clear form and function.
- **Public realm**: maximize usable open space when possible. Smart growth emphasizes the public space (e.g., streetscapes and pedestrian environment), while sprawl emphasizes the private realm (Ewing [6]).
- **Secure environment**: orient windows and entrances to the public realm to provide opportunities for "eyes on the street" and community interaction (CNU [4]).
- **Uses and activities aspects**
  - **Mixed use**: promote the creation of mixed use neighborhoods that support the functions of daily life and enhance sustainability (CNU [4]).
  - **Land property value**: infill development increases the economic value of the surrounding land, attracting investors and residents to the area.
- **Access and linkage aspects**
  - **Parking**: parking regulations should be adjusted to accommodate infill development. Parking requirements in zoning ordinances can hinder infill projects.
  - **Integration**: development is to promote the integration of the infill development into the city through planning, urban design, community involvement, and the provision of public amenities.
  - **Walkability**: it offers increased mobility for people, it minimizes traffic congestion. Higher density community allows easier carpooling, maximising use of public transportation and increasing walkability.
  - Connectivity: infill that is not well connected to surrounding roads, sidewalks, is poorly planned (Ewing [6]).

5 Analytical examples

5.1 Southeast False Creek, Vancouver Canada.

False Creek was used by residents for fishing; its shoreline was developed by industry and businesses that filled in to create more industrial use. For the last few decades, these buildings have been abandoned and occupied by sawmills, shipbuilders, metalwork, etc. (City of Vancouver [7]).

5.1.1 Features of False Creek neighborhood

Infill scale: large scale – waterfront neighborhood development, site area: 67 hectares, population: 10,570 in 2006, density: 390 dwellings/hectare, built form: medium and high-rise towers ranging from 6–17 storey, open space: 1.0 hectare per 1000 residents, 25% of the total site area.

Figure 1:   Industrial site of False Creek before and after development.

5.1.2 Project objectives

- Transfer the industrial/brownfield site into a sustainable, mixed use neighborhood.
- Establish a foundation of sustainability principles, and environmental, social, and economic strategies to enable the development as a complete community, and to serve as a learning experience or application of such principles on a broader scale.
- Provide a framework for the creation of policies, zoning, public facilities, subdivision plans, design guidelines and forms of development (City of Vancouver [7]).

5.1.3 Design evaluation according to principles of successful infill development

Table 1 shows the design criteria.

Table 1:   Design criteria (source: City of Vancouver [7]).

• Promoting a variety of houses, social and physical infrastructure, enhancing accessibility and connecting it to the water edge with a variety of activities. • Develop a community that can grow and adapt itself to sustainability principles. • Street network is maintained to serve residents to achieve walkability and public ream	*Diversity, mixed use, connectivity, adaptability, public realm, integration, sustainability, liveability and walkability.*
• Creating a framework for economically viable community employment.	*Economic aspects and land property value.*
• Provides integration of land uses within a compact urban form	*Compatibility and integration*
• Design of row houses, legible development, building heights stepping down to the water front. • Re-zoning regulations adopted by Councils. Change of land use from industrial to mixed use conserving and managing the ecosystem health	*Design codes, building regulations mixed use and zoning regulations.*
• Encourage awareness among residents about sustainability and its role in creating fully developed neighborhoods.	*Education and public participation*

5.2 Al-Azhar Park Cairo, Egypt

The old Al-Azhar Park site has been a debris dump for over 500 years. The area had witnessed a marked decline and a thriving drug trade in the 1980s, left it with a reputation for being crime-ridden and unsafe. The Al-Azhar Park has created welcome opportunities for parallel rehabilitation efforts in Darb Al-Ahmar, the impoverished and densely built-up district that borders the Park.

5.2.1 Features of Al-Azhar Park

Infill type: vacant land/brownfield, infill scale: large scale – open space, site area: 30 hectares, population: 90,000 residents in Darb Al-Ahmar quarter.

It is located within the historic and touristic area of the old downtown in Cairo. The measures successfully carried out by the Agakhan Trust for cultures to restore and renew the Darb Al-Ahmar quarter, huge portions of the old Islamic quarter are overwhelmed by the decay of building fabric, very high population and occupancy density, a largely predominant lower class and informal commercial structures (Bandarin and van Oers [8]).

Figure 2: Al-Azhar Park infill before and after the development.

5.2.2 Project objectives

- Transfer the brownfield land into an open park providing a green lung for the highly compact historical area of Darb Al-Ahmar.
- Provides an ideal opportunity for renewed investment while preserve the area's urban qualities, to regenerate its economy and improve the area's physical assets through greater public and private investment.
- Comprehensive urban development to reverse the present decay, raise housing standards and introduce new commercial uses and economic activities on the blighted streets.
- Public and donor funding to improve the infrastructure and revitalize dormant assets, in particular its outstanding monuments.

5.2.3 Design evaluation according to principles of successful infill development

Table 2 shows the design criteria.

Table 2:   Design criteria (source Bandarin and van Oers [8]).

• Vacant lots on Burg Al-Zafar can be used to meet the current housing shortage with new residential developments that are attractive to residents. • Introducing new multi-functional commercial structure.	*Diversity, mixed use and sustainability, economic aspects.*
• Keeping the identity of the old Islamic architecture that was built with the area of Darb Al-Ahmar and providing the park with the same spirit in a modern approach. • Rejuvenating historic landmarks through adaptive reuse.	*Sense of place, historic preservation, public realm and identity*
• Encourage awareness among residents. Residents shared and employed in the development and renovation project of Darb Al-Ahmar and the park. • Social and educational programs introduced. • Preserving the social fabric by providing residents with security of tenure.	*Education, public participation economic aspect and secure environment.*
• Primary infrastructure serving the district, with neighborhood accessibility from the city's network of streets and the integration of a walkable pedestrian network connecting the neighborhood and its public spaces with the park.	*Infrastructure, accessibility, walkability, integration, connectivity and public realm.*

5.3 Solidere downtown, Beirut, Lebanon

The medieval city is largely lost because of the substantial urbanist deformations of the old town during the Ottoman period and the French Mandate and the demolitions during the war in the seventies and eighties and of the latest comprehensive renewal of the central district area. The Beirut city center is located at the heart of Lebanon's capital.

5.3.1 Features of Solidere, Beirut downtown
Infill type: vacant lands within the city center, infill scale: large scale downtown development, site area: 191 hectares, population: 40,000 residents, built form: medium scale buildings, from 5–6 storey, open space: 39 hectares.

5.3.2 Project objectives
• Transfer the abandoned, damaged buildings into high density mixed used development.
• Provide a functional and an attractive environment, using quality infrastructure, buildings and property management.
• Restoring life to this vital part of the country, traditionally a meeting place and the focus of economic and cultural activity.
• Delivering the tangible benefits of comprehensive planning, Beirut's downtown has re-emerged as a prime, active district, at the same time historic core, mixed use and social arena.

Figure 3:   Infill development carried out in Solidere downtown (source: Solidere [9]).

5.3.3 Design evaluation according to principles of successful infill development

Table 3 shows the design criteria.

Table 3:   Design criteria (source: Solidere [9]).

• Providing a variety of housing types, new residential quarters emerging in the center. • A broad mix of land uses ranging from business and institutional to residential, cultural and recreational facilities. • Mixed densities and commercial opportunities for the creation of an inclusive urban environment.	*Diversity, density, compactness, compatibility, land use, mixed use and sustainability.*
• Quality built form contributes to urban design of the old city of Beirut. Preserving features of townscape, restoring the old downtown.	*Sense of place, historic preservation and identity*
• The Solidere private company and the government both invested in the downtown infill project, allowing further local and international investments to take place.	*Economic aspects, land property value.*
• Public parking facilities which has a capacity to withstand the amount of residents of the downtown area and the outside daily visitors. • Reconnecting the urban environment to the water's edge, creating a high quality public realm that promotes integration of a wide variety of outdoor recreation activities.	*Infrastructure, parking, accessibility, walkability, integration, vitality, connectivity and public realm.*

6 Comparative analysis

Table 4 shows the comparative analysis between the previously discussed examples.

Table 4: Comparative analysis of examples.

Criteria	False Creek, Vancouver	Al- Azhar park, Cairo.	Solidaire, Beirut.
Type of infill development	City edge	Open space	Downtown
Sociability			
Diversity	●	●	○
Sense of place	●	●	●
Public participation	●	●	●
Political support and commitment	●	●	●
Economic aspects	●	○	●
Education	●	●	●
Density	○	●	○
Comfort and image			
Compatibility	●	●	●
Comprehensive plan	●	●	●
Zoning Regulation	●		●
Design Codes	●		○
Preserve Identity	○	●	●
Adaptability	●	●	●
Public realm	●	●	●
Secure Environment	●	●	●
Uses and Activities			
Vitality	●	●	●
Public Amenities	●	●	●
Mixed use	●	○	●
Land property value	●	●	●
Sustainable	●	○	○
Access and Linkage			
Parking	●	○	●
Integration	●	○	●
Walkability	●	●	●
Connectivity	●	●	●
Network of streets	●	○	●
Renewal of infrastructures	●	○	●

Source: researcher (Strong ●, Moderate ○).

By comparing the three examples, the paper came to the following findings. False Creek waterfront neighbourhood transferred the industrial abandoned site into one of the largest urban redevelopment projects in North America, and has been recognized for bringing residents into the downtown core and people closer to their place of work, which has greatly reduced their commuting times and need for a private vehicle, managed urban sprawl and density problems. Although a flexible approach is required to allow optimal use of parking space and a more sufficient social infrastructure is necessary to reflect the needs and income ranges of the community. Infill development at city edge requires an appropriate plan for the extension of infrastructure and a detailed study of its surrounding land uses. On the other hand, infill development carried in the Al-Azhar Park "open space" allowed the revitalization of the whole surrounding context of Darb Al-Ahmar. Based on these studies, the area's land use map was found to be of very high dense residential neighborhood, lacking mixed use and low social interaction. It has survived the economic, environmental and social changes through focusing upon its culture background, urban transformation, establishing magnet projects within the area. The project was aspiring to educate the people living in the area, increasing their awareness about the historical neighborhood of Darb Al-Ahmar. Encouraging them to participate in the renovation project, promoting their sense of belonging to the area. However, with the introduction of this unique infill development in the city of Cairo, a problem was raised in which the infrastructure wasn't planned to handle the increased bearing capacity of the outsiders from the rest of the city. Finally, infill development carried at the downtown of the city of Beirut has considered some major urban development aspects such as, the existing and renewed infrastructure, the need to build a high standard streetscape and public spaces. It also considered the surrounding density of the existing context as it will attract residents and new investment into the area. Outside the historic core of the downtown a mechanism that relates adjacent green areas to successful land sales and rising land values. The restoration of old buildings with the preserving of the surrounding identity of historical context and adding new ones that contribute to the architectural design.

7   Conclusion

Infill development was carried out in different urban contexts (at the city edge, at the downtown and as an open space); a comparative analysis on the criteria of infill development was carried out on each example (shown in table 4). Infill development could be applied in vacant lands at the edge of the city where land use maps of surrounding context are considered, keeping the city's edge defined.

It could be applied to high density areas changing the land use into an open space while providing the surrounding context with central features in organizing the community, and connecting it with the adjacent areas. When carrying infill development in downtowns, there is an increased emphasis on using the existing infrastructure and providing a mixed use commercial center with the need of preserving its cultural and historical identity, creating liveable city centers.

Infill development promises to contribute to the solution of the problems associated with sprawling land use patterns. It can support increased transportation choices, a more efficient use of land and infrastructure, more varied and affordable housing types, savings for local government budgets, reduced pollution, improved economic health and better quality of life.

8 Recommendations

- A successful infill development program will require more than a narrow focus. Instead, a cooperative partnership with the broader focus of competing the existing community fabric.
- Downtown should include relatively high-density mix of retail, office, services, and employment in downtown to serve a regional market area.
- Residential development should reinforce the traditional town center through a combination of restoration of historic buildings in the downtown area and compatible new infill development targeted to a broad range of income levels.
- Open spaces introduced as infill development project should consider the surrounding density, accessibility and existing infrastructure.
- Examine existing codes and searching for more flexible ways to shape development. A creative combination of strategies will best accomplish a comprehensive infill development.
- Concerns about safety, quality of education and quality of public and commercial services may need to be addressed, in addition to concerns about design, finance and political interference.

References

[1] Faris, J. Terrence, The Barriers to Using Infill Development to Achieve Smart Growth, *Housing Policy Debate* 12 (1): 1–30, 2001.
[2] Robinson and Cole LLP *Best Practices to Encourage Infill Development.* Association of prepared for the National Associaion of Realtors, 2002.
[3] Downs, Anthony. *Neighborhoods and urban developement.* Washington DC: The Brookings Institution, 1981.
[4] Charter of New Urbanism. *Charter of New Urbanism.* New York: McGraw, www.cnu.org, 2000.
[5] Lynch, Kevin. *Good City Form.* Massachusetts Institute of Technology, 1981.
[6] Ewing, Reid. "Best development practices." Chicago Press. 1996. www.planning.org (accessed 12 20, 2012).
[7] Official Development Plan By-laws. "City Of Vancouver." April 2007. http://vancouver.ca/green-vancouver.aspx (accessed January 20, 2013).
[8] Bandarin, Francesco and van Oers, Ron *The historic urban landscape.* UK: Wiley Blackwell, 2012.
[9] Solidere, 2010. [Online]. Available: http://www.solidere.com. [Accessed 12 2 2012].
[10] Trancik, R. Finding Lost Space –Theories of Urban Design, New York: Van Nostrand Reinhold, 1986.

Enhancing sustainable infrastructure with the aid of the Green Infrastructure Toolkit

S. H. Saroop & D. Allopi
Durban University of Technology, South Africa

Abstract

It is globally acknowledged that there is a growing need for co ordination of design, sustainability, economic and environmental requirements of infrastructure projects.

The provision of civil infrastructure plays a major role on the natural environment and on the quality of life.

The lack of appropriate tools and skills for sustainable design is often quoted as a barrier to sustainable design Richardson *et al.* (Design and Sustainability: A Scoping Report for the Sustainable Design Forum, 2005).

A systematic and iterative analysis of the environmental impact of various design solutions is commonly suggested for infrastructure projects, but rarely happens.

In order to stay competitive and to meet upcoming stricter environmental regulations and customer requirements, designers have a key role in designing civil infrastructure so that it is environmentally sustainable. These and other factors have compelled the engineer to design with greater care and in more detail. The changing roles of engineers will be highlighted, in order to react to changes in climate.

In the area of sustainability, there is an urgent need to apply technologies and methods that deliver better and more sustainable performance in a way that is cost effective.

Sustainability, adaptive and mitigative approaches to climate change, in the design of infrastructure are therefore important steering elements (FIDIC, State of the World Infrastructure Report 2009). This paper discusses the application of 'green technology' on infrastructure design projects. It gives an overview of the proposed Green Township Infrastructure Design Toolkit and looks at a number of recommended green practices on infrastructure services design, that are environmentally sound, placing fewer burdens on the environment.

WIT Transactions on Ecology and The Environment, Vol 173, © 2013 WIT Press
www.witpress.com, ISSN 1743-3541 (on-line)
doi:10.2495/SDP130391

The use of the proposed model would ensure a sustainable design of township infrastructure services through the consideration of scare resources and ecological sensitivity in the design and planning of infrastructure projects.

Keywords: green technology, infrastructure design, eco-efficiency, sustainable development, green infrastructure.

1 The need to implement green technology on civil engineering infrastructure projects

Civil engineering projects can have significant site-specific and cumulative impacts on ecological and social systems if not correctly planned, designed and implemented.

In the area of sustainability, there is an urgent need to apply technologies and methods that deliver better and more sustainable performance in a way that is cost effective. Sustainability, adaptive and mitigative approaches to climate change, in the design of infrastructure are therefore important steering elements (FIDIC [2]).

Relatively few designers have as yet explored the transformative potential of ecological design and have preferred to remain apolitical and unconcerned with the distributional impacts of design as they affect the health of humans and ecosystems (Van Wyk [3]).

Infrastructure development has been focused mainly on financing issues and engineering aspects in the region. Mainstreaming environmental aspects and incorporating the eco-efficiency concept into various stages of infrastructure development have not been considered as much as they should have been.

Infrastructure elements such as roads, water, sewage and stormwater can result in loss of critical ecosystems and biodiversity. There is a need to create an eco sensitive infrastructure design rating system that encourages and promotes the use of "softer" design solutions.

The rating of green buildings evaluates the environmental impacts of buildings but with little emphases on the environmental performance of civil engineering infrastructure. The proposed research uses the concept of the green rating of green buildings and creates a decision toolkit that assesses the environmental impacts of infrastructure design decisions on development.

By utilising improved environmentally friendly-seeking design solutions, this study aims to introduce environmentally friendly design decisions prior to the infrastructure design approval process. This increases overall competitiveness by bringing a whole new class of productive solutions to problems while at the same time adding a fresh perspective to the traditional infrastructure design process.

Diligent attention to greener infrastructure solutions from the very earliest phases of a project will help guarantee that quality design environmental solutions are "built in" from the beginning. Figure 1 shows the declining influence of environmental interventions on a project. It is important to implement the environmental management from the early stages of the process, since the "freedom" to make decisions, of importance for the environment, decreases with the progress of the project.

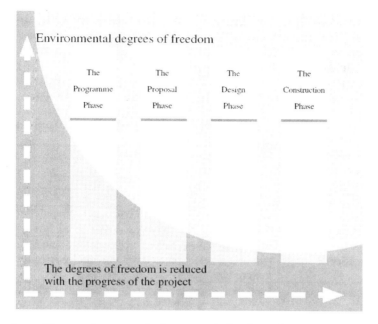

Figure 1:   The environmental degrees of freedom (European green cities network [4].

2   Infrastructure environmental sustainability criteria

Environmental Sustainability criteria are the set of performance measures that characterize sustainable criteria of infrastructure as listed in Table 1.

The Eco Efficient Infrastructure Sustainability Criteria namely Efficient Layout Planning ensures that infrastructure is placed in environmentally responsible ways. The Resources criteria encourage an efficient utilisation of materials/ resources. Environmental Quality mitigates environmental impacts of infrastructure. Functional Efficiency ensures that infrastructure is designed optimally. Future Maintenance maximizes the opportunities for integrating capital and operation of infrastructure. Economy maximizes the opportunities for integrated cost effective adoption of green infrastructure options. Safety minimises the environmental impact of infrastructure by incorporating safety into the design and convenience provide a range of mobility choices and accessibility options for infrastructure

The Infrastructure Sustainability criteria used in the proposed Green Township Infrastructure Design Toolkit were developed to:

- Determine the means by which eco- environmental efficiency can be assessed, monitored, quantified and verified at any stage of the project, to ensure a value-added, quality driven, green approach to infrastructure design;

- Provide a basis for the consultants and clients to work together on creating and evaluating sustainable infrastructure solutions thereby ensuring comprehensive infrastructure planning with maximum stakeholder involvement;
- Achieve the required balance of sustainability, expenditure, value for money and quality, between the various elements of the project;

Table 1:   The eco efficient infrastructure performance criteria.

Eco-efficient infrastructure Sustainable criteria	Measure
1. Efficient Layout planning	Placement of infrastructure in environmentally responsible, efficient ways, conserve land,
2. Resources	Encourages the efficient utilisation of materials/ resources, selection of environmentally friendly materials,
3. Environment quality	Design features that mitigate environmental impacts of infrastructure, by reducing effects of pollutants
4. Functional efficiency	Design of infrastructure that maximizes functional efficiency of infrastructure
5. Future maintenance	Maximizes the opportunities for integrating capital and operation of infrastructure, ensuring reliability of level of service
6. Economy	Maximizes the opportunities for integrated cost effective adoption of green infrastructure options
7. Safety	Minimizes the environmental impact of infrastructure by incorporating safety into the design
8. Convenience	Provide a range of mobility choices and accessibility options for infrastructure

3   The Green Township Infrastructure Toolkit: a green rating system on infrastructure projects

This paper proposes a toolkit that enforces environmentally sustainable design on township infrastructure services by integrating a consideration of resources, the environment, ecologically sensitive innovative design, maintenance and recyclable materials, from the early design stages of a project.

The Green Township Infrastructure Design Toolkit, as illustrated in Figure 2, uses the concept of eco-efficiency and would allow the designer to evaluate design options, enabling him/her to choose the one likely to yield the best performance with the least environmental impact, based on proven technology.

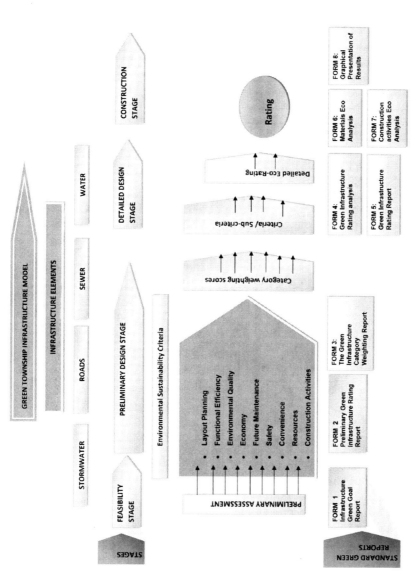

Figure 2:   The Green Township Infrastructure Design Toolkit.

This toolkit is intended to encourage developers to consider green methods and practices in the earliest stages of project planning, by assessing a number of recommended green practices and its environmental impacts on infrastructure services design, placing fewer burdens on the environment.

The various Green Report Forms, enables the client to select a combination of alternatives and evaluate a number of possible design options – with their environmental implications – at each stage of the design process

During the briefing and preliminary design stage, (1 and 2), the client and engineer have a joint responsibility of deciding just how green the project should be, or alternatively of deciding what environmental quality of services can be provided. During the detailed stages (3), the engineer has the responsibility of designing, while maximising the green value of the project. Stage 4 gives the designers an opportunity to add environmental value at the construction stage, by analysing eco-friendly construction material.

The underlying structure of the Green Township Infrastructure Design Toolkit is based on a hierarchical breakdown of the project into five stages described in Table 2 below:

The various green reports developed for use at different stages of the project, provide clients and consultants with more control over the environmental impact of design decisions taken and enable a comparison of the options of various engineering solutions.

Table 2:   Stages in the Green Township Infrastructure Design Toolkit.

Stage		Activities
Stage 1	Feasibility Stage	Establishing environmental objectives
Stage 2	Scheme Design Stage	Preliminary eco rating
Stage 3	Preliminary Design Stage	Weighting of environmental sustainability categories and targets
Stage 4	Detailed Design Stage	Detailed eco rating analysis
Stage 5	Construction Stage	Materials and construction activities eco analysis

4   Advantages of using the eco approach to infrastructure design

Green township infrastructure technologies will contribute to greenways and green corridors and provide linkages between habitats, and wetlands. Green technologies have a number of environmental, economic benefits and community benefits. The benefits of this approach are as follows:

- Conservation of natural resources;
- Reduces the ecological footprints of roads, sewer, stormwater and water, allowing ecosystems to function more naturally;
- Uses energy-efficiency systems and materials;

- Minimizes impervious surfaces reducing soil erosion;
- Enhance and protect ecosystems and biodiversity;
- Conserves and reuses water and treats stormwater runoff on-site;
- Recharges ground water flow for streams, conserving water supplies.

5 Conclusions

Engineers will have to be at the forefront of developments finding innovative solutions to maximise water capture, ensuring conservation of the resource from supply through to distribution, and the issues of innovation, technology, design ensuring environmental impacts are avoided or mitigated. Understanding the context of the environment in which they work is thus essential (Kilian and Gibson [5]).

Improvement in the awareness of eco-efficiency concepts is urgently needed among policy-makers, planners and decision-makers. However, the criteria applicable to, and measures for developing eco-efficient and sustainable infrastructure are yet to be fully identified (United Nations Economic and Social Commission for Asia and the Pacific [6]).

Engineers need to look at greener technologies rather than just using traditional engineering solutions. By using this green approach, sustainable design of township infrastructure services can be achieved by enforcing the consideration of resources, environmental impacts of ecologically sensitive design decisions, innovation, maintenance and materials, at the design stage of a project. As can be seen in this paper, there are numerous opportunities for improving eco-efficiency in infrastructure design. A new paradigm for infrastructure design is required in order to ensure environmental sustainability on infrastructure projects

The weighting and rating of environmental sustainability criteria provide adaptation benefits and also provide the means to measure projects.

Taking a greener approach to infrastructure development not only mitigates the potential environmental impacts of development but makes economic sense as well. By softening the environmental footprint, avoiding waste and finding efficiencies, clients and local governments can increase their long term sustainability.

References

[1] Richardson, J, Irwin T. and Sherwin C. 2005. *Design & Sustainability: A Scoping Report for the Sustainable Design Forum.* [online]. Available at: http://webarchive.nationalarchives.gov.uk/tna/+/http://www.dti.gov.uk/sustainability/pdfs/design_and_sustainability_report_June_2005.pdf [Accessed 1 December 2010].
[2] FIDIC, 2009. FIDIC State of the World Infrastructure Report 2009.
[3] Van Wyk, L. 2009. EcoBuilding: Towards an Appropriate Architectonic Expression, In *Green Building Handbook for South Africa* [online].

Available at: http://researchspace.csir.co.za/dspace/bitstream/10204/3262/1
/vanWyk1_2009.pdf [Accessed 13 April 2011].

[4] European Green Cities Network, 2004. *Manual and Guidelines for Sustainable Housing Projects*. [online]. www.europeangreencities.com/pdf/publications/manualSustainableHP.pdf
[Accessed 1 April 2004].

[5] Kilian D and Gibson D. 2007, Environmental information for decision-making, Civil Engineering, August 2007vol 15,8, ISSN 1021-2000.

[6] United Nations Economic and Social Commission for Asia and the Pacific. 2006. *Sustainable Infrastructure in Asia* [online]. http://www.unescap.org/esd/environment/mced/singg/documents/Sustainable Infrastructure in Asia.pdf [Accessed 1 April 2010].

The thermal performance of green roofs in a hot, humid microclimate

U. D'Souza
F-o-CUS: Focus on Construction Urbanism Sustainability, UAE

Abstract

Green roof applications can alleviate the heat island effect in cities and positively contribute to sustainable development by regulating building temperatures and enhancing its impact and effectiveness on the built environment. Green roofs are an innovative concept for the planning and development of future cities. The aim of this research paper is to review evidence of the environmental impact of using green roofs when compared to a conventional roof in the hot and humid microclimate of the United Arab Emirates (UAE). In order to achieve this, a micro-scale urban ENVI-met model of the Dubai Marina is tested. The parameters measured in this experiment include Surface Albedo (SA), Mean Radiant Temperature (MRT), Relative Humidity (RH) and Predicted Mean Vote (PMV). Improvements in plant to air interaction were also studied using ENVI-met simulation software; a three-dimensional microclimate model was designed to simulate surface-plant-air interactions in the urban environment. The programme was used in order to gauge the temperature variations of green roofs when compared to using conventional roofs. A study was conducted on June 21st, 2011 at 1:00 pm and December 21st, 2011 at 1:00 pm which depicted variations in temperature due to the impact of green roofs between these two different periods. During the hot, humid months SA and PMV were the predominant changes documented due to the impact of green roofs. However, during the winter months temperature changes such as, MRT and RH were clearly visible in the ENVI-met simulations. The research revealed findings to suggest that a green roof can contribute to a significant improvement in the thermal comfort levels of the surrounding built environment. These findings can be used by the relevant stakeholders, planners, architects, engineers and developers to recommend green roofs as a necessity for the sustainable development of future cities.
Keywords: thermal performance, green roofs, hot, humid micro-climate, sustainable development, planning, sustainable architecture, built environment and heat island.

 WIT Transactions on Ecology and The Environment, Vol 173, © 2013 WIT Press
www.witpress.com, ISSN 1743-3541 (on-line)
doi:10.2495/SDP130401

1   Introduction

Densely populated urban area in the Dubai microclimate is characterized by numerous buildings, infrastructure and hard scapes that absorb heat rapidly leaving massive hot spots also known as heat islands. In an effort to alleviate heat levels in the region, the Dubai municipal government adopted a green building initiative in 2008. This initiative encouraged the use of green roofs on buildings because of the positive impact on cooling hot and humid areas, reducing carbon emissions and controlling energy consumption levels within buildings, all leading to an energy savings solution for sustainable development.

A high land value in urban areas has led to an immediate need for green space alternatives. Several environmental benefits include; promoting biodiversity, reducing air pollution and dust, absorbing solar radiation by the provision of reflective materials, creating attractive open spaces, providing a habitat for wildlife, opening more doors for re-using and recycling building materials. This research will explore the performance of green roofs in the hot and humid micro-climate. It will assess the research covered by past academics and by using simulation software ENVI-met evaluate a conventional roof model in comparison to a green roof model under UAE microclimatic conditions and then formulate results and encourage discussion based on the modelled scenario.

2   UAE climate

According to climate data from National Centre of Meteorology and Seismology in the UAE (NCMS) [1], the temperature ranges of hot and humid summer months reaches a high of 48°C (118.4°F) to the warm winter months dropping to a minimum of 14°C (50°F and 57.2°F). Humid south-eastern winds (sharqi) dominate the coastal region during the summer, whereas cool north-westerly winds (shamal) develop during the winter months. Humidity is high during the summer, reaching over 90%, but it declines to 50–60% in the coastal regions during the winter NCMS [1]. Rainfall is limited, arriving in short sharp bursts during the winter months. Thunder and dust storms occur during the summer accompanied by severe flash floods over the south-eastern mountains. The region is characterised by a regular formation of dew that assists in the survival of plants and wildlife.

3   Green roof research through observation

Green roofs can help regulate the urban microclimate and minimize the occurrence of heat islands [2–5]. Based on prior research experiments in hot and humid climates, the following parameters Surface Albedo (SA), Mean Radiant Temperature (MRT) and Relative Humidity (RH) have been observed.

Surface Albedo (SA) determines the solar reflectivity on a surface. According to Taha [6], albedo levels for most cities range from 0.10 to 0.20. North African towns are considered a good example of SA ranging from 0.30-0.45. Extensive the vegetation in towns lead to a higher the SA. A mesoscale simulation model developed by Taha [6] found that SA in Los Angeles, USA can result in a 2°C temperature decrease. This decrease suggested lower electricity consumption by 10% by air conditioning. Sailor [4] simulated the effects of albedo in the Florida, USA urban environment and found that a higher in albedo using vegetation can result in a 2°C decrease in air temperature while extreme increase in albedo can result in a 4°C temperature reduction. It was deduced that SA can aid temperature reduction in cities.

Mean Radiant Temperature (MRT) is calculated based on ambient air temperatures, global temperatures and air velocity. Wong *et al.* [7] measured the MRT in Singapore above hard surfaces and vegetated surfaces and found that solar radiation exposure on hard surfaces during the day emitted more long-wave radiation to the surrounding environment at night leading to uncomfortable thermal comfort levels. MRT measured for vegetated roofs confirmed a reduced long-wave radiation emission regulated by plants and absorbed to the roof surface. Kakon and Nobou [8] studied the effects of MRT on a modelled canyon in Dhaka, Bangladesh and found that levels vary during the day depending on air flow movements affected by surrounding built environment such as, building heights, vegetation, climate, sky view factor (SVF) and global temperatures. Air flow can also regulate humidity levels in the urban areas.

Humidity levels in Singapore studied by Wong *et al.* [9] on hard surfaces and vegetated surfaces were around the same levels. Kakon and Nobou [8] found that Relative Humidity (RH) levels in an urban canyon in Dhaka, Bangladesh were higher during the day especially in places with a higher sky view factor (SVF). Higher SVF resulted in higher air temperatures (Ta) causing higher RH levels because of the amount of solar radiation absorbed. Increased building heights and tree canopies decreased the SVF resulting in lower Ta and RH levels. Air flow can impact RH levels on urban environments.

Knowledge gaps from these studies include consistent simulated temperature profiles that can validate the research of thermal performance of green roofs in the UAE. An investigation on a local site study of Dubai, UAE in section 7 will involve a discussion on the results of the green roof thermal performance levels.

4   Green roof research through ENVI-met simulation

ENVI-met micro-climatic numerical modelling software was developed by Michael Bruse and designed to assess conditions in urban developments. It has the capacity to easily translate numerical data founded on the fundamental laws of fluid dynamics and thermo-dynamics to simulate surface, vegetation and atmospheric exchanges within the urban environment. ENVI-met software validity falls under the scrutiny of several scientific entities, government organisations and researchers. Previous studies [10–12] found limitations in the software flexibility required to create the urban environment. However, a conceptual surface can be suggested. Evidence of such is apparent in the research literature conducted by Bruse [10], which validate the ENVI-met results.

5 Site in context

Dubai is located in UAE north (see figure 1). The Dubai Marina Master Plan (see figure 2) was developed by architectural firm HOK comprising of a total land area of approximately 578 ha NRI [13]. The initial concept is based on a 'city within a city' model which houses a waterfront community development consistent of luxury apartments, condominiums and villas. The Dubai Marina not only serves a high density residential community, it encompasses offices and retail facilities making it a pedestrian friendly environment.

Figure 1:   Location of Dubai (Maps 2011).

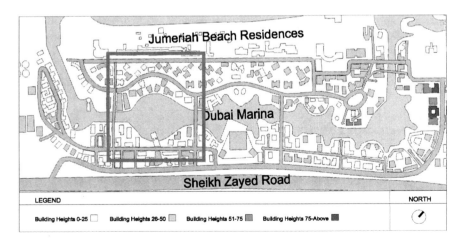

Figure 2:   Site area and density on AutoCAD.

6 Modelling the context with ENVI-met

Modelling the Dubai Marina context on June 21st, 2011 at 1:00 pm and December 21st, 2011 at 1:00 pm using ENVI-met involves a calculation of fluid dynamics and thermodynamic processes at surfaces/walls/roofs and plants Bruse [10]. The four processes are defined below:

- **Model area inputs**
  According to Bruse [10], this is based on the model size, location, dimension and building environment. Building heights, soil types, plants and surface conditions can be defined in the area input editor.

- **Model configuration**
  Including a model configuration file can help the model run an analysis for that period to test the thermal comfort levels. In this case the measured performance parameters include humidity, temperature and Surface Albedo.

- **Model run and outputs**
  Model is tested and run following the assigned time frame (June 21st, 2011 at 1:00 pm and December 21st, 2011 at 1:00 pm because of variations in temperature due to the suns angle during the two periods) input into the configuration while generating the necessary output field for the tested parameters specified in the model configuration.

- **LEONARDO visualisation**
  LEONARDO visualises the output files generated from the model run. This is based on the selected time frame, outputs and area recorded.

The simulation date is set during the summer solstice June 21st, 2011 and the winter solstice December 21st, 2011. The sun is at peak intensity on June 21st. During the winter period, the sun is at a lower angle. Seasonal variation is tested to validate thermal performance levels purely because during winter months, the earth surface does not receive as much solar energy from the sun in the Northern hemisphere when compared to the summer months.

7 Results and discussion

ENVI-met documented results of the numeric simulation tests done to measure the thermal performance levels of a conventional roof and a green roof by programming the inputs into the two models on a built up section of the Dubai Marina on June 21st, 2011 at 1:00 pm and December 21st, 2011 at 1:00 pm. The major difference between the two models included different inputs programmed in the base and green roof model along with the location and building details. In the green roof scenario, additional inputs such as plant and soil typology were programmed based on the ENVI-met database selection available. A comparison of these changes is documented in the tables of the following four parameters.

Parameter 1: Surface Albedo (SA)

A Surface Albedo (SA) assessment was conducted using ENVI-met to measure the difference in albedo levels during the summer period for the base and green roof scenario. In doing so the simulation was run and the derived edi. file was taken to the LEONARDO to define the results. By including green roofs in the Dubai Marina ENVI-met sectional model, the SA increased from a low of 0.12–0.16 in the summer and winter conventional roof model to 0.16–0.20 in the summer and winter green roof model (see figure 3).

There is no major difference in the SA increase as the tested inputs did not yield significant changes. This could be due to several factors which influence the SA of green roofs, such as the type of plants used for the roof and the materials used in installation. A rise in SA rise represents the potential for green roofs to reduce surface temperature and long wave radiation emitted from the roof surface.

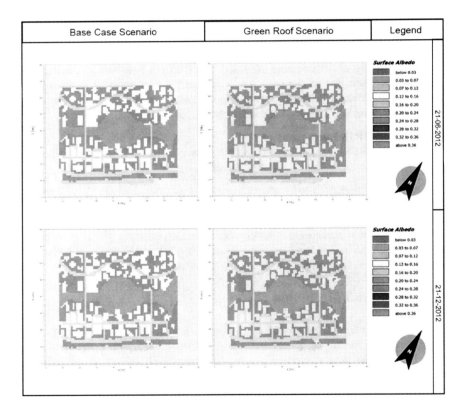

Figure 3:   ENVI-met Surface Albedo (SA) results of base and green roof.

Parameter 2: Mean Radiant Temperature (MRT)

A Mean Radiant Temperature analysis was conducted using ENVI-met to measure the difference in levels during the summer period for the base and green roof scenario. The Mean Radiant Temperature (MRT) in the summer time ENVI-met simulation remains between 49.62°C–51.73°C in the base roof and green roof scenario. The winter time base roof and green roof scenario was measured at 36.91°C–39.03°C when compared to the summer time MRT from 49.62°C–51.73°C (see figure 4).

There is not much change in temperature when compared to the base case winter time roof scenario. Changes in MRT can occur due to green roof installation typology as green roof soft surface emits less long wave radiation when compared to hard surfaces such as in the base roof. Leaf foliage and density can also affect MRT and therefore temperature variations can depend on the inputs programmed. At present the plant inputs were limited to the ENVI-met database selection.

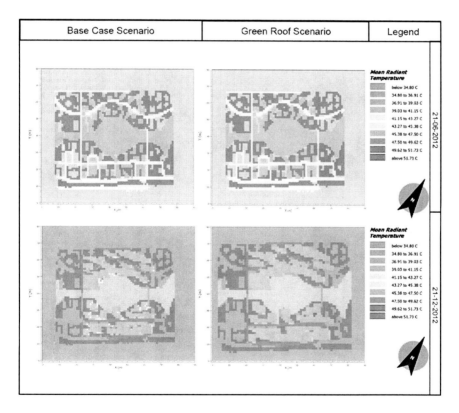

Figure 4:   ENVI-met Mean Radiant Temperature (MRT) results of base and green roof.

Parameter 3: Relative Humidity (RH)

A Relative Humidity (RH) study was conducted using ENVI-met to measure the difference in RH levels during the summer period for the base and green roof scenarios. In doing so the ENVI-met simulation was run for all four models and once the edi. file was derived; it was taken to the LEONARDO program to define the results. The RH study (see figure 5) reveal values at a range of 83.44% to 86.87% during summer base case and green roof scenario.

RH is recorded above 108.05% during the winter, slightly higher when compared to the winter base case conventional roof scenario. The average RH was measured at 85% in a dense urban context at 13:00 hours. Since there was no change yielded in RH between the base roof and green roof in both seasons during the ENVI-met experiment, it is recommended that further research be conducted on soil and substrate depth and its influence on RH.

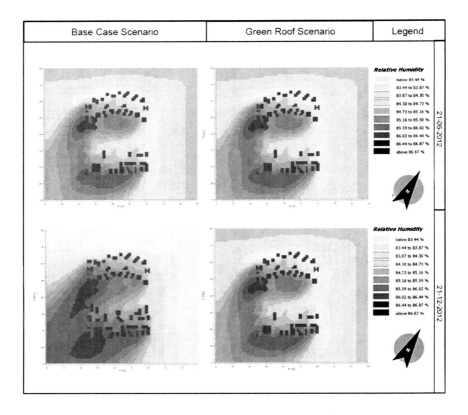

Figure 5:   ENVI-met Relative Humidity (RH) results of base and green roof.

Parameter 4: Predicted Mean Vote (PMV)

The Predicted Mean Vote (PMV) simulated by ENVI-met depicts a slight change in PMV numbers from the summer base case and green roof scenarios (See figure 6). This slight change is represented by a change from -0.51 to -0.35 in the base case scenario to -0.01 to 0.33 in the green roof scenario. As this satisfies the ANSI/ASHRAE Standard 55 [14, 15] and ISO 7730 [16] of human thermal comfort range -0.5 to +0.5 (neutral) the level of thermal sensations experienced by an individual is minor when measured on a small section of the Dubai Marina (refer to section 5, figure 2), but this could be due to the nature of plants assumed. A large area when tested may suggest different results.

Consequently, the ENVI-met green roof modelled during the winter measured PMV at -1.15 to -0.16 which resulted in a slight change in PMV numbers from the base case winter roof scenario measured at -1.48 to -0.82. When compared to summer green roof measured at -0.01 to 0.33, the winter PMV range is cooler. PMV is found to be cooler in winter due to the UAE experiencing warm/cool winter months and the north-westerly shamal winds.

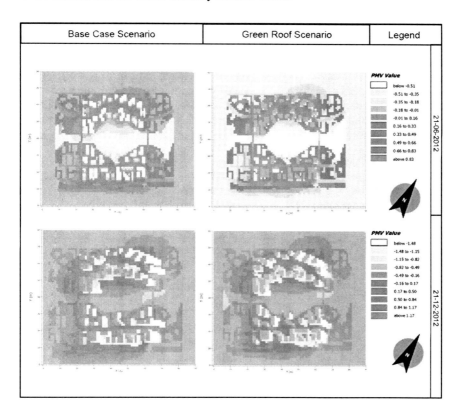

Figure 6:   ENVI-met Predicted Mean Vote (PMV) results of base and green roof.

Climatic factors such as Mean Radiant Temperature (MRT) and Relative Humidity (RH) were found to be consistent in both simulation scenarios, one possibility is because the green roof inputs were simply normalised ENVI-met inputs and variation in plant selection or foliage density could result in a change of either of the above parameters. Green roofs also provide protection to the roof membrane from incoming solar radiation and so although the Mean Radiant Temperature (MRT) value does not change, green roofs can moderate both the long wave radiation emitted and the heat transfer coefficient. By protecting the roof membrane from long wave radiation, green roofs provide an effective insulation barrier which can reduce indoor cooling loads and regulate energy consumption. The Predicted Mean Vote (PMV) recorded an improved levels in thermal comfort compared to that of the base roof, these changes were not significant and were still considered in the neutral range satisfying the ANSI/ASHRAE Standard 55 [14, 15] and ISO 7730 [16]. However, it gives an indication that planted roofs could effectively mitigate the Urban Heat Island (UHI) effect in an urban environment.

8   Conclusions

The thermal implications of using green roofs in the built environment as the main aim of this study involve testing the introduction of vegetation in a hot and humid climate through investigation of previous research and ENVI-met simulation. The ENVI-met study was undertaken to observe the impact of green roofs in the hot and humid micro-climate of the Dubai Marina development. It is recommended that the outdoor thermal implications of this study are essential for developers, architects and engineers to progress towards innovative strategies for heat island mitigation.

- In the hot and humid Dubai climate adding vegetation to roofs has been shown to raise Surface Albedo (SA). Experimentation by Taha [6] and Sailor [4] concluded that vegetation can result in higher albedos. The SA rise recorded in the ENVI-met study is considerable but still not considered a significant increase. The slight SA increase has resulted in reduced surface temperatures. Further increase in SA can be accomplished depending on the type of vegetation selected. Vegetation that meets the minimal water requirements and is climate specific is ideal for any green roof scenario.
- When measuring Mean Radiant Temperature (MRT) on a vegetated roof long wave radiation was significantly reduced compared to a conventional roof and consistent with similar findings by Wong et al. [7] and Kakon and Nobou [8]. The ENVI-met simulation on the Dubai Marina confirmed changes in MRT in the winter months when compared to summer months. This is a consequence of a climatic condition such as a lower sun angle in the winter when compared to summer.
- Relative Humidity (RH) levels in the ENVI-met simulation study on the Dubai Marina found to have decreased levels in the summer when compared to that depicted in the winter. The change could be the result of higher wind

temperatures during winter months and consistent with those results founded by Wong *et al.* [9] and Kakon and Nobou [8] on the influence of building heights and air flow on RH. However, RH on green roofs changed very little from those levels found on the conventional roof in both winter and summer scenarios. Again this could be because of the efficient variation of building heights in the Dubai Marina regulating air flow movements.

- According to ANSI/ASHRAE Standard 55 [14, 15] and ISO 7730 [16] of human thermal comfort for Predicted Mean Vote (PMV) ranges between -0.5 to +0.5 (neutral). Consequently, the ENVI-met green roof model for December 21st 2011 measured PMV at -1.15 to -0.16 which resulted in a slight change in PMV numbers from the base case winter roof scenario which was measured at -1.48 to -0.82. Compared to the summer time green roof measured at -0.01 to 0.33, the winter time PMV range is cooler.

Finally, limitations of the ENVI-met software do not allow for a detailed assessment of plant and substrate details to influence all the parameters discussed above. However, ENVI-met does provide a general analysis through a conceptual model of the potential impacts of using green roofs and the potential benefits of that application. The outcome of the results provided through the numeric ENVI-met model show that there is evidence to suggest that green roof applications can effectively increase SA, reduced surfaces temperatures and improve outdoor thermal comfort as studied through PMV. Climatic conditions and urban planning practices studied in ENVI-met support the development of the green roof in a hot and humid micro-climate, however, possible monitoring of large scale sites, developments with different densities and available technical solutions for green roof systems such as layers, materials, plants, and soil thickness can also be observed. In order to deduce quantitative results the parameters will have be standardised to suit previous research findings and can be recommended for further research to determine the similarities and differences of possible outcomes. Furthermore, a more specific technical objective can then be suggested based on the quality of green roof performance and the involved components of the system. This can then be developed as a successful dialogue to address the design and planning of green roofs for sustainable development and construction.

Acknowledgements

Dr Hanan Taleb, Faculty of Engineering and IT at The British University in Dubai, UAE and Welsh School of Architecture, Cardiff University, UK.

References

[1] National Centre of Meteorology and Seismology in the UAE. [Online] http://www.ncms.ae/english/ 2010.

[2] Dubai Municipality, Green Roof Manual: Guidelines for Planning, Execution & Maintenance of Green Roof Various Applications. Dubai

Municipality, Government of Dubai, UAE. [Online] pp. 1–46 www.dm.gov.ae 2009.

[3]   Dubai Municipality, Dubai Green Building Regulations. Dubai Municipality, Government of Dubai, UAE. [Online] pp. 1–46 www.dm.gov.ae 2010.

[4]   Sailor, D.J., A green roof model for building energy simulation programs. *Energy and Buildings*. Vol. 40 (8), pp. 1466–1478, 2008.

[5]   Shashua-Bar, L. and Hoffman, M., (2004). Quantitative evaluation of passive cooling of the UCL microclimate in hot regions in summer, case study: Urban streets and courtyards with tress. *Building and Environment*. Vol. 39 (9), pp. 1087–1099, 2004.

[6]   Taha, H., Urban climates and heat islands: albedo, evapotranspiration, and anthropogenic heat. *Energy and Buildings*, Oxford, vol. 25 (2), pp. 99–103, 1997.

[7]   Wong, N., Cheong, D., Yan, H., Soh, J., Ong, C., and Sia, A., The effects of rooftop garden on energy consumption of a commercial building in Singapore. *Energy and Buildings*, Vol. 35 (4), pp. 353–364, 2003b.

[8]   Kakon, A.N., and Nobuo, M., The sky view factor effect on the microclimate of a city environment: A case study of Dhaka City. *Proceedings of the 7th International Conference on Urban Climate, June 29-July 3, Yokohama, Japan*, pp.: 1–4, 2009.

[9]   Wong, N., Chena, Y., Ong, C. and Siab, A., Investigation of thermal benefits of rooftop garden in the tropical environment. *Buildings and Environment*. Vol. 38 (1), pp. 261–270, 2003a.

[10] Bruse, M., *Modelling and Strategies for Improved Urban Climates.* [Online]   http://www.envi-met.com/documents/papers/strategies1999pdf 1999.

[11] Okeil, A., A holistic approach to energy efficient building forms. *Energy and Buildings.* Vol. 42 (9), pp. 1437–1444, 2010.

[12] UAEInteract, *UN Conference on Trade and Development (UNCTAD).* [Online] www.uaeinteract.com/docs/UAE_population 2010.

[13] NRI, Dubai Marina, Dubai, U.A.E. [Online] *Net Resources International* http://www.designbuild-network.com/projects/dubai-marina/ 2011.

[14] American Society of Heating Refrigerating and Air Conditioning Engineers (ASHRAE). *Thermal Environmental Conditions for Human Occupancy.* (ASHRAE Standard 55-1992). Atlanta, GA. 1992.

[15] American Society of Heating Refrigerating and Air Conditioning Engineers (ASHRAE). *Thermal Comfort. ASHRAE Handbook: Fundamentals* (p. 8.1–8.29). Atlanta, GA. 2001.

[16] ISO Standard 7730, Moderate Thermal Environments Determination of the PMV and PPD Indices and Specifications of the Conditions for Thermal Comfort. *International Standards Organizations*, pp. 1–26, 1994.

Recognizing socioeconomic risks and benefits related to biofuel production in developing countries: framework for analysis

M. Havukainen, S. Väisänen, V. Uusitalo, M. Luoranen,
J. Havukainen & R. Soukka
Laboratory of Environmental Technology,
Lappeenranta University of Technology, Finland

Abstract

The aim of the paper is to carry out an analysis on socioeconomic risks and benefits of biofuel production on different stages of biofuel production chain. Biofuels have gained increasing attention as an alternative to fossil fuels and as a potential way to reduce the greenhouse gas (GHG) emissions while contributing rural development in developing countries. In this paper socioeconomic risks and benefits related to biofuel production in developing countries were studied by going through related literature. In addition to greenhouse gas emission reductions, biofuel production is also expected to improve rural development. However, according to several studies, they pose some social and economic risks among the local farmers. First of all, the land for biofuel production is often acquired by clearing forest or replacing food production. Second of all, farming may cause some socioeconomic issues if farmers lose the control of their land. On the other hand, sustainable biofuel production could improve rural development and employment in developing countries. The results show that sustainability certificates should be developed further to avoid risks and gain benefits.
Keywords: biofuels, socioeconomic risks and benefits, sustainable development, certificates.

WIT Transactions on Ecology and The Environment, Vol 173, © 2013 WIT Press
www.witpress.com, ISSN 1743-3541 (on-line)
doi:10.2495/SDP130411

1   Introduction

Biofuel production has been growing during the last decade. There are two main reasons for this growth. First of all, biofuels are considered as a clean sources of energy, which are helping Annex 1 countries, as stated by Kyoto protocol, to reach their greenhouse gas (GHG) emission targets. Second of all, there is an increased need for energy and fuel prices are getting higher. In this paper biofuels mean biodiesel and bioethanol produced from crops and oil crops and the studied feedstocks include sugarcane, palm oil and jatropha. The paper aims to summarize the identified socioeconomic risks and benefits of biofuels in developing countries and find out the potential ways to overcome risks and improve the benefits from biofuels. In addition the paper gives an insight to the political forces and agendas that have led to the growth of biofuels.

Many countries have implemented mandatory targets to promote biofuels and governments such as the United States and the European Union have established biofuel mandates to be achieved at target dates. A blend mandate means that a minimum share of biofuel in mixed fuel is required (Harmer [1]) Table 1 presents biofuel mandates of major biofuel consumers.

Policies to promote biofuel production have impact on agricultural commodity production, prices and trade flows. Especially effects of EU biofuel policies are studied. The main effects of EU biofuel policies by 2020 are (Fonseca et al. [2]):

- EU production of biofuels and feedstocks will be higher
- It is uncertain whether the EU's energy independence might be improved by its biofuel policies, particularly when reliance on imported feedstocks is taken into account
- The long-run trend of decreasing agricultural area in EU is slowing down
- World market prices for biofuels will be higher, as a response to increased EU demand for imported biofuel

Table 1:   Biofuel mandates by major consumers (Harmer [3]).

Country	Mandate
USA	Mandatory target of 7.5 billion gallons of biofuels by 2012, rising to 36 billion by 2022
Brazil	Mandatory blend of 20–25% anhydrous ethanol with petrol, mandatory minimum blend of 3% biodiesel with diesel by July 2008 and 5% by end of 2010
EU	Mandatory target of 10% share of renewable (including biofuels) in transport energy by 2020
China	15% of transport energy needs from biofuels by 2020
Canada	5% renewable content in petrol by 2010; 2% renewable in diesel fuel and heating oil by 2012
India	Proposed blending mandates of 5–10% of ethanol and 20% of biodiesel

Reduction of GHG emission to mitigate climate change is one of the main drivers for biofuel production. Kyoto Protocol has set binding targets for industrialized countries to reduce their GHG emissions. As a result The EU's Renewable Energy Directive RED (2009/28) was created which sets an overall binding target of 20% for renewable energy in Europe by 2020. Also at least 10% of each Member State's transport fuel use must come from renewable sources (including biofuels). RED (2009/28) includes criteria for sustainable biofuel production and procedures for verifying that these criteria are met. The criteria are related to GHG savings, land with high biodiversity value, land with high carbon stock and agro-environmental practices. In addition the Commission reports every two years the European Parliament and the Council on the impact on social sustainability in the Community. Also the impact of Community biofuel policy on food security and wider development issues are stated (European Union [4]).

2 Expectations and concerns related to socioeconomic aspects of biofuels

The WTO Agreement on Agriculture (AoA) obliged agriculture under a set of international rules in 1995. The agreement required many countries to open agricultural production to international markets and it has been criticized for reducing protections of small farmers in developing countries. According to the WTO's Agriculture Agreement many countries agreed to improve market access and reduce trade-distorting subsidies in agriculture (WTO [5]). However, at the same time developed countries are continuing paying their farmers massive subsidies which developing countries cannot afford (WTO [5]). Even before the massive growth of biofuel production small farmers in developing countries were already struggling to survive.

Land clearing for biofuels production potentially increases deforestation and puts pressure on food prices. The link between biofuel development and deforestation is complicated and very difficult to measure at the global level. Biofuel production potentially causes deforestation both directly and indirectly. However, there is no clear accepted method to assess these indirect effects of biofuels on deforestation (Gao et al. [6]).

If biofuels replace food production, less area is available for food production and the food prices will be increased. According to FAO unavailability of food, insufficient purchasing power, inappropriate distribution, or inadequate use of food at the household level are the main issues endangering food security (FAO [7]). The spike in food prices in 2008 is estimated to have pushed more than 100 million people below the poverty line. However, biofuels could supply 20–30% of global fuel demand in an environmentally responsible manner without affecting food production (Koonin [8]). Attention to food security has shifted interest toward second-generation that is not based on food crops (Pfuderer et al. [9], Abbot et al. [10], Chen et al. [11]).

Rural development is one of the expectations from biofuels. There is an inevitable link between biofuel production job creation, enhancement of rural development and improvement of rural livelihood. In addition rural development is also part of the International Energy Agency (IEA) policy goals. If biofuel productions as well as other agricultural activities are well planned, it could stimulate rural development. However, if biofuel production is not well implemented, it could have adverse impacts on rural development. Appropriate biofuel policies, laws and regulations could enhance the benefits of biofuels (Fargione *et al.* [12]).

The role of small farmers is extremely vital for rural development. The benefits for small farmers depend on whether they own their own land or simply are forced to sell their village land to investors. In addition rural infrastructure has a key role to play in rural development and improving rural infrastructure will promote biofuel development and agriculture in general. Without appropriate infrastructure biofuel production may not bring any benefits on rural development (Mitchell [13]).

The expanding production of biofuels raised concerns about socioeconomic risks and benefits in developing countries. As a result efforts towards formulation and application of standards and certifications also increased. Roundtable on sustainable palm oil (RSPO) was formed in 2004 and the Roundtable on Sustainable Biofuels (RSB) launched its global certification system to assure the sustainability and traceability of feedstocks and fuels (RSB [14]). International Sustainability and Carbon Certification (ISCC) is another international certification system that can be used to prove sustainability and GHG savings for all kinds of biomass and bioenergy. ISCC has been operating since the beginning of 2010 and is already used by leading companies internationally (ISCC [15]).

3 Results and discussion

Based on studies several potential social aspects have been recognised and collected in table 2. Biofuel production comprises of three stages that are land clearing, farming and refining and within each stage different socioeconomic issues take place. In this study we have focused on small farmers and landless people in developing countries. In this paper the most significant potential impacts on small farmers are caused though deforestation, food price increase, livelihood and job creation. The potential socioeconomic risks and benefits of biofuel production are presented in table 2.

3.1 Land clearing

Socioeconomic risks related to land clearing has been a concern all over the developing world. South Korea and China operate in 4.4 million hectares of overseas plantations in Southeast Asia, Africa and Latin America. For example Cambodia and Laos are losing agricultural resources for their richer neighbors such as Thailand and Vietnam. In addition Indonesia and the Philippines lease out large areas to foreign investors, primarily from China and South Korea, with Japan and Malaysia on their heels (Fargione *et al.* [12]).

Table 2: Potential socioeconomic issues of biofuel production.

Stage	Issues	Description of the issues	Source
Land clearing	Deforestation	The impacts depend on feedstock used, land available, the comparative advantages of biofuel crops versus other food crops, the technologies and financial capital and the existing land use regulations.	Chen *et al.* [11] FAO [16] Murphy [17]
	Food production replacement	If food crops are replaced with energy crops, less area for food production is available and food prices will go up. The food price effects depend largely on policy design.	Braun [18]
Farming	Livelihood	Livelihood impacts depend greatly on contracts with biofuel companies, knowledge of farmers on biofuel harvesting, scale of production, socioeconomic and policy context of the country.	Saturnino *et al.* [19]
	Job creation	On average biofuel production requires 100 more workers per Joule than fossil fuel industry. Job effect depends on scale and mechanization of biofuel production.	Renner and McKeown [20]

Some estimation on deforestation in Malaysia has been done. According to World Bank in Malaysia the area under cereal production has declined from 696,000 hectares in 2003 to 680,000 hectares in 2010. However, the deforestation rate between 2000 and 2010 in Malaysia has been 1.4%. At the same time the area for palm oil production has grown from 338 000 hectares in 2000 to 448,000 hectares in 2008 (World Bank [21]).

The possible deforestation rate caused by biofuel production depends on the area and feedstock. Palm oil plantations are estimated to be one of the main drivers of deforestation in Indonesia while the direct deforestation resulting from sugar-based ethanol in Brazil and Colombia seems to be insignificant. In Brazil the plantations locate approximately 2000 kilometers from Amazon. While in Malaysia, Indonesia are sometimes found in rainforest areas specifically cleared for this purpose, or in areas that had been cleared earlier but planted with rubber or coconut (Gao *et al.* [6]) In addition land is a crucial issue for many indigenous people and others forest dependent people in Indonesia. The Indonesian law does not acknowledge native rights and ownership of lands, as lands are all owned by the government (Friends of the Earth [22]).

Evidence suggests that, at least in Latin America, sugarcane is generally expanding on lands cleared for agriculture a long time ago; it mainly replaced other field crops. Thus, expanded production of ethanol from sugarcane is unlikely to cause direct deforestation, although it may cause indirect land use change by displacing crops or livestock into forests or grasslands (Gao *et al.* [6]).

In recent years, jatropha has been promoted as a crop that uses 'wastelands', marginal lands or abandoned agricultural lands. However, in practice, dry secondary forests have often been affected, although jatropha's establishment is so recent that it is difficult to find evidence on this feedstock's impact on deforestation (Gao *et al.* [6]).

Land clearing can also have impact on food security. At the moment only a marginal share of agricultural land is used for biofuel production but the future scenario is not clear. If EU biofuel polices are implemented total land used for cereals, oilseeds and sugar crops worldwide would increase 3.4% over the period 2008–2020 (Fonseca *et al.* [2]). At the moment accelerating demand for palm oil is contributing to the 1.5% annual rate of deforestation of tropical rainforests in Indonesia and Malaysia (Fargione *et al.* [12]). The role of biofuel policies in the food-price hikes has become particularly controversial. On estimate is that the contribution of the biofuel is 30–75% of the food price increase in 2008. However, there are large methodological difficulties in measuring the role of biofuel production on food prices (Mitchell [13]).

Before the global food crisis in 2008, an analysis of bioenergy policies showed that despite global reductions in food production, undernourishment may decrease in certain locations, where bioenergy production occurs. It also shows that these income effects can substantially increase agricultural land and food commodity prices while at the same time undernourishment decreases in some locations. However, such effects are not globally valid and are sensitive to policy design (Schneider *et al.* [23]).

Concerning food security there are number of regional and global initiatives that are currently underway, e.g. the RSB, the RSPO, developing ISO and CEN standards and the existing FSC, PERC and other forestry schemes. The biofuels roles in food security issues were also discussed after the global food crisis in 2008. Despite the recent controversy surrounding the expanding role of biofuels in the transport sector, it is not obvious that the use of food crops for 1st generation biofuels is an automatic cause of conflict. In a best case scenario, energy demand could dispose of unwanted surpluses, keeping crop prices stable and high enough to warrant the investment that has been lacking in the past decades. These schemes are based on rapidly-developing, though presently incomplete, scientific knowledge and modeling tools (Murphy *et al.* [17]). Also studies indicate that Jatropha can be intercropped with food or use presently unfarmed land unsuitable for other crops. Therefore it is regarded as a potential feedstock to secure food production. However, this would require massive improvements of genetic potential of oil yields and the production practices (FAO [24]).

3.2 Farming

Impacts of biofuels on job creation have been studied. A study made on liquid biofuel production in 2008 showed how the potential environmental and socio-economic risks associated with large-scale production of liquid biofuels in developing countries might affect male- and female-headed households differently. This depends on the specific socio-economic and policy context. In some cases liquid biofuels production might even complicate such inequalities, contributing to the socio-economic marginalization of women and female-headed households and threatening their livelihoods, with negative implications in particular for their food security. Men and women might also have different employment opportunities and conditions on plantations of biofuel feedstocks, and might therefore be exposed to different work-related health risks (Rossi and Lambrou [25]).

An outgrower approach might be beneficial for small farmers in developing countries. A case study from Mozambique biofuel sector (2009) covering sugarcane and jatropha concluded that to producing biofuels is more beneficial for small farmers compared with the more capital-intensive plantation approach. The outgrower approach means that the farmer agrees to provide established quantities of a specific agricultural product and in turn, the buyer commits to purchase the product, often at a pre-determined price. In addition the expected benefits of outgrower schemes will be further enhanced if they result in technology spillovers to other crops. However, while welfare and food security broadly increased due to enhanced purchasing power, certain households may be adversely affected due to the price and quantity adjustments associated with rapid growth in biofuel production (Channing et al. [26]). Studies have shown that projects based integration of local communities through outgrower schemes have the potential to contribute to socioeconomic development in African countries by offering additional income opportunities for the rural population (Janssen et al. [27]).

Jatropha is a marginal feedstock in biofuels but it has gained interest especially in South Asia. A case in India showed that after a while a large share of Jatropha plantations were discontinued due to perceived poor performance. Problems arose from limited knowledge about jatropha cultivation, poor planning and implementation of the national jatropha program (Axelsson et al. [28]).

Biofuels production can have impact on job creation since biofuel production requires 100 times more workers per joule of energy content produced than the highly capital-intensive fossil fuel industry (Renner and McKeown [20]). A study made in 2010 Asia-Pacific area concluded that biofuels can create jobs in rural areas through new biorefineries and new feedstock harvesting, seeding, and transportation activities. In addition it is believed that biofuels also provide a logical growth path into increased mechanization. However, one of the issues recognized was that women face some barriers to be engaged in the biofuels sector. However, it is believed that women are able to increase gradually their participation in the sector (APEC [29]).

4 Policy implications

Biofuels certificates are developed to assure sustainability of biofuel production. For instance RSPO is a global, multi-stakeholder initiative on sustainable palm oil (RSB [14]). With expansion of biofuel productions number of certificates also increased. Large number of certification systems is hard to manage and some experts argue that an increasing number of certification initiatives would just lead to beneficial competition, resulting in constant improvement in standards and standard application. Others point out that further proliferation of standards will lead to a substantial confusion among various stakeholders (Lebandowski and Faaij [30]). According to studies biofuel policies should concentrate on market development and promote sustainable international biofuel trade. Free trade of biofuels should be linked with social and environmental standards and verification systems (World Energy Council [31]).

Certification systems are going to develop in the future. There has been a suggestion of universal standard since there are many similarities and synergies among the different existing schemes. They could be integrated into a single system, thereby reducing the complexity of the current approach. However, it has to be borne in mind that standards are only a single tool to deal with socioeconomic risks and benefits of biofuels (Kaphengst et al. [32]). Independent sustainable palm oil certification can be a useful approach to promote sustainable palm oil production. However, RSPO certification scheme are likely to be above the capacity of most smallholders (World Bank [21]).

However, in the future it is expected that number of areas and countries producing biofuels will also increase, which is making creation of universal sustainability standard more important but also more challenging. In addition number of feedstocks will also increase and possibly bring new socioeconomic risks and benefits that are not yet recognized.

To deal with social concern some investors and companies have adopted a special strategy. One example is The International Finance Corp (IFC), the World Bank's private sector lender, stated in 2009 that it had suspended new investments in palm oil businesses. IFC carried out a study on palm oil plantations and found that did not have adequate approach to social concerns within Indonesian palm oil sector (Reuters [33]). The specific complaints included [34]: illegal use of fire to clear lands, clearance of areas of high conservation value, seizing of indigenous peoples' lands without due process, failure to carry out free, prior, and informed consultations with indigenous peoples leading to broad community support, failure to establish agreed areas of smallholdings, social conflicts that triggered repressive actions by companies and security forces, failure to carry out or wait for approval of legally required environmental risks and benefits assessments.

After all the problems related to palm oil production were recognized World Bank lifted suspension in 2011 and IFC created a new strategy for sustainable palm oil based on meeting with 3,000 stakeholders. IFC stated that palm oil investments have potential to economic growth and reduce poverty, while also being environmentally friendly (Reuters [35]). At the moment biofuel feedstocks in general share only a marginal portion of all the agricultural production

As IFC is a relatively small provider of finance and advice within the sector and therefore IFC aims to concentrate on (WTO [5]) investing in relatively underdeveloped areas, such as in poorer countries or frontier regions, where projects will have a relatively larger positive impact (e.g., through direct employment or by supporting smallholders) and where access to capital is constrained; (RSB [14]) engaging selectively with key private sector partners throughout the industry's supply chain (producers, traders, and processors) who are able to demonstrate best practice in environment and social sustainability and community and smallholder engagement; (Renner and McKeown [20]) working with multi-stakeholder initiatives to develop voluntary industry-wide standards for sustainable development (World Bank [36]).

5   Conclusions

Rural development was recognized as the main socioeconomic benefit if job creation and technology transfer expectations are met. The most significant risks recognized are related to deforestation and food security. Certificates are one of the most important tools recognized to overcome socioeconomic risks and enhance the benefits. Due to mandates and biofuel policies biofuel production is increasing and therefore socioeconomic issues related to biofuels will become more significant in the future. Some of the risks and benefits that still are in the local level have potential to expand to global level in the future if they are not considered by decision makers, authorities and biofuel producers. To date many of the issues are not yet completely measured and certificates are based on inadequate knowledge. Certificates should be developed further to secure the sustainable biofuel production. Also biofuel schemes should be planned and implemented better and also ensured that the farmers have enough knowledge to harvest feedstocks.

References

[1]   T. Harmer, "Biofuels subsidies and the law of the World Trade Organization," 2009.
[2]   M. B. Fonseca, A. Burrell, S. Hubertus, M. Henseler, K. Aikaterini, R. M'Barek, I. Dominguez ja A. Tonini, "Impacts of the EU Biofuel Target on Agricultural Markets and Land Use," Joint research centre, Institute for Prospective Technological Studies, 2010.
[3]   T. Harmer, "Biofuels subsidies and the law of the WTO, ICTSD Global Platform on Climate Change," *Trade policies and sustainable energy,* 2009.
[4]   European Union, "Directive 2009/28/EC on the promotion of the use of energy from renewable sources," European Union, 2009.

[5] WTO, "World Trade Organisation," 7 7 2011. [Online]. Available: http://www.wto.org/english/docs_e/legal_e/14-ag_01_e.htm. [Haettu 16 1 2013].

[6] Y. Gao, M. Skutsch, O. Masera ja P. Pacheco, "A global analysis of deforestation due to biofuel development," Center for International Forestry Research, 2011.

[7] FAO, "State of food insecurity in the World," FAO, 2012.

[8] S. E. Koonin, "Getting serious about biofuels," 2006.

[9] S. Pfuderer, G. Davies ja I. Mithcell, "The role of demand for biofuel in the agricultural commodity price spikes of 2007/08," Food and Farming Analysis, 2010.

[10] P. C. Abbott, C. Hurt and W. E. Tyner, "What's driving food prices?" Farm foundation, 2008.

[11] X. Chen, H. Haixiao, M. Khanna and H. Önal, "Meeting the Mandate for Biofuels: Implications for Land Use, Food, and Fuel Prices," 2012.

[12] J. Fargione, J. Hill, D. Tilman, S. Polansky and P. Hawthorne, "Land Clearing and the Biofuel Carbon Debt," Science, 2007.

[13] D. Mitchell, "Note on rising food prices," *World Bank Policy Research Working Paper,* 2008.

[14] Roundtable for sustainable biofuels, "Roundtable for sustainable biofuels," [Online]. Available: http://rsb.org/. [Haettu 17 1 2013].

[15] International sustainability and carbon certification, "International sustainability and carbon certification," [Online]. Available: http://www. iscc-system.org/. [Haettu 11 2 2013].

[16] Food and Agriculture Organization of the United Nations, "Global forest resource assessment," Food and Agriculture Organization of the United Nations, 2005.

[17] R. Murphy, J. Woods, M. Black and M. McManus, "Global developments in the competition for land from biofuels," *Food policy,* pp. 52–61, 2011.

[18] J. Braun, "Impact of Climate Change on food security in times of high food and energy prices," *Land management 2,* 2008.

[19] M. Saturnino, J. Borras, P. McMichael and I. Scoones, "The politics of biofuels, land and agrarian change: editors' introduction," 2010.

[20] M. Renner and A. McKeown, "Promise and pittfalls of biofuels jobs," *Biofuels,* pp. 7–9, 2010.

[21] World Bank, "The world bank," [Online]. Available: http://data.worldbank. org/. [Haettu 11 2 2013].

[22] Friends of the Earth, "Losing Ground The human rights impacts of oil palm plantation expansion in Indonesia," Friends of the Earth, 2008.

[23] U. A. Schneider, C. Llull and P. Havlik, "Bioenergy and Food Security Modeling Income Effects in a Partial Equilibrium Model," 12th Congress of the European Association of Agricultural Economists, 2008.

[24] Food and Agriculture Organisation of the United Nations (FAO) and Policy Innovation Systems for Clean Energy Security (PISCES), "Small-Scale Bioenergy Initiatives:Brief description and preliminary lessons on

livelihood impacts from case studies in Asia, Latin America and Africa," PISCES and FAO, 2009.

[25] A. Rossi and Y. Lambrou, "Gender and equity issues in liquid biofuels production minimizing the risks to maximize the opportunities," FAO, 2008.

[26] A. Channing, R. Benfica, F. Tarp, T. James and U. Rafael, "Biofuels, Poverty and Growth A computable general equilibrium analysis of Mozambique," *Environment and Development Economics,* 2009.

[27] R. Janssen, D. Rutz, P. Helm, J. Woods and R. Diaz-Chavez, "Bioenergy for sustainable development in Africa: Environmental and social aspects," 2010.

[28] L. Axelsson, M. Franzén, M. Ostwald, G. Berndes, G. Lakshmi and N. Ravindranath, "Jatropha cultivation in southern India: assessing farmers' experiences," *Biofuels, Bioproducts and Biorefining,* 2012.

[29] APEC Energy Working Group, "A Study of Employment Opportunities from Biofuel Production in APEC Economies," APEC Energy Working Group, 2010.

[30] I. Lewandowski and A. Faaij, "Steps towards the development of a certification system for sustainable bio-energy trade," *Biomass and Bioenergy,* p. 83–104, 2006.

[31] World Energy Council, "Biofuels: Policies,standards and technologies," World Energy Council, 2010.

[32] T. Kaphengst, M. Mandy and S. Schlegel, "At a tipping point? How the debate on biofuel standards sparks innovative ideas for the general future of standardisation and certification schemes," *Journal of Cleaner Production,* 2009.

[33] Reuters, "Reuters," [Online]. Available: http://www.reuters.com/article/ 2009/09/09/us-worldbank-palmoil-idUSTRE5886OD20090909. [Haettu 11 2 2013].

[34] International Finance Corporation (IFC), "Audit report: CAO Audit of IFC's investments," 2009.

[35] Reuters, "Reuters," [Online]. Available: http://www.reuters.com/article/ 2011/04/01/worldbank-palmoil-idUSN011595420110401.

[36] World Bank, "The World Bank Group Framework and IFC Strategy for Engagement in the Palm Oil Sector," 2011.

[37] International land coalition, "Meals per gallon. The impact of industrial biofuels on people and global hunger," *Action Aid,* 2 2010.

[38] S. Pradhan, "Biofuels and Its Implications on Food Security, Climate Change, and Energy Security:A Case Study of Nepal," Tufts University, 2009.

[39] T. Rice, "Meals per gallon, The impact of industrial biofuels on people and global hunger," ActionAid, 2010.

[40] C. Schott, "Socio-economic dynamics of biofuel development in Asia Pacific," 2009.

[41] B. Richardson, J. Anderson, H. Heath, I. Mostad and V. Sivalingam, "Sugarcane and the global land grab:A primer for producers and buyers," 2012.

[42] K. Hermele, "Regulating Sugarcane Cultivation in Brazil," Lund University, 2011.

[43] S. Wiggins, "Institute of development studies," 21 10 2009. [Online]. Available: http://www.ids.ac.uk/news/do-small-scale-farms-in-africa-have-a-future.

[44] A. Mabiso and D. Weatherspoon, "The Impact of Biofuels Crop and Land Rental Markets on Farm Household Incomes: Evidence from South Africa," 2011.

[45] Malesyan Palm oil board, "Official Portal of Malesyan Palm oil board," [Online]. Available: http://www.mpob.gov.my. [Haettu 11 2 2013].

[46] House of commons, Environmental audit committee, "Are biofuels sustainable," the House of Commons, 2008.

[47] J. S. E. W. R. M. H. Sanders, "Bio-refinery as the bio-inspired process to bulk chemicals," *Macromolecular Bioscience,* pp. 105–117, 2007.

Community participation in comprehensive upgrading programmes in developing countries

S. Restrepo Rico

URBANgrad, Technische Universität Darmstadt, Germany

Abstract

Urban life defines the character of communities and the life quality of urban dwellers. Urban expansion, unequal incomes and social conflicts create gaps of development, which lead cities towards intolerance and segregation, compromising the ability of low-income communities to participate in the improvement of their environment. Furthermore, the failure of governments to foresee the consequences of urban policy in weak economies denies the urban poor their rights as citizens. In consequence, the meaning of participation is distorted, development is achieved through top-down processes, negotiation and manipulation of communities.

Sustainable development in the global south relies on understanding the role of communities in urban expansion, along with the emergence, growth and consolidation of informal settlements. A framework for comprehensive upgrading programmes that supports community initiatives could become the basis for sustainable urban development. In this sense, it is essential to understand the main constituents of comprehensive upgrading and the requirements, in terms of spatial improvement, legitimacy, social development and governance. These programmes would not only become a holistic and effective strategy to react to existing problems in informal settlements, but also would prevent the proliferation, and improve the life quality of the urban poor. Comprehensive upgrading programmes address efficiently the needs of the poor and empower them to participate. Participative processes become catalysts for city-wide integral development, prevent the proliferation of informality and encourage social integration, which could diminish the gap throughout the different sectors of society.

Keywords: community participation, comprehensive slum upgrading, informal settlements, sustainable urban development, governance.

WIT Transactions on Ecology and The Environment, Vol 173, © 2013 WIT Press
www.witpress.com, ISSN 1743-3541 (on-line)
doi:10.2495/SDP130421

1   Introduction

Globalisation driven by political and economic pressures influence urban policy, which in the context of weak economies lead to segregation of communities and deprives them from their rights as citizens [2]. As governments fail in the task of conceiving an appropriate vision of the future, consequent with their context-specific necessities, the problem of restricted citizenship engenders tensions in urban development and hinders sustainability, especially in developing countries, where urban expansion is encouraged by unstable political structures, social conflicts and scarcity of opportunities.

Sustainable development could become the answer for prompt growth in urban areas, as sustainability combines in the same idea social, economic and urban development. However, current urban growth processes in the developing world become the strongest obstacles to implement sustainability. Furthermore, urban expansion is aggravated by the incidence of poverty in cities, evidenced by the exponential increase of low-income population in the past decades. Poverty has conquered developing societies, forcing them to look outside governmental structures for the means to survive in hostile urban environments.

2   Urban growth and informality

Informality emerges from scarcity of resources and opportunities to address the needs of the growing urban poor. Exclusion and economic stagnation reinforce the position of the informal sector, while the formal city isolates and stigmatises these communities. The ability of informality, as urban actor, to adapt in size and scope becomes a significant factor in development. These invisible marginal societies accumulate power, human and physical resources [6].

Understanding the situation of informality in urban areas is recognising the importance of these invisible societies in the lives of the urban poor to satisfy necessities. The informal sector provides employment, along with housing for a large share of the urban population, covering between 40% to 60% of the overall housing stock in developing cities [7]. The need for affordable housing leads the urban poor to create new informal communities. In the last decades, these communities grew promptly, allowing them to be visible in the city, accounted for 31,6% of the total urban population [8]. The urban image declined, poverty became customary rather than exceptional and forced governments to implement institutional transformations in order to address the rising urban problems in a holistic way [5]. The urban poor live with and from the informal sector which makes the task of planning for sustainability even more intricate, since the influence of informality is not constrained to housing; it expands to economy, welfare, as well as the social necessities that the local government fails to provide.

> *"Policies must address the current situation of socio-economic and institutional systems, removing inefficiencies and making them flexible with an integrative multi-sectorial goal"* [5].

3 Upgrading strategies for informal settlements

The problem of informal settlements has forced governments to react to urban expansion in diverse ways. Former efforts translated into reactive upgrading strategies i.e. eviction, paternalism, site and services and self-help, measures generally associated to the influence of international institutions in urban policy throughout the 1970s and 1980s. The United Nations, the World Bank and many Non-Governmental Organisations have promoted upgrading strategies in the developing world through loans and grants, accompanied by imposed foreign development processes, which neglect the specific cultural, social and physical context of communities. Furthermore, the concept of informality and informal settlements is not yet clear in every context. The inability of imposed strategies to adapt to diverse contexts challenges the effectiveness of measures and quality of outputs, since the conditions of informal settlements differ in each country. The approaches have been naïve and constrained by budgets, political willingness and lack of comprehension of the dimensions of poverty. The limited success of the improvements is a consequence of implementing partial measures that address one single aspect of poverty. Overlooking the multidimensional complexity of poverty exposes the lack of understanding about the real needs of the urban poor, along with the reluctance of municipal authorities to engage in holistic upgrading programmes. As result, informal settlements expand, gentrification boosts, supported by paternalistic social policy, and the urban boundaries stretch to unthinkable limits [10]. These strategies, although implemented in several countries, have shown to be inefficient and unsustainable in the long term [9].

Upgrading strategies generally address land tenure regularisation, financing mechanisms, provision of infrastructure and services, and partnerships for participatory approaches in planning [7]. The main characteristic of these strategies is that governments continue to be owners, as well as providers of infrastructure and housing, approaching low-income communities through conciliatory policy.

> "Perhaps the single and most important factor in the limited success or scope of so many housing and urban development projects supported by governments and international agencies over the last 40 years is the lack of influence allowed groups of urban poor in their conception, location, design, resource mobilisation and management, and evaluation" [11].

As Marisa Guaraldo [3] exposes, the inclusion of communities rarely grasps the real meaning of participation, understood as the empowerment of communities to influence decision-making processes. On the contrary, urban development is driven through conciliation, diplomacy and, in many cases, manipulation of the population. Thus, informality is transformed into an urban phenomenon which spreads throughout the city, from urbanisation to the economy and social networks, becoming the means for the urban poor to survive in disadvantaged conditions, where sustainability is unrealistic, unattainable and perpetuates poverty cycles, propagating problems and necessities.

4   Comprehensive upgrading of informal settlements

The future scenario shows that 70% of the world's population growth is expected to occur in developing countries, challenging the ability of governments to manage an increase of two billion dwellers in cities, where the local situation is already severe [12]. In order to achieve sustainable development in the global south, urban policy must address the survival of the urban poor [13]. Low-income communities are now the majority in developing countries, with 60% of the population living below the poverty line U$2 per day [14].

Comprehensive upgrading programmes can confront the challenges of exponential population growth in contexts of limited economic resources. Understanding the intrinsic dynamics of population change is recognising the potentials of low-income communities and their real needs. Community-based initiatives and participative projects have shown multiple strengths, as well as efficiency of results to meet the specific needs of informal dwellers, thus, ensuring sustainability of improvements through sense of place and empowerment [6]. Increased participation of low-income communities in upgrading projects give rise to strategies which address the problem from a bottom-up perspective, transforming rigid schemes into adjustable structures, where the community becomes an important element of the process [15].

"The appropriate role of government would seem to minimise direct intervention, allowing the urban poor to find solution that they can afford in their traditional way" [3].

An significant element in the transition from top-down approaches to participatory strategies is legitimacy, understood as the acknowledgment of the existence of the urban poor in the city and their right to citizenship, as well as their ability to become actors in urban development [16]. Although not completely comprehensive of the dimensions of poverty, this recognition as urban dwellers and citizens modifies the perception of policies, programmes and encourages participation in urban projects. Renewed citizenship provides slum dwellers *De facto* tenure [17], recognises their right to shelter and promotes self-help as the means for improving their own dwelling through incremental construction. However, the vision of John Turner [18], where self-help is the answer to the problem of slums is far from becoming a reality , since self-help imposes time and budget burdens on the poor, in addition to diverse limitations and setbacks regarding resources, the improvement of public spaces, urban infrastructure and mobility. These communities lack, in most cases, technical, financial and legal means for upgrading the built environment and connecting themselves to the city. Hence, support of government agencies in terms of funding, design and management is essential, in cooperation with the private sector and professionals, in order to promote holistic approaches [9], Additionally, government support must come with institutional changes and flexibility to manage the unforeseen factors associated to informal settlements. Advice and guidance to address the needs of the people solve local and context-specific problems, thus, encourages project replication and modifies measures to the evolving needs.

The research in the field of sustainable upgrading of informal settlements in developing countries exposes the main factors to address in order to formulate comprehensive upgrading programmes. Similarities in the foundation of programmes suggested that, although understanding the cultural context is essential to formulate integral strategies, the core constituents to promote sustainable upgrading are comparable and can be classified in terms of *Physical Development, Legitimacy, Social Development and Governance* [4]. Furthermore, these constituents can become the framework for the formulation of comprehensive upgrading programmes in the context of informal settlements.

4.1 Spatial improvement

Small-scale improvements have great impacts on the livelihood of the urban poor and empower them to organise and execute community-initiated projects via incremental construction of housing and public space. Basic infrastructure, combined with secure connection to public services, reduce the living costs for, which, at the same time, improves their socio-economic condition. Access to services promote the creation of on-site employment and local retail [1]. Urban mobility and physical accessibility allow spatial and structural relationships with the urban structure, while open spaces become social places for recreational, social and economic activities and provide opportunities to develop community cohesion [19].

SPATIAL IMPROVEMENT		
COMPONENT	ACTIONS	INSTRUMENTS
URBAN INFRASTRUCTURE	Water Sanitation Drainage Public lighting Waste disposal	In-Situ Community Work Partnerships for implementation Funding for infrastructure by municipalities Community Working Groups
MOBILITY & ACCESSIBILITY	Roads & Walkways Access to the city Restricted access for automobiles	Construction of roads and foothpaths Physical connection to urban transport systems Promotion of non-motorised transport modes Layout adjustment
PUBLIC SPACE	Urban renewal Social Facilities Housing improvement	Improvement of open spaces Incremental construction Training skills for local construction
URBAN ENVIRONMENT	Dwellings for essential relocation Elimination of hazards	Relocation near former settlement Reforestation Management and prevention

Figure 1:   Spatial improvement [4].

Infrastructure and community facilities generate an overall improvement in the sense of place of the residents, which combined with increased incomes encourage incremental construction, consequent with the needs and resources of families [18].

4.2 Legitimacy

Legitimacy allows individuals and communities to become part of the formal city and encourages sense of place and participation. The urban poor understand their rights and obligations, as well as the opportunities and responsibilities in the development of communities.

The evolution of strategies in addressing informal settlements relies on the importance of legitimacy, since illegality hinders the possibilities for self-help, access to welfare, education and labour [14]. Upgrading programmes grant instant *De facto* tenure, eliminate the fear of eviction and mend the relation of the inhabitant with the city [17]. The degree of participation in decision-making processes, from planning to execution and supervision, legitimates the programme in the community and boost trust, as well as commitment from the city and the inhabitants [20].

LEGITIMACY		
COMPONENT	**ACTIONS**	**INSTRUMENTS**
TENURE	Occupation rights Property rights Land tenure	*De facto* tenure Collective ownership of land Education about civil rights
LEGALITY	Community-Based Organisations Financial support Assistance in Planning	Legitimation of CBO's Guidance provided by municipal agencies Legitimation of Incremental construction
PARTICIPATION & SENSE OF PLACE	Community leadership Private-Public partnerships Diversity of Stakeholders	Local committee Partnerships with other actors Shared project ownership Acknowledgement of social responsibilities

Figure 2: Legitimacy [4].

A difference has to be made between legitimacy and legality [16]. Although legality is necessary for social development, legal tenure is neither a guarantee for legitimacy, nor for community participation. Legitimacy is an implicit agreement generated by understanding the programme, accompanied by the possibility to participate and influence decision-making [16]. Additionally, self-organisation is fundamental for securing the means to finance improvements and protect the most vulnerable population. Community cohesion and legitimacy are encouraged through recognition of the ability of the poor to manage their own resources, grants them a renewed citizenship, which nourishes new partnerships with the municipality and the private sector [21].

4.3 Social development

Social development is a learning process where empowerment, social capital and community capacity foster further social and economic activities to support the development of communities.

Social development was the main component missing in former upgrading strategies, also the reason for the limited scope and success. While physical results are important for legitimacy, social development signifies an improvement in the socio-economic condition of the settlement. The isolation of the poor is not only a physical limitation, is also a problem of restricted access to opportunities, ignorance about their rights and negligence of the state. Building social capacity encourages integration to the society [22]. Partnerships, shared ownership, collective tenure and legitimacy generate networks and spread knowledge.

SOCIAL DEVELOPMENT		
COMPONENT	ACTIONS	INSTRUMENTS
EMPOWERMENT	Community commitment Local Associations Participation	Encouragement for self-organisation Integration to the formal society Education about democratic processes
SOCIAL CAPITAL	Social Services Local management and financing Community cohesion	Open spaces as stage of social activities Facilities for knowledge transfer Community saving funds
COMMUNITY CAPACITY	Social networks Economic Development Education and Training	Self-organisation for managerial capabilities Small-scale businesses Open spaces for economic development Community groups

Figure 3:   Social development [4].

The horizontal structure of networks demands open spaces for discussion and participative decision-making, mobilising the people towards integration and community cohesion [23]. Empowerment reduces vulnerabilities by supporting community-driven initiatives for physical, social and economic improvement. However, the strength of communities relies on the stability of organisations and legitimacy of actions. Community-based organisations build social capital, educate the people in participatory processes and provide working skills that could be employed later in the development of other settlements or in the formal labour market.

4.4 Governance

Participative approaches demand the construction of city-wide networks to spread knowledge, otherwise improvements of informal settlements become isolated projects with restricted relevance in the overall development of the city.

Governments experienced a learning process with the past strategies, where they understood the limits of internationally driven initiatives along with rigid programme frameworks. Decentralisation is the institutional transformation, which allows the emergence of comprehensive upgrading programmes. Local authorities realised the need for institutional reorganisation in order to answer the call for empowerment. Moreover, self-organisation demands participative approaches for implementation and planning. Participation steers municipalities to innovate in policy and institutional structures, open to social networks and include diverse stakeholders in decision-making processes.

The urban poor need guidance and financing opportunities, as community organisations are not sufficient to overcome poverty, illegality and stigmatisation. The municipality provides funding and guidance in management, while the academy assists in planning, the private sector in partnership with government agencies and the community support implementation and sustainability.

GOVERNANCE		
COMPONENT	**ACTIONS**	**INSTRUMENTS**
INSTITUTIONAL RENOVATION	Decentralisation Institutional autonomy Institutional reorganisation	Encouragement of local initiatives Flexibility and Innovation Delegate responsibilities to local authorities
INTER-INSTITUTIONAL CO-OPERATION	Coordination of activities Partnerships Inclusion	Joint work between government agencies Diversity of stakeholders Economic motivation for inclusion of civil society Community participation in decision-making Guidances for CBO's in the conception of projects
INCLUSIVE DECISION-MAKING	Empowerment Government as enabler Renewed citizenship	Promotion of community-driven initiatives City-wide community development plan
INTEGRAL PLANNING	Mapping Prevention Project replication	City-wide comprehensive survey Projects as learning centres Pilot projects for promotion Comprehensive development plan for the city

Figure 4: Governance [4].

4.5 Framework synthesis

The poor are as well part of the city, calling for inclusive development policies. Responding to the challenges of informal settlements relies on the formulation of integral development strategies at a city-wide scale encouraging social integration, especially in urbanised areas, where life quality decreases as low-income population expands.

COMPONENT		ACTIONS	INSTRUMENTS
SPATIAL IMPROVEMENT	URBAN INFRASTRUCTURE MOBILITY & ACCESSIBILITY PUBLIC SPACE URBAN ENVIRONMENT	Public Services Waste Management Road Construction Public Transport Urban Renewal Community Facilities Incremental Construction	In-Situ participative design Partnerships for Implementation & Financing Guided Self-Help Incremental Construction
LEGITIMACY	TENURE LEGALITY PARTICIPATION	Property Rights De Facto Tenure CBO's Inclusion Assistance & Support Stakeholders Commitment PPP's	Collective Ownership Legal Tenure Legitimation of CBO's Guidance Shared Ownership Shared responsibilities
SOCIAL DEVELOPMENT	EMPOWERMENT SOCIAL CAPITAL COMMUNITY CAPACITY	Participation Information Community Cohesion Self-Management Social Networks Education & Training	CBO's Knowledge Transfer Skill Training Small-Scale Improvement Local Economy
GOVERNANCE	INSTITUTIONAL INNOVATION INCLUSIVE DECISION-MAKING INTEGRAL PLANNING	Decentralisation Coordination Participation Enablement Citizenship Mapping Prevention Replication	Flexibility Innovation Reorganisation Diversity of Stakeholders Encouragement & support Community-driven initiatives Comprehensive Development

Figure 5:   Synthesis [4].

Spatial Improvement embraces the provision of urban infrastructure, improved mobility and accessibility through the improvement of roads, walkways and the built environment, which in turn would improve the quality of open spaces. These changes in the public realm encourage incremental construction of housing and an overall improvement in the built environment. In order to implement these spatial improvements programmes need to include communities, recognise the potentials of diverse stakeholders for planning and decision-making processes in urban upgrading

Legitimacy is an essential constituent for participation and encouragement of communities, promotes sense of place, and legitimises institutions, organisations and associations. Legitimacy initiates learning processes and capacity building for both communities and municipal agencies, allows knowledge transfer through social networks, and generates new relationships between residents and the state.

Social development is both basis and outcome of sustainable development, a continuous cycle where empowerment, social capital and community capacity foster further social and economic activities.

Governance for the development of informal settlements brings together diverse sectors of society, involving low-income communities in the urban agenda. Participatory approaches demand social integration to avoid gentrification and isolation of projects. Communities need guidance and flexible regulatory frameworks, along with financing that supports community-driven initiatives.

These components can be used to create a flexible basis, an integral structure to support the definition of upgrading programmes in developing countries, address the diverse dimensions of informal settlements and allow adaptation of programmes to the context-specific conditions of each culture.

5 Conclusions

The components exposed above are some of the lessons learned from the previous research, which have been organised and integrated into a framework, where each constituent is defined by the main components. Actions and instruments for the implementation are suggested, revealing that the understanding of poverty leads to the identification of the real needs of low-income communities and the importance of including them in the upgrading planning process. Thus, the combination of the following components can be the basis for comprehensive slum upgrading programmes.

The framework proposed in the section above suggests a flexible structure for comprehensive upgrading programmes, however the participation component is yet to be defined and revealed in order to propose a programme structure which emphasises the importance of community participation in upgrading programmes and the instruments and modes to achieve a participatory approach.

The proposal of a framework aims to provide the planning tools to government agencies, as well as communities, transforming the idea of governments as single stakeholders. It has been observed the limited success of improvements and brittle impact of top-down upgrading strategies. Low commitment and absent sense of place weaken the effectiveness of measures, compromising the sustainability of outcomes and replication of projects.

Communities gradually understand the importance of participation in the development of their own environment; consequently, the state must recognise the potential and ability of community-based organisations to manage implement and maintain their neighbourhood, guided, and supported by every sector of society.

References

[1] Jenks M., Burgess R. Compact Cities: Sustainable Urban Forms for Developing Countries. London: Spon Press, 2000.
[2] Davis M. Planet of Slums. London: Verso, 2006.
[3] Guaraldo M. A ladder of community participation for underdeveloped countries // Habitat International. 1996. Vol. 20, № 3. P. 431–444.
[4] Restrepo Rico S. Sustainable Upgrading of Informal Settlements in Developing Countries: Brazil, Indonesia and Thailand. University of Applied Sciences Frankfurt am Main, 2010.
[5] Briassoulis H. Sustainable Development and the Informal Sector: An Uneasy Relationship? // The Journal of Environment and Development. 1999. Vol. 8, № 3. pp. 213–273.
[6] Pugh C. Squatter settlements. 2000. Vol. 17, № 5. pp. 325–337.
[7] UNCHS. Informal Settlement Upgrading: The Demand for Capacity Building in six Pilot Cities. Amman, Ankara, Caracas, Concepcion, Ibadan and Nkayi. Nairobi: UN-HABITAT, 1999.
[8] UN-HABITAT. Enhancing Urban Safety and Security: Global Report on Human Settlements. London, 2007.
[9] Environment and Urbanization. Aid and Urban Development: Where are the Views of the "Recipients"? // Environment and Urbanization. 2001. Vol. 13, № 1. pp. 3–9.
[10] Bank T.W., Pugh C. Housing policy development in developing countries. 1994. Vol. 11, № 3. pp. 159–180.
[11] Satterthwaite D. The Rise of Participatory Society: Challenges for the non profit sector // 33rd annual conference of the Association for Research on Non Profic Organisationa and Voluntary Action. Los Angeles, 2004.
[12] Cohen B. Urbanization in developing countries: Current trends, future projections, and key challenges for sustainability // Technology in Society. 2006. Vol. 28, № 1-2. pp. 63–80.
[13] Barredo J.I., Demicheli L. Urban sustainability in developing countries' megacities: modelling and predicting future urban growth in Lagos // Cities. 2003. Vol. 20, № 5. pp. 297–310.
[14] Wakely P., Mumtaz B., Clifford K. Slum Spatial Analisis // UN-Habitat, The Challenge of Slums: Global Report on Human Settlements. London: Earthscan Publications Ltd, 2003. pp. 79–95.
[15] Chiu H.L. Four decades of housing policy in Thailand // Habitat International. 1984. Vol. 8, № 2. pp. 31–42.
[16] Macedo J. Urban land policy and new land tenure paradigms: Legitimacy vs. legality in Brazilian cities // Land Use Policy. 2008. Vol. 25, № 2. pp. 259–270.
[17] Van Horen B. Informal Settlement Upgrading: Bridging the Gap Between the "De Facto" and "De Jure" // Journal of Planning Education and Research. 2000. Vol. 19. pp. 389–400.

[18] Turner J.F.C. Housing in three dimensions: Terms of reference for the housing question redefined // World Development. 1978. Vol. 6, № 9-10. pp. 1135–1145.

[19] Newman P., Kenworthy J. Sustainability and Cities: Overcoming Automobile Dependence. Washington, DC.: Island Press, 1999.

[20] Brakarz J., Engel Aduan W. Favela-Bairro: Scalled up Urban Development in Brazil // Inte-American Development Bank. 2004.

[21] CODI. Community Organisations Development Institute [Online] // Strategic Plans.

[22] Sophon P. Social Capital and the Government Housing Program: A Case Study of Baan Mankong Program in Bangkok. Thammasat University, 2006. № May.

[23] Newman P., Jennings I. Cities As Sustainable Ecosystems. Washington, DC.: Island Press, 2008.

Section 9
Environmental economics

Systematic monetisation of environmental impacts

H. Krieg, S. Albrecht & M. Jäger
Department of Life Cycle Engineering (GaBi), Chair of Building Physics, University of Stuttgart, Germany

Abstract

Integrating environmental aspects in planning and controlling processes is an increasing challenge for companies and organisations, especially in times of growing environmental awareness of customers and increasing regulative pressure. Monetisation of environmental impacts can help here to include environmental impacts of products and processes in established planning and controlling structures and thereby contribute to organisational sustainability efforts. The method proposed here allows for a systematic integration of environmental impacts and economic factors. It does so by using the simplex algorithm, a heuristic approach that is used in classic business theory for, for example, planning of production processes within companies. The approach presented is based on the outcomes of a Life Cycle Assessment of products and processes. Furthermore, all environmental aspects to be included in the planning have to be limited. Such limitation can come, for example, from an organisation's environmental policy. Resources with unlimited availability are considered to be free of charge in business theory and can therefore not be monetised. Through the limitation towards a target value, scarcity is created. Through the iterative application of the simplex algorithm, an optimal allocation of the scarce resources, in this case environmental impacts, can be reached. The approach thereby allows for systematically planning programs with the constraint of limited environmental impact. This results in a portfolio that fulfils the goal of reduced environmental impact with minimal costs, while also giving information on the internal value of scarce parameters, such as emissions, through shadow prices.
Keywords: monetisation, LCA, portfolio planning, reducing impacts, environmental policy, carbon tax, carbon trading, linear optimisation.

WIT Transactions on Ecology and The Environment, Vol 173, © 2013 WIT Press
www.witpress.com, ISSN 1743-3541 (on-line)
doi:10.2495/SDP130431

1 Introduction

Monetisation of environmental impacts describes the effort of expressing emissions into the environment in monetary values with the goal of an economic quantification of environmental damage caused through a product or process, which then can be the basis for a monetary incentive to avoid said impacts (Beckenbach *et al.* [1]). Current approaches for the monetisation of environmental impacts are mostly based on a separate assessment of both economic and environmental factors that are then combined retrospectively. Due to the retrospective approach, it is hard to use monetisation for planning processes, as it is always delayed to actual organisational actions (Schultz [2]). Most approaches for the monetisation of environmental impacts are based on the willingness to pay, which again is a quite subjective measure as for each region, individual or organisation and situation this willingness can vary (Reap *et al.* [3]).

Other approaches focus on determining the actual environmental damage costs caused through environmental impacts. This again is based on soft criteria. An analysis found that the environmental damage costs for the same system can differ by a factor of 40,000 (German Federal Environment Agency UBA [4]). Due to those problems, monetisation of environmental impacts is still an unresolved issue for Life Cycle Assessment (LCA) practitioners.

The approach presented within this paper picks up at this point. It offers an integrated approach that allows combining environmental aspects with economic factors in an objective way and avoids using subjective or soft criteria to determine a monetary value for environmental impacts. The determination of monetary value is hereby calculated organisation specific. That means that the outcomes of the assessment are only valid for the given situation and is not generally valid for other organisations or situations. Still, it offers a method of objectively determining the internal value of environmental impacts of an organisation. It does so by using the simplex algorithm in order to optimise a company's portfolio while establishing a price for environmental impacts. In a first step, the underlying methodologies used within the presented approach are explained, followed by a description of the integrated approach for monetisation as well as a case study that shows the application of this method. Results of the assessment are then discussed and interpreted. The article ends with a conclusion on the potential of the method and an outlook.

2 Methodological approach

2.1 Life cycle assessment

Life Cycle Assessment (LCA) is a method widely accepted and applied in industry and science. It allows quantifying the environmental impacts of products, processes and services and is standardised in ISO 14040 [5] and 14044 [6]. Within those standards, requirements for the method to ensure transparency and reproducibility of are defined. Through the quantification of environmental impacts, LCA supports environmental product improvement, strategic planning, benchmarking with other technologies or products as well as decision making. LCA is based on life cycle thinking; therefore all life cycle stages during a products life are assessed, from raw material extraction, material production, manufacturing over utilisation to end of life. For those life cycle stages, all energy carriers, materials and auxiliaries as well as waste and emissions are taken into account and summed up.

This life cycle approach avoids shifting environmental impacts from one life cycle stage to another. Through the consideration of the entire life cycle, total environmental impacts are taken into account, allowing for a systematic analysis and reduction of environmental impacts using a well-established method.

As LCA requires a lot of data on inputs, outputs and their respective impact on the environment, software tools such as the GaBi LCA [7] software are used. This allows creating environmental models of products and processes, using extensive background databases with information on environmental impacts of different materials, processes or products. The results of an LCA are expressed in impact categories such as Global Warming Potential (GWP) and characterised by their significance in relation to a reference unit, e.g. kg CO_2-equivalent for GWP. This allows taking systematic steps for product improvements, benchmarking or strategic decision making.

2.2 Environmental aspects in business theory

Goods can be classified according to several criteria. An example of this is the classification based on excludability and rivalry in consumption. Excludability is based on whether it is possible to exclude individuals from the consumption of such goods. An example can be a levee and pay-tv. No one can be excluded from the benefits of a levee, as it protects everybody behind it. On the other hand, individuals can be excluded from the consumption of pay-tv, simply not by activating the channels. Rivalry in consumption describes an interference of the usability of a good that is being used by another individual. An example can be breathing and bread. Under normal conditions, no one's potential to breath is influenced by other breathing organisms around. On the other hand, an individual's potential to consume bread is strongly impacted by the consumption of said bread through another individual. Based on those criteria, four categories of goods exist, as shown in Figure 1 (Endres and Martiensen [8]).

	No rivalry of consumption	Rivalry of consumption
Non-excludable	Public goods e.g. levee	Common goods e.g. environment
Excludable	Club goods e.g. pay-tv	Private goods e.g. food

Figure 1:   Classification of goods.

The environment is here categorised as a common good. Individuals can't be excluded from using it, while there is a rivalry of consumption. This is described as the so-called *Tragedy of the Commons*, postulated by Hardin [9]. As an example, he uses grazing land open to all. Several shepherds use it to feed their cattle. Each shepherd, being a rational actor, tries to maximise his earning, which can be achieved by increasing the size of his herd. This has two opposing effects. For the shepherd, the earning is increased by the benefit he has from having more cattle. On the other side, the same grazing land has now to accommodate one additional cattle to feed. However, this effect is smaller for a single shepherd, as it is shared by all shepherds. Therefore the rational decision for each shepherd in this example is to add more cattle to his herd. This is the tragedy of the commons: while each individual follows his own rational agenda to maximize his earning; the total availability of grazing land is limited. So while pursuing their own best interest, the group of shepherds is driving themselves to ruin. The same is the case for pollution and emissions, only in a reverse way. Instead of consuming too much of a limited resource, something is emitted in a system that has only a limited capacity to hold those emissions. Again, each actor will find that it is cheaper for him to emit into the common good environment and pay his share of the costs to compensate the impact, than to pay for the actual costs of avoiding or purifying his waste and emissions (Hardin [9]). From an economic point of view, the rational thing is therefore to rather participate in social repair costs, e.g. in form of tax than to take more expensive individual measures to reduce an organisations environmental impact.

On the other hand, environmental awareness in society, industry and politics has grown over the last years. Politics impose laws that aim at preserving the environment (European Commission [10]) while customers awareness for the environmental impacts of products and services increased. Industry answered to these new challenges through organisational environmental policy, sustainable product design or systematic improvement of products and processes, e.g. based on LCA studies. As a result, sustainability efforts of companies become a competitive factor, as it can be used to diversify own products and services from those of competing organisations (Meffert and Kirchgeorg [11]). Especially in saturated markets, diversification can be an important step to get a competitive edge over other organisations. This rising awareness and measures taken due to it can help to solve the tragedy of the commons.

2.3 The simplex algorithm for portfolio planning

The simplex algorithm is a method presented by George Dantzig that allows solving linear optimisation problems (Dantzig [12]). In classical business theory, it is e.g. used to identify optimal production programs with the constraint of limited availability of machining time and/or materials. In a first step the target value to be optimised has to be selected. The Contribution to Margin (CtM) is here often selected; as it takes into account both costs and revenues related to a product. The Contribution to Margin (CtM) is the key parameter for short-term production planning. The CtM is generally the difference between the selling price and the variable costs of a product (Wöhe and Döring [13]). Both target value and constraints are then transferred in a matrix structure (see Table 2 in section 3). Starting from a basic feasible solution, it takes iterative steps to find a solution better than the previous one. This is done until an optimal allocation of available resources is reached. The basic feasible solution is often chosen with a total Contribution to Margin of zero, correlating to not using any means of production, while generating no income at all. From this feasible solution, pivot operations are conducted in order to improve increase the target value and reach an optimal allocation of scarce resources (Geiger and Kanzow [14]). The application of the simplex algorithm is described within the case study.

2.4 Integrated approach for systematic monetisation of environmental impacts

In a next step, the previously presented methodological approaches are combined to an integrated approach for the systematic monetisation of environmental impacts. The procedure of this is shown in Figure 2.

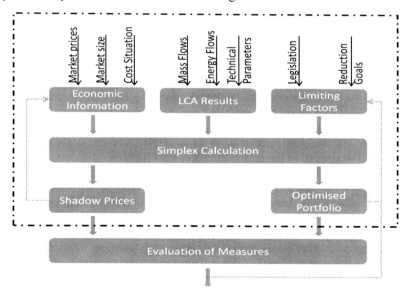

Figure 2: Integrated methodological approach.

Economic factors such as market prices, market share and product prices deliver the required economic information. At the same time, LCA studies are conducted for all products under assessment, giving out the environmental profiles of products based on mass and energy flows. Finally, there are limiting factors, e.g. legislation or reduction goals, that put a certain boundary to the amount of environmental impacts. All those factors are used as input parameters for the simplex calculation. This calculation aims at an optimal allocation of scarce factors, in this case environmental impacts. It thereby allows reaching environmental reduction goals with minimal economic impact. The output is an optimised portfolio, which results in the largest economic success under the given constraints. Furthermore, shadow prices are calculated. Those determine the internal value of scarce factors. This can then be used to prioritise measures or to compare the internal value of scarce factors with external prices, e.g. coming from an emission trading scheme.

3 Case study

The application of the simplex method as a tool for portfolio planning with the consideration of environmental impacts is presented through a case study. The case study is based on a virtual logistics company. This company operates a portfolio of multi-use plastic crates for the transport of fruits and vegetables and aims at optimising this portfolio with consideration of environmental aspects. The value to be optimised is selected to be the contribution to margin (CtM) of both products. There are two kinds of crates available, one made of conventional, crude oil based polyethylene (PE) and one made of polyethylene based on the renewable feedstock sugar cane, each with its own environmental profile but identical technical properties. The composition of the portfolio will thereby impact the company's environmental impact.

The environmental information is based on a study conducted by the Department Life Cycle Engineering of Fraunhofer IBP and University of Stuttgart on behalf of Stiftung Initiative Mehrweg (Albrecht *et al.* [15]). Within this study, the life cycle of multi-use plastic crates for the transportation of fruits and vegetables in Europe was assessed and quantified through an LCA study. Environmental data models, assumptions, documentation of system boundaries as well as results have been subject to a critical review according to ISO 14040/44. The quality of the data is therefore very high.

Subject of the study are among other multi-use plastic crates. Those crates have a weight of 2 kg and a capacity of 15 kg of fruit or vegetables. Logistic processes take place between five selected producing countries and four consuming countries, respectively representing the most important markets within the European Union. The study covers initial production of crates, replacement of broken crates during use, transport, washing of used crates and recycling of crates at their end of life. Life span of plastic crates is assumed to be 10 years and 5 fillings per year, corresponding to 50 circulations per crate total.

For those system boundaries and same underlying assumptions as realised in the study mentioned above, two multi-use plastic crates are analysed, one made of conventional crude oil based polyethylene as in the original study and the other made of bio-based polyethylene from sugar cane.

Based on those assumptions and system boundaries, environmental data models are created within the GaBi LCA software [7]. The model is evaluated in order to identify the environmental impacts of the entire life cycle of the plastic crates. Results of the LCA study for both packaging systems are expressed in impact indicators. Those impacts are shown in Table 1. All properties refer to one circulation of each system. For the sake of simplicity, the LCA is not described here in detail.

Economic aspects differ from organisation to organisation; no general statements can be given here. Therefore assumptions on the CtM have to be made for this case study. It is assumed that per circulation of a conventional PE crate the CtM is 0.50 €, due to the higher production costs for sugar cane based PE crates, the CtM is set to 0.45 €.

For the sake of simplicity, this case study only takes two environmental impact categories into account, Global Warming Potential (GWP, expressed in kg CO_2-equivalent) and Acidification Potential (AP, expressed in kg SO_2-equivalent).

Table 1:   Product properties per circulation.

	GWP [kg CO_2-eq.]	AP [kg SO_2-eq.]	CtM [€]
Conventional PE crate	0.33	0.0015	0.50
Bio-based PE crate	0.10	0.0025	0.45

It is assumed that the company currently operates a portfolio that consists of respectively 50% of each type of crate. The total number of circulations is 3,333,350, corresponding to the transportation of 50,000 t of fruits and vegetables. Therefore, 1,666,675 circulations of each type of crate carried out.

In a first step, the current environmental impact is determined. This can be done by multiplying the number of crates with the respective environmental profile of one circulation. Based on this, the environmental profile sums up to 717,500 kg CO_2-eq. and 6,667 kg of SO_2-eq. while generating a total CtM of 1,583,341 €. Apart from the environmental restrictions, there is also a market restriction; the total amount of circulations can't be higher than 3,333,350.

The company now aims at optimising their environmental profile. Therefore, the product properties as well as the restrictions are transferred in a simplex starting tableau with a basic feasible solution. Table 2 shows the first simplex tableau. The first two columns represent the product properties for conventional (Y) and bio-based crates (X) that were already shown in Table 1. Columns S1–S3 are slack variables that transform the inequations into an equation. The column on the right quantifies the limitations. RHS stands hereby for Right Hand Side. These are the environmental and market-based limitations for the portfolio. The first numerical line in the tableau represents contribution to GWP. The number in the RHS-column describes the yet available amount. The second numerical line represents AP; the third line the market restriction with a maximum number of circulations of 3,333,350. The numbers in the table represent the negative marginal impact of an increase of the product or slack variable in that line on the RHS.

Table 2:   Simplex tableau basic feasible solution.

	X	Y	S1	S2	S3	RHS
GWP	0.1000	0.3300	1	0	0	717,500
AP	0.0025	0.0015	0	1	0	6,667
Market	1	1	0	0	1	3,333,350
	-0.45	-0.50	0	0	0	0

The bottom line is the target function, containing the CtM of each product, while on the RHS the organisations total CtM is shown. In this case it is still zero, as the basic feasible solutions starts with an output of zero before taking iterations to optimise the outcome.

On the very left, the restriction to which the line relates is named. Note that this will change when applying the simplex method, depending where a pivot line with one "1" and the rest "0" is. Values on the RHS always correspond to the line where the "1" is found, representing the variable in the column of the "1".

Starting from this basic feasible solution, iterative steps are taken to optimise the portfolio. Within each iterative step, a column is selected, for example the one with the largest negative number in the target function line, as it has the strongest marginal impact on the target value. From the selected column the pivot element is chosen by dividing the number in the right column by the respective number in the previously chosen column and choosing the line with the smallest number as pivot element. In this case, the pivot column is Y, the pivot element is the contribution of product Y to GWP in the first line. The pivot line is then divided by the pivot element, so that the pivot element has a value of 1. In a next step, multiples of the pivot row are subtracted from the other rows so all non-pivot elements in the pivot column become 0. In the next step, another negative value from the target function line is selected and the steps are repeated. This is done until there are no negative values in the target function line left. As soon as this is the case, the available resources are allocated in an optimal way, as no adaption of the portfolio can increase the CtM anymore. Based on this allocation, shadow prices of scarce resources are determined. Those shadow prices describe the internal value of each respective resource in the current organisation-specific situation (Geiger and Kanzow [14]).

In a first step it is analysed if the current portfolio is optimal. Therefore, a simplex analysis is run with constant constraints. The result is shown in Table 3.

Table 3:   Simplex tableau optimised basis scenario.

	X	Y	S1	S2	S3	RHS
Y	0	1	4.330	0	-0.430	1,666,675
AP	0	0	0.004	1	-0.003	0
X	1	0	-4.330	0	1.430	1,666,675
	0	0	0.220	0	0.430	1,583,341

It can be seen that the lines now relate to different parameters, as the pivot columns and thereby the reference value of the pivot element changes. Both X and Y have an output of 1,666,675, generating a total CtM of 1,583,341 €. This means that the original portfolio represents an optimal allocation of available factors. In this case, this is not surprising, as one product has a lower GWP, while the other has a lower contribution to AP. In order to have the largest benefit from the available parameters, the original split is a logical consequence.

In a next step, the company aims at reducing its environmental impact. It is decided to reduce GWP by 10%. This results in adapted constraints of the simplex tableau, as the maximum emission of CO_2-equivalents is now only 90% of the original level. Based on the new constraints, the simplex analysis is run again. The outcome of this optimisation is shown in Table 4.

Table 4: Simplex tableau optimised with GWP-reduction.

	X	Y	S1	S2	S3	RHS
Y	0	1	3.69	-147	0	1,401,737
X	1	0	-2.21	488	0	1,825,637
Market	0	0	-1.47	-341	1	105,976
	0	0	0.85	146	0	1,522,405

As the acceptable amount of CO_2-emissions is reduced, the portfolio changes. The new portfolio now consists of about 1,402,000 conventional PE crates and 1,826,000 crates made of sugar cane based PE. This results in a total of 3,228,000 circulations, generating a total CtM of 1,522,405 €. In this situation, the market still has an unsaturated demand of almost 106,000 circulations. As it can be seen, a reduction of the companies' contribution to GWP by 10% can be realized by changing the portfolio and without taking other steps. This results in a reduction of the total CtM by 3.8%. The total market saturation is then down to 97%. Under the new constraints, the highest possible CtM was realized, therefore fulfilling the environmental reduction target at the lowest possible reduction of CtM. Still, in this scenario, the company would lose some of its market share, as it can't saturate the entire demand of the market.

The company therefore wants to assess whether a bio-based crate that is produced in sustainable agriculture is a reasonable extension of the portfolio. It can be expected that the environmental impacts of such a product are lower, e.g. by not relying on slash-and-burn agriculture. This on the other hand causes higher production costs and thereby a lower CtM. An adapted LCA for the new product is conducted and its results are used as parameters in the simplex algorithm. Again, the goal is to reduce the contribution to GWP by 10% while not increasing the contribution to AP. The calculated environmental impacts per circulation are 0.08 kg of CO_2-eq. and 0.002 kg of SO_2-eq., while it is assumed that the CtM is only 0.42 € due to higher production costs. Furthermore, it is assumed that all three crates have the same technical properties and no additional costs are caused by introducing an additional type of material, namely the bio-based PE from sustainable production without slash-and-burn agriculture here referred to as "Z". The new situation results in an updated simplex tableau with a new basic feasible solution, as shown in Table 5.

Based on this new situation, the simplex algorithm is now applied again. The results of this are presented in Table 6.

As can be seen, the total amount of circulations can remain at 3,333,350, so no market share is lost. To saturate the demand, 518,990 circulations of sustainable bio-based PE crates are used. Furthermore, the total CtM is higher by 32,400 € compared to the basis reduction scenario. Even though the bio-based PE crate

Table 5:   Basic feasible solution for product alternative with GWP-reduction.

	X	Y	Z	S1	S2	S3	RHS
GWP	0.1000	0.3300	0.080	1	0	0	645,800
AP	0.0025	0.0015	0.002	0	1	0	6,667
Market	1	1	1	0	0	1	3,333,350
	-0.45	-0.5	-0.42	0	0	0	0

from sustainable agriculture looks at first sight less favourable from an economic point of view, it can contribute to the organisations business success. A comparison of the shadow prices of scarce factors shows that the situation is less stressed as the shadow prices are lower. Compared to the basis scenario, the total CtM is 28,500 € lower than in the initial situation. A reduction of more than 71 t of CO_2-eq. can therefore be reached only through a change of the portfolio mix and the introduction of a new product variant for costs of 28,500 €. Compared to the best solution with the established crates, this increases the company's total CtM by almost 33,000 €.

Table 6:   Optimised simplex tableau for product alternative with GWP-reduction.

	X	Y	Z	S1	S2	S3	RHS
Y	0	1	0	3.6	-165.0	0.1	1,407,180
X	1	0	0	3.6	1.8	-3.9	1,407,180
Z	0	0	1	-7.2	-1.7	4.9	518,990
	0	0	0	0.4	41.9	0.3	1,554,797

4   Results and discussions

Through the application of the proposed method, environmental reduction goals of organisations can be reached by adapting their product portfolio with the lowest possible economic impact. In the first case, a reduction of 71,750 kg of CO_2-equivalents was realised through changing the portfolio. This results in a reduction of the total CtM by 61,000 €. This corresponds to 0.85 €/kg CO_2-eq. This value is referred to as the shadow price. It describes the internal value of one unit of a scarce factor in the current situation of a company. As it can be seen, this value is also shown in the bottom line under S1 in Table 4. The simplex algorithm describes the scarcity of all factors through their shadow price. For AP (represented through S2), this shadow price is 146 €/kg SO_2-eq. This means that the emission of one additional kg SO_2-eq., the total CtM can be increased by 146 € in the organisations current situation, while the emission of one additional kg of CO_2-eq. will increase the total CtM by 0.85 €. This can be the basis on which an organisation can decide e.g. whether or not to buy CO_2-certificates.

For the second application example with sugarcane grown in sustainable agriculture it could be seen that even the introduction of an at first sight economically not favourable product can contribute to the success of an organisation. For the situation assessed here, the introduction of a third product variant is a good choice, as it allows to fully saturate the demand of the market while increasing the total CtM of the organisation. Through the new product, the contribution to GWP could be reduced while other environmental impacts remain the same while reducing the costs compared to basis scenario. At the same time, the total CtM could be increased by over 32,400 € compared to the first scenario, while the entire demand of the market is saturated.

As it could be seen, the presented approach allows for an objective and systematic monetisation of environmental impacts. It uses economic information, environmental profiles of products and limiting factors in order to determine an optimal allocation of all scarce factors, by minimizing the economic impact. This can give decision makers a basis on which they can decide whether or not to take measures to reduce environmental impacts; to introduce new products or if and to what extent to by emission certificates.

5 Conclusion and outlook

This paper describes a systematic approach for monetizing environmental impacts as well as ways to improve environmental performance of organisations with the lowest possible economic impact. The described approach is therefore a valuable extension of current monetisation methods. Through the systematic and objective combination of ecologic and environmental aspects, it helps to include the outcomes of LCA studies in existing management procedures and thereby increases the relevance of LCA for decision making support.

As it could be seen in the case study, an optimal portfolio and thereby an optimal allocation of scarce factors, is reached through the application of the simplex algorithm with the smallest possible economic impact. Furthermore, shadow prices for scarce factors are calculated. Those can help companies with their decision making; e.g. the costs of measures to reduce emissions can be compared with the internal value of the reduction and thereby give information on the efficiency of measures. Also, the monetisation of environmental impacts can be the basis for internal programs, such as e.g. a carbon tax, as it helps to determine the price of such a tax. Another application shown is the evaluation whether to introduce a new product variant in order to fulfil environmental targets.

Those possibilities make the described methodological approach a useful extension of current approaches for the monetisation of environmental impacts, which again helps to increase the relevance of LCA for organisational decision making and thereby supports overall sustainability efforts. It helps organisations to define priorities when it comes to choose measures to reduce the environmental impact through shadow prices; a higher shadow price means a higher priority for measures that reduce the respective impact. Furthermore, objectively determined internal costs can be compared to external costs, e.g. for emission certificates or trade-off costs and thereby allows to systematically enhance sustainability efforts.

References

[1] Beckenbach, F., Hampicke U. and Schulz, W., *Möglichkeiten und Grenzen der Monetarisierung von Natur und Umwelt*, Schriftenreihe des IÖW 20/88, Berlin, pp. 3–18, 1998.

[2] Schultz, A.; *Integrated environmental and economic assessment of production processes and technologies. Doctoral Dissertation accepted by: Otto-von-Guericke-Universität Magdeburg, The Faculty of Engineering*, pp. 13–31, 2002.

[3] Reap, J., Roman F., Duncan, S. and Bras, B., A survey of unresolved problems in life cycle assessment – part 2: impact assessment and interpretation *Int Journal of Life Cycle Assessment*, pp. 374–388, 2008.

[4] German Federal Environment Agency UBA, *Ökonomische Bewertung von Umweltschäden – Methodenkonvention zur Schätzung externer Umweltkosten*, pp. 7–14, 2007. http://www.umweltdaten.de/publikationen /fpdf-l /3193.pdf

[5] ISO 14040:2006: *Environmental management – Life cycle assessment – Principles and framework.*

[6] ISO 14044:2006 , *Environmental management – Life cycle assessment – Requirements and guidelines.*

[7] PE: *GaBi 5. Software-System and Databases for Life Cycle Engineering.* Copyright, TM. Stuttgart, Echterdingen 1992–2012.

[8] Endres, A. and Martiensen, J., *Mikroökonomik. Eine integrierte Darstellung traditioneller und moderner Konzepte in Theorie und Praxis*, Kohlhammer-Verlag: Stuttgart, p. 768, 2007.

[9] Hardin, G., The Tragedy of the Commons. *Science*, New Series, Vol. 162, No. 3859 (Dec. 13, 1968), pp. 1243–1248, 1968.

[10] European Commission (2003), *Directive 2003/87/EC of the European Parliament and of the Council of 13 October 2003 establishing a scheme for greenhouse gas emission allowance trading within the Community and amending Council Directive 96/61/EC.*

[11] Meffert, H. and Kirchgeorg, M., *Marktorientiertes Umweltmanagement. Konzeption, Strategie, Implementierung*, Schaeffer-Poeschel-Verlag: Stuttgart, pp. 23–27, 1998.

[12] Dantzig, G., *Linear Programming and Extensions.* Princeton University Press: Princeton (NJ), pp. 94–119, 1963.

[13] Wöhe, G. and Döring, U., *Einführung in die Allgemeine Betriebswirtschaftslehre*, Vahlen-Verlag: München, pp. 386–387, 2005.

[14] Geiger, C. and Kanzow, C., *Theorie und Numerik restringierter Optimierungsaufgaben*, Springer-Verlag: Berlin, Heidelberg and New York, pp. 77–120, 2002.

[15] Albrecht, S., Beck, T., Barthel, L., Fischer, M. *The Sustainability of Packaging Systems for Fruit and Vegetable Transport in Europe based on Life-Cycle-Analysis – Update 2009.* On behalf of Stiftung Initiative Mehrweg SIM (Foundation for Reusable Systems under German Civil Law)). Stuttgart/Michendorf, pp. 17–98, 2009.

Value chain costing analysis as an approach to evaluate market price volatilities due to changing energy prices

S. Albrecht, H. Krieg & M. Jäger
Department Life Cycle Engineering (GaBi),
Chair of Building Physics (LBP), University of Stuttgart, Germany

Abstract

The commercial availability of resources and preliminary products is of essential importance for the industry. One aim of manufacturing companies is to know about structural dependencies in the availability of resources along the entire value chain of their products and to also not only know about environmental impacts of a product but also to have information about the economic life cycle and the value chain. Life Cycle Costing (LCC) is a technique to evaluate the costs of a product over its entire life cycle. Existing approaches give no sufficient answer on how input price alterations in upstream processes influence the value chain costs of materials. But for decision makers, it is crucial to know e.g. at what oil price investments in new materials or the change of feedstock from fossil to renewable become profitable from a life cycle perspective. Therefore, a new approach is suggested, combining LCC and Life Cycle Assessment (LCA). LCA provides the fundamental basis (a functional system model with energy and mass flow balances of all upstream processes) which is enhanced with economic parameters. It basically combines most of the elements of Life Cycle Assessment, environmental Life Cycle Costing according to the method suggested by SETAC and Total Cost of Ownership avoiding restrictions of the respective methods. The paper will describe the procedure of modelling, an exemplary process model and combined static LCA and dynamic LCC results for insulation materials along the value chain of the product. The model is validated using alternating energy prices.
Keywords: energy costs, Life Cycle Engineering, supply chain risks, green procurement, Life Cycle Costing, price sensitivity.

WIT Transactions on Ecology and The Environment, Vol 173, © 2013 WIT Press
www.witpress.com, ISSN 1743-3541 (on-line)
doi:10.2495/SDP130441

1   Introduction

The commercial availability of resources and preliminary products is of vital importance for the industry. One aim of companies is to know about structural dependencies in the availability of resources within the entire value chain of their products. Also, forecasting of price developments is of great importance for planning processes. Therefore, an approach that combines and extends the methods of Life Cycle Assessment (LCA) and Life Cycle Costing (LCC) and thereby allows identifying the impact of changing energy prices on the selling price of products is presented.

This paper describes the methodological foundation of the method, and then gives a validation for the approach.

2   Method

Within the next section, an outline of the method compared to existing approaches will be explained and the procedure of the developed approach itself will be described. Furthermore, a calculated evaluation of the method is applied.

2.1   Analysis of existing methods and demarcation of the value chain energy cost analysis method

Life Cycle Costing (LCC) is a technique to evaluate the costs of a product over its entire life cycle [1]. However, existing approaches give no sufficient answer on how input price alterations in upstream processes influence the value chain costs of materials. But for decision makers, it is crucial to know about e.g. at what oil price an investment in new materials or the change of feedstock from fossil to renewable becomes profitable from a life cycle perspective.

By combination and further development of existing economic assessment methods, identified gaps are filled according to the goals of this approach. The following table 1 summarizes the essential methodical requirements and the differences of the respective approaches.

The comparison of the existing methods indicates that none of the presented approaches can meet the requirements of the goal of the value chain energy costs analysis method. Previous approaches of LCC such as conventional LCC / TCO [3] or the flowcost accounting [4] are no appropriate methods as they do not consider interactions of companies within the value chain. Further approaches that integrate upstream processes either do not include economic aspects (such as LCA [2]) or focus only on organisational aspects of the value chain (Supply Chain Management, Supply Chain Costing [3]).

Therefore, a new approach for LCC is suggested using the Life Cycle Assessment (LCA) method as the fundamental basis (a system model with energy and mass flow balances of all upstream processes) enhanced with economic aspects. With this, it will be possible to calculate more precisely e.g. the influence of energy price alterations and its influences regarding the value chain of a product considering all upstream processes.

Table 1:   Comparison and evaluation of existing methodical approaches.

Description	Life Cycle Assessment LCA [2]	Conventional LCC/ Total Costs of ownership TCO [3]	Environmental-LCC	Flowcost Accounting [4]	GaBi [8]	Supply Chain Management/Supply Chain Costing [3]	Experience Curves [5]
Modelling/ Integration of upstream processes	✓	(✓)	✓	(✓)	✓	✓	(✓)
Energy input per module of the upstream process	✓	x	✓	x	✓	(✓)	x
Costs for the energy input	x	(✓)	(✓)	(✓)	(✓)	(✓)	x
Consideration of margins / surcharges	x	(✓)	x	x	x	x	x
Compounding over the links of the upstream processes	x	x	x	x	x	x	x
Summation / transfer of the sum	✓	(✓)	(✓)	(✓)	(✓)	✓	x
Physical life cycle	✓	x	✓	x	✓	✓	x
Dynamic projection into the future	(✓)	(✓)	x	x	x	(✓)	✓

✓ = component of the method;

(✓) = possible; not up to now, indirect or only applied for some players of the value chain (application for single process modules);

x = not component of the method

2.2 Procedure of the energy cost analysis through a combination of a technical process chain analysis and dynamic cost accounting

The first step is the definition of the technical system and the functional unit, according to the procedure of an LCA study. The functional unit according to ISO standard DIN ISO 14044 [6] is defined as "[...] the quantified performance of a product system for use as a reference unit".

After defining the functional unit of the product system, the next step is to set up a Life Cycle Inventory model corresponding to the LCA procedure. This is based on mass and energy flows for each step of the upstream value chain. The relevant Life Cycle Inventory data must be available in non-aggregated form. The process model should be broken down to the energetic input resources like naphtha, gas or electricity.

The technical model is then extended with economic quantities, such as costs for material and process energy for every process step as well as the product selling price. Data sources used for this are described in detail in section 2.3.

To provide a stable basis, data from a year with slight price fluctuation has to be used. Thus, prices from 2009 were used to set up the static model, since energy prices (oil and naphtha price, gas price, electricity price) fluctuation was relatively low in this period.

Processes which take place within the organisation underlie a special analysis interest. It is possible to depict the functional dependence in maximum detail by using manufacturer-specific data, thus providing the opportunity for a very explicit analysis. According to classic cost accounting theory, the following costs are identified:

> + Direct material costs
> + Direct energy costs
> + Direct manufacturing costs
> + Overhead costs
> = Production cost per unit
> + Selling, general and administrative costs
> = Original costs
> + Profit margin
> = Product selling price

Direct manufacturing costs are mainly wages directly corresponding to the manufactured product.

Investment costs are usually included in the overhead costs. Within investment decisions, with the goal of a certain return on investment, the realistic possibility to realise this return rate, is a decisive factor. Therefore, it is recommended to identify investment costs for one product- or process-specific analysis based on the produced functional unit and to integrate those costs with a reference to time according to the projected life span. The production costs and other, nonspecific overhead costs accumulate to the original costs. Those, together with the profit margin, result in the products selling price.

To analyse upstream processes where no detailed information is available, a surcharge margin has to be calculated. The margin is determined by the data from Life Cycle Analysis and price databases. The margin in this method contains overhead costs as well as the profit margin and is defined as:

$$\text{Margin} = \text{sales price} - \sum \text{material costs} - \sum \text{energy costs.}$$

Depending on the availability of data, the margin can be further subdivided. This can only be done with additional information.

In a next step, the margin is related to the direct material and energy costs, in order to identify the percental mark-up. Based on these assumptions, it is possible to identify the direct cost basis and the margin for every process step. The product selling price is then calculated with the formula:

$$\text{Product selling price} = (\text{Direct material costs} + \text{Direct energy costs}) * (1+\text{margin})$$

The functional linking serves the creation of a mathematic model alongside the value chain. Thereby, the separately analysed process steps are combined over the entire value chain. The final prices of preliminary products are at the same time the material costs of the following process step (Input costs). Consequently, there is a functional mathematic relationship along the value chain for used substances (mass balance), energies (energy balance) as well as costs and prices (economic balance).

The up to date static model is complemented with variable costs for the energetic inputs naphtha, gas and electricity. Therefore, the product price p depends on the prices of the energetic input resources:

$$P(t) = (P_{Naphtha}(t); P_{Electricity}(t); P_{Gas}(t))$$

The developed method can for example further be used for
- Evaluation of expected cash flows to calculate net present value;
- Determination of the energy costs share of the product price to evaluate the dependence on resources and supply guarantee;
- Comparison of product prices subject to variable energy costs: Comparing the "Break-Even-Point" of product alternatives based on different feedstock.

2.3 Data requirements

A general need for all simulation tools and models is the availability of input data. For this method, both LCA and LCC data is required. The specific requirements for data are described in the following.

2.3.1 Technical and environmental data requirements

LCA models are in principle system models of the life cycle of a product or parts of the life cycle like the value chain of the production phase. Each process step requires a mass balance and energy balance model, which is called unit process according to ISO standards [6, 7], to describe physically the production process as single steps in the value chain. Combining the respective mass and energy balances of singles processes of the value chain of the respective production phase then describes the whole production process, starting with the extraction of raw materials. This kind of modelling requires knowledge of all upstream processes including detailed knowledge of process specific materials and energy carriers. These data requirements are normally handled by using databases like GaBi [8].

2.3.2 Economic data requirements

For the creation of the value chain energy cost analysis model, price and cost data along the entire value chain are required. Most important are the prices of all physical inputs (materials and energy carriers). Also, selling prices for all pre-products along the value chain should be known, since those market prices are input prices on the next higher level of the value chain. Based on the sum of input costs for a product and the selling price, the margin is calculated. If information on input prices and the margin of all upstream processes is available, a functional composition for the entire value chain can be made.

Economic information for materials and energy carriers can be gained from various price databases. Here public available information was chosen for energy carrier prices. On a national German level the German Ministry of Economics and Technology (BMWi) [9] provides long term price data for energy carriers like crude oil, natural gas and electricity both for industrial and private customers.

On a European level Europe's Energy Portal [10] provides current energy price ranges for each European country, for private customers and for industry. Price data for Germany for a bulk of traded goods are available by the German statistics office (destatis) [11]. On a European level EUROSTAT provides import and export prices of traded goods in Europe [12]. Special prices and additional information like volatility, average prices and price ranges for specific sectors like the plastics industry are provided by commercial database providers such as KI Web [13], which offer price information for most commercial thermoplastic polymers and its most important pre-products.

Further information, like labour costs, ROI factors or average overhead costs can be gained (if available) from branch specific reports, for example the report of the chemical industry in Germany [14].

3 Model validation

Based on the newly developed method, an LCA based economic price model of Expanded Polystyrene (EPS), which is mainly used for insulation and packaging applications, was set up. This price model is validated to check its accuracy.

The following Figure 1 shows a simplified model of the production value chain of EPS. It comprises all relevant upstream processes including the steps where energy carriers enter the system.

EPS and Polystyrene (PS) are polymerised from styrene, which is based on the fossil feedstock oil. The share of fossil feedstock dominates the used materials and energy carrier within the value chain of the production.

To validate the model, a retroactive forecast, based on historic energy and product prices, is carried out for the product "Expanded Polystyrene". The data used as a basis for the static model is from 2009, most of it being taken from destatis [11] foreign trade statistics and KI-Web (synthetic materials and preliminary products) [13]. After the static model was set up, average energy prices for every month in 2008 and 2009 were used as input prices, while other prices remained fixed. While 2009 saw a quite constant oil price rise from 0.23 €/kg in January to 0.36 €/kg in June and then prices quite constantly fluctuating around 0.36 €/kg until December, 2008 was a year with very volatile oil prices. Starting with 0.44 €/kg in January, prices peaked at 0.62 €/kg in July, only to drop to 0.21 €/kg in December. This offers the opportunity to validate the model both for quite constant and volatile surrounding conditions.

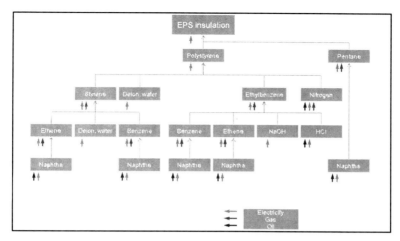

Figure 1: Simplified flow chart of the production of polystyrene foam EPS including input of energy carrier.

The calculated product price based on varying energy prices showed a mean variation of less than 5% over the assessed two-year period, compared to the market price of the product.

When comparing the real market price with the simulated price, it was found that there was a lag between them. A phase-postponement of one month of the naphtha price (t) to the resulting product price (t) resulted in an improvement of the mean deviation from about 5% to about 3% in average. This is due to temporary delayed transmission of the price variation. It shows that the approach is working as a basic principle and generates accurate results.

The simulated and actual market prices for this period are shown in Figure 2.

It can be seen that the forecasted prices depict the actual market prices quite accurate and follow all market price trends. This shows that the approach is working as a basic principle.

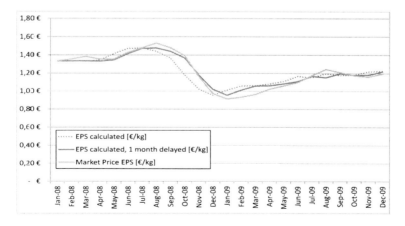

Figure 2: Validation of the economic model for EPS.

4 Conclusions

With the value chain energy cost analysis method, an innovative approach is developed that allows calculating the influence of energy price alterations more precise, taking into account the whole upstream value chain. This method combines the deep process knowledge of the environmental Life Cycle Assessment method with economic information to create a new procedure for a more detailed knowledge of where and in which intensity energy prices influence product prices along the products value chain.

An exemplary model was set up for German boundary conditions and prices and was evaluated with real market prices from 2008/2009 for Expanded Polystyrene by varying naphtha, electricity and gas price monthly. The modelled mean prices show a very high precision compared to real market prices of the product. The deviations mean value for the examined 24 months-period is about 2.9%. Due to its ability to potentially create relatively precise predictions of a product price depending on energetic input prices, this method is an innovative enhancement of existing Life Cycle Costing approaches.

References

[1]   VDI 2884, *Purchase, operation and maintenance of production equipment using Life Cycle Costing (LCC)*, 2005.
[2]   Klöpffer, W. & Grahl, B., *Ökobilanz (LCA)*, Wiley: Weinheim, 2009.
[3]   Herrmann, C.: *Ganzheitliches Life Cycle Management,* Springer-Verlag: Berlin, pp. 63 et seq., 2009.
[4]   Umweltbundesamt, *Ansätze der Umweltkostenrechnung im Vergleich.* Online: http://www.umweltdaten.de/publikationen/fpdf-l/2292.pdf
[5]   Simon T., Patel M., Junginger M., *Experience Curves in the World Polymer industry,* Utrecht University, Faculty of geosciences, Netherlands.
[6]   ISO, *Environmental management– Life cycle assessment – Requirements and guidelines* (ISO 14044:2006). German and English version EN ISO 14044:2006.
[7]   ISO, *Environmental management– Life cycle assessment – Principles and framework* (ISO 14040:2006). German and English version EN ISO 14040:2006.
[8]   LBP, PE (1992-2010*), GaBi 4.3. Systems and Databases for Life Cycle Engineering.*
[9]   BMWi – German Ministry of Economics 2010, *Gesamtausgabe der Energiedaten - Datensammlung des BMWi.* Report and tables provided by German Ministry of Economics 2010 regarding any questions of the energy supply in Germany.
[10] Energy Europe Portal. URL: http://www.energy.eu/#industrial. 12-05-2010.
[11] Statistisches Bundesamt, *Aus- und Einfuhr (Außenhandel)*, 2009. Report and tables available under URL: www.destatis.de
[12] Eurostat. URL: http://epp.eurostat.ec.europa.eu/portal/page/portal/eurostat /home/ 12-05-2010.

[13] KI Web. URL: http://www.kiweb.de/ 12-05-2010
[14] Association of the Chemical Industry in Germany (Verband der Chemischen Industrie e.V.), *Chemiewirtschaft in Zahlen*, 2009.

Section 10
Energy resources

Distributed energy generation:
case study of a mountain school campus in Italy

M. Anderlini, L. de Santoli & F. Fraticelli
Department CITERA, University of Rome, Italy

Abstract

Distributed energy generation is a technologically feasible reality. That requires rethinking buildings as nodes in a network for energy production and utilization and implementing best strategies according to the characteristics of the site. This paper concerns an ecologically sustainable school campus in the city of Contigliano (Rieti, Italy) that has specific environmental characters. Climate in the valley is continental: very cold in winter (which lasts 140 days) and hot in summer with wide temperature ranges. For this reason the valley records the lowest temperatures in Italy during the period from April to September. The research was carried out considering envelope characteristics, infrastructures and available renewable energy sources, taking into account the economic and environmental impacts with a particular attention to CO_2 emissions reduced by 93% if compared with traditional systems. The project of the school complex was analyzed by energy analysis. This has led to excellent results with a significant reduction of greenhouse gas emissions and a considerable reduction of energy consumption.

1 Introduction

Since the beginning of the Industrial Revolution, the atmospheric concentration of carbon dioxin has increased by 30%, concentration of methane is more than twice and the concentration of N_2O has increased by 15%. In addition, recent data show that the increasing speed concentrations of this gas, despite being low during the first part of the 90s, now are comparable at the high concentrations of the 80s.

WIT Transactions on Ecology and The Environment, Vol 173, © 2013 WIT Press
www.witpress.com, ISSN 1743-3541 (on-line)
doi:10.2495/SDP130451

In developed countries, the fossil fuel used for cars, for the heating flat and as alimentation of a lot of power stations are responsible for 95% of carbon emission, 20% of methane and 15% of N_2O.

The growth of soil depletion, industrial production and mining activities, contribute to the emissions in the atmosphere. Deforestation has an important role in the increment of CO_2 concentration, because plants can reduce the percentage of CO_2 with the process of photosynthesis. Vegetal respiration and decomposition of organic matter release in the air a quantity of CO_2 10 times higher than human activities; that emissions were balanced with photosynthesis and absorption by oceans.

If the global carbon emission will be the same of last years, atmospheric concentration will reach the value of 500 ppm until the end of this century, a value that is almost twice than the pre-industrial value (280 ppm). The problem is bigger because greenhouse gases can remain in the atmosphere for hundreds years.

For the energetic production, Italy consumes as much gas as Latin America. Our consumptions are equal to the total consumptions of Turkey, Poland, Romania and Austria all together: 59 millions of people that consume as 138 millions people. Of the all energy that we need, we product only 12%, for the remaining 88% we depend on other countries. Of this 88%, 76% is produced with the importation of gas, petroleum and coal and the other 12% bought from adjacent countries and produced by an equivalent of 8 nuclear plants. So in Italy, energy costs 30% more than other countries. In 2011, energetic demand is reduced by 0.5%, from 184 to 178.4 Mtep, relative to the last year. It has recorded a loss for gas (-4%), importation of electric power (-4.5%) petroleum (-1.4%). At the same time there was an increment of demand for solid fuel (+9.2%) and renewable sources (+8.1%).

During 2010, photovoltaic plants in Italy increased by 215% (84.777 photovoltaic plants installed) and increased by 314% in terms of power (2.4 GW). During the last period this field is amazingly increased; reaching on 10th April 2012, 13.06 GW for a total of 343,433 photovoltaic plants; reaching and exceeding the 12 GWP installed in 2011 photovoltaic covered 3% of electric demand in Italy, with the possibility of reaching 5.5% in 2012.

2   Italian School architecture

For a rapid description of the Italian School architecture situation, we refer to the Legambiente dossier [1], called *"ecosistema scuola"*, which is an analysis instrument of the Italian School situation. With this report it is possible to evaluate and analyse data from the main cities about the quality of the structures, first and secondary school.

Legambiente's report is anything but comforting; it is strongly necessary to invest on emergency maintenance, because more than 30% of the structures need urgent interventions of maintenance.

Six schools out of ten have been built before 1974 and there is an incredible difference between North and South Italy: only 50% of South Italy's buildings have been built after 1974, in the central part of Italy the percentage is 42% and in the North, 31%.

Positive data are derived from energy conservation: the number of the schools that use low consumption illumination is increased, in the last 4 years, from 45% to 65%, in addition thanks to "Il Sole e la Scuola" there has been an awareness campaign.

From the surveys, the most active region in this program is Sicily with 80 schools, follow to Lazio, Abruzzo and Puglia with 60 schools.

In Italy will have the reduction of working expenses and make improvements to school's structures thanks to the project "Nuovo piano di edilizia scolastica", approved by Cipe according to the propose of "Ministero delle infrastrutture e dei trasporti"," Ministro dell'economia e delle finanze" and the "Ministro dell'istruzione, dell'università e della ricerca".

Once this plan will be effective, the schools will have 2 years for refurbish their structures, respecting specific technical index (art. 52).

With this measure, Italy will adapt to European standard, aligning the Country with specific laws on maximum and minimum index of energetic efficiency [2].

3 Specific situation of Rieti

The province of Rieti is an Italian province of region Lazio of 160,467 inhabitants whose capital Rieti. It covers an area of 2,749.16 km^2 and includes 73 municipalities. Founded in 1927 it is, together with Latina, one of the youngest Italian provinces. It born, therefore, as a result of a long process of gathering historical and political consolidated over time - such was the case for many of the provinces of Lombardy boasting a long tradition of such federation - but rather a result of an act that brought together an archipelago of municipalities and territories with very different histories and social identities, cultural traditions, by natural gravitation, dialects, customs and lifestyles.

Another anomaly in the province of Rieti lies in the fact that it was lapped only marginally from that vast process of industrialization and urbanization that has characterized the development stage of quantitative analysis of the 50s and 70s. This process has greatly changed the economic and social postwar background in Italy.

The climate is continental capital of the valley: very cold in the winter (which lasts 140 days) and high temperature during summer season, with large temperature ranges, which make the province under consideration the first of the Italian provinces with the lowest minimum temperatures during the period from April to September. Rainfall exceeds 1,000 mm annually; with two maxima, the largest in autumn and a secondary one in late spring. There is mist occasionally but rarely persistent for the entire day.

More rare snowfall in the valley, mainly with movement from the north-west, while the surrounding hills are numerous. There are also frequent summer thunderstorms. In 2008 average annual temperature +12.7°C, absolute minimum -10.3°C, absolute maximum +35.4°C, rainfall 1411.2 mm of rain in 106 days, average daily excursion 13.9°C, moderate excursion in August 19.2°C, 3 months (January, February and December) with average minimum temperatures below zero degrees, seven months without frost, maximum temperature of the coldest day of +3.3°C, minimum temperature of the hottest day +17.8°C [17]. The winter in Contigliano lasts about 4 months. Record cold in 1956 and 1985, respectively, -20°C and -18°C. The summer has an average life span of a hundred days.

4 Analysis of current situation

The research has touched every aspect of the educational sector in the city of Contigliano and the following paragraph describes the results of statistical-descriptive analysis and the current quality of the old school campus. In the following we will highlight the critical factors divided into 3 groups according to: technical-administrative analysis, technical and environmental analysis and energy performance analysis.

In the first one, a comparison is made between the current legislation and regulations applicable at the time of implementation, in particular the regulations being studied are L.5 August 1975, n. 412 and the l. January 11, 1996, n. 23.

In the analysis has not found a strong innovation on the part of the 1996 Act in that it takes into account purely economic and financial aspects for local authorities, ignoring current issues including the functional and morphological appearance of the building as a whole. The complex in question appears to be

Primary school   Secondary school

Figure 1:   The school living complex.

devoid of a structure to accommodate the school canteen to the appropriate legislation. From the functional point of view the plexus results to be made according to a horizontal structure which faces the various classrooms, are also provided for the central areas of the collective, all in a view of the 60s.

The analysis has led to technical and environmental results for the critical noise impact due to the high intensity of vehicular passing just below the school structure in the early hours of the day. The school complex of Contigliano was built around the 60s so in the absence of energy legislation, especially it refers to the Law 10/91 and Decree 192/05 as amended [3] establishing the criteria, conditions and ways to improve the energy performance of buildings in order to facilitate the development, enhancement and integration of renewable sources and energy diversification, help to achieve the national targets for limiting greenhouse gas greenhouse set by the Kyoto Protocol and European legislation known as 20-20-20, to promote the competitiveness of the sectors by developing more advanced technology. Not taking into account the regulations in force in the school campus are to be present sanitation situation is not sufficient to ensure an acceptable level of learning capacity of the areas.

5 Description of site and description of intervention

The research was developed based on a design from scratch of a school campus to serve Contigliano and Greccio. This requirement stems from a feasibility study developed upstream of where research has evaluated the ability to adapt structurally and energetically, the old school facilities or change the intended use and convert them to office or to build a new school edge trying to achieve goals of building passive. The latter solution was the most advantageous from the standpoint of economic, regulatory and energy.

The study area is located in the municipality of Contigliano and more specifically in the area east of the old city in front of the train station that connects the town with neighboring countries and cities like Rieti, Terni and L'Aquila.

The research is geared to design scenarios for the realization of the new school complex and sustainable urban redevelopment, with the definition of the

Figure 2:   Site location.

new urban edge of the city and the creation of public spaces to serve the sporting and cultural communities. The area is characterized by wide open spaces and buildings scattered expands to an area of about two hectares, from the east is the railway station from where the main road that leads through the town, the historic village. To the north of the lot there is a nursing home and a series of residential and commercial buildings to no higher than 3 floors. On the opposite side there is a sports and entertainment complex that lies on the axis leading to the main urban center of the town, which are aligned along the newly built residential buildings. On the west side of the opening scene of the beautiful historic village of Contigliano. The study area is presented as a site with excellent potential to build a place characterized by a strong identity and a high quality urban area.

A predominant factor that significantly affects the microclimate of the site chosen is the sunshine of the area, particularly the sides that slope in directions between southeast and southwest. The analysis has resulted in important basic data for the purposes of architectural design, as the zenith angle of the sun, according to the latitude where we are, is a parameter characterizing strong and together with the analysis of the wind allows us to create characterization of distribution spaces in our buildings for optimum comfort environment. To do this you must plan taking into account the zenith angle of the sun, the latitude of the place under study, equivalent to $72.00°$ and $24°$ in summer and winter [4]. The indication of the considered against the zenith angle of the sun is to have an excess of energy due to radiation during the summer; this situation is easily solved through the use of solar shading systems that allow the reduction of irradiation within the living space in summer. To take full advantage of solar energy incident on the site were used in an active and a passive one. The active system used is a photovoltaic system capable of ensuring electrical energy sufficient to power the heat pump, which is necessary to ensure the thermal requirements of the interior, and provide electricity to meet the needs of the electrical structure, while for the passive system has made use of a greenhouse bioclimatic control of hygrothermal flows through the building, aimed at improving home comfort and to reduce energy consumption: physically consists of a glazed area, located adjacent to the building and living in some periods of the year, which contributes to the heating and cooling of spaces occupied by humans. Below will be described the analytical results obtained for the different technologies used.

6 Solar greenhouse

These solar systems for environmental control are based on the use of renewable energies, mainly solar radiation to help control the environmental conditions of space with the aim of reducing energy consumption and improve comfort such systems are called passive solar systems to distinguish from the active solar systems which require auxiliary energy for operation, mainly used for the circulation of the fluid. In the case study you are working in a site characterized, in winter, just to be clear days or high frequency of overcast days while estete

warm and sunny days, so it is useful to evaluate the contribution of scattered radiation. Looking at the climate data of Contigliano is known as in winter the average monthly contribution of scattered radiation on a horizontal plane is roughly equivalent to the contribution paid by direct radiation. An analysis carried out shows there is the advantage of having a transparent cover for the purposes of an increased uptake, compared to several disadvantages including:
-a greater heat loss greater radiation;
-night summer internal in conclusion.

An opaque cover has been adopted to decrease the dispersions at night and the glass area has been increased between the heated room and the greenhouse to increase the lighting comfort of a heated room.

In scenario planning, there are three different types of solar greenhouse, for reasons related to the architectural structure also opposite to the passive structures has created a body of water which can cool the air. Figure 3 shows a plan with the localization of the three types.

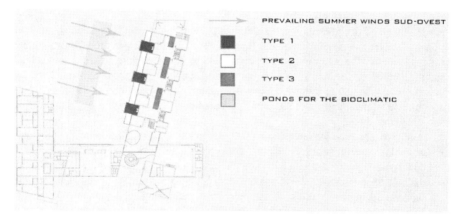

PREVAILING SUMMER WINDS SUD-OVEST

TYPE 1

TYPE 2

TYPE 3

PONDS FOR THE BIOCLIMATIC

Figure 3:   Position of the green house.

The third type is a solar greenhouse that is able to ensure internal levels of environmental comfort of the classrooms facing north. In the classrooms it was deemed appropriate to exploit the effect of solar chimneys to allow air inside the classrooms, in so doing has made an energy-economic benefits by reducing the energy demand for summer air conditioning.

The estimate of the benefit of a greenhouse can be developed with simulation software under thermodynamic variable which have the advantage of providing data simulated microclimate inside the greenhouse, hour by hour, on the basis of detailed climatic database. The disadvantage of these systems is the complexity of use which would result in many detailed while if they are used with other methods developed a calculation easier steady using average climate data and ignoring the fluid dynamic phenomena involved are reached acceptable results.

The software used are a transposition in the form of an automatic spreadsheet UNI EN 832 2001 and Method 5000 [5]. Both allow you to evaluate the energy

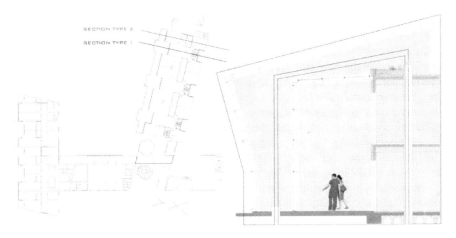

Figure 4:   Section of the green house – type 1 and type 2.

contribution of the greenhouse so steady for the winter months but with software you will study the dynamics of the fluid mass of air inside the greenhouse so that it may have, in the summer, good ventilation to its procedure that ensures a high thermal comfort for users.   Analysis conducted in the area identified by the greenhouse effect has led to temperature-humidity conditions to ensure it is acceptable to the occupants can enjoy a comfortable area of the building during sunny winter days.

In order to reduce overheating in summer some solutions have been prepared:
-   glazed opening, controlled by appropriate sensors, to provide for heat dissipation,
-   installation of semi-transparent PV panels and photovoltaic cells that serve as screens during the middle of summer days and spring.

The system allows a certain accumulation of heat due to the large glass area and its operation from the solar collector, although obviously low heat capacity. the solar radiation absorbed by the floor, or any other opaque surface, is stored and outputted based on the characteristics of emissivity of the various surfaces and to the thermal inertia of the components. Here are the results in the form of images, produced by the fluid flow analysis software GID. Fluid from the analysis carried out it has been noted how the design of the type 2 does not create air zone stagnated in all its height, while for the greenhouse 1 has been necessary to install a grid of ventilation on the balcony, the first floor, to prevent it would create an area where air stagnation, while the type 3 occurred the proper establishment of the effect of fire inside classrooms located to the north, in order to ensure a climate of spring and autumn. In addition to this analysis has verified the correct sizing of the transom windows, placed inside the northern classrooms.

The simulation results show that, in winter, the temperatures inside the greenhouse following the trend for the outdoor and are higher by 3–4°C. The only data that might seem strange is the low energy advantage brought about by the greenhouse building in October, this is because the simulation takes into

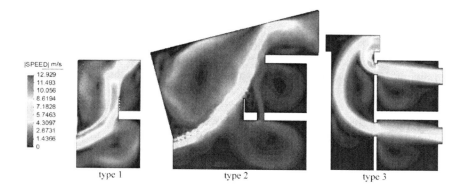

Figure 5:   Computational fluid dynamics of the greenhouse.

account the thermal inertia accumulated during the summer months and sold in the autumn so the advantage of the greenhouse is lowered considerably. In conclusion, considering the size of the greenhouse and the surface of the classrooms means less greenhouse heat loss to the outside and bring benefits to the building adjacent to substantial energy.

7   Heat pump and distribution of heat

In conclusion, considering the size of the greenhouse and the surface of the classrooms means less greenhouse heat loss to the outside and bring benefits to the building adjacent to substantial energy.

For the system of generation of heat, we have chosen a solution to the geothermal heat pump energy supplied by electricity from solar photovoltaic panels positioned above the roof of the school structure. This choice was made primarily for the hours of use of school facilities, which are 8:00 AM to 4:00 PM. For this reason it was decided to exploit the effect to produce electricity with photovoltaic power a geothermal heat pump in order to have a high value of energy efficiency and cede most of the electricity to neighboring users.

In the first part of the research was a study for the evaluation of energy can be drawn from underground through the study of stratigraphic and energy characteristics of the subsoil and the definition of the heat exchanger more suited for taking energy. The second part is identified, the heat pump fitter in synergy with thermal calculations necessary for the identification of potential, estimated hours of machine operation on an annual basis, design of distribution systems between soil hydraulic and thermal power plant and verification of the refrigeration cycle between school structure and the net uptake of energy in the subsurface.

In the third part the system of distribution of thermal energy within the building is identified.

The geological analysis has led to the construction of the stratigraphy that consists of 4 layers identified with the first layer of topsoil to 1.5 m, 12 m of limestone breccia with sharp corners in the clayey matrix, 1.5 m of brown clay dark of weak consistency and finally 12 m of limestone breccia with sharp corners in the sandy clay matrix. The aquifer is located at a depth of 15 m from ground level.

The distribution of geothermal systems with horizontal probes in the Italian territory is less than those with vertical probes. the reasons for this difference is mainly due to the limited availability of land at low prices in the vicinity of building sites and in the widespread conception of the project that this type of system is less efficient and handsome than that with vertical probes.

In the study of the design scenario of Contigliano's school campus, it was decided to proceed with an absorbing surface in horizontal closed loop geothermal because it is operating in an area free of water courses, this is to use a geothermal system in open circuit, and because it has wide open spaces in which to install the module surface horizontal and in the end because the material near the ground level has good energy parameters. The solution to geothermal probes horizontal, in contrast to the vertical, uses as an energy source a volume of soil of great extension but of little depth, the overall cost of excavation of the soil, which is necessary to prepare the area to the laying of the probes, is generally not significant compared to the installation of vertical probes, the implementation of horizontal probes is simple and requires no special technical skills. Obviously, the extension of the intercepting surface is proportional to the thermal power of the heat pump.

In the winter period the reference temperature of the first subsoil is variable between 4–6°C of less than about 6–8°C with respect to those occurring at depths greater. A heat source at a lower temperature than usual for the vertical systems, if exploited in the same manner, may result in a lower thermal efficiency of the geothermal heat pump. To overcome this problem, the systems of horizontal wells are designed, for the same thermal power, with a number of meters probe uptake greater than the equivalent vertical solutions. The efficiency of the heat exchange probe-soil is improved by increasing the total surface area of exchange. Given the low cost for the construction of the trench and the pipe for the supply of exchange plastic PEAD (high density expanded polyurethane) you can afford to oversize the field capturing, however, imposes limitations on its use in future use of these areas which will not be possible to build products, planting trees to tall buildings or schedule future.

For the calculation were used the following parameters: temperature of the water in the evaporator outlet, of 8 ° C and a thermal gradient of 5°C for the capacitor, while an outlet temperature of 45°C with a thermal gradient of 5°C it reaches a torque of 4.52 with a heat output of 345.63 kW and a power input of 43.66 kW. These results are obtained using the machine coolant water to water under reference dell'aermec NXW 750 D. For the calculation of the geothermal probe can use two methods: an analytical and a tabular, you use the analytical method is preferred because it is more accurate by taking into account the heat exchange at steady state and the amount of energy in the domain of groundwater uptake. In almost all of the literature used for the study of the feasibility of the geothermal sizing of geothermal probes uses the heat exchange relationship below [6].

$$Q = L \frac{(T_g - T_w)}{R}$$ (1)

Q = heat flow of fluid between single probe and the ground [k];
L = total length of the probe [m];
T_g = average temperature of the ground before installing the probe [k];
T_w = average temperature of the fluid in the probe [k];
R = thermal resistance of the soil per unit length of the probe [mK/W].

In the above formula the value of the subsurface temperature along the heat flow, are the main parameters of reference necessary for assessing the economic viability of a geothermal plant. At our latitudes this value is greater than the minimum winter temperatures and less of the maximum summer. The temperature of the fluid coming from the intercepting surface, which is sent to the heat pump allows to establish the yield of the latter, the thermal output is equal to the C.O.P. (coefficient of performance) = 4.82. The value of q to be used in the above formula is equal to the difference between the thermal power output and power input to the compressor; that difference in power is equal to 301.97 kW.

The average temperature that we find in our latitudes, and at a depth of 2.5 m is about 5°C. This data was obtained by a comparison between the different experiments carried out in the geothermal field and can be found in technical literature.

Obtaining the horizontal length of the probe, by the formula quoted above, and integrating the known data with the thermal calculations carried out with the software 10 to estimate the net electrical energy necessary for the operation of the compressor but also for the handling of fluids is obtained a length equal to about 14,350 linear meters of pipes to be laid inside the lot under study. Inside the school campus has decided to use a mixed system composed of channels of air to ensure clean air and radiant panels embedded in the floor to provide thermal comfort indoors. One of the clear advantages, radiant panels, it is the optimal temperature distribution within the environment, heat only at head height and avoid the feeling of cold feet, low temperatures also allow you to transfer heat to irradiation and not by convention avoiding the handling of hot air typical of radiator systems, and the consequent lifting of dust [7]. This type of heat emission maximizes the yield of the pampa of heat that has the maximum yield just in correspondence of low temperatures of operation of the radiant heating.

8 Photovoltaic plant

The first stage of the design consists in collecting a range of information on environmental and technical conditions of the site where the intervention will be realized. The first step is the inspection and it is known exactly how to install solar power at this stage will assess any logistical difficulties during the construction of environmental constraints and obstacles that could create shade.

The next step is to prepare a parametric study of the possible consumption for the entire school year and expand by acquiring the consumption of school buildings in the town of Contigliano and Rieti.

Obviously, in this calculation was considered the use of electrical devices other than low-consumption for which the new complex of the same size will have the lowest consumption. The numerical analysis has identified a predicted consumption of about 137,000 kWh to 70,000 kWh which must be added to power the heat pump. The plant has been split into two sections, one installed on the roof of the gym and the other on the roof of solar greenhouses. The plant located on the roof of the solar greenhouse is made up of 84 polycrystalline modules with peak power of 235 Wp, that plant can supply 272,000 kWh/year while the section located on the roof of the gym is also composed of 266 modules in polycrystalline from 235 Wp for a total year of electricity equal to 873,000 kWh.

This amount of energy is much higher than needed to power the school structure, the surplus energy will be distributed to users adjacent to the structure under study.

9 Conclusion

In conclusion we can say that the plan design of the school campus of Contigliano, falls into the category of passive house reaching a value of 0.1 kWh/sq m of annual energy requirements, this value was calculated by simulating energy the project the school campus of Contigliano. The diffusion of the passive house standard brings important and significant results for climate protection through rational use of fossil energy resources [8]. The very low power requirements of passive houses, allows the use of renewable sources not only as a supplement, but as the main source of energy throughout the year [9]. The large surplus of electricity generated by the photovoltaic means that the school acts as a power plant to neighboring users in order to create a system of distributed generation.

The plant subject of this discussion, given that it consists of photovoltaic panels and heat pump, results to have a lower environmental impact as regards the emission of carbon dioxide. Assuming to realize the school pole with traditional systems, we could create a structure capable of generating a quantity of carbon dioxide equal to 160 T/year while using the systems listed in the discussion is cut down by 90% the values of CO_2 emission reaching 12 T/year.

References

[1] XII Rapporto di Legambiente sulla qualità dell'edilizia scolastica, delle strutture e dei servizi, http://www.legambiente.it
[2] Calice, C., Clemente, C., De Santoli, L., Fraticelli, F., *Guidelines for the retrofit of the school building stock for sustainable urban regeneration of the city of Rome in Sustainable City VII, Urban regeneration and Sustainability,* Ecology and the Environment, Volume 155 WIT Press 2012, ISBN 978-1-84564-578-6.

[3] Decreto Legislativo 19 agosto 2005, n. 192, *Attuazione della direttiva 2002/91/CE relativa al rendimento energetico nell'edilizia.*

[4] De Santoli, L., Fraticelli F., Fornari, F., Planning the integration of new technologies for sustainability: case study of a school building's restoration project in Rome, in *ECO-Architecture III, Harmonization between architecture and nature* WIT Press, 2010, pp. 423–434, ISBN 9781845644307.

[5] Zappone C. *Serre Solare*, Sistemi Editoriali, 2009.

[6] Tornaghi M. *Geotermia*, Sistemi Editoriali, 2010.

[7] Dascalaki, E.G., Sermpetzoglou V.G., Energy performance and indoor environmental quality in Hellenic schools, *Energy and Buildings*, Volume 43, Issues 2–3, February–March 2011, Pages 718-727, ISSN 0378-7788.

[8] Rifkin J., *Economia all'idrogeno*, Mondadori, 2002.

[9] AA.VV. Edilizia scolastica ecocompatibile . *Il Progetto Sostenibile*, 17–18, Edicom, 2008.

Small hydroelectric plants: the hydraulic auger

G. Perillo
Department of Technology, Naples Parthenope University, Italy

Abstract

Small-scale hydroelectric plants are an important source of renewable energy and can actively contribute to the sustainable development of the local area, while also being cost-competitive with other renewable energy sources. This paper presents the application of a hydraulic auger used for flow rates up to 5–6 m³/s and heads up to 10 m. Unlike other turbines, this equipment works by gravity with water producing torque on a transmission driving a generator connected to the auger in order to produce electricity. We present a case study on a plant located at an existing dam where, by evaluating the river's mean daily flow, we have obtained duration curves that make it possible to determine the power and annual energy production obtainable from the plant. This is then compared with the energy that can be obtained from a plant equipped with a Banki-Mitchell turbine, highlighting that, at equal flow rates, the annual production obtainable from the two systems is nearly the same, confirming the effectiveness of the inverse auger in the energy production process. The economic aspects are then analyzed by comparing the plant construction costs with revenues from energy sales.
Keywords: hydroelectric plants, hydraulic auger, turbine comparison.

1 Introduction

The use of hydraulic energy dates back to ancient times and, ever since its origins, hydro-electricity has been the most widely used source of renewable energy after biomass.

The first dam known to mankind was built around 4000 BC in Egypt, its purpose being to divert the flow of the Nile and establish the city of Memphis on the reclaimed land. Many ancient dams, including those built by the Babylonians, were part of complex irrigation systems which transformed barren regions into fertile plains. The main 'inanimate' source of energy in the ancient

WIT Transactions on Ecology and The Environment, Vol 173, © 2013 WIT Press
www.witpress.com, ISSN 1743-3541 (on-line)
doi:10.2495/SDP130461

world was the so-called Greek mill, comprising a vertical wooden plank with small blades on the lower end submerged in the water, which was mainly used to grind wheat.

The Romans used hydraulic energy to till their fields instead of using horses and, by 85 BC, the kinetic energy of a river or the potential energy of a waterfall were exploited to power simple machines. A type of watermill with a horizontal axis and a vertical wheel was designed by the military engineer Vitruvius in the 1st century BC and mills of noteworthy dimensions were built in the Roman Empire from the 4th century AD.

In the Middle Ages, the Islamic world made important contributions to hydraulics. In the geographical area where the first Islamic civilizations developed, important work to reclaim land and distribute water was carried out.

Between the 9th and the 10th centuries, the need to find an energy source alternative to muscle power led to the considerable technical development of water-powered machines. In England, the Doomsday Book (the record of a census commissioned by William I in 1086) reported the presence of 5,624 water mills. This number gradually rose to 20,000 but the power generated by these water mills rarely exceeded 10 kW. In 1770, the French engineer Bernard Forest de Bélidor wrote the book "Architecture Hydraulique" in which he described hydraulic machines with horizontal and vertical axes.

The first important attempt to formulate a theoretical basis for the design of water wheels was carried out in the 18th century by the British civil engineer John Smeaton, who was the first to build large, cast-iron water wheels. The Frenchman Jean-Victor Poncelet came up with the idea of an underwater wheel with curved blades, which increased efficiency by 70%.

Another French engineer, Claude Burdin, invented the term "turbine", introducing it into a theoretical relationship in which he highlighted the importance of the rotation velocity; Benoit Fourneyron designed and built impellers for the French ironworks which reached speeds exceeding 60 RPM and generated power up to 50 HP. It was the British-American engineer James B. Francis who, in 1849, designed a turbine with a centripetal flow, i.e. in which the flow was directed inwards.

The first hydroelectric plant was built in Northumberland in 1880. In 1858 Antonio Pacinotti built the first dynamo and in 1860 the first direct current electric engine. In 1895 Le Blanch experimented with the brushed DC electric motor to be inserted in cascade with an induction motor. The combination of hydraulic turbines and electric current gave birth to the use of hydroelectric energy on an industrial scale, based on a technology that has remained almost unaltered to the present day [1–3].

According to the classification adopted by UNIDO (United Nations Industrial Development Organization), hydroelectric plants can be classified on the basis of their rated power as follows:

- Micro hydroelectric plant P < 100 kW;
- Mini hydroelectric plant P < 1.000 kW;
- Small hydroelectric plant P < 10.000 kW;
- Large hydroelectric plant P > 10.000 kW.

It is worth remembering that, in terms of power classification, the term 'Small Hydro Power' (SHP) refers to hydroelectric plants capable of producing a maximum of 10 MW (10,000 kW).

2 Current world situation

Hydraulic energy amounts to a quarter of the total energy produced in the world and its importance has been increasing in recent years.

Hydroelectric power production was prominent at the beginning of the 1960s when, due to the progressive use of available hydraulic resources, it stabilized at around 40–50 billion kWh per year, with oscillations caused mainly by the different hydraulic conditions over the years. In percentage terms, hydroelectric production, which in the 1960s constituted 82% of the total power production, fell to 25% in the 1980s, while thermoelectric production increased in the same time frame from 14% to 70%.

Today, over 20% of the world's energy production comes from hydroelectric power plants, for a rated power of 870 GW.

The market for large hydroelectric plants is almost saturated, especially in Europe, so increasing importance is being attributed to smaller plants. Furthermore, while large hydroelectric plants require large surface areas, which causes a considerable environmental and social impact, a smaller plant will integrate itself perfectly into the local ecosystem, since it exploits the flow of the river directly [4, 5]. Such plants have a number of advantages:

- Their installation is very straightforward and can be carried out in short construction times;
- They require only a limited water supply to generate electricity;
- The plants are usually located near the users, which minimizes energy loss due to electricity transport;
- They occupy less space.

There is no specific law concerning the classification of small hydroelectric plants, however the literature offers the following definitions:

- micro-turbines, machines with $P \leq 100$ kW;
- mini-turbines, machines with power between 100 kW and 3 MW;
- small turbines, machines with power between 3 MW and 12 MW.

Various turbines are present on the international market, a brief description of which is given below [6–8].

2.1 Pelton Turbine

The Pelton Turbine was invented by the carpenter Lester Allen Pelton in 1879, and to this day it is still the most efficient turbine and very simple to operate. The way it works resembles the classic mill wheel, but revised and corrected to increase efficiency. This type of turbine is generally used for large heads (between 20 and 200 m) and modest flow rates Q.

2.2 Turgo turbine

The Turgo turbine is an impulse turbine. It works with heads between 10 and 300 m and has a maximum output of 5MW. It differs from the Pelton turbine in that the blades have a different shape and arrangement and the jet hits several of them at the same time. The smaller diameter of the Turgo turbine makes it possible to have a higher angular velocity, so there is no need for a gearbox coupled to the generator. This reduces costs and increases the mechanical reliability of the system.

2.3 Francis turbine

The Francis turbine is a reaction turbine developed in 1848 by James B. Francis, a British engineer who moved to the United States. The Francis Turbine makes use of lower heads and considerable water flow rates; it is suitable for heads between 10 and 350 m and generates power between 0.2 MW and a maximum of 10MW.

2.4 Axial flow turbine (Kaplan)

In the Kaplan turbine (or similar) the water runs through the wicket gate with a flow normal to the machine's rotation axis; therefore, the water will have to move through about 90° to run axially over the runner, which obviously causes loss. In order to reduce this drawback, tubular axial turbines (TAT) have been built and patented for fairly large heads (up to 30–40 meters) and generating power from 0.3 MW up to 10 MW.

2.5 Bulb turbine

The bulb turbine is a reaction turbine which has both a generator and a gear box, if present, inside a watertight, bulb-shaped housing submerged in water. The bulb turbine, like all tubular axial turbines, is not equipped with a spiral case supplying the runner and is inserted directly inside the penstock. This allows for considerable engineering savings and simplifies routine maintenance operations. Water flow variation is much lower than in normal axial tubular turbines, even if the axis is horizontal.

2.6 Banki-Mitchell turbine

This kind of turbine is not suitable for use in large plants, but only in small-scale ones. It is well adapted for medium-low heads (from a few meters up to 200 meters) and for low power production, and hence also low flow-rate, below 700–800 kW. This impulse turbine is also called the Cross Flow or Ossberger turbine, after the factory that has manufactured it for over 50 years. It is a two-stage machine, which allows a double action of the water on the blades. Although its efficiency is less than 87%, it remains constant when the flow-rate falls as low as 16% of the nominal flow and can, in theory, operate with a minimum flow rate 10% lower than that envisaged in the design specifications.

WIT Transactions on Ecology and The Environment, Vol 173, © 2013 WIT Press
www.witpress.com, ISSN 1743-3541 (on-line)

Figure 1 shows a diagram from which the applicability field of the above mentioned turbines can be determined, at least in a first approximation.

2.7 Inverse hydraulic auger

The hydraulic auger employs the same principle as the Archimedes' screw, used by the ancient Egyptians to transport water for irrigation.

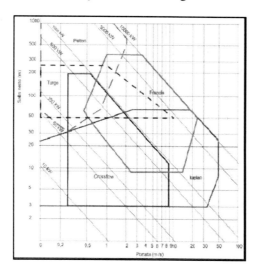

Figure 1:   Performance curve of the hydraulic auger (red line) compared.

According to this principle, the energy is transferred to a shaft/rotor and the water is transported upwards. A power-generating machine can be made by using this principle in the inverse way. Unlike the above-mentioned turbines, the hydraulic auger harnesses gravity to work, i.e. water flows downwards from the higher chambers to the lower ones. In so doing, the falling water generates a torque on the transmission shaft. Since the auger must extend from the upper water surface to the lower one, it can only be used for short heads. The design flow determines the angle of incidence of the helix, the number of revolutions and the external diameter, while the head determines the length of the auger. The auger is manufactured by welding an optimized-flow helix onto a stiffened hollow shaft. The motor assembly comprises elastic joints, support frames, gear box, generator and, if needed, a transmission belt.

These augers can be used to harness hydraulic energy at flow rates between 0.2 and 5.5 m³/s and for a maximum head of 10 m.

Hydraulic augers do not require the fine-mesh grills used in turbines and water wheels to prevent flotsam and fish from entering the machinery. This means that there is no loss of energy due to head reduction or a fall in performance because of the grills.

Figure 2:   Inverse hydraulic auger.

The wide-mesh grill (10–20 cm) greatly reduces the formation of debris, and hence lowers costs for cleaning and related disposal operations, as any flotsam entering the plant is transported downstream. Variations in flow rate have a negligible impact on performance and do not affect the operation and service of the hydraulic auger. Very low flow rates do not damage the hydraulic auger and hydroelectric power plants fitted with them are therefore more feasible than traditional turbine-driven plants. As can be seen in the figure reported below, the performance of hydraulic augers can be as high as 90% and is, in any case, high in a range from one third of the flow rate to the maximum flow rate. This means that hydraulic augers achieve a high performance even when water supply is low.

Moreover, dams and turbines generally represent a major obstacle and a threat not only for fish heading upstream but also for migratory fish. Hydroelectric plants of any kind also constitute an obstacle for fish migrating to lay eggs. Experts' tests on hydraulic augers, on the other hand, have shown that both small fish (longer than 8 cm) and large fish (up to 58 cm) can pass through the plant unharmed, making the inverse hydraulic auger 'fish-sustainable' [9].

3 Case study

The study focuses on the possible installation of an inverse auger hydroelectric plant at the Persano dam (figure 3) situated between the Picentini and the Alburni mountains (Italy) at an elevation of 52.10m asl and measuring 158.80 m in length.

The foundations of the dam comprise layers of cemented large conglomerate over an impermeable concrete diaphragm covering 2500 square meters. The dam has four gates in line between five concrete piles (figure 2). The dam continues onto the left bank with a masonry structure. The gates have a 17m aperture and are 6m in height and are balanced with counterweights set in shafts inside the piles and are opened/closed by acting on the water level in the shafts. Obviously the speed with which the gates can be opened or closed depends on the quantity of water evacuated from or diverted into the shafts housing the floats.

Figure 3:   Aerial image of the dam.

Plant maintenance can be performed by diverting the course of the river to a spillway located along the left bank at 38.20 m asl. This spillway also has a gate measuring 4.8m x 4m and can divert a flow of about 50 m^3/s. The dam greatly reduces the river flow velocity, which results in the depositing of large quantities of silt and sand both at the mouth of the spillway and in the shafts housing the floats that operate the gates. These areas therefore need to be dredged periodically to ensure efficient plant operation. This dam has raised the river level by 6m (from 40.50 m to 46.50 m) and created a reservoir in a large bend in the river Sele which is also supplied by its tributaries (the Tanagro and the Tenza).

Figure 4:   Frontal view of the dam.

The main data for the reservoir are as follows:

- maximum reservoir height: 46.50 m asl.
- maximum regulation height: 46.50 m asl.
- minimum regulation height: 43.50 m asl.

- freewater surface
  1. at maximum reservoir height: 0.6 km^2
  2. at maximum regulation height: 0.6 km^2
  3. at minimum regulation height: 0 km^2
- total reservoir volume: $1.5 \times 10^6 \text{ m}^3$
- regulation working volume: $1 \times 10^6 \text{ m}^3$
- lamination volume: 0 m^3
- directly subtended basin surface area: 2336 km^2.

The first step was to calculate the confined flow from the gates; as already mentioned, these are 17m in length and are regulated automatically. Raising the gates allows the water to flow into the afterbay. System operation is similar to that of a sluice, as the entire aperture is below the freewater surface.

The data provided by the Bonifica Destra Sele Consortium for the period 2003–2009 made it possible to calculate the river's mean daily flow rate. The calculations performed made it possible to obtain the duration curves for every year from 2003. Of course, the measured flow rates vary from day to day between a maximum and a minimum.

The inverse auger plant was located on one of the two diversion channels on the hydraulic right which are used for irrigating the fields in the Sele valley. The water from the reservoir is diverted into these channels only during the irrigation season (essentially from June to September). In our case, as the aim is to site the production plant on the diversion works and as it would be necessary to have a constant supply throughout the year, it was decided that the augers should be installed immediately downstream of the diversion works with a spillway immediately downstream of the turbines to channel the water back into the river when irrigation is not required. The Bonifica Destra Sele Consortium has provided us with the data necessary for our case study. Specifically:

- the diverted flow varies between 4 m3/s and 8 m3/s;
- the bottom of the diversion tunnel is at an elevation of 43.70 m asl;
- the reservoir elevation is, as already mentioned, 46.50 m asl and maintains this level for most of the year.

4 Assessment of the power and energy produced

Plant power can be obtained from the formula:

$$P_{kW} = \frac{g \cdot \rho \cdot \eta \cdot H \cdot Q_p}{1000} \tag{1}$$

where:
- g is the acceleration of gravity $= 9.81 \text{ m}^2/\text{s}$;
- ρ is the water density $= 1000 \text{ kg/m}^3$;
- η is the plant efficiency;
- H is the net head $=$ reservoir height – height of the tunnel bottom, assumed to be 2.80 m;
- Qp is the projected flow.

The available data shows that the maximum flow rate obtainable from the diversion works is 8 m³/s, which is greater than the maximum flow that the auger can manage. It was therefore initially decided that the power should be assessed with the plant operating at Q_p = 5.5 m³/s, which is the maximum flow rate at which an auger can operate. Thus we calculated the percentage ratio between Q_p and Q_{max} (maximum flow that the plant can manage) which, in this case is 100 % and, using the graph shown in figure 6 with the abscissa value known, the auger performance was calculated.

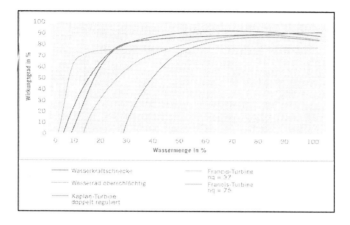

Figure 5: Auger performance curve (in red) compared.

We thus have all the data needed to calculate the power. The plant can be used with a flow rate which is at least 10%–12% of the maximum flow. For values below 10 % of this figure, machine efficiency falls to zero. Adding the flow Q_p to the DMV (3.7 m³/s) yields the minimum flow in the river bed needed to ensure a flow to the auger of Q_p. At this point, it was possible to evaluate the number of days for which the flow rate in the river bed (specifically 9.2 m³/s) is reached or exceeded.

Looking at the number of hours during which a flow rate of 5.5 m³/s is guaranteed then makes it possible to calculate the obtainable energy:

$$E = P \cdot n [kWh] \tag{2}$$

Obviously the plant will also work for Q_p flows below the maximum rate. In a second stage this value was reduced in steps of 0.5 m³/s and the previously analysed calculations were repeated. For every step, therefore, it was possible to evaluate the power and the energy obtainable from the plant. The calculations then make it possible to evaluate the energy obtainable in a year from an inverse auger plant, which is:

$$E_{total} = 752,216.7 \text{ kWh}$$

4.1 Comparison with a Banki-Mitchell mini-turbine

In order to assess the economic viability of an inverse auger plant, its productivity was compared with that obtainable using Banki-Mitchell turbines. The latter was chosen because, as shown in section 2, it can exploit very low heads (we have a working head of 2.80 m) as reported in figure 1.

The calculations were performed using the previously described procedure, initially hypothesising a maximum flow rate of 5.5 m^3/s (like that considered for the inverse auger, while the maximum flow at which this turbine can operate is 12 m^3/s) , and then reducing the Q_p value as previously, in steps of 0.5 m^3/s. Efficiency was assessed using the graph reported in figure 6.

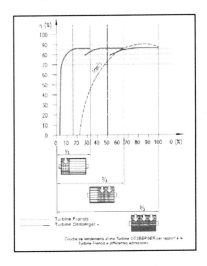

Figure 6:   Banki-Mitchell performance curve.

The annual total energy obtained is:

$$E_{total} = 729,891 \quad [kWh];$$

which is almost the same as the total energy obtainable from an inverse auger plant. This was expected, as a comparison of the two performance curves shows that for both plants the value of η varies between 0.8 and 0.9 up to a percentage value of the Q_p/Q_{max} ratio of around 10%.

Then, given the characteristics of the Banki-Mitchell turbine, a maximum turbine flow rate of 8 m^3/s (i.e. the Q_{max} obtainable from the diversion works) was considered.

The annual total energy obtained is:

$$E_{total} = 997,157 \quad [kWh].$$

Another comparison was then performed between a plant fitted with a Banki-Mitchell mini-turbine ($Q_{p,max} = 8$ m^3/s) and a plant fitted with two inverse augers, each working with a maximum flow rate of 4 m^3/s. The calculations performed for the plant fitted with two inverse augers show that the annual productivity obtainable is:

$$E_{total} = 1,099,520 \quad [kWh].$$

Here too, the comparison shows that the annual productivity obtainable from the two plants is almost the same.

5 Conclusions

This paper has analysed the issue of small-scale hydroelectric power production. For almost 150 years, dams and hydroelectric power stations have been part of the mountain landscape, consolidating the idea that hydroelectricity is a clean, available and renewable energy resource [10, 11].

In particular, there are considerable environmental benefits in the construction of mini-hydroelectric plants: they can supply electricity to areas that would otherwise be isolated or reachable only with works having a greater environmental impact; they exploit water resources in a balanced way controlled by the communities involved; they contribute to reducing energy dependence on fossil fuels and do not produce greenhouse gases or other pollutants; moreover, by locating these plants near the users of the electricity produced, there is a much smaller network loss compared to large-scale hydroelectric plants.

Small-scale hydroelectric plants are therefore an important source of renewable energy and can actively contribute to the sustainable growth of the area in which they are situated.

If well located and appropriately sized, small-scale hydroelectric plants can also be economically competitive with other renewable energy sources and, considering the actual overall costs, even with traditional energy sources. On the basis of these considerations, we have specifically examined the feasibility of an inverse auger plant to be located on the Persano barrage dam, near the diversion and clarification works which channel the water from the river Sele into the fields in the Sele valley. The inverse auger works for small flows (up to a maximum of 5.5 m^3/s) and for small heads (10 m maximum). The head in the case in question (2.80 m) falls well within the auger's field of application. Moreover, thanks to the data provided by the Bonifica Destra Sele Consortium, it has been possible to determine that the maximum flow rate in the diversion channel is 8 m^3/s. Once the mean daily flows over the year were determined (a calculation performed using data provided by the Consortium for the period 2003–2009), the duration curves were obtained and the annual obtainable power and productivity of the plant were established for such conditions. A comparison was then made with the energy obtainable from a plant equipped with a Banki-Mitchell turbine, which highlighted that the annual obtainable productivity of the two plants was practically the same for the same flow rates, confirming the efficacy of the inverse auger in energy production.

References

[1] C. d'Amelio, *Elementi di macchine: Le turbine idrauliche.* Fridericiana editrice Universitaria, 1991.
[2] F.H. White, *Fluid Mechanic.* McGraw-Hill, USA, 2001.
[3] *Atlante europeo del potenziale idroelettrico minore* (ATLAS). Institute of Hydrology of United Kingdom, UK, 2004.
[4] *European commission, Externalities of Energy – vol.6: Wind and Hydro. Ed. EUR 16525 EN, 2005.*
[5] De Siervo, Lugaresi, *Moderns trends in selecting and designing Pelton turbines.* Ed. Water Power and Dam Construction, 1988.
[6] Libro bianco Unione Europea, *Energia per il futuro, le fonti energetiche rinnovabili.* Ed. UE, 1997.
[7] N.H.C. Hwang and C. Hita, *Fundamentals of hydraulic engineering systems.* Ed. Prentice Hall Inc. Englewood Cliffs, New Jersey, 1987.
[8] *Manual de minicentrales hidroelectricas.* Ed. Cinco Dias, 1997.
[9] Massa Lugaresi, *Moderns trends in selecting and designing Kaplan turbines.* Ed. Water Power & Dam Construction, 1989.
[10] Celso Penche, *Guida all'idroelettrico minore – Per un corretto approccio alla realizzazione di un piccolo impianto.* Ed. European small hydropower association (ESHA), Bruxelles, 1998.
[11] G. Raffaellini, *Manuale di Progettazione HOEPLI, "Criteri Ambientali ed Impianti" vol.2.* – Ed. Hoepli, Milano, 1994.

Passive zones, bio-climatic design and scale hierarchic urban fabric

S. Salat & L. Bourdic
Urban Morphology Lab, CSTB, France

Abstract

Bioclimatic design in cities widely relies on the optimization of the interface between the city and the outside. With this in mind, passive zones are a crucial aspect of building sustainability: the zones located less than 6 meters from the façade can benefit from natural lighting, natural ventilation and passive solar gains. The passive volume ratio of an urban structure thus widely impacts on the energy requirements associated with lighting, ventilation, cooling and heating. Based on a twofold approach, this paper shows how complex urban structures with courtyards allow optimizing passive volumes ratios. Building on a geometric model, the paper shows how the passive volume ratio increases along with the scale hierarchy of courtyards within the urban fabric. A massive tower displays a passive volume ratio of 17% whereas a fabric with 3 scales Sierpinski carpet-like urban fabric displays a passive volume ratio of 100%. This geometric model is enhanced by a comparison of real urban structures. It shows that many historical urban tissues display passive volume ratios that are up to 6 times higher than in simple modernist urban fabrics. These results on passive volumes are then put in perspective with the buildings envelope/volume ratio, leading to the introduction of a climatic-dependant trade-off.
Keywords: passive zones, urban morphology, scale hierarchy, urban fabric, bio-climatic design.

1 Introduction

Modernism led to the near complete disappearance of courtyard types, which were supplanted by freestanding buildings. This paper undertakes an environmental comparison of these two main families of urban types. Compared to the freestanding towers or pavilions, exposed on all sides, courtyards

WIT Transactions on Ecology and The Environment, Vol 173, © 2013 WIT Press
www.witpress.com, ISSN 1743-3541 (on-line)
doi:10.2495/SDP130471

integrated into a continuous fabric create a sheltered exterior space, that can be appropriated by the residents and that offers great potential for passive energy gains. This paper investigates the issue of building energy consumption on the neighborhood and district scale. On this scale, the city can be analysed as a large membrane separating the inside and the outside. One of the many ways to tackle the issue of building energy consumption is thus investigate the structure of this interface and to find ways to optimise it. The first section of the paper shows how fractal theory provides innovative tools to optimise this interface. Based on 6 geometric neighborhood patterns, the following section shows how the fractalisation of court textures allows an optimisation of the passive volume ratios on the neighborhood scale. These results are then compared with 4 existing urban fabrics. Putting these passive volume aspects into perspective with the building envelope/volume ratio, the last section shows how the trade-off between both is climatic dependant.

2   The fractal optimization of court textures

Natural structures respond to laws of optimized exchanges across membranes. In urban forms, courtyard textures and their implications in terms of energy have been investigated by several authors [1, 2]. They respond to the need of bioclimatic optimization. This is why they almost universally characterize historical cities from China [2] to India and from the Islamic world [3] to Greece [4] and Italy. They did not disappear until the emergence of artificial means of controlling interior environments, means that are very costly in fossil fuels.

We shall illustrate this aspect by a simple example. Suppose that a system needs to increase energy gains from the environment, across a membrane. This is the case for natural lighting and passive solar gains, and this is also the case today for the potential to capture photovoltaic energy through the building's envelope. Energy gains (and bioclimatic exchanges, more generally) are proportional to the surface area of the membrane. Consequently, the system necessitates maximizing a quantity of topological dimension $D = 2$. Exchanges of energy, air, and light take place across the external surface of the body. Optimization would thus lead to an increase in the body's size. However, the result of such a process is negative for energy gains: the increase in size by a factor ρ increases the surface by ρ^2, but also the volume by ρ^3, so that the energy by unit of volume decreases as $1/\rho$.

This decrease was advocated in the 1970s by thermal engineers in cold countries for the purpose of limiting heat losses and constructing airtight buildings. Rather than reducing heat loss by sacrificing solar gains, lighting and natural ventilation, a bioclimatic architecture must on the contrary resolve the following optimization problem: Is it possible to optimize the exchange surface without increasing the body's volume? The only solution for increasing the bioclimatic exchanges (or the energy capture potential) is to increase the surface inside the given limits of the building via fractal complexification. At a given scale, the increase displays a limit that can only be exceeded by a new complexification at a smaller scale, and so on. The fractal iteration stops when the advantages are balanced out by other constraints or physical limits.

It would be interesting to examine in vernacular architecture whether the variation of the size of courtyards according to the different climates, results from a process of energy exchange optimization across the membranes. The process of complexification optimizes both the passive volume and the volumetric compactness (S/V), as we have observed on blocks in Turin that starting from the Roman foundation have evolved toward a significant inner complexity and have strongly increased their exchange surfaces (40 km of façades on the street and 16 km on the courtyards in an 710 x 770 meter selection corresponding to the old Roman colony) without degrading their thermal performance. Conversely, the square blocks in Barcelona, designed on a grid twice the size of Turin's (113 x 113 meters rather than 70 x 70 meters) and which, after only a century and a half of existence, densified without complexifying like those in Turin, two thousand years old, do not display the same optimal character.

We could study from this perspective dozens of different types of urban textures with courtyards because they not only offer the most bioclimatic advantages but also the greatest flexibility to optimize energy exchanges through the membranes, depending on the climate, the season, and the time of day, because membranes themselves can also be fractalized and transformed into porous surfaces filtering air and light (as Indian, Islamic, and Chinese architecture show). The fractality of Islamic architecture, with its countless openings, from the Arab countries to India, evinces a desire to increase the number of envelope surface components almost ad infinitum and to create porous membranes through which air moves. They filter the sunlight, subduing its intensity and attenuating its heat. What we learn both from the history of urban and architectural forms and from recent calculations is that the form of an urban texture, and the more or less porous and variable conception of the membranes that make up the envelopes, depend above all on latitude and climate.

3   Passive volumes

The concept of passive zone is described in the LT-method [5, 6] as being the area in the building within a distance from a perimeter wall, usually between 6 and 8 meters, depending on the floor to ceiling height (see Figure 1). These passive zones benefit from natural lighting and natural ventilation, but also from useful solar gains in winter. The energy consumption associated with lighting and ventilation is thus expected to be lower in these zones, an important part of lighting and ventilation being 'free'. On the contrary, these zones suffer from heat loss through the envelope and from unwanted solar gains in summer.

But as building technologies improve significantly at the present time, notably concerning glazing and insulation, the share of this unwanted phenomenon in the overall energy consumption figure will tend to diminish significantly in the future. In the office buildings, energy consumption is mostly

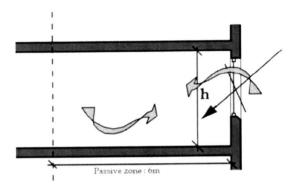

Figure 1:   The passive zone is located less than 6 meters from the façade [5].

associated with lighting, ventilating and cooling, even though the outside temperature is low. Concerning residential buildings, improved glazing and insulation will diminish the share of heating in the overall energy consumption figure in a close future. As it is already the case in office buildings, the share of ventilation, lighting and cooling will increase.

Strategically speaking, the role of passive zones will become more and more significant in the coming years and decades, as the benefits from improvements of insulation and glazing will become marginal. The more passive zones in the building, the better. Unfortunately, it is much harder to improve the passive volume ratio - the ratio of the volume of passive zones over the total volume - of an already built building than its insulation. This ratio entirely depends on the original form of the building. If the passive volume ratio of a building is low, it is almost impossible to change it, but to destroy and rebuilt. Whereas improving insulation or glazing is a matter of months or years, improving passive volume ratios is a matter of several decades, *i.e.* the lifespan of the building.

The approach presented in this paper rests upon an ability to scale up urban issues. Passive volume ratios are a characteristic on the building scale. But considering this issue from the neighborhood or the district scale provides interesting insights. The following analysis is based on the neighborhood scale. It aims at showing how passive volume ratio may increase as urban fabric becomes more complex. In the six situations, the zone under consideration is a 200x200m square, in which the building occupies 70% of the available floor area. The first three examples display simple urban organizations on which most of modernist cities have been based.

Figure 2 displays a mono-block structure, typically a tower. Passive zones are in green whereas non-passive zones are in black. The passive volume ratio (PVR) is only 17%, which is extremely low and leads to high energy consumptions notably for lighting, ventilation and cooling (even in cold climates). The reader will certainly notice that unfortunately most of the office buildings – where energy consumption is mainly associated with lighting, ventilation and cooling – are towers...

Figure 2:   One block, PVR=17%.

Figures 3 and 4 display two other structures, with the exact same floor area ratio. The passive volume ratio remains below 60% in both cases.

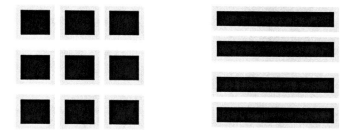

Figure 3:   9 blocks, PVR=46%.   Figure 4:   Linear   buildings, PVR= 58%.

Figure 5, 6 and 7 show three structures based on square courtyards, with a growing complexity. The construction is directly inspired from fractal theory, and more precisely from a Sierpinski carpet. Several authors have highlighted the potential of fractal theory to better grasp urban complexity [7–9] and to optimize urban structures [10, 11]. Figure 5 displays a massive building with only one block, with one big courtyard: the passive volume ratio is low. In figure 6, a second level of smaller courtyards has been added in the building. This leads to an almost doubling of the passive volume ratio. Finally, another level of courtyards is added in the building (Figure 7), leading to a passive volume ratio of 100%.

This simple geometric analysis shows that complex urban fabrics, based here on fractal theory, display a much higher passive volume ratio than simple ones. Fractal theory is a way to optimize the "urban membrane" – the interface between the inside and the outside. In figure 7, the pattern is distributed over three scales, instead of one in figure 1. The careful reader will then certainly notice that the multiplicity-size distribution of courtyards in figure 7 follows a power law. Further research is currently carried out to understand how size and

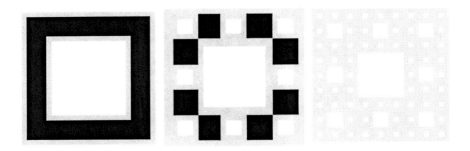

Figure 5: One courtyard, PVR=33%. Figure 6: 2 levels of courtyards, PVR=60%. Figure 7: 3 levels of courtyards, PVR=100%.

scale hierarchy of courtyards impact on energy consumption patterns according to the different climates.

Pushing further this geometric analysis, we have investigated numerous urban tissues, historical and modernist ones, in cold and hot climates. When analyzing real cities, the same kind of results emerge: the more complex the urban tissue, the higher the passive volume ratio. The four following figures display two modernist districts (800x800 m squares) and two historical ones. Passive zones are in dark grey, whereas non passive zones are in light grey. The two first districts are made of simple blocks, without any courtyard. In Shanghai Lujiazui Central Business District (Figure 8), elements are so massive that the passive volume ratio is smaller than 50%. In Thianhe district (Figure 9), there are two predominant scales of buildings. The small ones have an acceptable passive volume ratio, but the big ones have a dramatically low one, leading to an average passive volume ratio of 66%.

In the two historical urban tissues, Shanghai's Lilongs in figure 10 and a Parisian district in figure 11, there are still some big elements. But they are

Figure 8: Lujiazui (CBD), Shanghai, PVR = 43%.

Figure 9: Tianhe, Guangzhou, PVR = 66%.

organised around numerous courtyards of all scales that allow a much better interface with the outside, and a passive volume ratio higher than 80%. The analysis of the building size distribution and of the courtyards size distribution shows that the two historical urban fabrics display a high scale hierarchy, close to an optimal power law distribution [2].

Urban scale-free complexity is a way to optimise passive volumes in the urban fabric. Urban complexity is not about scattering numerous small elements, but on the contrary about respecting an adequate scale hierarchy: a small number of big buildings and courtyards, a medium number of medium size elements, and a big number of little elements. Modernist urban fabrics based on one are structurally speaking unsustainable. On the contrary, urban fabrics based on several scales (up to three or four fundamental scales in figures 10 and 11) allow optimizing crucial parameters for sustainability, such as the passive volume ratio.

Figure 10:   Lilongs, Shanghai PVR > 80%.

Figure 11:   Paris district, 19th century, PVR > 80%.

4   A climate dependant trade-off between passive volumes and S/V ratio

Along with the passive volume ratio, the building envelope/volume ratio widely impacts on urban sustainability. By widely influencing the structural needs (in heat, cooling, light or air) of buildings, they both widely influence the associated energy needs. As we explained earlier in this paper, a low S/V ratio was advocated in the 70s by thermal engineers in cold countries: the more compact the better.

These two fundamental parameters are somehow antagonist. Table 1 displays the S/V and passive volume ratios for the 6 theoretical neighborhood presented earlier in this paper. The more compact (small S/V ratios), the lower the passive volume ratio.

Table 1:   S/V and Passive volume ratios for 6 theoretical neighborhoods.

Type of neighborhood	One Block	1-level courtyard	9 blocks	Linear Buildings	2-levels courtyards	3-levels courtyards
S/V (m^{-1})	0.08	0.10	0.13	0.12	0.12	0.19
Passive volume ratio (%)	17%	33%	46%	58%	60%	100%

In septentrional latitudes, simple buildings with big courtyards are more adapted to the cold climates. They display a "good" S/V ratio – that is a small one – that limits thermal losses.

On the contrary, in hot and arid climates – the medinas of Sfax or Marrakech (fig. 12) for instance displays more than 1000 small courtyards on 24 ha – the main objective is not to limit thermal losses through the envelope but to insure passive ventilation and cooling. The "good" S/V ratio is a high one that increases passive volumes while protecting the inside and outside spaces from direct light and solar radiation. In this context, according to Ratti et al. [12], several authors such as Fahty [13] and Bahadori [14] claim that small courtyard allow the creation of an open sheltered zone, the adoption of ingenious natural cooling strategies, the protection against wind-blown dustor sand and the mitigation of the effects of solar excess.

Figure 12:   Small courtyards in central Marrakech [12].

The benefits of high S/V ratios in hot climates are also related to inertia phenomena. Indeed, the order of magnitude of inertia phenomena directly correlates with the amount of material used in the buildings – notably the walls – and thus to the surface of the envelope. According to Ratti et al. [12] the high thermal mass can be used to store heat during the day to benefit from it during the cooler nights. The maximization of S/V ratios acts as a heat sink.

Today, with the rise in insulation standards and internal gains, the most important concerns in energy consumption have shifted to lighting and mechanical ventilation, for which the effects of urban geometry are different and even reversed. To maximize natural light, the passive volume needs to be increased and hence the compactness diminished. The impact of these values needs anyway to be put into perspective by an analysis separating size and form factors. Indeed, the S/V ratio can be broken down for buildings or groups of connected buildings, into:

$$\frac{S}{V} = \frac{1}{V^{1/3}} \cdot \frac{S}{V^{2/3}} \tag{1}$$

In this equation $\frac{1}{V^{1/3}}$ represents the building size factor (the bigger the building, the smaller this factor) and $\frac{S}{V^{2/3}}$ is an adimensional factor that describes the form of the building. This breakdown makes no sense on the texture scale. The impossibility, on the texture scale, of separating size effects from form effects in the S/V parameter leads to a considerable loss of information on an essential aspect of the texture. Here we see that the volumetric compactness of the texture is an overly simple parameter because it does not allow us to apprehend the "grain" of the texture, that is, the fact that the texture is composed either of many small buildings that can be combined in a complex, continuous way (which, due to the contiguity, leads to a good factor of compactness), or of large discontinuous buildings (which also leads to a good factor of compactness but degrades other energy parameters, like daylight availability or natural ventilation potential).

5 Conclusions

A proper urban complexity is a way to improve the passive volume ratio, and thus to optimize the interface between the city and the outside, and to benefit from natural lighting, cooling, ventilation and passive solar gains. This paper shows how fractal patterns may help in optimizing the passive volume ratio. It should be kept in mind, however, that the passive volume is only a potential: these passive areas must be designed in a technologically efficient way, notably using smart bioclimatic solutions like those that enable light control through sensors that prevent overheating in summer, and heat loss in winter. Combining smart bioclimatic façades with good thermal insulation makes it possible in part to neutralize the geometric contradiction in optimizing the form of the texture. Indeed, there is no universal answer to the question of optimal urban texture, which depends on climate and latitude.

Pushing the thought further, this approach aiming at optimizing the urban envelope may also have implications on the renewable energy potential of urban structures. An optimized and complex interface on the district and city scale is a way to increase, with the same land footprint, the available envelope area, and thus the available area for solar energy. Complexification of urban structures may thus also reveal to be a part of the answer to the higher land footprint of renewable energy compared to the one of fossil fuels.

References

[1] D. Raydan, C. Ratti, and K. Steemers, "Courtyards: a bioclimatic form?," in *Courtyard Housing: Past, Present & Future*. New York: Taylor and Francis, 2006, pp. 135–145.
[2] S. Salat, *Cities and Forms, On Sustainable Urbanism*.: Hermann, 2011.
[3] S. Ozkan, "Courtyard: a typology that symbolises a culture.," in *Courtyard Housing: Past, Present and Future*. New York: Taylor and Francis, 2006, pp. 15–29.
[4] B. Fletcher, *A history of architecture on the comparative methods*. London: Batsford, 1954.

[5] N. Baker and K. Steemers, "LT Method 3.0 - a strategic energy-design tool for Southern Europe," *Energy and Buildings* **23**, pp. 251-256, 1996.

[6] C. Ratti, N. Baker, and K. Steemers, "Energy Consumption and Urban Texture," *Energy and Buildings* **37(7)**, pp. 762–776, 2005.

[7] M. Batty and P.A. Longley, *Fractal cities: a geometry of form and function.* London Academic Press, 1994.

[8] Salingaros N.A. and B.J. West, "A universal rule for the distribution of sizes," *Environment and Planning B: Planning and Design*, vol. 26, pp. 909–923, 1999.

[9] N.A. Salingaros, "Complexity and Urban Coherence," *Journal of Urban Design*, vol. 5, pp. 291–316, 2000.

[10] S. Salat and L. Bourdic, "Power laws for energy efficient and resilient cities," *Procedia Engineering* **21**, pp. 1193–8, 2011.

[11] S. Salat and L. Bourdic, "Scale Hierarchy, Exergy Maximisation and Urban Efficiency," , ELCAS2, Nisyros, 2011.

[12] C. Ratti, D. Raydan, and K. Steemers, "Building form and environmental performance: archetypes, analysis and an arid climate," *Energy and Buildings* **35**, pp. 49–59, 2003.

[13] H. Fathy, *Natural Energy and Vernacular Architecture.* Chicago: The University of Chicago Press, 1986.

[14] M.N. Bahadori, "Passive cooling systems in Iranian architecture," *Scientific American* **2 (238)**, pp. 144–52, 1978.

Section 11
Sustainability assessment and management
(Special session organised by C. A. Poveda)

The Canadian oil sands: environmental, economic, social, health, and other impacts

C. A. Poveda & M. G. Lipsett
Department of Mechanical Engineering, University of Alberta, Canada

Abstract

As world energy demands increase, so will the exploration and exploitation of alternative energy resources. The present level of energy generation cannot meet the needs of future generations if the pace of population growth and energy consumption continues at the current rate. While some unconventional energy sources are still in research and development phase, others have been effectively implemented. The impacts of different energy operations are still being debated, with respect to environmental, social, economic, and health effects. The definition of sustainable development adopted by United Nations (UN) uses the expression "…meets the needs of the present…" to indicate the required development by a current generation to maintain its standard of living while minimizing environmental, economic, social impacts. Large industrial developments will affect a range of stakeholders, and may entail cultural and political change. The level of impacts and their implications depends on many characteristics of the development, such as its size, production rate, duration of exploitation, processes used (including treatment of waste streams), and regulatory standards. While local communities, businesses and surrounding areas are first expected to be impacted, certain developments can attract global attention. Canadian oil sands developments are of interest to oil producers because of the size of the proven reserves; but the scale of development and the perceived enduring impacts are of concern to different stakeholders. This work presents a discussion and analysis of the economic, social, health, and other impacts of current operations in Canadian oil sands that are of concern to different stakeholders, including some uncertainties in levels and persistence of

WIT Transactions on Ecology and The Environment, Vol 173, © 2013 WIT Press
www.witpress.com, ISSN 1743-3541 (on-line)
doi 10.2495/SDP130481

impacts. An overview is provided of efforts undertaken by government and developers to minimize impacts; and comments are offered on possible future strategies.

Keywords: impacts, oil and gas, oil sands, sustainable development, energy consumption, unconventional oil.

1 Introduction: oil and gas resources

With continued growth in emerging economies around the world, the global oil demand has steadily grown over the past 20 years from 60 million barrels per day to 88 million [1]. Crude oil is not only one of the most traded commodities in the world, but also one of the most volatile; the commodity is influenced by a variety of factors that produce fluctuations in oil prices, thereby affecting supply and demand.

Production of oil and gas is classified as either conventional and unconventional: unconventional oil is extracted or produced using techniques other than the conventional oil well method. Since the sources of conventional oil are in decline, efforts are turning to unconventional reserves to meet the growing demands; however, unconventional oil production carries not only some extra monetary extra costs, but also a bigger environmental footprint. Moreover, conventional oil is easier extract, and creates fewer greenhouse gas emissions than unconventional oil production [1].

Conventional oil is either light or heavy, depending on its consistency (API gravity). Light oil can flow naturally to the surface or be extracted using pumpjacks (i.e., the oil well method). Extraction techniques for conventional oil have been used for decades; therefore, certain acceptable levels of efficiency in the extraction process have been accomplished, with incremental improvements in enhanced oil recovery. In contrast, development of efficient techniques for unconventional oil production. takes high levels of investment and considerable time; however, producers and developers recognize the necessity of optimizing extraction techniques, not only to increase production but also to reduce their environmental footprint.

The International Energy Agency (IEA) reports different sources of unconventional oil and gas: oil sands-based synthetic crudes and derivative products, oil shales, coal-based liquid supplies, biomass-based liquid supplies, and liquids arising from the chemical processing of natural gas [2]. Out of these unconventional oil sources, oil sands is at the top of the list, because the amount of proven reserves is very large, and the largest deposits are located in stable geo-political regions (e.g. Canada).

Canadian energy production has almost doubled since 1980 due to the rapid development of the proven oil sands reserves in the province of Alberta. As of 2010, Canada produces 1.22 million barrels per day of conventional oil, 1.5 million barrels per day of oil sands, and 14.7 billion cubic feet per day of natural gas, making Canada part of the global crude oil markets [2]. In fact, Canada's richness in oil and gas resources can be measured based on its global presence: it is the third largest producer of natural gas, the fifth largest energy producer, and the largest producer of crude oil with the biggest deposits of oil sands in the world [3].

The oil and gas industry in Canada is currently present in 12 of its 13 provinces and territories. In global oil reserves, Canada places third, following Venezuela and Saudi Arabia; however, the scenario is promising if feasible oil sands deposits in the province of Saskatchewan change from the non-proven to the proven reserves category.

Unconventional oil and gas extraction and production from any of the different sources raises a variety of concerns. Social, economic, health, and especially environmental impacts are expected; however, finding a balance among the three pillars of sustainability offers a feasible sustainable path. The primary affected pillar of sustainability noticed by stakeholders refers to environmental impacts; in unconventional oil and gas extraction and production, those impacts of major concerns include waste management, use of chemicals and energy, and air pollutions (e.g., GHG emissions). Major concerns arise due to the large amounts of mildly hazardous tailings and waste in the mining process during oil extraction and production. In addition to the concerns in light oil production, heavy oil requires the use of heat to pump the product out of the ground. Exploration of oil shale raises questions regarding net unit energy production efficiency and carbon dioxide emissions, in addition to oxides and pollutants and the use of chemicals mixing with underground water. Similarly, oil obtained from coal or natural gas produces large amounts of carbon dioxide.

Environmental impacts are not the only concerns related to unconventional oil and gas extraction and production; however, the general first impression of government, developers, local communities, and stakeholders regarding sustainable development refers to that specific pillar of sustainability (i.e., environmental). Social, economic, and health impacts involving the development of unconventional oil (e.g., oil sands) can be equally, if not more, relevant than those affecting the environment, as they are interconnected.

2 The Canadian oil sands

Put simply, oil sands are an unconsolidated mixture of sand, clay and/or other minerals, water, and bitumen; therefore, the extracted product must be treated before it can be used by refineries to produce usable fuels. Even though oil sands deposits can be found around the world, including Russia, Venezuela, the United States, and Colombia, Canada possesses not only the largest deposit in the world, but also the most developed, as advanced technology is used in the production process.

While Alberta's oil sands proven reserves are currently stated to be 178 billion barrels, the estimated total volume of bitumen in place is 1.6 trillion barrels [4]. The 178 billion of barrels can be recovered with current technology, and would be sufficient to meet the Canadian crude oil demand for approximately 250 years. The current developed area of the Canadian oil sands concentrates in three main areas (i.e., Peace River, Athabasca, and Cold Lake) located in the Province of Alberta; however, the development will eventually be extended to the Province of Saskatchewan. Surpassing Canada's conventional oil production, the daily production for Alberta's oil sands is approaching 1.7 million barrels [5]. And because a combination of unique factors – large untapped reserves, a stable political environment, and openness to investment in an environment of high oil prices [6] – Canada is expected to be the fourth largest oil producer by 2035.

The rapid development of the oil sands, which appears to be exponential, has raised major concerns for different sectors of society. Although Albertans recognize the economic benefits of the oil sands development, environmental, social, and health impacts that may be present in each phase of the life cycle are not to be ignored by those directly affected. These projects have grabbed not only national but also international attention.

The oil sands resource life cycle, as shown in Figure 1, starts with the assessment of prospects and ends with a reclamation process, which consists of leaving the exploration and production areas as equally productive (or equivalent environmental capability) as they were before their use. Independent of the extraction method utilized – surface mining or in-situ – companies proposing a development go through similar project approval processes, which generally include public consultation and a variety of required studies. The major impacts are encountered in the processes of recovery, upgrading, and refining: Canada's oil sands projects (extraction, upgrading, and distribution to downstream refineries) require multi-billion-dollar infrastructure, for which construction, operation, and maintenance affects primarily uninhabited land as well as local and Aboriginal communities.

3 Sustainability: The triple bottom line

Before 1987, when the Brundtland Commission (formally known as the World Commission on Environment and Development [WCED]) defined sustainable development, the movement did not enjoy major support, and its origins can be debatable. Since then, the development of sustainability assessment tools has faced unprecedented growth, and sustainable strategies have grabbed the attention of public and private organizations and stakeholders in general.

In Canada, the concept of sustainable development has been integrated into federal government policies, programs, and legislation; however, provincial and territorial governments are key partners in the development of projects in a sustainable manner [7, 8].

Canada's oil sands are not only an unconventional oil and gas resource, but also a non-renewable resource for which exploration, extraction, and production challenge the different stakeholders' ability to meet the needs of the present without compromising for the needs of future generations. As social, economic, environmental, and health impacts occur during the development of the oil sands, a sustainable path consists of finding the balance to different stakeholder needs, which are influenced by the different positive and negative impacts encountered in any of the three pillars of sustainable development (i.e., social, economic, and environmental).

Interdependency and balance between impacts and gains (benefits) is meant to be understood by observing the graphic representation of sustainable development, which is usually shown using 3 mutually intersected circles. Gibson *et al.* [9] describe the fundamentals of sustainability as a mindset where "economic imperatives rule, social arrangements are judged by how well they serve the economy, and the biosphere (environment) is treated mostly as a source of resources." But economic factors are major drivers in the decision-making process [10].

The balance between impacts and gains is influenced by perception and subjectivity. While environmental impacts are usually observed as negative, economic impacts place on the other side of the spectrum. Subjectivity refers to factors like priorities and emphases, which level of confidence stakeholders and experts have regarding the feasibility and sufficiency of certain approaches, and what makes the list of priorities and considerations to meet the needs of policy and project activities [9]. Oil producers are advertising in public media to emphasize that economic benefits are not regional, but rather national.

Economic impacts are mostly interpreted as positive. Negative environmental impacts are obvious, but progress is being made on reducing energy intensity and disturbed land footprint (although with additional projects the overall rate increases). Social impacts, for the most part, are uncertain and immeasurable due to subjectivity and qualitative factors. Health impacts unpredictable, as some effects may appear long after the exposure to contaminants, and demonstrating the illness and source linkage needs credible and reliable evidence resulting from scientific intervention.

3.1 Environmental impacts

The rapid development of the oil sands has increased the pressure on Alberta's natural environment. The total area of Alberta's oil sands covers 140,200 km². To date, about 715 km² of land have been disturbed by surface mining activities, and up to 1.25 percent of Alberta's boreal forest could potentially be disturbed, although not permanently [11].

The World Resources Institute (WRI) [12] reports well-documented environmental impacts of mining: presently [mining] is the primary method of oil sands extraction with 53% of the total production in 2010 and the other 47% using in-situ methods; however, only 20% of the oil sands is recoverable through mining, while approximately 80% is recoverable by in-situ processes [11]. While the WRI reported impacts make reference to mining in general, Alberta's oil sands are not excluded from facing similar challenges: waste management issues (sedimentation, acid drainage, metal deposition), impacts on biodiversity and habitat, indirect impacts, and poverty alleviation and wealth distribution. Furthermore, environmental impacts involving the oil sands development can be divided into impacts on land, air, and water resources.

As part of the land management and reclamation program and Alberta's legislation, disturbed lands must be productive again; therefore, companies must remediate and reclaim such areas meeting Alberta Environment's strict standards

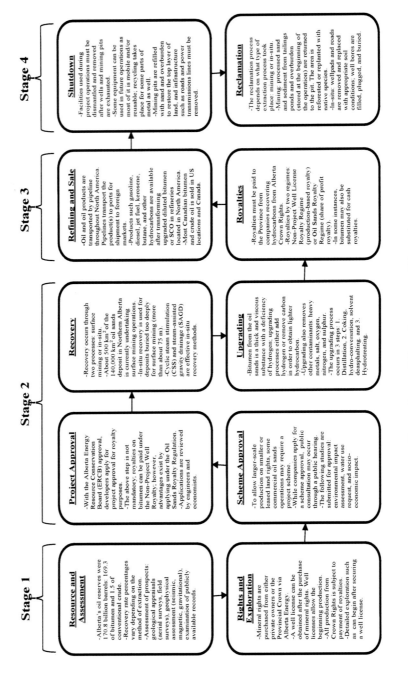

Figure 1:   Oil sands resource life cycle.

guaranteeing the land can support activities similar to its previous use. Currently, only 67 km² of disturbed land have been reclaimed but not certified, which indicates less than 10 percent of the total disturbed area [13]. Moreover, Gosseling *et al.* [10] report on reclamation and adequacy of financial security, underlining that reclamation is not keeping with the pace of development, and "current practices for obtaining financial security for reclamation liability leave Albertans vulnerable for major financial risks" [10].

Impacts on air as a resource are one of the major worries for government, developers, local communities, and other stakeholders. More than 1,400 known pollutants are emitted by oil sands operations, but only a few are monitored: sulphur oxides (SO_x), nitrogen oxides (NO_x), hydrocarbons, and fine particulate matter ($PM_{2.5}$) [10]. Even though the Canadian oil sands projects have reduced their carbon dioxide emissions intensity by up to 33 percent since 1990, their contribution to the Canadian greenhouse gas emissions (GHGs) account for 6.5 percent of the nation's total, and less than 0.1 percent to the world's total GHG emissions. Additionally, the GHG emissions per barrel have been reduced between 1990 and 2009 by an average of 29%; however, emissions of (SO_x) and other sulphur compounds (NO_x), as well as total hydrocarbons, have been rising for the past decade due to the growing increments in production [10]. Alberta Environment measures the cleanliness of outdoor air, also known as ambient air, through the Air Quality Index (AQI), which includes the measurement of concentration of five major air pollutants: carbon monoxide, nitrogen dioxide, ozone, sulphur dioxide, and fine particulate matter. In reference to air quality, the Royal Society of Canada (RSC) concluded that there has been minimal impact from the oil sands, except for noxious odour emissions, over the past two years [10]. However, odours can only be assessed subjectively, using trained observers.

In 2009, 90 facilities in Alberta reported that their combined GHG emissions equalled 113.1 megatonnes in carbon dioxide equivalent (Mt of CO2e). About 41.9 Mt of CO2e are emissions from oil sands facilities: 26.9 Mt of CO2e are from the oil sands mining and upgrading, and 15 Mt of CO2e are from in-situ projects' facilities. In 2011, oil sands production emitted an estimated 80 million tons of CO2 [14]. The production and upgrading of the oil sands are more energy-intensive than the production of conventional oil; as a result, higher GHG emissions are expected. However, if considering the complete life cycle, which includes the refinement, transportation, and consumption of oil, 80 percent of the total emissions occur at the end of the cycle (consumption) from burning fuel. Nevertheless, the new levels of bitumen production create challenges for Canada to meet international commitments for overall GHG emissions reduction, which the current technology does not resolve [10].

Water consumption, contaminants emissions, and groundwater quality and quantity are three of the major concerns in reference to water resources. Water consumption in the oil sands development projects varies based on whether the extraction method utilized is in-situ or surface mining. In mining operations, 2.5 to 4 barrels of water is used for every barrel of bitumen produced; however, up to 90 percent of the water utilized is recycled, and as a result, only 0.5 barrels of water is needed to make up for the deficit [11]. As for surface mining operations, 7.5 to 10 barrels of water is used per barrel of bitumen, but the recycle rate is currently up to 70 percent, translating to 3 to 4.5 barrels of water to make up for the deficit to maintain production [11].

Almost all of this water is captured in the pores of tailings deposits, produced in the process of separating bitumen from the oil sands. Inventories of hydrocarbon-contaminated water are impounded in earth dams or in mined-out pits. Untreated water is not to be released to water bodies off the mine site. Oil sands tailings comprise water, sand, clay, residual bitumen, and chemicals, which includes small amounts of polycyclic aromatic hydrocarbons (PAHs), naphthenic acids, heavy metals, and mineral ions. The functions of the ponds are to provide a disposal area for coarse and fine tailings, to allow water to separate from solid waste materials, to store water from recycling, and to hold contaminants [13]. Even though new technologies have emerged for improving tailings management, these have not stopped the growing inventory of tailings ponds.

An additional factor in water management refers to groundwater quantity and quality. Not only concerns about the Regional Aquatics Monitoring Program (RAMP) have been raised, but also the regional cumulative impact on groundwater quantity and quality has not been assessed [10].

3.2 Social impacts

If sustainability is still in its infancy, then the social dimension is the youngest of the three pillars; however, it is not less relevant than the other two (economic and environmental). Based on the equality factor, the three dimensions are interchangeably relevant, and a sustainable path translates to a balance between the three dimensions. The social dimension of sustainable development is subjective, qualitative, difficult to assess, and involves stakeholders' diverse views on the issues; but it is recognized that social impacts occur at different social scales involving individuals, families, businesses, community groups, communities as a whole, ethnic groups, cultures, and broader society [8]. Individuals will identify with some or all of these divisions.

Social impacts are, as expected, linked to other types of impacts such as health. In the Athabasca region, the health indicators are consistent with the "boom town" effect. Small towns suddenly face rapid growth, which affects communities' health and social infrastructure. Gosselin et al. [10] indicate that the Government of Alberta has recognized some of the shortfalls due to the rapid population growth caused by the accelerated pace of the oil sands development; however, there is no evidence of addressing the serious population health issues. In fact, it has been recognized that better understanding is needed about the social impacts of development on some Alberta regions (e.g., Forth McKay, Fort McMurray), including demographic information regarding population changes, migration, and the impact of migration patterns (such as labour force statistics and income statistics) [15].

Even though the lack of statistical data makes it difficult to assess the different impacts, concerns have been raised by Aboriginal and local communities, including the influx of non-Aboriginal people onto traditional lands, the loss of traditional resources due to development, the level of migration of people to local communities, the outward migration of First Nation and Métis communities due to lack of housing, and the loss of traditional culture. Additionally, Shipley [15] highlights some effects of the oil sands development on education: funding conditions, infrastructure costs, staff recruitment and retention, and the effectiveness of adult education programs and their barriers.

Additional concerns have been raised due to the use of industrial camps. Because of the size of the oil sands development and the large number of personnel required to build, operate, and maintain the projects, developers often use industrial camps to allocate personnel, rather than relying on housing in the community (which has a very low vacancy rate). This type of allocation generates a series of additional concerns, including but not limited to the increased potential of forest fires, recreational pressure on the environment, safety (primarily the increased number of vehicles on local roads), and the potential destruction of sacred sites [15].

Social impacts are expected to occur as the development of the oil sands projects goes on; however, in order to mitigate and/or eliminate the impacts, the first step towards a sustainable development consists of assessing the impact, followed by monitoring the programs. The main challenge encountered in achieving the assessment and monitoring the social impacts revolves around the fact that scientists and industry seem to be facing a major obstacle regarding two main questions: what should be measured (e.g., indicators), and how should they be measured (e.g., metrics). Government, developers, local communities, and other oil sands stakeholders are not exempt from stumbling upon similar issues.

3.3 Economic impacts

As one of the largest development projects in Canada's history, the cumulative investment in oil sands in the past decade alone has surpassed $100 billion [6]. However, any discussion of the future and current economic impacts of Alberta's oil sands development is based on a series of assumptions and constraints, including (1) that the current announced project will proceed, (2) the size of the initial, remaining, and new established reserves, and (3) the current project will keep and/or increase production. The economic impacts (benefits) of Alberta's oil sands may differ from study to study based on the assumptions, constraints, and methodology used; however, findings always point toward a series of positive economic impacts instead of negative, as presented in some statistics ahead. Most studies measure economic impacts (therefore, the terms "positive" or "benefits" are used) in terms of changes in three major indicators: gross domestic product (GDP), employment and labour income, and government revenue [5 16 17]. Naturally, any major development of a resource with large reserves (e.g., unconventional oil) of national and/or international interest has inherently positive impacts on major economic indicators (e.g., GDP, employment, revenue); however, "real" (negative) impacts on the average citizen may be overlooked in the decision-making process, with the aim of giving the "green light" to development projects.

The analysis of the economic impacts of the oil sands must not only take into consideration current operations, but also those projects that have grabbed the attention of government, stakeholders, and the public in general, related to transport of hydrocarbon products from oil sands projects: TransCanada's Keystone XL Pipeline; Enbridge's Northern Gateway Pipeline from Bruderheim, Alberta to the port of Kitimat, British Columbia; and Kinder Morgan's Trans Mountain Pipeline system's Northern Leg expansion to Kitimat, British Columbia.

Over the 2010–2035 period for different scenarios, the estimated investment, reinvestment, and revenues from the operation of the oil sands projects range from $2,197 to $4,783 billion [16]. The $4,783 B estimate is reached with the assumption that announced oil sands projects will proceed and pipelines will be built to get the product out. While all provinces in Canada are affected by the development of the oil sands, Alberta carries the highest positive economic impact of all, followed by Ontario, British Columbia, Quebec, and Saskatchewan, respectively [6].

Honarvar et al. [5, 16] offer an analysis of the economic impacts of the oil sands development under these different scenarios over the 25-year period:
- The total Canadian GPD impact as a result of the investment shocks is estimated to range from $2,283 to $4,925 billion.
- Canadian employee compensation can range from $650 billion to $1,417 billion.
- Employment creation, including direct, indirect, and induced, is expected to grow from 390,000 up to 1,600,000 jobs in 2035 if the best scenario presents.
- Alberta royalties may grow from $3.56 billion to $65.2 billion.

Additionally, the US market is expected to be economically impacted by the oil sands development:
- US GDP impacts as a result of the investment shocks is estimated to range from CAD$210 to CAD$775 billion.
- US employee compensation can range from $100 billion to $68 billion.
- US employment, including direct, indirect, and induced, is expected to grow from 80,000 up to 600,000 jobs in the best of the scenarios.

The lower range value in each case represents the economic impacts of existing operations and those that are still under construction. The top range value assumes that all the announced oil sands projects will proceed, and pipelines will be constructed with adequate capacity to move the product. Existing pipeline export capacity is at 3.5 million barrels per day (MMBPD) of crude oil, and in the best scenario, the capacity will increase up to 7 million barrels per day (MMBPD).

Although still positive, the Conference Board of Canada presents a slightly different employment forecast through a detailed supply chain analysis. $364 billion in price-adjusted investment is expected for the next 25 years, which will support 3.2 million person-years of employment in Canada (880,000 person-years of direct employment) [6].

Not everything regarding economic impacts of the oil sands is positive, and even though economic impacts mostly sound positive due to high levels of cash flow as a consequence of the rapid development of the project, there is another side of the coin. Shipley [15] discusses negative impacts, which include the cost of living as impacted by development. This translates into suitable accommodation for new residences, affordable and comfortable homes for regional residents, and the ability to attract and retain employees. Additionally, concerns regarding housing include increased costs of building material, increased costs and scarcity of tradespersons, high building and maintenance costs, and high costs of rental property, which affect those with low-paying jobs.

3.4 Health and other impacts

Similar to other impacts, the oil sands development projects' impacts on health require rigorous monitoring. Though some effects on health are measurable in the short term, other impacts affecting local communities may not appear until after several years have passed.

For those health indicators that are monitored in the Regional Municipality of Wood Buffalo (RMWB), the majority of those indicators show poorer levels than other Alberta regions and the provincial average. Based on current levels of monitoring, there is not credible evidence of environmental contaminant exposures causing elevated human cancer rates; however, rigorous monitoring is needed to find the causes and to address the concerns of First Nations and other communities [10]. Additionally, public health cannot be limited to exposure to environmental contaminants, since there are other health indicators to assess major negative effects on local communities. Health impacts are tightly linked to other impacts (e.g., environmental and social); therefore, finding the link between cause and effect becomes a priority in areas of rapid development (e.g., the Athabasca region [Alberta]) to effectively, rapidly, and efficiently mitigate and/or eliminate the risks.

In addition to economic, social, environmental, and health impacts, Alberta's oil sands development carries other potential impacts due to disruption to ecosystems and local communities. The oil sands projects require access to land, other natural resources such as water, and subsequent land development to accommodate the needs for the execution, operation, and maintenance of the projects, not only during construction but also during operations and decommissioning.

In addition to conflicts between different land users that may arise, Aboriginal and local communities may oppose the development of the projects. Government provides funding to address community needs and develops new regulations to address social concerns. Some stakeholders criticize that the regulations imposed by regulatory bodies are not stringent enough. Developing companies have implemented programs for stakeholder engagement to improve their relationships and obtain the so-called "social license." Furthermore, local communities in the role of "active" or "inactive" stakeholders are ready to act as issues concerning them arise.

A common worry amongst Albertans involves the equality factor. The oil sands resource results in not only provincial but also national economic growth. However, the benefits of mining are not always equally ("fairly") shared [12];

the same feeling of "unfairness" is shared by some Albertans who believe that the resource belongs to the province, and it is argued that Albertans do not get their "fair" share from other industries/resources (e.g., fishing) existing in other provinces. This issue of fairness is felt in other regions, and it can affect inter-jurisdictional negotiations, such as conditions for British Columbia approval of the Northern Gateway pipeline project.

4 Conclusions

Canada's oil sands are in an advantageous and unique position as the biggest deposit of unconventional oil and gas in the world. Conventional oil sources face not only the threat of scarcity, but also unequal geographic distribution of the remaining oil; therefore, unconventional oil sources have grabbed national and international attention. For most, the volume of the deposits has taken the back seat, since the current technology will enable 178 billion of barrels to be recovered and meet the Canadian demand for about the next 250 years. The attention has now shifted to improving technology involving the extraction of the remaining resource, and identifying and mitigating the increasing impacts (social, economic, and environmental) inherent in the exploration, extraction, and production processes of the resource.

Indisputable, varied impacts are expected with the development of large scale projects; the focus of government, developers, local communities, and other stakeholders is not only to mitigate and/or eliminate impacts, but also to find a balanced approach for social, economic, and environmental needs. The rapid development of the Canadian oil sands may have taken government and developers by surprise; such development is under pressure by oil importers who see Canada as an ally that brings a feasible energy resource alternative with considerably-sized deposits that are in the middle of a stable geo-political scenario.

Efforts made by government and developers towards mitigating and/or eliminating impacts are falling short from the standpoint of local communities, environmentalists, national and international watchdogs, and other stakeholders. Not only is the on-going assessment, monitoring, and reporting of performance required, but stakeholder engagement in decision-making and informing/educating the public is also essential to facilitate and benefit the process.

References

[1] Canadian Association of Petroleum Producers (2012). Oil. Retrieve from http://www.capp.ca/canadaIndustry/oil/Pages/default.aspx. December 2012.
[2] International Energy Agency (2012). Oil Market Report. Retrieve from http://www.capp.ca/energySupply/canadaPetroleumResources/Pages/default.aspx. December 2012.

[3] Canadian Association of Petroleum Producers (2012). Canada's Petroleum Resources. Retrieve from http://www.capp.ca/energySupply/canada PetroleumResources/Pages/default.aspx. December 2012.

[4] Alberta Energy and Utilities Board (2004). Alberta's Reserves 2003 and Supply/Demand Outlook 2004–2013, June 2004 Revised Version. Retrieve from http://www.eub.gov.ab.ca/bbs/products/STs/st98-2004 December 2012.

[5] Honarvar, A., Rozhon, J., Millington, D., Walden, T., and Murillo, C.A. (2011). Economic Impacts of New Oil Sands Projects in Alberta (2010-2035). Canadian Energy Research Institute. Study No. 124.

[6] The Conference Board of Canada (2012). Fuel for Thought: The Economic Benefits of Oil Sands Investment for Canada's Region. The Conference Board of Canada: Report October 2012.

[7] National Resources Canada.(2011a). Whitehorse Mining Initiative. Retrieve from http://www.nrcan.gc.ca/minerals-metals/policy/government-canada /3882. December 2012.

[8] United Nations. (undated). Canada National Reporting to CSD-18/19 – Thematic Profile on Mining. Retrieve from http://www.un.org/esa/dsd /dsd_aofw_ni/ni_pdfs/NationalReports/canada/Mining.pdf December 2012.

[9] Gibson, R. B., Hassan, S., Holtz, S., Tansey, J., and Whitelaw, G. (2010). Sustainability Assessment: Criteria and Processes. London, UK: Earthscan.

[10] Gosselin, P., Hrudey. S. E., Naeth, M. A., Plourde, A., Therrien, R., Van Der Kraak, G., and Xu, Z. (2010). The Royal Society of Canada Expert Panel: Environmental and Health Impact of Canada's Oil Sands Industry. The Royal Society of Canada.

[11] Alberta Energy (2012). Facts and Statistics. Retrieve from http://www.energy.gov.ab.ca/OilSands/791.asp. December 2012.

[12] WRI (undated). Appendix 2: Environmental and Social Impacts of Mining. Retrieve from http://pdf.wri.org/mining_background_literature_review.pdf . December 2012.

[13] Environment Canada (2009). Environmental Management of Alberta's Oil Sands: Resourceful. Responsible. Government of Alberta.

[14] Salameh, M. G. (2012). The potential of Unconventional Oil Resources: Between Expediency & Reality. International Association for Energy Economic. Fourth Quarter 2012 Report.

[15] Shipley, K. (2005). Socio-Economic Impact Assessment Review: Albian Sands Energy Inc. Muskeg River Mine Expansion. Report prepared for The Fort McKay Industry Relations Corporation: August 2005.

[16] Honarvar, A., Rozhon, J., Millington, D., Walden, T., and Murillo, C.A. (2011). Economic Impacts of Staged Development of Oil Sands Projects in Alberta (2010-2035). Canadian Energy Research Institute. Study No. 125 – Section I.

[17] Timilsina, G. R., LeBlanc, N., and Walden, T. (2005). Economic Impacts of Alberta's Oil Sands. Canadian Energy Research Institute. Volume I. Study No. 110.

Sustainability assessment framework for engineering and sciences educational institutions in developing countries

M. M. G. Elbarkouky[1], A. M. Aboshady[2] & A. S. Salem[3]
[1]Construction Engineering and Management, School of Business,
School of Science and Engineering,
The American University in Cairo, Egypt
[2]Structural Engineering Department, Faculty of Engineering,
Cairo University, Egypt
[3]Comparative Education and Educational Administration Department,
Faculty of Education, Ein Shams University, Egypt

Abstract

There are different factors that may impact the technological, organizational, social, and pedagogical innovation necessary for improving the existing Governmental Egyptian Engineering and Sciences educational institutions to enable offering a more sustainable learning environment for Egyptian students and faculty members. This paper proposes a sustainability assessment framework that can help these educational institutions in achieving the required transformation towards a more sustainable education. First, a literature review is conducted to identify the sustainability factors that need to be considered in achieving a more sustainable education environment in Egypt. Those factors are then tailored to satisfy the Egyptian educational environment through experts' interviews and gap analysis. The factors are then ranked through a survey questionnaire and experts' judgment using a 5-point Likert scale to identify the most significant factors, based on the Pareto principal. A case study of a learning institution in Egypt is adapted to identify the gaps in light of the highly prioritized factors in order to develop guidelines and provide recommendations for improvement.
Keywords: sustainable education, engineering and sciences, pedagogical innovation, gap analysis.

WIT Transactions on Ecology and The Environment, Vol 173, © 2013 WIT Press
www.witpress.com, ISSN 1743-3541 (on-line)
doi:10.2495/SDP130491

1 Introduction

In general, sustainability education is considered one of the most critical aspects of education that may hinder the future of a nation. Today's graduates will take the positions of future management, and leadership in any given society, and they will be in need to acquire knowledge and decisions to make correct choices. They should be coupled with information about their society, economy, and environmental issue that change dramatically year over year. Plank [1] stated that education for sustainability development aims at enabling everyone to gain the values, skills, and knowledge, which contribute to building more sustainable society. This implies revising teaching content to respond to global and local challenges. It should also promote teaching methods that enable students to grasp skills, such as interdisciplinary thinking, integrated planning, understanding complexities, cooperating with others in decision-making process, and participating in local, national, and global processes towards sustainable development. Also, Simpson [2] suggested that higher education has a tremendous contribution to enhance sustainability development. For example, University researchers were the first to alert the global warming issue, and researchers are now seeking to find technological and social solutions to assist nations to face this environmental challenge. Therefore, higher education institutions should play their part as centres of teaching and research in their local communities.

2 Literature review

According to the World Commission on Environment and Development [3], sustainable development was defined as *"development that meets the needs of the present without compromising the ability of future generations to meet their own needs."* Different researchers have tackled the issue of sustainability education. Cole [4] assessed sustainability on a Canadian University Campus. He proposed a framework for the development of Victoria Campus sustainability assessment. West *et al.* [5] recommended international perspectives to flourish the quality in higher education for educational research. Martin *et al.* [6] studied sustainability development in higher education. He proposed some recommendations for future development, such as universities should function as places of research and learning for sustainable development. Also, he proposed that new sustainable development strategy means securing the future, which emphasis the role that education can play in both raising awareness among youth about sustainability development as well as giving them the skills apply sustainability development into practice. Wigmore and Ruiz [7] developed a sustainability assessment framework in higher education institutions. Kaviola and Rochmeder [8] studied sustainability development in higher education in Finland. Koehn and Demment [9] overviewed higher education and sustainability development in Africa. Zilaly [10] investigated the role of higher education and recommended a clean technologies, and environmental policy toward enhancing the higher educational institutions. In addition, some authors have studied the factors affecting

Sustainability development. Evans *et al.* [11] assessed the sustainability indicators that affect the renewable energy technologies. Ghose [12] technological challenges for boosting coal production with environmental Sustainability. Urban *et al.* [13] designed self-reliant networks of technological ecological systems. Smith [14] studied the organizational elements affecting Sustainability. Pluye *et al.* [15] designed a program for sustainability, which focuses on organizational routines. Smith [16] highlighted the importance of organizational learning for Sustainability. Gonzalès and Parrott [17] developed a network theory for the assessment of Sustainability of Socio-Ecological Systems. Assefa and Frostell [18] studied social sustainability and social acceptance in technology assessment. Daniel *et al.* [19] discussed social Sustainability in urban renewal communities. Yuen *et al.* [20] developed a comparative case study for the pedagogical orientation in Hong Kong. Finally, Johansson [21] discussed Pedagogical approaches and their implications for sustainability. All the above researchers did not develop a framework that deals with the sustainability development of the Engineering and Science Institutions in Egypt. Therefore, the Sustainability assessment framework was developed in this paper to overcome this limitation and provide recommendations not only applicable to Egypt, but also to any other developing country.

3 Objectives

The main objective of this paper is to prioritize critical factors affecting sustainability development in Egypt. This is achieved through the development of the sustainability development framework. The consent of framework development can be generalized and applied to other countries by changing related sustainability development factors and expert opinions. The framework solves a major problem that faces educators who want to prioritize critical factors affecting the sustainability development process in order to produce a list of prioritized sustainability factors.

4 Methodology and model development

The proposed framework is composed of six stages: Identifying critical Sustainability Factors, Creating Linguistic Scale to Rate Different Critical Factors and Collecting Experts' Opinions, Performing Statistical Analysis, Assessing the Relative Importance Index (RII) for Prioritization, Conducting a Case Study in Egypt, and Suggesting Recommendations as per in Figure 1.

4.1 Identifying Critical Sustainability Development Factors

Critical Sustainability Development Factors were determined using literature review and interviews with ten experts each of them had twenty years of experience in Sustainability Development Education. Experts agreed that Sustainability Development Factors can be divided into four groups: Technological Factors, Organizational Factors, Social Factors, and Pedagogical Innovation Factors (Table 1).

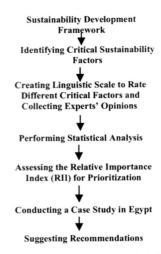

Figure 1:   Methodology and model development.

Table 1:   Critical sustainability development factors and their groups.

	Group (1) Technological factors		Group (3) Social factors
1	Need for acquiring skills for developed industries	21	Ensure participation of different groups (students, women) in social activities
2	Enhance university's curriculum with main changes in energy resource	22	Being aware of environmental injustice and its direct and indirect effects on higher education
3	Enhance students' creativity	23	Understand internationalization of core curriculum
4	Promote the higher education requirements for radical improvement in human technology interfaces	24	Promote lifelong learning
5	Aware the staff about changing in technological skills to enhance these skills in students.	25	Prepare students to post graduation life
6	Establish vocational courses	26	Monitor and evaluate team performance
7	Teach students giving positive respond to global and local challenges	27	Need to avoid in equality within nations and develop internationally recognized curriculum
8	Prepare students to the technological effects on employment	28	Promote community engagement
9	Understand technology and its negative and positive effect on our daily life	29	Implement the university policies
10	Enhance industry intervention in higher education	30	Need to have the ability to work well with others
	Group (2) Organizational factors		**Group (4) Pedagogical innovation factors**
11	Need to face the deficit in real demands in goods and services existed in industrial organizations.	31	Need for distance learning
12	Enhance students' loyalty to working organizations.	32	Need for industries involvement in research
13	Need to know about employment terms and conditions	33	Need for graduating innovative students
14	Need to be aware about number of job vacancies	34	Being aware with changing nature of market needs
15	Promote skills understanding between students and staff	35	Need for providing training to deans and chairs to their work
16	Learn students how to solve problems	36	Need for gaining worldwide accreditation
17	Develop and run international offices	37	Promote experiences in labor market research
18	Need to cope with international division of labour market and its effects in industrial organizations.	38	Being aware of economic challenges for 21st century
19	Being aware of financing development and growth	39	Giving rise to international equity
20	Support learning for life and work	40	Develop staff to cope with international education standards

4.2 Creating Linguistic Scale to Rate Different Critical Factors and collecting experts' opinions

In this step, a survey-based questionnaire was designed to assist experts in ranking Critical Sustainability Development Factors based on the impact of these Sustainability Development factors on the sustainable education enhancement of engineering and science educational institutions, using a five-point Likert scale (Saaty [22]). The scale ranged between (1) *Very Low* and (5) *Very High*, while the term (3) *Medium* was placed as a midterm value on the scale. Moreover, the questionnaire included a section that contained experts' demographic information that defined five qualification criteria of experts: Q1: Years of experience, Q2: Years of experience in Science or education Fields, Q3: Position, Q4: Academic record, and Q5: Public vs. Private Institutions. Table 2 lists experts' qualifications and their attributes.

4.3 Performing statistical analysis

The statistical analysis of the experts' ratings determined the Mean, Median, Mode, Standard Deviation, Standard Error, and 95% Confidence Range to advise on whether the opinions are converging or not. The 95% Confidence Range is a type of interval estimate of a population parameter and is used to indicate the reliability of an estimate, where the 95% Confidence Range reflects a significance level of 0.05 in the current study. The Standard Error was computed to measure the extent to which the means from different samples is expected to vary from the population mean, owing to the chance error in the sampling process, which was computed by dividing the Standard Deviation by the square root of N, where N is the sample size. According to Montgomery [23], computing the Standard Error implies an acceptable agreement among experts. Abdelgawad [24] demonstrated that the calculated Standard Error is to be compared to 0.2, as this value indicates a relatively precise point estimate of agreement among experts on the results (Shen *et al.* [25]).

4.4 Assessing the Relative Importance Index (RII) for prioritization

In this step, the Relative Importance Index (RII) was utilized to prioritize Critical Sustainability Development Factors, based on the ranking of the experts (collected from step 2). This approach was applied because of its simplicity and ability to provide subjective and objective assessments of multiple factors (Elbarkouky *et al.* [26]).

The average rating of the fifty experts (Table 2) who participated in the process of prioritizing Critical Sustainability Development Factors was computed. 'Equation (1)' illustrates the RII computation.

$$RIIj = \sum_{i=1}^{n} \frac{yj}{z} \tag{1}$$

where, yj is the rating score assigned to each risk event (j) by each expert (i) on the Likert scale from 1 to 5, and z is the highest possible rating value of the

Likert scale [22], which is 5 in this case. The *RII* value has a range between 0 to 1 (0 not inclusive), such that the higher its value, the more important the risk event is.

Table 2:   Experts' qualifications (attributes).

Expert No.	Q1 Years of Experience	Q2 Years in Education or Science Fields	Q3 Position	Q4 Academic record	Q5 Public vs. Private
1	11–15	6–10	Professor	PhD	Public
2	11–15	6–10	Professor	PhD	Public
3	11–15	6–10	Assco Prof	PhD	Public
4	11–15	11–15	Assco Prof	PhD	Public
5	11–15	6–10	Assco Prof	PhD	Public
6	11–15	6–10	Assco Prof	PhD	Public
7	6–10	6–10	Assco Prof	PhD	Public
8	1–5	< 1	Ass Prof	PhD	Public
9	1–5	1–5	Ass Prof	PhD	Public
10	< 1	< 1	Ass Prof	PhD	Public
11	1–5	< 1	Ass Prof	PhD	Public
12	1–5	1–5	Ass Prof	PhD	Public
13	16–20	16–20	Professor	PhD	Public
14	16–20	16–20	Professor	PhD	Public
15	11–15	11–15	Professor	PhD	Public
16	16–20	16–20	Professor	PhD	Public
17	16–20	11–15	Professor	PhD	Public
18	11–15	6–10	Assco Prof	PhD	Public
19	< 1	< 1	Ass Prof	PhD	Public
20	16–20	11–15	Professor	PhD	Public
21	11–15	6–10	Assco Prof	PhD	Public
22	1–5	1–5	Ass Prof	PhD	Public
23	1–5	< 1	Ass Prof	PhD	Public
24	1–5	< 1	Ass Prof	PhD	Public
25	1–5	1–5	Ass Prof	PhD	Public
26	16–20	16–20	Professor	PhD	Public
27	16–20	16–20	Professor	PhD	Public
28	6–10	6–10	Assco Prof	PhD	Public
29	16–20	16–20	Professor	PhD	Public
30	6–10	6–10	Assco Prof	PhD	Public
31	16–20	16–20	Professor	PhD	Private
32	6–10	6–10	Ass Prof	PhD	Private
33	1–5	1–5	TA	Master	Private
34	16–20	16–20	Professor	PhD	Private
35	1–5	< 1	TA	Master	Private
36	16–20	11–15	PM	Master	Private
37	1–5	< 1	SPE	Bachelor	Private
38	16–20	16–20	PM	Master	Private
39	16–20	16–20	PM	Master	Private
40	1–5	1–5	SPE	Master	Private
41	11–15	6–10	SPE	Bachelor	Private
42	16–20	11–15	PM	Bachelor	Private
43	16–20	16–20	PM	Master	Private
44	11–15	6–10	PM	Bachelor	Private
45	11–15	6–10	PM	Master	Private
46	6–10	1–5	SPE	Bachelor	Private
47	11–15	11–15	PM	Bachelor	Private
48	11–15	11–15	PM	Bachelor	Private
49	11–15	11–15	SPE	Master	Private
50	16–20	6–10	PM	Master	Private

As illustrated in Table 2, the PM stands for Project Manager, SPE stands for Senior Project Engineer, Ass Prof stands for Assistant Professor, Assco Prof stands for Associate Professor and TA stands for Teaching Assistant.

5   Conducting a case study in Egypt (Ain Shams University)

Sustainability development plays a vital role in enhancing the understanding of youth and developing there needed skills in order to be able to cope with the changes in the technological, economical, and social requirement. The Sustainability assessment framework was applied in this case study to be able to identify and qualify the factors affecting the development of the sustainability objectives. Case study is conducted on Ain Shams University, which is public university, and is considered as one the biggest universities in the field of Engineering and Science, and 6 October University, which is a private university and considered one of the most growing private universities in Egypt.

The forty sustainability factors that have been previously identified in step 1 of the framework were introduced to fifty Egyptian experts to solicit their opinions regarding the linguistic criticality of factors that would affect the development of sustainability objectives. The survey was conducted using the linguistic rating scales and questionnaire-based survey (step 2). The experts were carefully selected to possess different levels of experience, represent different sizes and maintain different experience levels in sustainability. The statistical Analysis was performed in (Step 3) in order to ensure the correctness of the data collected from experts, and to ensure that their final assessment is a result of common agreement. The Relative Importance Index (RII) was computed using equation (1) Step 5 to rank different factors affecting the sustainability development based on their consequence on sustainability assessment. Table 3 illustrates the computations of the Mean, Median, Mode, Standard Deviation, 95% Confidence Range, Average Rating, Relative Importance Index (RII), and rank of different factors.

6   Recommendations

A set of recommendations were developed to enhance the sustainability development using literature review and interviews with experts with fifty experts.

1. Graduates' skills should be developed in order to meet the needs of the modernized industries.
2. Both university curricula and methods of teaching should be examined in order to improve the mentality of the students, and cope with the radical technological changes.
3. Higher education institutions have to include local and global challenges in their curriculum, and motivate students to learn how to respond to these challenges positively.
4. Higher education institutions have to aware students about the changing demands of employment, and labor markets.
5. Higher education institutions have to contain international offices for
6. Famous universities in order to acquire a variety of knowledge.
7. Team work skills should be strengthened within the university
8. Curriculum in order to develop students' skills in this field.

Table 3:   List of prioritized sustainability development factors.

Factors ID	Mean	Median	Mode	Standard Deviation	Standard Error	95% Confidence Range	RII	Rank
19	4.88	5	5	0.385	0.088	[5.035, 4.725]	0.976	1
15	4.76	5	5	0.591	0.109	[4.952, 4.568]	0.952	2
2	4.7	5	5	0.505	0.1	[4.876, 4.524]	0.94	3
26	4.68	5	5	0.471	0.097	[4.851, 4.509]	0.936	4
1	4.56	5	5	0.501	0.1	[4.736, 4.384]	0.912	5
7	4.5	5	5	0.814	0.128	[4.725, 4.275]	0.9	6
39	4.48	4.5	5	0.544	0.104	[4.663, 4.297]	0.896	7
18	4.46	5	5	0.788	0.126	[4.682, 4.238]	0.892	8
29	4.46	5	5	0.734	0.121	[4.673, 4.247]	0.892	8
34	4.46	5	5	0.762	0.123	[4.677, 4.243]	0.892	8
33	4.44	5	5	0.705	0.119	[4.65, 4.23]	0.888	9
11	4.42	5	5	0.758	0.123	[4.637, 4.203]	0.884	10
24	4.42	5	5	0.731	0.121	[4.633, 4.207]	0.884	10
40	4.42	5	5	0.859	0.131	[4.651, 4.189]	0.884	10
4	4.38	4.5	5	0.697	0.118	[4.588, 4.172]	0.876	11
10	4.36	4	5	0.693	0.118	[4.568, 4.152]	0.872	12
5	4.3	5	5	0.814	0.128	[4.525, 4.075]	0.86	13
8	4.3	4	4	0.463	0.096	[4.469, 4.131]	0.86	13
30	4.26	4	4	0.723	0.12	[4.471, 4.049]	0.852	14
3	4.24	4	4	0.687	0.117	[4.446, 4.034]	0.848	15
9	4.14	4	5	0.783	0.125	[4.36, 3.92]	0.828	16
24	4.12	4	4	0.659	0.115	[4.323, 3.917]	0.824	17
27	4.1	4.5	5	1.111	0.149	[4.362, 3.838]	0.82	18
6	4.08	4	4	0.778	0.125	[4.3, 3.86]	0.816	19
32	4.06	4	4	0.512	0.101	[4.238, 3.882]	0.812	20
35	4.06	4	5	0.818	0.128	[4.285, 3.835]	0.812	20
37	4.06	4	5	0.89	0.133	[4.294, 3.826]	0.812	20
16	4.04	4	4	0.832	0.129	[4.267, 3.813]	0.808	21
20	4.02	4	4	0.795	0.126	[4.242, 3.798]	0.804	22
13	3.98	4	5	0.958	0.138	[4.223, 3.737]	0.796	23
38	3.98	4	4	0.82	0.128	[4.205, 3.755]	0.796	23
31	3.96	4	3	0.925	0.136	[4.199, 3.721]	0.792	24
28	3.92	4	4	1.085	0.147	[4.179, 3.661]	0.784	25
12	3.92	4	4	1.027	0.143	[4.172, 3.668]	0.784	25
14	3.86	4	4	0.729	0.121	[4.073, 3.647]	0.772	26
17	3.78	4	4	0.815	0.128	[4.005, 3.555]	0.756	27
22	3.78	4	5	1.148	0.152	[4.048, 3.512]	0.756	27
36	3.68	4	3	0.683	0.117	[3.886, 3.474]	0.736	28
21	3.52	4	5	1.474	0.172	[3.823, 3.217]	0.704	29
23	3.18	4	4	0.919	0.136	[3.419, 2.941]	0.636	30

9. Administration in Universities should aware the staff and faculty members about financing development and the rate of growth in order to provide this experience to students.

10. Universities have to provide social services, and social activities, and advice students to participate in this field.

11. Higher education institutions have to promote lifelong learning.

12. Higher education institutions have to aware students about post graduation life, and how to develop their skills.

13. Universalities have to develop internationally recognized curriculum.

14. Higher education institutions have to develop students' skills in order to obtain finally an innovative graduate.

15. Universities should have a linkage with international organizations, such as UNESCO, International Bank, and International Monetary Fund in order to achieve worldwide accreditation.
16. Universities have to promote research activities in the field of international education.
17. Universities have to develop their staff to cope with international education standards.

7 Conclusion

A Sustainability Assessment Framework was developed in this paper to prioritize different factors affecting the development of Sustainability objective. The proposed framework was composed of six stages: Identifying critical Sustainability Factors, Creating Linguistic Scale to Rate Different Critical Factors ,and Collecting Experts' Opinions, Performing Statistical Analysis, Assessing the Relative Importance Index (RII) for Prioritization, Conducting a Case Study in Egypt, and Suggesting Recommendations. Factors affecting the sustainability development were identified using literature review and interviews with experts. A case study was conducted to demonstrate the validity of the Sustainability assessment framework in identifying, and qualifying different factors affecting the sustainability development. The framework provided an improvement over previous sustainability models by incorporating the use of the Relative Importance Index (RII) to prioritize different factors affecting the sustainability development. The framework improves over the previous models, which rely on the subjective assessment. In the future, the highly prioritized sustainability factors will be introduced to another quantitative sustainability assessment model that quantify these factors that is currently under preparation.

References

[1] Plank, D., "The Emerging Markets and Higher Education: Development and Sustainability", *Economics of Education*, **22(3)**, 337–338, 2003.
[2] Simpson, J., "A Shared Vision for Development in Higher Education", Higher Education Funding Council for England, www.sd.defra.gov.uk, 2010.
[3] The World Commission on Environment and Development (WCED), *Our common future*. Oxford, Oxford University Press, May 21, 1987.
[4] Cole, L., "Assessing Sustainability on Canadian University Campus: Development of a Campus Sustainability Assessment Framework", University of Victoria, Canada, www.neumann.hec.ca/.../campus.../ campus_memoire.pdf, 2003.
[5] West, A., Noden, P. and Gosling, R. "*Quality in Higher Education; An international Perspective*", Centre for Educational Research London School of Economics and Political Sciences, www. citeseerx.ist.psu.edu, 2000.

[6] Martin, S., Dawe, G., and Jucker, R. "Sustainable Development in Higher Education Current Practice and Future Development", Higher Education Academy, UK, www.thesite.eu/sustdevinHEfinalreport.pdf, 2005.

[7] Wigmore, A. and Ruiz, M. "Sustainability Assessment in Higher Education Institutions", *Romonllull Journal of Applied Ethics,* **1(1)**, 25–42, 2010.

[8] Kaviola, T., and Rochmeder, L. *"Towards Sustainable Development in Higher Education"*, Ministry of Education, Department for Education and Science Policy, Finland, www.minedu.fi/export/sites/default/.../opm06.pdf, 2007.

[9] Koehn, P.H. and Demment, M.W. "Higher Education and Sustainable Development in Africa and Why Partner Transnational?", Paper for the Ministerial Conference on Higher Education in Agriculture in Africa, Kampala, www.aplu.org, 2010.

[10] Zilaly, G. "Towards Sustainability: The Role of Higher Education", Clean Technologies and Environmental Policy, **8(1)**, 1–2, 2006.

[11] Evans, A., Strezov, V. and Evans, T.J., "Assessment of sustainability indicators for renewable energy technologies", *Renewable and Sustainable Energy Reviews,* **13(5)**,1082–1088, 2009.

[12] Ghose, M.K. "Technological challenges for boosting coal production with environmental sustainability", *Environmental monitoring and assessment,* **154(1–4)**, 373–381, 2009.

[13] Urban, R.A., Bakshi, B.R., Grubb, G.F., Baral, A. and Mitsch, W.J. "Towards sustainability of engineered processes: Designing self–reliant networks of technological–ecological systems", *Computers and Chemical Engineering,* **34(9)**, 1413–1420, 2010.

[14] Smith, P.A.C. "Elements of organizational sustainability", *The Learning Organization,* **18(1)**, 5–9, 2011.

[15] Pluye, P., Potvin, L., Denis, J.L. and Pelletier, J. "Program sustainability: focus on organizational routines", *Health Promotion International,* **19(4)**, 489–500, 2004.

[16] Smith, P.A.C. "The importance of organizational learning for organizational sustainability", *The Learning Organization,* **19(1)**, 4–10, 2012.

[17] Gonzalès, R. and Parrott, L. "Network Theory in the Assessment of the Sustainability of Social–Ecological Systems", *Geography Compass,* **6(2)**, 76–88, 2012.

[18] Assefa, G. and Frostell, B. "Social sustainability and social acceptance in technology assessment: A case study of energy technologies", *Technology in Society,* **29(1)**, 63–78, 2007.

[19] Daniel C.W.H., Yung, Y., Chi K.L., Sun W.P., Hak K.Y. and Ervi L. "Social sustainability in urban renewal: An assessment of community aspirations", *Urbani Izziv,* **23(1)**, 125–139, 2012.

[20] Yuen, A.H.K., Lee, M.W. and Law, N. "School leadership and teachers' pedagogical orientations in Hong Kong: A comparative perspective", *Education and Information Technologies,* **14(4)**, 381–396, 2009.

[21] Johansson, T. "Pedagogical approaches and their implications for sustainability", *EUROGEO Seminar and Annual Meeting Sustainable Geographies*, University of Helsinki, 1–17, 2010.

[22] Saaty, T.L. Multi–criteria Decision Making: *The Analytic Hierarchy Process*. RWS Publications, Pittsburgh, PA, 1980.

[23] Montgomery, D.C., Runger, G.C. and Hubele, N.F. *Engineering Statistics*, John Wiley and Sons, New York, 1998.

[24] Abdelgawad, M. "Construction Schedule Delay Assessment in Joint Venture Projects: A Fuzzy Logic Method" Master of Science Thesis, Structural Engineering Department, Cairo University, Egypt, 2005.

[25] Shen, L.Y., Wu, G.W.C. and Ng, C.S.K. "Risk Assessment for Construction Joint Ventures in China." *Journal of Construction Engineering and Management*, **127(1)**, 76–81, 2001.

[26] Elbarkouky, M.G., Ezzeldin, A.S. and Elassaly, A. A multi–criteria decision–making (MCDM) framework for prioritizing damaged infrastructure and services facilities in Egypt using sustainability objectives. *Proceedings, CSCE Annual Conference, 1st International Specialty Conference on Sustaining Public Infrastructure*, Edmonton, Alberta, June 6–9, 2012, INF–S11–1011–1/11, 2012.

Section 12
Waste management

IDES project: an advanced tool to investigate illegal dumping

G. Persechino[1], M. Lega[2], G. Romano[1], F. Gargiulo[1] & L. Cicala[1]
[1]CIRA, Italian Aerospace Research Centre, Italy
[2]Department of Environmental Sciences, University of Naples, Italy

Abstract

IDES – Intelligent Data Extraction System – is the name of a new project, founded by Campania Regional Government (Italy) and developed by the CIRA – Italian Aerospace Research Centre that aims at implementing an advanced tool to support Government Bodies in the discovery and localization of environmental criticalities. In detail, this project will develop a software and hardware platform for image, data and document analysis in order to support law enforcement investigations. The fight against illegal waste dumping is the first objective of the IDES project and the main goal is to develop algorithms for image analysis in order to automatically identify this environmental criticality. The first task is to identify the statistical link between specific features extracted from satellite images or acquired by airborne sensors, possibly in combination with punctual information (results of chemical analysis, physical property measurements, information pertaining to the population), and environmental criticalities (e.g. illegal dumping, illegal landfills etc). IDES will offer an integrated Geographic Information System (GIS) repository of information extracted and collected by various government bodies. Furthermore, an innovative aspect of IDES is the integration between information extracted from remotely sensed images and information extracted from textual documents through a semantic analysis. The results of this last analysis will be a taxonomy-driven document searching and browsing system in which all documents are categorized and all relevant entities in documents (e.g. people, organizations, places and events) are extracted and represented by means of concept maps. Finally, these results: a) provide support to government bodies "end-users"; b) can be included in a GIS; c) can constitute the basis for the application of Artificial Adaptive Systems used in the domain of semantic analysis of

WIT Transactions on Ecology and The Environment, Vol 173, © 2013 WIT Press
www.witpress.com, ISSN 1743-3541 (on-line)
doi:10.2495/SDP130501

unstructured information providing unknown relationships between entities (e.g. criminal associations, people, places, activities, buildings, towns and dates).

Keywords: illegal dumping, landfills monitoring, interoperability, unmanned aerial systems, synthetic aperture radar, multispectral images, infrared images, text semantic search, geographical information systems.

1 Introduction

A recent census of the Italian illegal dumping sites estimates the presence of 4866 illegal dumping. Only 21% of surveyed landfills have been reclaimed and more than 700 contain hazardous waste (Persechino *et al.* [1]).

In Italy, the Campania Region might be associated with a history of illegal dumping and disposal of hazardous waste.

The citizens' exposure to toxic waste is a major public health problem; therefore, the responsible public authorities have the need to act as soon as possible in the identification of such environmental issues. Identifying the problem, as soon as it occurs, would reduce reclamation costs. So it is necessary a more frequent and more targeted monitoring of large areas.

On the other hand, public authorities do not have large budgets, so the required solution must also be economically feasible. Many employers and gears are involved in territory control requiring high costs for this activity. But control of the territory is a necessary action for the prevention of such unlawfully. It is a difficult challenge to perform long-term environmental monitoring with today's manned aircraft because of vehicle, cost, and mission limitations.

Moreover, where there are small sources of pollution and contamination over a wide area, the illegal dumping is very difficult to detect. The use of satellite monitoring exceeds the current limits of traditional methods of detection. The satellite images are able to continuously monitor, in terms of space and time, large part of the territory. Early intervention on the waste accumulation is the only way to prevent its transformation in illegal landfill. The continuous satellite scanning allows the detection of anomalies connected to the dumping area employing a smaller number of operators. In this way the operators can arise only in aimed interventions having more time for other important police activities. Another plus of early warning in the contaminated area is a more effective remediation so that the territory can be back to his old self again. The treatment of small accumulations of waste requiring disposal and reclamation entails much smaller costs than those for the remediation of large volumes of waste and it's more safety for exposure to the risk of contamination from the people living around there.

Early warning also prevents the contamination of wider areas due to the dispersion phenomena mediated by trophic chain and atmospheric agents. government bodies must ensure to citizens the healthy avoiding their exposure to contaminants.

2 IDES – Intelligent data extraction system

IDES – Intelligent Data Extraction System – project aims at implementing an SW platform for data analysis within the domain of environmental criticalities.

IDES will offer an integrated repository of information extracted from heterogeneous, physically distributed, unstructured sources (satellite and airborne data, web pages, etc.) by means of a capture, extraction and analysis process. Based upon the integrated information stored in a Geographic Information System and elaborated with the aid of advanced data analysis techniques and tools, IDES will be able to extract the *hidden* information, that is information non immediately identifiable through a mere reading or a deeper analysis, even if performed by a domain expert; at this end, IDES will be able to uncover patterns, multi-disciplinary correlations not known a priori and it will be able to extract relevant information useful for government bodies.

There are available, with regard to these issues, a large amount of data that describe anthropic activities with heavy impact on environmental health; so to this end, the project team focussed on the following dataset:

- dumping and landfills data related to specific industrial installations;
- urban solid waste temporary deposits/facilities;
- statistical data about urban people.

All above data, coming from different sources available in the project, are different for semantics (chemical, emissions, county people, installations address, etc.) and structure (tabular, vector, raster, structured, unstructured). IDES is an environmental Geographical Information System (GIS) with the strategic mission to be a centralized and unified informative system containing all data coming from different sources (satellite, airborne, terrain data) and tools enriched with geographical information enabling detailed spatial analysis tasks.

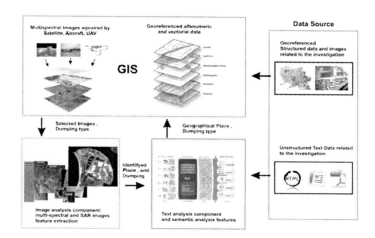

Figure 1:   IDES components workflow.

In order to deal with different types of data and to enable user analysis, the IDES SW platform is based on different SW components each of which with a well defined responsibility:

- text analysis component with semantic analysis features; its objective is to analyse text document coming from intranet and web sources in order to automatically extract entities and relationship among them with which to build conceptual map useful for a primary illegal crime detecting;
- image analysis component for analysing multi-spectral and SAR images through advanced algorithmic features to mine pattern among data; this represents a powerful key to identify and geo-locate sites with potential illegal activity;
- geographical information system and geostatistical analysis component for spatial data exploration and analysis with the capabilities to create statistically valid prediction information from a limited number of data measurements.

2.1 IDES Geographical Information System

The IDES project involves several government agencies including: Autorità di Bacino, Arpa Campania, Genio Civile, Provincia di Caserta, etc. Each agency also participates in the project by providing its own data. Such data are always geo-referenced or they could be geo-referenced with a little effort. Then, the first step is to collect all this information into a GIS.

A geographic information system is a software system used to describe and characterize the earth and other geographies for the purpose of visualizing and analyzing geographically referenced information.

GIS is one of the most powerful of all information technologies because it focuses on integrating knowledge from multiple sources (for example, as layers within a map) and creates a crosscutting environment for collaboration. In addition, GIS is attractive because it is both intuitive and cognitive. It combines a powerful visualization environment, using maps to communicate and visualize geographic data through a strong analytic, statistical and modeling framework.

A GIS utilizes a layer-based geographic information model for characterizing and describing our world and models geographic information as a logical set of layers or themes. For example, a GIS can contain data layers for the following:

- streets represented as centerlines;
- land-use areas that represent vegetation, residential areas, business zones, and so forth;
- administrative areas;
- water bodies and rivers;
- parcel polygons representing landownership;
- a surface used to represent elevation and terrain;
- an aerial photo or satellite image for an area of interest.

A GIS uses maps to visualize and work with geographic information.

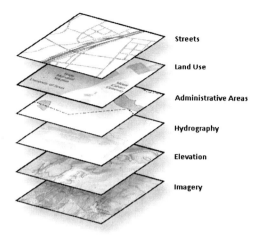

Figure 2:   GIS layers.

Each GIS includes a set of interactive maps and other views (such as 3D globes) that show features and relative relationships on the earth's surface. Various map views of the underlying geographic information can be constructed to support query, analysis, and editing of geographic information. Maps can also be used to access geographic modeling tools that are used to derive new information.

A GIS has a comprehensive set of analytic and data transformation tools to perform spatial analysis, data processing and geostatistical analysis.

Geo-processing is the methodical execution of a sequence of operations on geographic data to create new information. GIS includes a large set of geo-processing functions to take information from existing datasets, apply analytic functions, and write results into new result datasets. Each geo-processing tool takes existing information as input and derives a new result, which can be used in subsequent operations. This ability to string together a logical sequence of operations so that you can perform spatial analysis and automate data processing, all by assembling a model, is one of the key elements of GIS.

The emphasis of spatial analysis is to measure properties and relationships, taking into account the spatial localization of the phenomenon under study in a direct way. That is, the central idea is to incorporate space into the analysis to be made (Camara *et al.* [7]). Spatial analysis is useful for evaluating suitability and capability, estimating and predicting, and interpreting and understanding.

Geostatistics is a branch of statistics focusing on spatial or spatiotemporal datasets. It is related to interpolation methods, but extends far beyond simple interpolation problems. Geostatistical techniques rely on statistical method to model the uncertainty associated with spatial estimation and simulation. Geostatistical algorithms are incorporated in GIS.

For example, starting with industrial dumping registered in the province of Caserta, we use the geostatistical analysis to identify areas where the distribution of these dumping is "abnormal" with respect to the density of population and productive activities. This may provide a guideline for the presence of potential illegal dumping.

2.2 Text analysis component and semantic analysis features

An innovative aspect of IDES is the integration between information extracted by remotely sensed images and information extracted from textual documents. There is a huge amount of information in unstructured documents (for example, it has been estimated that about 80% of corporate information is unstructured and contained in spreadsheets, presentations, e-mails, web pages and .pdf files).

Thanks to search methodologies based on deep linguistic analysis (semantic engines), it is possible to grasp the "meaning" of the content and go beyond traditional search tools

Such a kind of semantic engines relies on a semantic network, (e.g. ontologies), that contains all information about terms, grammar rules, meaning relations (i.e. synonyms, hyponyms, hypernyms, and so on) of the language (i.e., Italian, English). The semantic network is the core of the semantic engine, it contains about half a million concepts and four million relations.

In addition to basic linguistic analysis (grammar and morphology), the semantic engine used in the IDES project performs: logical and sentence analysis, disambiguation of polysemic terms and entity extraction (i.e. people, place and organization).

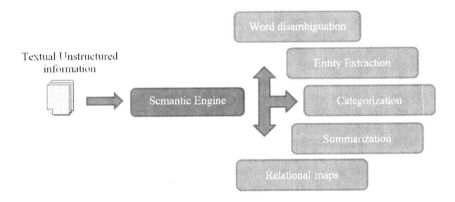

Figure 3: The relationships between the extracted entities represented by the "relational map".

A customization, also called "training", of the semantic engine must be performed in order to obtain: a better automatic comprehension of the content, a correct disambiguation of terms and a high level of quality of semantic-based categorization in specific domains, such as environmental criticalities domain.

There are two types of customization: Extensions of the semantic network and Definition of domain specific taxonomies. The former is a deeper personalization because a relevant number of new concepts (e.g. pollutant, criminal associations) and their relations are hard-coded in the semantic network. Through the semantic network, the semantic engine reconstructs the meaning of each word and each sentence of text. The definition of specific domain taxonomies instead allows us to classify each document in one or more categories with a certain percentage of membership. The documents are classified by the application of specific rules. A training set allows analysts to derive the classification rules. For example, the taxonomy may include a category for each environmental criticality and, during the step of classification, the semantic engine inserts each document in the right categories. In this way the user can access the documentation in a selective manner. Furthermore, advanced automatic semantic summarization allows the user to examine a summary of a set of documents. Then, the user can decide very quickly whether or not these documents are useful.

In the context of the IDES project, the semantic analysis of large amounts of unstructured information is guided by information obtained from the analysis of images.

By means of the semantic engine specifically trained documents both in the public domain (e.g. news and technical reports from public agencies or industry, blogs) and reserved domain (e.g. documentation of real investigations) will be analysed.

The results of this analysis will be a taxonomy-driven document searching and browsing system in which all document are categorized and all relevant entities in documents (e.g. persons, organizations, places and events) are extracted and represented by means of concept maps. These results: a) provide support to end-users; b) can be included in the GIS layer if they could be geo-referenced; c) can constitute the basis for the application of Artificial Adaptive Systems used in the domain of semantic analysis of unstructured information that allow to visually represent obvious connections and probable links between entities (e.g. criminal associations, persons, places, activities, buildings, towns and dates).

2.3 Image analysis component: multi-spectral and SAR images feature extraction

Remote sensed images from satellite platforms have been used to derive interesting feature maps suitable for environmental applications.

The aim is to localize high environmental risk regions. The localization process is performed by terrain classification, change detection and data fusion with not imagery derived data. A GIS is used to combine the imagery derived data with the others.

Two kinds of very high resolution (VHR) imagery sensors have been used:

- multispectral (MS) Images, GeoEye-1 sensor, operating in blue, green, red and near infrared spectral bands;
- synthetic aperture radar (SAR) images, Cosmo SkyMed sensor, operating in microwave X band.

Different acquisitions have been committed for the same region to analyse.

In the MS case, we planned to acquire new data in the same month and with the same sensor pose with respect to available archive data, so that a multi-temporal analysis can be performed without introducing errors due to the different acquisition geometry.

In the SAR case, we planned to use a long time series (8 scene) of the Map Italy project (ScanSAR acquisition mode of the Cosmo SkyMed sensor), obtained with the same acquisition geometry and interleaved approximately by one month, and a pair of interferometric couple, acquired in a committed mission.

Table 1:   Used sensors.

Sensor	Sensor type	Sensor mode	On ground resolution	Temporal acquisition	Time series length
GeoEye-1	Multispectral	MS (4 ch) + Panchromatic	4 m /pixel + 1 m/pixel	1 year	2
Cosmo Sky Med	SAR	ScanSAR	3 m /pixel	1 month	8
		Spotlight interferometric couple	1 m /pixel	1 month	2

The imagery raw data has been processed, obtaining, as final products, some indexed maps, each of them related to a specific phenomenal to be observed. The maps, originally rasters, can be easily vectorialized for an immediate use in a GIS.

The processing workflow can be summarized in the following table.

Table 2:   Used processing workflow.

General case	MS	SAR
Pre-processing	Pan Sharpening	Spatial Multilooking
Temporal Alignment	Coregistration	Coregistration + Temporal Despeakling
Feature Extraction (spectral, spatial, temporal)	Spatial Feature Extraction, Spectral Feature Extraction	Interferometry
Segmentation	Terrain Classification Map	Coherence Maps
Geometry Correction (using DTM)	Ortorectification	Geocoding
Fusion		
Change Detection		

In general the processing workflow consists in five phases. The first step is the pre-processing of the images. The resolution if the MS images can be improved, using the panchromatic channel, by pan-sharpening. The SAR images, that suffer from the speckling phenomenon, can be enhanced using a spatial multilook strategy. The second step consists in the multitemporal coregistration of the time series. It can be performed, using control points. In the SAR case, the coregistration can be simultaneously performed with a temporal filtering, in order to further reduce the speckle. Then features of interest can be extracted.

The feature can be of spectral type (in the MS case), of temporal type (like in the SAR case, where interferometry is performed), of spatial type (in both cases, in order to exploit spatial patterns like that well characterize manmade objects like building or roads). Extracted the interest features, the source image is partitioned in homogeneous regions, in order to finally create polygons that can be easily handled by the GIS geostatistical analyser. At the end of the processing workflow, the geometry of the maps has to be corrected. For this purpose we planned to use the Digital Terrain Model of Italy (DTM), 20 m on ground resolution, produced by the Military Geographic Institute.

Two separate workflows have been designed for the Multispectral and the SAR cases, because the different geometry of the two sensors. The final product of the MS workflow is a terrain classification map (with associated probability levels), the final product of the SAR workflow is a coherence map. The geo-corrected segmentation maps are the final output of the two processing workflows, while the environmental analysis, consisting in a data fusion and a change detection, is performed with the GIS tools.

The used features are summarized in the following table.

Table 3:   Used spectral/spatial/temporal features.

Environment feature	Image feature	Map index
Multispectral		
Vegetation / Culture	Spectral Angle	Vegetation Presence Probability Level
Water	Spectral Angle	Water Presence Probability Level
Soil	Spectral Angle, Corner Detectors (low response)	Soil Probability Level
Rocks	Spectral Angle, Corner Detectors (low response)	Rock Probability Level
Buildings	Spectral Angle, Corner Detectors (high response)	Urban Area Probability Level
Roads	Spectral Angle, Line Detectors (high response)	Urban Area Probability Level
Legal Garbage	Spectral Angle, Corner Detectors (high response)	Legal Garbage Probability Level
Illegal Garbage	Spectral Angle, Corner Detectors	Illegal Garbage Probability Level
SAR		
Incoherence in non vegetation areas	Interferometric Coherence	Change Probability Level

The analysis is focused mainly on temporal changes. The change detection is obtained statistically combining two approaches:

- comparing two MS segmentation map;
- analysing the SAR interferometric map, evaluating the coherence information only for the some terrain types (excluding, for example, roads, water or vegetation).

The main changes of interest are reported in the following table.

Table 4:   Temporal changes of interest (I=interesting, DC=don't care, -= not frequent, the not considered, E=excluded from the analysis.

Time 2 (right) \ Time 1 (down)	Vegetation	Water	Soil	Rock	Building	Road	Legal garbage	Illegal garbage	Coherence information
Vegetation	DC	DC	I	I	DC	I	I	I	E
Water	DC	DC	DC	DC	DC	DC	I	I	E
Soil	DC	DC	DC	-	DC	I	I	I	I
Rocks	I	-	-	DC	DC	DC	I	I	I
Buildings	DC	-	DC	-	DC	DC	-	-	DC
Roads	DC	-	I	DC	DC	DC	-	-	E
Legal Garbage	DC	-		I	-	-	I	I	I
Illegal Garbage	I	-	I	I	-	I	I	I	I

3   Preliminary results

The project IDES is now in the test phase of the software components. Some preliminary results of individual software components are outlined here.

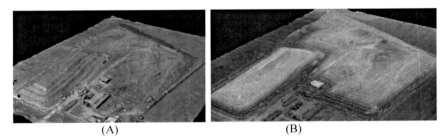

(A)   (B)

Figure 4:   (A) Example of a landfill 3D reconstruction by set of aerial images. (B) Example of a landfill characterization and geometrical analysis.

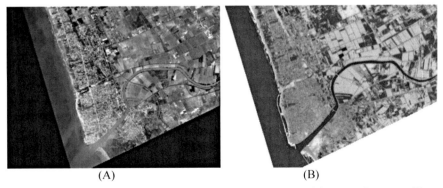

(A)   (B)

Figure 5:   (A) Example of multispectral remote sensed images from satellite: Volturno (2011). (B) Example of a multispectral remote sensed images feature extraction: vegetation, soil, com, stone, sand, houses, water, etc.

Thanks to the reconstruction of the investigated site by a 3D model, it's possible to create a multi-layer structure that permits to represent in one shot and in overlap all the data acquired during the mission. This approach simplifies the interpretation of data and allows us to filter the anomalies related to the specific morphology of the land (Lega *et al.* [2]).

Starting with industrial dumping registered in the province of Caserta, we use the geostatistical analysis to identify areas where the distribution of this dumping is "abnormal" with respect to the density of population and productive activities.

This may provide a guideline for the presence of potential illegal dumping.

Figure 6:   Example of a geostatistical map.

Geostatistical techniques rely on statistical model to exceed the uncertainty associated with spatial estimation and simulation. Geostatistical algorithms are incorporated in GIS.

4   Conclusions

If today a conventional investigation begins with the evidence of the crime that defines the scenario to be investigated, in the environmental field the investigation often begins with the evidence of the damage and not of the illegal polluting act. Often the consequences of pollution appear indeed in a different place or a long time after the polluting act has been committed and the correlation between the source and the damage depends from the morphology of the scenario and the physical phenomena that permit the transport of the pollutants. For these reasons the environmental police investigations must be realized alternating a bottom-up and top-down approaches (Lega *et al.* [2]).

In this paper we demonstrate the added value of the use of an integrated approach that combines several IT tools in the environmental police investigations.

IDES offer an integrated Geographic Information System (GIS) repository of information extracted and collected by various Government Bodies. The main novelty of this research lies in the integration between information extracted from remotely sensed images and information extracted from textual documents through a semantic analysis.

Thanks to a GIS multi-layer structure it's possible an advanced analysis of the investigated macro-area that permits to represent in one shot and in overlap all the data acquired and/or correlated.

This approach simplifies the interpretation of data and allows filtering the results.

The results of this last analysis will be a taxonomy-driven document searching and browsing system in which all documents are categorized and all relevant entities in documents (e.g. people, organizations, places and events) are extracted and represented by means of concept maps. Finally, these results: a) provide support to government bodies "end-users"; b) can be included in a GIS; c) can constitute the basis for the application of Artificial Adaptive Systems used in the domain of semantic analysis of unstructured information providing not obvious relationships between entities (e.g. criminal associations, people, places, activities, buildings, towns and dates).

Moreover, this IDES project provides an example of where law enforcement and research teams can collaborate on developing enhanced environmental protection methods.

References

[1] Persechino G., Schiano P., Lega M., Napoli R.M.A., Ferrara C., Kosmatka J. "Aerospace-based support systems and interoperability: the solution to fight illegal dumping", Waste Management 2010, Tallin, Estonia, 2010.

[2] M. Lega, C. Ferrara, J. Kosmatka, G. Persechino and R.M.A. Napoli "Thermal Pattern and Thermal Tracking: fingerprints of an environmental illicit", Quantitative Infrared Thermography (QIRT), Naples, Italy, 2012.

[3] M. Lega, R M.A. Napoli. Aerial infrared thermography in the surface waters contamination monitoring.

[4] G. Persechino, P. Schiano, M. Lega, R.M.A. Napoli, "Environment Monitoring performed by Advanced Hybrid Airship at low altitude", TIES 2009 – the 20th Annual Conference of The International Environmetrics Society – Conference 2009, Bologna, Italy, July 5–9, 2009.

[5] M. Lega, R.M.A. Napoli, G. Persechino, P. Schiano, "EMPA project: the conquering of the third dimension in the ambient air Monitoring", Airnow 2009: Air Quality Conferences: Air Quality Forecasting and Mapping, Dallas, USA, 2–5 March, 2009.

[6] M. Lega, R.M.A. Napoli – "A new approach to solid waste landfills aerial monitoring", Waste Management 2008, Granada (Spain) 2–4 June, 2008.

[7] Câmara, G., Monteiro, A. M., Fucks, S. D. and Carvalho, "Spatial Analysis and GIS: A Primer", 2004.

Promoting sustainable waste minimisation in the built environment: a case study of urban housing in Akure, Nigeria

Y. M. D. Adedeji, A. A. Taiwo, G. Fadairo & O. A. Olotuah
Department of Architecture, Federal University of Technology, Nigeria

Abstract

The construction industry is one of the largest solid waste generators all over the globe. Because waste generation from both new construction works, as well as renovation works has been on the increase, it is absolutely necessary for the construction industry to adopt ecologically sound planning and construction practices for the purpose of creating a healthy and sustainable built environment. This is the focus of this paper. It appraises the management of construction waste in Nigeria and Akure in particular. A survey of selected construction sites in Akure is used as a case study to demonstrate the magnitude of poor management level of construction waste generation observed and the implications on the built environment. Research findings reveal that the Ondo State Waste Management Board is responsible for the management of solid waste in the city and over 78% of the construction waste is disposed indiscriminately or burnt on site, since the mandate of the board does not cover construction waste. Contractors were observed to cart away a sizeable junk of the waste for other uses. The paper suggests a wide range of measures for minimisation of waste on construction sites. These include modularisation of design, standardisation of building components, industrial production of building materials, efficient specification writing, retraining of building professionals, reuse and recycling among others. The paper concludes that there is colossal deficiency in the management of construction waste in the study area and recommend ways of ameliorating it.
Keywords: built environment, construction waste, management, modularisation of design, standard building components, sustainable.

WIT Transactions on Ecology and The Environment, Vol 173, © 2013 WIT Press
www.witpress.com, ISSN 1743-3541 (on-line)
doi:10.2495/SDP130511

1 Introduction

Waste generation in building construction and renovation processes is in the increase in many developing nations including Nigeria without commensurate efforts on its management. This waste can be as high as 10–15% of the materials that goes into a building [1]. DETR [2] reported that a similar large quantum of waste was recorded within the UK, with total construction wastage estimated at around 70 million tonnes per annum. Construction industry is one of the largest solid waste generators, a major consumer of non-renewable resources and is responsible for the emission of almost half of the global greenhouse gases [2]. A recent study in developed countries reveals that 30-40% of natural resources were exploited by the building industry, 50% of energy used for heating and cooling in buildings, almost 40% of global consumption of materials convert to built environment and 30% of energy used due to housing [3, 4]. The rate of generation of solid waste increases by the day in Nigeria with increase in urban population. An estimated 20kg of solid waste is generated per capital per annum in Nigeria, equivalent to 2.2 million tons a year [5, 6].

Waste in the building industry is made up of materials such as wood, laterite, concrete bricks and blocks damaged or unused for various reasons during construction. Others include sand, granite, insulation, nails, electrical wiring, tree stumps as well waste originating from site preparation such digging for foundations or dredging, rubbles, asbestos and other hazardous substances. Studies on waste generation shows that it can arise at any stage of the process, from inception, through to the design, construction and operation of the built facility [5, 7, 8]. These studies have also shown that the 3 most significant sources of construction waste relate to design changes (usually stemming from over-specification, poor detailing, late variations, changing materials previously ordered and alterations to complete work), leftover materials, waste from packaging and non-reclaimable consumables, design/detailing errors, poor storage and handling of materials and insufficient protection of the completed works [9]. Pressures on cost and programme delivery also lead to working practices that are not conducive to conserving materials and avoiding damage [10].

Faniran and Caban [8] noted that levels of waste generated are clearly dependent upon the attitudes of key individuals (in the supply chain) engaged with the project especially the clients, which have the greatest influence over waste issues. This is based on the clients' responsibility to set the environmental standards to which the project team must comply. Besides, professional lapses such as design errors, poor detailing, over-specification, late variations, leftover materials, waste from packaging and non-reclaimable consumables, poor storage and handling of materials are all causes waste generation in the building industry [10]. Conversely, Teo and Loosemore [11] opined that efforts to influence waste management will be less appreciated if those further down the supply chain do not buy-in to more effective waste management practices. It would seem that waste management is often considered a low priority in the strategic planning of projects. Indeed, by the time that construction commences, many of the opportunities for waste reduction have already elapsed, with the management team only being able to control waste through reactive management measures.

2 Waste management and sustainable development

Sustainability plays a vital role in the development of modern societies. It is an inevitable factor in the enhancement of efficient and strategic development of any society [12]. Consequently, governments and other agencies involved in development s are consciously evolving sustainability in their existing and future vision. Adewole [13] observed that towards the end of the 1980s, there were growing concerns over a radical reappraisal of resource availability and use, the environmental consequences of resource exploitation and the correlation between the environment, poverty and economic change. This re-appraisal has given rise to a new approach to environment and development issues, which seeks to reconcile human needs and the capacity of the environment to cope with the consequences of economic system. This view has been expressed by many researchers on the subject of sustainability. All these hang around the continuous validity of a healthy development that perpetuates a long life status without jeopardising the needs of future generations [2, 3].

It is important to note that there must be a balance between levels of development and the stock of natural resources, that is, development must be at a level that can be sustained without prejudice to the natural environment or to future generations. The construction industry cannot be left out. Therefore, if there is to be sustainable development in waste management in Nigeria, the availability of land (for landfill), human resources, plant and equipment and other tools including capital must be readily available. There is the need to protect future for the next generation by cleaning up the environment of all types of waste, taking into consideration both physical and population development of the state [13]. Hence, waste management must mean the collection, keeping, treatment and disposal of waste in such a way as to render it harmless to human and animal life, the ecology and the environment generally.

2.1 Waste generation, disposal and management in Akure, Ondo State, Nigeria

Akure faces daunting environmental problems that are compounded by the daily influx of people in search of a better life, domestic, industrial and construction waste generated daily. These problems include dumping of heterogeneous mass of throw-arrays from residential and commercial and industrial activities, ineffective solid waste management, insufficient sanitary infrastructure; soil, air and water pollution; flooding, ocean surge, insecurity, and limited access to basic infrastructure [5]. The waste generated in Akure can be classified into two namely:

    i. Municipal waste (these include domestic and commercial); and

    ii. Industrial waste.

Figure 1:   Ondo State government waste bin for waste collection.

2.2 Ondo state waste management authority

The agency of government responsible for waste management in Akure is the State Waste Management Authority. It was established on the 23rd April 1999 with the purpose of [5]:

 i. enhancing effective waste collection, transportation, disposal and management;

 ii. ridding the state (Ondo) of undesirable refuse pilation;

 iii. setting guidelines and organizing waste scavenging for recycling;

 iv. erasing environmental blightedness and development of epidemic;

 v. proffering waste management strategies and turning the state accumulated waste into wealth; and

 vi. ensuring a clean and healthy environment.

The Waste Management Authority zoned Akure into ten (10) zones, which were further subdivided into five (5) districts each to facilitate effective discharge of responsibilities [5]. The authority provides dino bins and cat bins to the densely populated areas and commercial centres, while dustbins (drums and buckets) are sold to the less populated areas. Currently, the authority employs two methods of waste collection.

2.2.1 House-to-house collection

This method is usually adopted in areas with good road networks within the city capital. This enables easy movement of the waste collection vans. Domestic waste from residential buildings is kept in containers to await removal by the waste collection vans into their refuse side loaders. The type and capacities of the containers used depend on the characteristics of the solid waste to be collected, the frequency of collection and the space available for the placement of the containers.

2.2.2 Communal/designated collection

Solid waste that are generated in offices, commercial and industrial buildings (banks, institutions, hotels) and open spaces including market and religious places are usually collected in relatively large containers known as dino bins or cart wagons. Empty bins are usually kept in open spaces to be filled up by users and thereafter removed by the authority for disposal. The filled containers are removed by means of roll-on-roll-off trucks, emptied and returned to their original location. Records from the authority shows that the bins are collected twice daily in areas where generation is very heavy (such as the market areas). Each dino bin contains 4.6 tons of waste [5].

During peak seasons, when waste generation is higher than usual, pay loaders and open tippers are used to compliment the collecting vans. However, the activities of the Waste Management Authority does not cover construction waste generated at the construction sites as these are left for the discretion of clients and contractors.

3 Research methodology: case studies

A survey of selected construction sites in Akure was used as a case study to gather data through observations and photographic prints. Selected cities were purposively chosen as study areas to reflect the magnitude of waste generated from construction processes. Data were collected through visits to selected sites, investigation and observations. Interview schedules prepared in question forms and written in English language were administered to professionals and site supervisors on site by the authors to collect data on the causes of waste observed on sites. Many of the surveyed projects, in various stages of completion were observed to be littered with unused and overused building materials together with others to be disposed after use.

4 Findings and discussion of results

Construction waste observed on surveyed sites include wood, bamboo, nails, tree stumps, laterite, sandcrete blocks, concrete bricks and blocks damaged or unused for various reasons during construction. Others include bags of used cement, waste from packaging and non-reclaimable consumables, sand, granite, pieces of roofing sheets, insulation, electrical wiring, as well waste originating from site preparation such digging for foundations or dredging, rubbles, asbestos and other hazardous substances as shown in Figs 2–4.

Much of this waste, such as sandcrete blocks, granite and interlocking tiles, resulted from over specifation and ordering of materials to sites, late alterations to works and changing materials previously ordered. Others such as planks, bamboos, pieces of roofing sheets, nails were left over and waste from formworks after use. A more rational precision in professional expertise and management of construction projects could reduce such waste to a minimal level.

Standard materials for formworks that could be dismantled and used in other sites as used in many big construction works should be adopted to avoid waste resulting from formworks.

Figure 2:   Wood and bamboo used as formwork after use on a construction site.

Figure 3:   Construction waste: laterite soil from digging, sandcrete blocks, roofing sheets, laterite, bamboo and wood on a construction site.

Figure 4:   Unused interlocking tiles, granite and refuses on a recently completed building project.

4.1 Standardisation of design/modular design

It was observed that the conventional methods of designs and constructions contributed to waste generation on site. Adedeji [14] opined that modular design and standardisation of spaces to improve buildability and reduce the quantity of off-cuts are strategies to significantly reduce construction waste resulting from the conventional methods of designs. By designing spaces and ceiling heights in multiples of standard material and sizes, a substantial reduction in off-cuts would be achieved [10]. Standardization of design and building components should be explored beyond the accessibility to materials only, but the assessment of baseline for the continuous initiatives for designs and intelligent usage of available materials for construction [14].

4.2 Use of renewable building materials for construction

In most of the site surveyed, sandcrete blocks were used for masonry works. This material is often associated with off-cuts and enormous waste. Minimisation of waste in masonry works can be achieved by adopting renewable building materials for construction [14]. One of such materials is unfired solid interlocking laterite/clay (Hydraform blocks) [15]. The usage of Hydraform blocks, in place of conventional fired ones, can significantly reduce the energy use and also cut down CO_2 emissions and minimize generated waste [16]. Usually, solid laterite blocks are produced on the site where the materials are available. Laterite soil with good grain size distribution and good cohesive performance is a good material for production of interlocking block, but the proportion of clay and aggregates has to be checked [17]. Interlocking blocks are manufactured by hydraulically compressing a soil and cement mixture in a block-making machine. Where the material is unused, excess can recycled on site and reused.

The development of interlocking blocks (solid interlocking laterite blocks) shows some merits over the conventional types. First, substantial cost savings can be achieved due to elimination of bedding mortar in the superstructure (except in ring beams and in high gables), thereby reducing workmanship.

Figure 5:   Renewable solid laterite (Hydraform) blocks produced in-situ.

Figure 6:   School of Earth and Mineral Sciences, Federal University of Technology, Akure. Use of brick facing as wall finishing

In this system, freely-available subsoil is the main raw material and the blocks do not require costly burning; transport costs are minimised since production of Hydraform blocks takes place on site in hydraulic block machines, available from Hydraform International (Pty) Ltd., headquartered in Johannesburg, South Africa. In addition, speed of construction is a valuable feature of the system, which is much faster than other building methods [17].

The main disadvantage of using these products is susceptibility to water damage, which can be avoided by stabilizing the laterite soil with the addition of small quantity of cement or lime.

4.3 Dry methods construction/use of prefabricated materials

Off-site prefabrication and industrial production of building materials and components are advocated for in order to minimize waste in the building industry. Prefabrication should be strictly based on designers' specification and standard sizes recommended in the industry. Also, the use of dry construction methods with appropriate standardised components to reflect the designer's specification would reduce or completely eliminate wastages, reduce labour to be engaged, reduce cost as well as the time for construction if the building operation is professionally handled [14]. In view of this, dry construction method is therefore more cost-effective and preferred above the conventional method as confirmed by this research.

Similarly, the application of standardised components has the potential of regularising dimensional units of spaces in a modular form. Professionals and stakeholders in the building industry can easily visualise with clearer perception their proposed building projects, thus, making materials and cost planning easier. Other advantages of the use of prefabricated materials include flexibility of space arrangement, dry construction, industrial production and comparative cost effectiveness.

4.4 Design management to ensure efficient specification of materials

Designers and allied building professionals are to ensure accurate dimensions of spaces and building components together with efficient specification of materials for construction in order avoiding over ordering of materials to the site. This will facilitate considerable waste reduction and financial cost savings on projects. Similarly, the engagement experienced project managers for a large scale project is another effective step in ensuring waste reduction. A similar study carried out by Dainty and Brooke [10] made similar observation.

4.5 Retraining of building personnel

It is vital for the Nigerian Institute of Architects, Ministry of Housing and Urban Development, and other Institutions and agencies responsible for teaching and training professionals to organise seminars and regular training programmes on effective waste minimization strategies to equip professionals with adequate knowledge on their relevance [13, 18]. Similar retraining should be extended to workmen on site on the usage of materials towards waste reduction in the building pro. These will not only publicise the contents of this research and other related ones but will generate better opportunity to advance the current status of the research in this direction.

5 Policy implications and recommendations

The built environment in Nigeria is faced with numerous urban challenges. Similarly, there are problems encountered on construction sites such as over-specification and delivery of materials, leftover materials, waste from packaging and non-reclaimable consumables, poor storage and handling of materials are all causes of waste generation in the building industry. Professionals in the building industry must rise up to these challenges with the adoption of waste minimisation strategies that will enhance sustainability in the sector. These strategies should stem from design stages to the specification of materials and methods of construction to be adopted. Modularisation of designs is strongly advocated for to enhance efficiency in materials specification and reduce off-cuts of materials associated with conventional methods of design and materials usage on building sites. Likewise, prefabricated materials are recommended for finishes and components in buildings as this would substantially minimise waste. The application of standardised components in construction of a building will enhance fast construction operations to be accomplished within couples of hours depending on the magnitude of the building. The policy makers should encourage standardisation of building components in Nigeria in line with the global trend as canvassed by the International Standard Organisation (ISO). This implies that building materials particularly timber and masonry materials should be available in the market in this form for users to purchase in finished forms to be assembled on site. Factories that produce standard components should be established. Besides, the use of renewable materials will enhance recycling of such materials where necessary. Design management towards ensuring efficient specification of building materials and retraining of building professionals and workmen are advocated for as ways of minimising waste in the built environment.

6 Conclusion

The focus of this paper is the adoption of ecologically sound planning and construction practices for the purpose of creating a healthy and sustainable built environment. The paper appraises the management of construction waste in Nigeria. A survey of selected construction sites in Akure is used as a case study to demonstrate the magnitude of poor management level of construction waste generation observed and the implications on the built environment. Management of construction waste in Akure, Ondo state, Nigeria (the study area) is highly deficient. Over 78% of the construction waste is disposed indiscriminately or burnt on site. Contractors cart away a sizeable junk of the waste for other uses. Waste minimisation on construction sites can be achieved through modularisation of design, standardisation of building components, industrial production of building materials, efficient specification writing, and retraining of building professionals.

References

[1] Evia O.W. Wong and Robin C.P. Yip, Promoting sustainable construction waste management in Hong Kong. *Construction Management and Economics,* As accessed on 4 October 2007, 2004.

[2] Department of the Environment, Transport and the Regions. *Guide to Waste Reduction on Construction Sites,* DETR, M0007184NP, London, 2000.

[3] Loucks, D.P., Qualifying trends in system sustainability. *Hydrological Sciences Journal,* 42(4), pp. 513–530, 1997.

[4] Sahley, H.R., Kennedy, C.A., and Adams, B.J., *Canadian Journal of Civil Engineering,* 32, pp. 72–85, 2005.

[5] Olotuah, A.O., Solid waste management and the built environment: the Nigerian urban housing situation. *In: E.H. Chan, and D.C. Ho (Eds.), Proceedings of the CII-HK Conference 2005 on Healthy Building, Community Health and Built Environment,* pp. 87–93, November, 2005.

[6] Ogunsote, O.O., Adedeji, Y.M.D. and Prucnal-Ogunsote, B.P., Combating Environmental Degradation through Sustainable Landscaping in Emerging Mega Cities: A Case Study of Lagos, Nigeria. Proceedings of the XXIV World Congress of Architecture, UIA 2011 Tokyo, 2011.

[7] Gavilan, R.M. and Bernold, L.E., Source evaluation of solid waste in building construction, *Journal of Construction Engineering and Management,* Vol. 120 No. 3, pp. 536–55, 1994.

[8] Faniran, O.O. and Caban, G., Minimising waste on construction project sites, Engineering *Construction and Architectural Management 5,* Vol. 2, p. 183, 1998.

[9] Dainty, A.R.J. and Brooke, R.J. Towards improved construction waste minimization. *Structural Survey, Volume 22, Number 1,* 20–29, 2004.

[10] Coventry, S. et al. (2001), Demonstrating Waste Minimisation Benefits in Construction, CIRIA Publication C536, 0-86017-536-7, London.

[11] Teo, M.M.M. and Loosemore, M., A theory of waste behaviour in the construction industry. *Construction Management and Economics,* Vol. 19 No. 7, pp. 741–51, 2001.

[12] Alsaqqaf, Z. and Zhang, H., Towards a sustainable system: application of temporal analysis on flood risk management. In C.A. Brebbia and E. Beriatos (Eds.), *Sustainable Development and Planning V,* WIT Press, Ashurst, Southampton, United Kingdom, 59–68, 2011.

[13] Adewole, A.T., Waste management towards sustainable development in Nigeria: A case study of Lagos state. *International NGO Journal* Vol. 4(4), pp. 173–179, 2009. Available online at http://www.academicjournals.org /INGOJ

[14] Adedeji, Y.M.D., Materials preference options for sustainable low-income housing in selected cities in Nigeria. An unpublished Ph.D Thesis,

Department of Architecture, Federal University of Technology, Akure, 2007.

[15] Oti, J.E.; Kinuthia, J.M.; Bai, J. Engineering properties of unfired clay masonry bricks. *Eng. Geol. 107*, 130–139, 2009.

[16] Joseph, P., Sustainable non-metallic building materials. *Sustainability Review 2*, 400–427, www.mdpi.com/journal/sustainability, 2010.

[17] Adedeji, Y.M.D., Housing economy: use of interlocking masonry for low-cost housing in Nigeria. *Journal of Construction Project Management and Innovation*, Vol. 1(1): 46–62, 2011.

[18] Adedeji, Y.M.D.; Taiwo, A.A.; Olotuah, A.O. and Fadairo, G., Architectural education and sustainable human habitat in Nigeria. In: C.A. Brebbia and E. Beriatos (Eds.); *Sustainability Today*, WIT Press, Ashurst, Southampton, United Kingdom, 89–99, 2012.

Impact of pretreatment on the landfill behaviour of MBT waste

A. A. Siddiqui[1], W. Powrie[2] & D. J. Richards[2]
[1]Department of Civil Engineering, Aligarh Muslim University, India
[2]Waste Management Research Group, University of Southampton, UK

Abstract

One of the main aims of the EU Landfill Directive is to reduce significantly the landfilling of biodegradable municipal waste. Mechanical-biological pre-treatment of municipal solid waste has become popular and is often adopted to enable compliance with this requirement of the Landfill Directive. This will have major implications for the nature of the waste that is disposed of to landfills and hence for the way in which the landfills should be managed. Pretreatment will cause changes in the composition and properties of the waste going to landfills including the gas generating potential, leaching behaviour and settlement characteristics. Germany has set strict allocation criteria for landfilling of mechanically biologically treated (MBT) waste. In contrast, there are no standards for MBT waste in the UK. Experimental studies were conducted to investigate the biodegradation and settlement behaviour of MBT waste samples treated to typical UK and German standards. The performance of large scale consolidating anaerobic reactors was monitored in terms of gas generating potential, leaching behaviour and waste settlement. The contributions of mechanical creep and biodegradation to secondary settlement were also identified.
Keywords: landfill, pretreated waste, leachate, biogas, waste settlement.

1 Introduction

Landfill has been the dominant municipal solid waste (MSW) management option for disposal of residual waste in the UK and many other countries for over a century. The EU Landfill Directive (EC [1]) sets targets for all Member States to reduce substantially the amount of biodegradable MSW going to landfill.

WIT Transactions on Ecology and The Environment, Vol 173, © 2013 WIT Press
www.witpress.com, ISSN 1743-3541 (on-line)
doi:10.2495/SDP130521

Many European countries (e.g. Germany, Austria) required to comply with the Directive earlier than the UK have chosen mechanical-biological pretreatment (MBP) as a technology for treating MSW to arrive at the targets set out in the Landfill Directive. MBP normally involves sorting to remove recyclables and, in some cases, combustible materials; particle size reduction (e.g. shredding and screening) and partial biodegradation by anaerobic digestion and/or aerobic composting processes. MBP facilities have been commissioned over recent years and its role in waste management is expected to become more popular in near future.

In Germany, waste pretreatment processes are more advanced and a Landfill Ordinance (German EPA [2]) has set very strict allocation criteria for the landfilling of MBT waste. In contrast, the UK has not defined standards for landfilled MBT waste and a quantitative approach is employed to reduce the amount of biodegradable municipal waste (BMW) which is landfilled in accordance with the Landfill Directive. Pretreatment will have major implications on the degradation and settlement characteristics of the waste in landfills. The long term behaviour of MBT waste will be different from that of unprocessed MSW since the pretreatment process may change its physical, chemical and biological properties. Biogas and leachate characteristics of pretreated waste based on small scale studies have been reported by a few authors (e.g. Bayard *et al.* [3]; Bockreis and Steinberg [4]; Horing *et al.* [5]; Leikam and Stegmann [6]). These studies demonstrate that MBT waste has reduced gas generating potential and leachate strength. None of the studies on MBT waste to date have included consideration of the settlement characteristics, and therefore uncertainties remain about the creep and biodegradation induced settlements.

This study represents experimental results for the long term biodegradation and settlement behaviour of the two specimens of MBT waste, treated to typical UK and German standards.

2   Waste samples

Two different waste materials were studied: UK MBT and German MBT. They originate from two different MBP plants, one in the UK and one in Germany.

2.1   MBT waste from Southern England (UK MBT waste)

A sample of about 500 kg of MBT waste was obtained from White's Pit waste processing plant, a mechanical-biological treatment facility in Southern England. This facility includes a shredder, conveyor belts, magnets, screens and windrows for aerobic composting. The waste was first sorted to extract recyclable material and then broken down into smaller parts by shredding and screened followed by recovery of ferrous metals. Waste was then aerobically composted in forced aerated windrows in fully enclosed halls for about six weeks. The material was screened again to extract any remaining dry recyclables, giving a maximum particle size for the waste of about 20 mm.

2.2 MBT waste from Northern Germany (German MBT waste)

A sample of about 120 kg of MBT waste was obtained from Hannover Waste Treatment Centre, a mechanical-biological treatment facility in Hannover, Northern Germany. The waste was sorted, shredded and screened, and recyclable materials and metals were removed. The high calorific value fraction (mainly non-recycled paper and plastics) was sent as a refuse derived fuel to the incineration plant. Waste was then anaerobically digested in fermentation tanks for a period of 3 weeks. The digested material was composted in enclosed windrows for about 6 weeks. The maximum particle size of the residual material was about 60 mm.

3 Waste characterisation

3.1 Particle size distribution

Representative samples of about 25 kg of both the UK and the German MBT waste were prepared by quartering the bulk sample. These samples were then sieved mechanically through a set of sieves into different fractions. The particle size distribution for both MBT samples is given in fig. 1. There were no significant differences between the results for the two wastes except that the German MBT waste had a higher fraction of large size particles and slightly less fine material than the UK MBT waste.

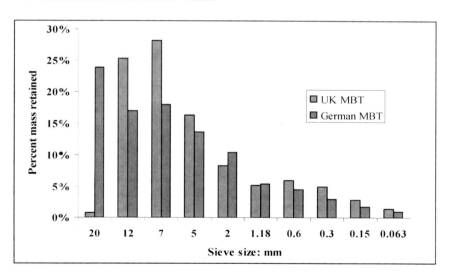

Figure 1:   Particle size distribution of UK and German MBT waste.

3.2 Waste composition

Each size fraction (except that less than 5 mm) from each MBT waste was sorted manually into various material categories i.e. flexible plastics, rigid plastics, textiles, paper, glass, wood, bones, rubber, ceramics, metals, stones and unidentified >5 mm. All material <5 mm was placed in the "unidentified <5mm" category. The "unidentified" category represents a mixture of different components that could not be identified or further separated. The unidentified >5 mm category consists of particles greater than 5 mm whose material could not be identified, usually because they were encased in soil-like material which was impossible to remove without breaking the particle. The composition of each waste sample by material type (expressed as percentage of the total dry weight) is given in table 1. Owing to different processing of waste in the pretreatment stages, UK MBT waste is slightly different from the German MBT waste.

Table 1:   MBT waste components expressed as dry weight percentages.

Component	Percentage of dry mass (%)	
	UK MBT waste	German MBT waste
Paper	0.43	0.18
Flexible Plastics	4.57	2.4
Rigid Plastics	6.27	5.91
Wood	1.57	3.22
Textile	1.33	0.63
Rubber	0.18	0.25
Bones	0.27	0.37
Metal	0.49	1.49
Ceramics	2.29	4.25
Stones	1.73	3.17
Glass	22.77	24.36
Unidentified >5 mm	28.95	26.75
Unidentified <5 mm	29.15	27.02
Total	100.00	100.00

4   Equipment

Large scale consolidating anaerobic reactors were set up in the laboratory to simulate anaerobic conditions in a landfill. The consolidating anaerobic reactor (CAR) comprises a Perspex cylinder 480 mm diameter, 900 mm tall, and a load delivery system that can apply a constant vertical stress to the waste. A 10 cm gravel drainage layer was placed at the base of the CAR followed by a geotextile membrane. The MBT waste (which had been dried in an oven at 70°C) was placed in the CAR in 10 successive layers of 4 kg each compacted to a thickness of 5 cm by hand tamping. A further layer of gravel (5 cm thick) was placed to give an even distribution of leachate over the top surface of the waste, and was again separated from the waste by a geotextile membrane. The CAR was placed within a compression loading rig, and the leachate was recirculated from the bottom to the top using a peristaltic pump. Biogas production was determined by allowing the gas to build up in the headspace volume to a small positive pressure above ambient atmospheric pressure measured by a pressure sensor. The details of CAR and gas measurement are given in Siddiqui *et al.* [7].

4.1 CAR start up and operation

Long term testing of each MBT waste was undertaken using two CARs: a control reactor (CAR1) and a test reactor (CAR2) (see fig. 2). Synthetic leachate containing mineral nutrients and trace elements dissolved in deionised water as described by Florencio *et al.* [8] was used in this study. CAR2 was filled with 80 litres of leachate comprising an inoculum of anaerobically digested sewage sludge (10% vol.) derived from an anaerobic digester. This was done to ensure the presence of viable methanogenic bacteria and to accelerate the initiation of methanogenesis. In the control reactor (CAR1), 80 litres of leachate mixed with acetic and propionic acids at a concentration of 10 grams per litre each was added to suppress microbial activity and prevent the onset of methanogenesis. The reactors were then sparged with nitrogen gas to remove any oxygen trapped within the reactor and the leachate was recirculated continuously from the bottom to the top of each reactor. CAR1 was operated at ~20°C in a controlled temperature room and CAR2 was maintained at a constant mesophilic temperature of 30°C using a heat blanket to establish a favourable growth environment for the microorganisms in the reactor.

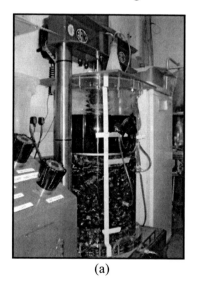 

(a)   (b)

Figure 2:   Consolidating anaerobic reactors (a) CAR1 (b) CAR2.

The operation of the CARs in this way was designed to isolate settlements due to mechanical creep from those due to biodegradation, by comparing the settlements measured in each. The CARs were operated for 347 and 279 days for the UK MBT and German MBT waste respectively. The load was maintained at 50 kPa for the first 286 and 202 days of the experiment on the UK and German

MBT waste respectively. Thereafter, load was increased to 150 kPa for the remainder of the test in order to investigate any dependence of the creep characteristics of the waste on the applied load.

4.2 Monitoring and testing programme

Biogas volume and composition, leachate characteristics and waste settlement were monitored on a regular basis to understand the degree of waste stabilisation. The volume of biogas produced was recorded daily and analysed for gas composition. Leachate samples were collected and analysed every three days during the first three months of operation and weekly thereafter. Waste settlement was monitored daily using a linear variable displacement transducer.

5 Analytical procedures

The biogas composition (methane and carbon dioxide) in the CARs was measured daily as a percentage by volume using an infra-red gas analyser GASCARD II Plus. The biogas composition was not analysed in duplicate. Total organic carbon (TOC) and ammoniacal nitrogen (NH_4-N) analyses of leachate were carried out using a high temperature Dohrmann-Rosemount DC 190 TOC analyser and Foss Tecator Kjeltec System 1002 distillation unit respectively. Leachate samples taken from the reactors were analysed in duplicate and the results presented are the average of these measurements.

6 Results and discussion

6.1 Biogas generating potential

The cumulative gas production for the UK and German MBT waste is illustrated in fig. 3. The gas production started soon after filling the test reactor, CAR2, for both the UK and German MBT waste. Biogas production was relatively low during the first week of operation, presumably due to the time taken for the acclimatisation of the methanogenic bacteria and the accumulation of VFA which kept the pH low. The biogas production then increased and methanogenic conditions were quickly established as confirmed by the change in biogas composition to about 60% CH_4 and 35% CO_2 by volume. The acidogenic phase was virtually absent; probably due to the degradation of some organic compounds during pretreatment. This is in agreement with the findings of Bayard et al. [3] and Bockreis et al. [9]. Biogas production continued at a much lower rate until day 280 and 195 when it had effectively ceased for the two wastes respectively. The gassing potential of the German MBT waste was low compared with the UK MBT waste. The total biogas yield was 49.46 L/kg DM (litres per kilogram dry matter) and 17.74 L/kg DM for the UK and German MBT waste respectively. The control reactor, CAR1, for the UK and German MBT waste did not produce biogas due to the acidification of the reactor with acetic and propionic acids at the start of the experiment.

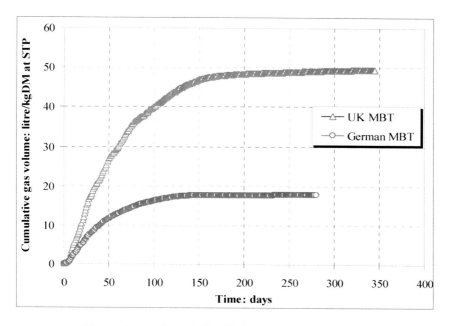

Figure 3:   Cumulative biogas production in CAR2.

6.2 Leachate quality

The total organic carbon in the leachate was analysed and the results for CAR2 for the UK and German MBT waste are presented in fig. 4. The TOC concentration increased during the first week due to the hydrolysis of organics from the waste into the leachate at the initial stage. After the first week, the TOC concentration began to decrease slowly with the progression of stabilisation processes and confirmed by the increase in gas production and the high methane content of the biogas. Towards the end of the study TOC concentrations were about 650 and 290 mg/L for the UK and German MBT waste respectively. This TOC is mostly recalcitrant or hardly biodegradable carbon present in the reactor as suggested by Kjeldsen *et al.* [10]. The organic strength i.e. TOC of the leachate from the German MBT waste was low compared with that from the UK MBT waste, owing to the different biological processing steps during pretreatment. The German MBT waste was produced after a longer duration (about 9 weeks) of anaerobic and aerobic biological treatment of raw MSW compared with 6 weeks of aerobic biological treatment for the UK MBT waste.

The concentration of ammoniacal nitrogen (NH_4-N) in the leachate from CAR2 for the UK and German MBT waste is shown in fig.5. The initial sharp increase in NH_4-N is the result of direct leaching of ammonia from the waste, and the microbial degradation of nitrogenous organics (Berge *et al.* [11]; Jokela and Rintala [12]). After an initial increase, ammoniacal nitrogen concentration decreased very slowly to a stable concentration of about 425 mg/L and 195 mg/L for the UK and German MBT waste respectively. The results indicated that the

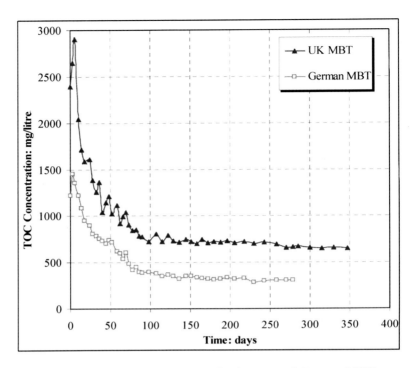

Figure 4: Leachate TOC in CAR2 for the UK and German MBT waste.

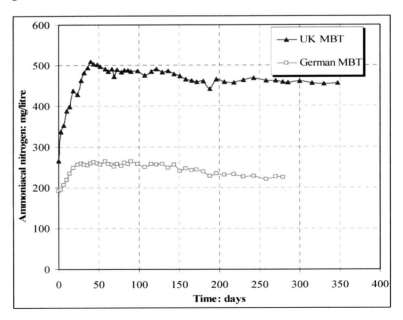

Figure 5: Leachate ammoniacal nitrogen in CAR2.

WIT Transactions on Ecology and The Environment, Vol 173, © 2013 WIT Press
www.witpress.com, ISSN 1743-3541 (on-line)

nitrogen content in the leachate from the German MBT waste was less than that from the UK MBT waste.

6.3 Waste settlement

The CARs were operated at 50 kPa load until day 286 for the UK MBT waste, and until day 202 for the German MBT waste. The load was then increased to 150 kPa for the remainder of the tests to investigate any dependence of the creep characteristics of the waste on the applied load.

The majority of the settlement occurred immediately in response to the application of the load which may be due to lack of compaction of the waste during emplacement of waste in CARs. The primary settlement by the end of 24 hours resulted in additional settlements in the range 5.9% to 7.8% after immediate settlement for the UK and German MBT waste.

The secondary settlements measured in the CARs at 50 kPa for the UK and German MBT waste are plotted against log-time in figs. 6 and 7 respectively. With data collected from both test and control reactors, it was possible to compare and quantify the net effects of creep and biodegradation on settlement. The total secondary settlement was 5.09% in CAR1 and 8.26% in CAR2 for the UK MBT waste, and 4.09% in CAR1 and 5.75% in CAR2 for the German MBT waste. The rate and magnitude of secondary settlement in CAR2 were higher than CAR1 (shown by the steeper slopes in figs. 6 and 7) for both the UK and German MBT waste due to the decomposition of organics, evidenced by the increase in biogas production and decrease in TOC.

For both waste, CAR1 remained biologically inhibited over the entire duration of the tests and as a result, settlement may be considered to be due to mechanical creep only. The settlement of the UK and German MBT waste in CAR2 can be attributed to both mechanical creep and biodegradation. Settlements due to mechanical creep can be isolated from those due to biodegradation, by comparing the settlements measured in each assuming that creep effects were the same in both CARs. Secondary settlement associated with mechanical creep was 5.09% and 4.09% and that associated with biodegradation was 3.17% and 1.66% for the UK and German MBT waste respectively.

7 Conclusions

The gas generation potential, leachate quality and settlements have demonstrated that waste stabilisation was achieved in less than a year under enhanced biodegradation conditions in the CARs for the UK and German MBT waste. The total volume of biogas produced at STP for the UK and German MBT waste was 49.46 L/kg DM and 17.74 L/kg DM respectively. The higher gassing potential of the UK MBT waste could be explained by the lower degree of biological pretreatment.

The organic strength of the leachate from the German MBT waste was low compared with that from the UK MBT waste owing to the different biological processing steps during the pre-treatment. The leachate load of ammoniacal

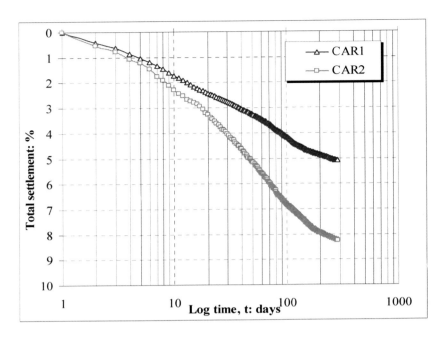

Figure 6: Secondary settlement in CARs at 50 kPa for the UK MBT waste.

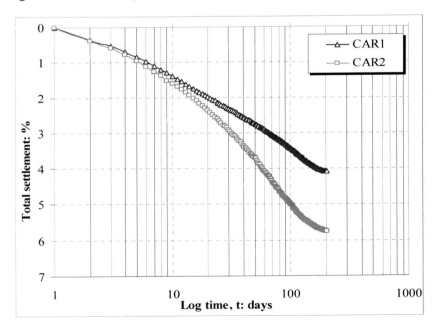

Figure 7: Secondary settlement in CARs at 50 kPa for the German MBT waste.

nitrogen from the German MBT waste was less than that from the UK MBT waste which was probably due to the lower nitrogen content of the German MBT waste.

Secondary settlement due to mechanical creep was more significant than that due to biodegradation, highlighting the importance of mechanical creep on the overall magnitude of secondary settlement.

References

[1]   European Commission Directive 1999/31/EC on the Landfill of Waste. Council of the European Union, Official Journal of the European Communities, L182, pp. 1–19, 1999.

[2]   German EPA. 2001. Ordinance on Environmentally Compatible Storage of Waste from Human Settlements and on Biological Waste Treatment Facilities (AbfAblV). Federal Ministry for the Environment, Nature Conservation and Nuclear Safety, Berlin, Germany, 2001. www.bmu.de/english/waste_management/downloads/doc/3371.php

[3]   Bayard R., de Araujo Morais, J., Rouez, Fifi M U., Achour, F. and Ducom, G., Effect of biological pretreatment of coarse MSW on landfill behaviour: laboratory study, Water Science and Technology, 58.7, pp. 1361–1369, 2008.

[4]   Bockreis, A. and Steinberg, I., Influence of mechanical-biological waste pre-treatment methods on the gas formation in landfills. Waste Management 25, pp. 337–343, 2005.

[5]   Horing, K., Kruempelbeck, I. and Ehrig, H.J., Long term emissions behaviour of mechanical-biological pretreated municipal solid waste. In: T. H. Christensen, R. Cossu and R. Stegmann (Eds.) Proceedings Sardinia 1999, Seventh International Waste Management and Landfill Symposium, S. Margherita di Pula, Cagliari, Italy, 1999.

[6]   Leikam, K., and Stegmann, R., Influence of mechanical–biological treatment of municipal solid waste on landfill behaviour. Waste Management and Research 17, pp. 424–429, 1999.

[7]   Siddiqui A. A., Richards D. J., and Powrie W., A preliminary analysis of mechanically biologically treated waste: biodegradation and settlement behaviour. Proc. of the twelfth International Waste Management and Landfill Symposium, S. Margherita di Pula, Cagliari, Italy, 2009.

[8]   Florencio, L., Field, J. A., and Lettinga, G., Substrate competition between methanogens and acetogens during the degradation of methanol in UASB reactors. Water Research 29(3), pp. 915–922, 1995.

[9]   Bockreis, A., Steinberg, I., Rohde, C., and Jager, J., Gaseous emissions of mechanically-biologically pre-treated waste for long term experiments. Proc. of the Ninth International Waste Management and Landfill Symposium. S. Margherita di Pula, Cagliary, Italy. 2003.

[10] Kjeldsen, P., Barlaz, M.A., Rooker, R., Baun, A., Ledin, A., and Christensen, T. H., Present and long-term composition of MSW landfill

leachate: a review. *Critical Reviews in Environmental Science and Technology* **32 (4)**, pp. 297–336, 2002.

[11] Berge, N.D., Reinhart, D.R., and Townsend, T.G., The fate of nitrogen in bioreactor landfills. *Critical Reviews in Environmental Science and Technology*, **35 (4)**, pp. 365–399, 2005.

[12] Jokela J.P.Y., and Rintala J.A., Anaerobic solubilisation of nitrogen from municipal solid waste. *Reviews in Environmental Science and Biotechnology*, **2**, pp. 67–77, 2003.

Municipal solid waste characterization and management in Uyo, Akwa Ibom State, Nigeria

E. N. Okey[1], E. J. Umana[2], A. A. Markson[2] & P. A. Okey[3]
[1]Department of Biological Sciences, Akwa Ibom State University, Nigeria
[2]Department of Botany, University of Calabar, Nigeria
[3]Solaris Energy, Barbados Ltd, Barbados

Abstract

Akwa Ibom state is one of the nine states in the Niger Delta region of Nigeria. This region is critical to sustainable economic development in the country being the main oil producing area. With its location within the tropical rainforest and dense population, Uyo, like other major cities in Nigeria generates enormous municipal solid waste which is not adequately managed. Municipal solid waste management has therefore emerged as one of the greatest challenges facing environmental agencies in the city. Solid waste management is simply reduced to waste transfer with overflow dump sites causing serious environmental pollution. Waste management practices are characterized by inefficient collection and poor disposal methods. Waste stream comprises: 65% of compostable materials, 10% plastics, 8% paper, 4% metal, 3% textile, 3% glass and 7% others. The rate of waste generation ranged between 0.49 to 0.60 kg/capita/day with an average of 0.54 kg/capita/day. Inadequate finances, lack of institutional arrangement, insufficient information on the quantity and quality of waste as well as inappropriate technology are the main constraints militating against effective solid waste management in Uyo. The findings in this research are useful in formulating adequate waste disposal procedures. In addition, the potential of waste recovery, reduction and reuse based on waste characteristics is projected at about $8million annually. However, further research is required in the area in order to maximize this potential.
Keywords: waste characterization, generation, recycle, reuse, reduce.

WIT Transactions on Ecology and The Environment, Vol 173, © 2013 WIT Press
www.witpress.com, ISSN 1743-3541 (on-line)
doi:10.2495/SDP130531

1   Introduction

Municipal Waste (MW) generally comprises urban garbage produced from households, industries, commercial and institutional establishments (including hospitals), markets, yards and street sweepings. This waste will normally include; solid, liquid and gaseous materials which if allowed to accumulate will pollute the environment. With growing concerns on Climate Change and Global Warming, the need for effective waste management cannot be over emphasized.

In order to maintain a clean Municipal environment, urban waste must be effectively managed through appropriate reduction, reuse and/or recycled practices (Dauda and Osita [1]). Waste management generally involves the collection, transfer, treatment, recycling, resources recovery and disposal of waste in any location. The goals of waste management are therefore, to promote a quality environment, generate employment, and thus, support the efficiency and productivity of the economy.

The volume of waste being generated continues to increase at a faster rate than the ability of the agencies to improve on the financial and technical resources needed to parallel this growth. Waste management in Nigeria is generally characterized by inefficient collection methods, insufficient coverage of the collection system and improper disposal of waste materials (Eja *et al.* [2]). What to do with Municipal waste (trash) has long been a topic of heated discussion. For years, the answer had been to either burn it (incineration) or bury it (landfills), two processes with obvious serious environmental consequences. Thus, the management of municipal waste has emerged as one of the most serious problems facing environmental protection in developing countries. In most of these countries including Nigeria, Municipal Waste Management if carried out at all, involves just the collection and transfer of waste with little or no conversion practices. These actions have resulted in the transfer of waste from different collection centers to designated dump sites as is the case in Uyo. Consequently, urban areas are often defaced with heaps of garbage, a situation that has earned Nigerian cities the dirtiest in the world.

Agunwamda [3] observed that, the quantity of waste generated in urban areas in industrialized countries is higher than in developing countries, still municipal solid waste management remains inadequate in the latter. Also, waste in developing countries differs from developed countries. Most developing countries, example Nigeria, would therefore have waste management problems different from those found in developed countries in areas of composition, density, political and economic framework, waste amount, access to waste for collection, awareness and attitude. Ogwueleka [4] also reported that, waste is in developing countries is generally heavier, wetter and more corrosive.

While Uyo is emerging as one of the cleanest cities in Nigeria, the problems of waste management in this city are still far from being solved as waste is merely transferred from the main city to dump sites. The Ministry of Environment and Natural Resources is the only government agency responsible for waste management in Uyo. Although this Ministry has recorded some success in the area of waste collection and transfer but are still seriously lacking in the final phase of waste management which is waste utilization- converting waste into useful products such as energy. In addition, information on municipal solid waste management in Uyo is scanty. Eja *et al.* [5] however, reported on the impact of municipal solid waste on the environmental and public health in Uyo.

In order to formulate adequate solid waste utilization strategies, information on the amount, rate of generation as well as type of waste produced is critical. Such information is lacking in Uyo. This study is therefore, aimed at characterizing municipal solid waste in Uyo municipality with the view of formulating adequate waste utilization strategies.

2   Materials and methods

For the purpose of this investigation, Uyo Municipality was divided into four zones: North, South, East and West. A variety of waste characterization methods can be used to assess Municipal solid waste USEPA [6]. In the field investigation, sampling directly from waste generation points was adopted. Sampling was designed for two seasons: November to April, 2011 (dry season) and May to October, 2011 (wet season).

2.1 Waste collection and transfer

An assessment of the methods of waste collection and transfer was conducted by monitoring collection bins along major roads within the municipality. Also, the vehicles used for the transfer of waste from bins to dump sites were observed daily in order to evaluate the type of vehicles used, their working conditions as well as the regularity of transfer.

2.2 Waste characterization

Residential assessment was undertaken by sampling twenty (50) households per zone. Two different colour bins; one bin for rapidly biodegradable materials and the second for slowly biodegradable and non-biodegradable waste were provided. Bins were emptied daily. Sampling was also conducted for commercial areas (open markets, shopping complexes and hotels/restaurants). Three markets, shopping complexes and hotels each were sampled per zone. The total number of markets, shopping complexes and hotels was obtained from the Uyo Municipal Authority, and this was used in computing the total amount of waste generated.

With respect to institutional areas, three primary schools, three secondary schools and one university were sampled. Three healthcare centers and a hospital were also surveyed. The daily average waste generation per student (for educational institution) and per bed (for health) were evaluated. The total amount of MSW generated in institutional areas was estimated by computing the total number of educational institutions with students and healthcare centers/hospitals with beds within Uyo.

Waste from street sweepings was also assessed. The waste generated per 100m of road length was determined by selecting ten paved roads (1km each). The total length of paved roads in Uyo was obtained from the Municipal

Authority and used in calculating the total amount of waste generated from street sweepings. Finally, the total MSW generated from residential, commercial and institutional areas as well as street sweeping was determined per zone and Uyo Municipal Area.

In the laboratory, the weight of collected waste samples was measured and then transferred for sorting. Portions of the waste were placed on sorting tables and sorting was carried out manually. Waste was categorized by adopting a modified method of AIT [7]. Waste was grouped into seven major categories namely: organic matter, paper, plastics, textiles, metals, glass and others.

2.3 Resource recovery and recycling

Four methods were adopted in evaluating the level of resource recovery and recycling in Uyo:

  i)   Interview of ten Ministry of Environment staff associated with waste management.
  ii) Visits to dump sites to compare waste composition with those from bins.
  iii) Evaluation of scavengers' recovery content
  iv) Cost projections on recyclable and composting materials were also assessed.

3 Results

3.1 Waste collection and transfer

Solid waste in Uyo is collected in bins that are located along major streets (fig 1). The bin sizes range between 400 and 560kg and are placed 1000m-2000m apart. Different types of vehicles are employed in the transfer of waste to dump sites. These include compactor trucks, tippers, pick-ups, side and rear loader and skip trucks. It was noted that most of these vehicles are in a state of disrepair and breakdown frequently. The efficiency of collection is quite low with less than 50% of generated solid waste actually conveyed to dump sites. The collection time is also irregular, thus waste accumulate in open dumps at road sides when the bins are full. Uyo has several designated dump sites which are often filled and now overflow (fig. 2).

Figure 1:   Waste bins on a major street in Uyo.

Figure 2:   Dump site.

3.2 Waste characterization

3.2.1 Waste generation
A total of 420 tons of waste was generated per day (table 1). The highest amount of waste (273t) was generated in the Southern zone of the city while the least amount of 49 tons was produced in the Western zone. The Northern and Eastern zones generated 96t and 73t respectively (table 1). The waste generation rate per capita ranged between 0.48 and 0.61 with a weighted average of 0.54 (table 2).

Table 1:   Component weight of MSW generated in four zones of Uyo.

Waste components	Waste generation (tons/day)				
	North	South	East	West	All waste streams
Biodegradable	64	150	40	19	273
Plastic	10	15	10	7	42
Paper	8	11	7	7	33
Metal	3	10	3	1	17
Glass	2	5	3	3	13
Textiles	1	5	3	4	13
Others	8	6	7	8	29
Total	96	202	73	49	420

Table 2:   Waste generation rate (Kg/capita/day).

Zones	Population	Amount (t)	Kg/capita/day
North	200,000	96.0	0.48
South	400,000	202.0	0.51
East	130,000	73.0	0.56
West	80,000	49.0	0.61
Total	**800,000**	**240.0**	**2.16**
Weighted Average	-	-	0.54

3.2.2 Waste composition

Sixty five percent (65%) of the total waste generated comprised biodegradable materials, fig. 3. The second largest percentage (10%) was taken up by plastics, while metal and glass materials constituted 7% combined. The remaining 7% was made-up of others which included ceramics, rubber, soil, bones and dust.

Chart Title

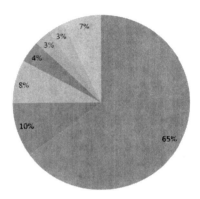

Figure 3:   Waste composition.

3.2.3 Contribution of different sources in total waste generation and waste disposal methods

The highest amount of waste (67.5%) was produced in the residential areas (table 3). Commercial areas followed with 28.3% while Institutions, street sweepings and others made up just 4.05%. With respect to waste disposal methods, 60% of municipal solid waste was disposed through open dumping, while 20% was by land filling. Composting comprised 10%, incineration 8% and 3R (Recover, Recycle, Reuse) just 2% (fig. 4).

Table 3:   Contributions of different sources in total waste generation (%).

Sources	MSW generation/day (%)				
	North	South	East	West	All waste streams
Residential	67.0	70.0	65.0	68.0	67.5
Commercial	29.0	25.0	31.0	28.0	28.3
Industrial	3.0	2.6	1.0	2.0	2.3
Street Sweeping	0.8	2.0	2.9	1.7	1.5
Others	0.2	0.4	0.1	0.3	0.3
Total	100	100	100	100	100

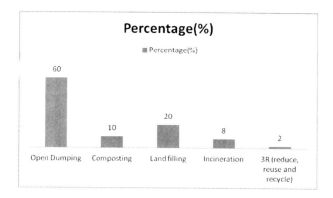

Figure 4:   Percentage of waste disposal methods.

3.2.4 Waste recovery

There are no formal waste resource recovery/recycling programmes in Uyo. However, very limited recovery operations are undertaken by the informal sector such as scavengers (fig. 5).

Figure 5:   Sorted plastic materials.

Following assessments in this study, a total of 329t of waste can be recovered daily (table 4). Out of this total amount of recoverable items, 250t are of compostable materials while 36t are plastics. Twenty five tons of paper can also be recovered daily (table 4). In monetary terms, based on the 2010 price projections (US$/t), $21,548 can be generated daily (table 4).

4 Discussions

Waste Management in Uyo municipality is the full responsibility of the Ministry of Environment and Mineral Resources. Like other Government activities, the collection, transfer and utilization of waste is grossly inadequate. Poor funding, lack of expertise and manpower, use of obsolete technologies as well as lack of

Table 4: MSW recoverable materials in Uyo.

Items	Recoverable materials/cost			
	Total weight (t)	Recovery weight (t)	2010 Price (US$/t)	Market value (US$)
Plastic	42.0	36.0	80.00	2,888.00
Paper	33.0	25.0	86.00	2,150.00
Metal	17.0	10.0	100.00	1,000.00
Glass	13.0	8.0	40.00	320.00
Textile	13.0	7.0	20.00	140.00
Others	29.0	5.0	10.00	50.00
Compostable	273.0	250.0	60.00	15,000.00
Total/day	420.0	341.0	-	21,548.00
Total/year	153,300	122,640	-	7,865,020.00

data are the main constraints militating against proper waste management practices in Uyo. Waste is collected through bins which are placed too far apart for effective collection. Residents therefore find it difficult to travel long distances in order to place their waste in such bins. As a result, waste is dumped indiscriminately along bushes and uncompleted buildings. The transfer of waste is also problematic. Most of the vehicles used for this purpose required urgent servicing and the rate of transfer is also inconsistent. Consequently, bins are often filled and most times they over flow causing spillage of waste. This shows lack of commitment on the part of the Government in tackling environmental issues.

The findings in this study also indicate that a high percentage of the waste generated in uyo is of organic matter. Similar results have been reported in other Nigerian and Asian cities [4, 8, 9]. Waste generation rates are generally reported to be higher in urban centers, Alsamawi [10], hence, the weighted average of 0.54 could be considered low since Uyo is a capital city and one of the top oil producing areas in Nigeria. This low estimated value could be a reflection of poor collection and transfer methods adopted. The complex composition of municipal solid waste in Uyo is an indication of the consumption pattern of the inhabitants and the heterogeneity of the waste stream. This type of waste is difficult to incinerate and therefore require other means of disposal. Open dumping is the most popular method of waste disposal. This form of waste disposal is grossly inadequate and could result in environmental pollution and so should be discouraged. Land filling is also practiced but at a lower percentage and most landfills often overflow causing land pollution.

In Uyo as well as in most cities in Nigeria, there is no formal recycling of waste materials [11]. At the moment, recovery functions are carried out by informal sector such as the scavengers who manually sort out garbage and recover only limited items such as plastics (fig. 3). Recycling is a more environmentally friendly method of disposing waste and should be encouraged. It not only reduces the amount of waste to be collected and transferred but also generates income for government and individuals. Composting is another means of utilizing municipal solid waste. This is a natural biological process that can be conducted under controlled aerobic or anaerobic conditions. Although, composting is a useful solid waste recycling process, it requires effective mechanical sorting which is not yet adopted in Uyo. However, there are available sustainable technologies than can produce everything that we currently derive from crude oil (both fuels and petrochemicals) from a more renewable source: municipal solid waste [12]. This green energy source can be obtained from garbage dumps and landfills. Recyclable materials can also provide papers, plastics, metals and glass that can be used for purposes.

The assessment of recoverable materials in this study indicate that 329t of municipal solid waste can be recovered from the total of 420t generated daily. Based on the 2010 price of recoverable items per ton, it is projected that about $8m (eight million US$) can be generated from recyclable materials. This amount could assist the Government in making Uyo cleaner and creating jobs for its inhabitants.

Although, there is increasing awareness on waste management in Nigeria, the findings of this study indicate that Municipal Solid Waste Management in Uyo is far from meeting WHO standards and suggest that effective waste management procedures be adopted. It is therefore recommended that Government should: hand over waste management to private agencies that will be more efficient and effective, put in place proper legislation and laws that will enable individuals and companies to comply and adhere to environmental safety regulations, provide adequate funding and adopt new technologies for effective waste management in Uyo municipality. These strategies should be extended to cover other parts of Akwa Ibom state.

References

[1] Dauda, M. and Osita, O.O., Solid waste management and reuse in Maiduguri, Nigeria. *Proc. of the 29th WEDC Int. Conf. towards the Millennium Development Goals*, Abuja, pp. 30–36, 2003.

[2] Eja, M.E., Asikong, B.E. and Arikpo, G.E., Solid waste management in South Eastern Nigeria: A case study of Ogoja development Area, *Tropical Environmental Research*, **5**, pp. 20–25, 2003.

[3] Agunwamba, J.C., Analysis of scavenger's activities and recycling in some cities of Nigeria, *Environmental Management*, **32(1)**, pp. 116–127.

[4] Ogwueleka, T.Ch., Municipal solid waste characteristics and management in Nigeria, *Iran Journal of Environmental Health Science Engineering*, 6(3), pp. 173–180.

[5] Eja, M.E., Alobi, N.O., Ikpeme, E.M., Ogri, O.R. and Inyang, A.O., Environmental and public health-related assessment of solid waste management in Uyo, Akwa Ibom State, Nigeria. *World Journal of Applied Science and Technology*, **2(1)**, pp. 110–123.

[6] United States Environmental Protection Agency (USEPA). Characterization of municipal solid waste in the United States, 1995 update, USEPA 530-R-96.

[7] Asian Institute of Technology (AIT), Sampling Techniques of municipal solid waste. School of Environment, Resource and Development, Thailand, EV. 04/11.

[8] Khajuria, A., Yamamoto, Y and Movioka, T., Estimation of municipal solid waste generation and landfill area in Asian developing countries. *Journal of Environmental Biology*, **31(5)**, pp. 649–654.

[9] Ministry of Forest, "Sustainable development study of urbanized areas", New Delhi, India.

[10] Alsamawi, A.A., and Zboon, A.R., Estimation of Bangladesh municipal solid waste generation rate. *Engineering and Technology Journal*, **29(1)**, pp. 131–140, 2009.

[11] Ogwueleka, T.C., Analysis of solid waste management and reuse in Maiduguri, Nigeria. *Proc. of the 29th WEDC Int. Conf. towards the Millennium Development Goals*, Abuja, pp. 64–74.

[12] Mutui, G. and Nakamura, E., Bioconversion of ligno cellulosic waste from selected dumping sites in Dares Salam, *Tanzania Biodegradation*, **16(6)**, pp. 493–499.

Analyzing reverse logistics in the Brazilian National Waste Management Policy (PNRS)

M. M. Veiga[1,2]
[1]Environmental Health Department, National School of Public Health, Oswaldo Cruz Foundation, Ministry of Health, Brazil
[2]Strategic Management Department, Business School, Federal University of Rio de Janeiro State, Ministry of Education, Brazil

Abstract

In the last 20 years, the Brazilian population has increased by 30%, while the amount of waste has risen by 90%. This demographic expansion associated with an increasing consumption of disposable products has switched the type (quality and quantity) of waste produced. Currently, many municipalities are facing difficulties in finding appropriate disposal sites. As a result, waste management has become a national priority. In 2010, after been on hold in the Nation's Congress for decades, the National Waste Management Policy (PNRS) was approved through formal legislation (Law 12.305/10). The PNRS represented a major political and judicial improvement, but, still, represents a major economical and operational challenge. The strategies for improving waste management in Brazil should include instruments provided in the PNRS. Extended product responsibility, which includes all supply chain stakeholders, and reverse logistics are two main instruments incorporated in PNRS. A post-consumption reverse logistics program is the most common strategy to make operational the extended producer responsibility concept. Usually, a reverse logistics program deals with a specific range of products requiring by legal enforcement to be: recycled; reused; remanufactured; finally disposed of; treated; or incinerated. An efficient reverse logistics program should stimulate producers to internalize all social and environmental costs, from cradle to grave, in their decision making process. Thus, it is necessary to analyze the costs and benefits of PNRS instruments in order to balance benefits (reducing social and environmental damages) and costs (keeping reverse logistics chain operational). Legislation is the most common instrument to change market behavior in order

WIT Transactions on Ecology and The Environment, Vol 173, © 2013 WIT Press
www.witpress.com, ISSN 1743-3541 (on-line)
doi:10.2495/SDP130541

to improve efficiency in returning numerous products. Even tough, reverse logistics has been successfully introduced in several national public policies; the instrument is still pending a further boost in the Brazilian regulatory system. This study discusses the strategies included in the PNRS.

Keywords: waste management, reverse logistics, extended producer responsibility, Brazil.

1 Introduction

In the last 20 years, Brazilian population has increased by 30%, while the amount of waste has risen by 90%. This demographic expansion associated with an increasing in the consumption of disposable products has switched the type (quality and quantity) of waste produced. Therefore, waste management is becoming a national priority for public officials [1, 2].

Currently, many municipalities are facing difficulties in finding adequate disposal sites. This site shortage for placing solid waste disposal facilities has leaded to inefficient logistics operations, and increasing environmental, social and economical costs [3].

Recycling, composting and reusing should be the natural alternatives for disposing waste, as they are associated with lower environmental impacts. Incineration, which has high costs, produces gas, ash and effluents should be the least desirable alternative [4–7].

Irregular and heterogeneous waste mix makes it difficult for recycling and composting processes to be economically feasible. High operational costs are usually linked to inefficient composting and recycling processes. Mixed waste needs to be segregated to improve technical efficiency, compost and recycled material quality. Most of the times, the use of low quality recycled material by industry is costly comparatively to the use of equivalent raw material [8].

In an attempt to reduce uncontrolled waste mix, many countries have implemented selective collection and recycling programs, which motivate segregation. Zhuang *et al.* [9] have indicated that segregation is a key component for improving the overall efficiency of any waste management process.

In Brazil, most of the selective collection and recycling programs are inefficient, with the exception of those in which the value of the material recycled is economical viable, which makes the whole reverse logistics chain efficient, e.g. aluminum and paper.

Due to these logistics difficulties, landfills are still the most common solution for disposing solid waste. Cost-benefit analysis indicated that landfills have comparatively low operational costs and simpler technical standards [10].

Thus, an increase in recycling and in composting would elevate existing landfill life, postponing the need for new disposal facilities. Due to the increase in waste generation ratio, public officials should prioritize investments in preventing (reduce waste generation) instead of just building more disposal facilities [11].

In Brazil, landfill disposal is still an exception. Most of the urban waste is disposed in illegal dumps. However, the PNRS dictated that all illegal dumping should be eradicated by 2014. The PNRS is the major Brazilian attempt to properly manage waste.

2 The national waste management policy (PNRS)

In Brazil, the first waste management regulations dated 25 years ago. Since the 80s, much legislation has been enacted. These regulations were not integrated, they were disperse throughout many legislative instruments, e.g. laws; administrative orders; and resolutions. This complex regulatory system made surveillance a hard task and had many conflicting legislation.

In 2010, after been on hold in Nation's Congress for decades, the National Waste Management Policy (PNRS) was approved through formal legislation (Law 12.305/10). The PNRS represented a major political and judicial improvement, but, still, represents a major economical and operational challenge.

PNRS promotes efficiency by stimulating innovation in waste management strategies and actions. There are three major instruments in the PNRS to implement and improve efficiency of waste management: Extended Producer Responsibility (EPR); Sectoral Agreement (SA); and Reverse Logistics (RL).

EPR establishes a shared responsibility among all stakeholders in the supply chain (suppliers-producers-consumers) throughout all product life cycle. It demands internalization of environmental costs in the decision making process of the supply chain.

In order to make EPR operational, PNRS requires a Sectoral Agreement (SA), which incorporates negotiation and contractual concept. It is a negotiation among public sector, producers, suppliers, importers, and dealers to implement EPR throughout product life cycle. Currently, these sectoral agreements are being negotiated.

PNRS strategy makes all stakeholders liable, internalizing environmental costs and stimulating innovation. The reverse logistics (RL) is the process of introducing recycled material after consumption on the supply chain. The reverse logistics is one main instrument of the PNRS (see figure 1).

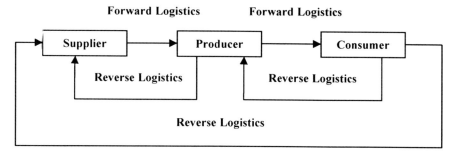

Figure 1:   Forward and Reverse Logistics flow.

The complete supply chain incorporates forward logistics activities (production, distribution, and consumption) and reverse logistics activities (collection, inspection, segregation, reprocess, recycle, and disposal). It is every stakeholder responsibility planning and operating this post consumption reverse logistics chain [12–14].

In most cases, even though it is not required, the stakeholders in the reverse logistics can be different from those in the forward logistics. Consumers operate in both edges of the supply chain, by returning post consumed products and by buying recycled products. Usually, suppliers and producers take into service third parties to make the reverse logistics operational. This strategy might be related to economical and technical issues [15].

The PNRS require the organization and the implementation of reverse logistics flow for producers, importers, distributors and retailers of selected products: pesticides (residues and containers); batteries; tires; lubricants (residues and containers); fluorescent lamps; and e-waste. This legal required reverse chain should comply with the sectoral agreement; consider technical and economical viability, social and environmental impacts.

The efficiency of any reverse logistics program is directly related to an efficient recycled material market. The PNRS states that it is producers, importers, distributors and retailers responsibility to implement: procedures for marketing empty containers and residues; receiving units for recyclable products; and partnership with recycling cooperatives.

However, the success of the PNRS is associated with the implementation of the extended producer responsibility (EPR), making liable any stakeholders of the supply chain (reverse and forward). The initiative for starting the reverse logistics relies on the consumer. A successful reverse logistics programs should stimulate end users to trigger the process.

OECD highlighted two related aspects of any EPR policy: "(1) the shifting of responsibility (physically and/or economically; fully or partially) upstream toward the producer and away from municipalities, and (2) to provide incentives to producers to incorporate environmental considerations in the design of their products" [16, 17].

Some economic instruments commonly associated to the effectiveness and the efficacy of reverse logistics is: Deposit and Refund Schemes; Advance Disposal Fees; Material Taxes; Upstream Combination Tax and Subsidy. Cost-benefit analysis of reverse supply chain should weight and balance benefits (reducing social costs of waste management) against the costs incurred in making the program operational [16].

Consequently, economics play a great role in making an efficient reverse supply chain. An efficient reverse logistics should be the one that is preferred over several alternative policy instruments. In the waste management decision-making process, there is a need for identifying, designing, and implementing cost-effective instruments by balancing economic, legal and environmental aspects. Reverse logistics is an instrument of EPR policy that makes operational taking back product or its packing after use [16–18].

3 Reverse logistics

Reverse and forward logistics are not differentiated in terms of operational aspects. Many particularities of reverse logistics have been continuously ignored. Forward logistics is an active process, where firms plan, produce, and supply distributors with products based upon forecasts. Reverse logistics is a reactive process with more unpredictable factors, which is usually initiated by end-user. The main trigger for reverse logistics process is the end-user, not the manufacturers themselves [12, 19].

Recent literature highlighted the importance of integrating all these processes. Stock [20] stated that successful reverse logistics solutions could only occur by efficiently merging forward and reverse flows into one process. Krikke et al. [29] ratified the need for a strong integration between forward and reverse chain.

Brito and Dekker [15] stated that reverse logistics is conceptually different from waste management. Waste management deals with effectively managing waste and its legal and environmental consequences. This assumption was only possible by defining waste in a controversial way, as products that have no value to be recovered. Reverse logistics, as a concept, focus on products that have some value to be recovered, creating a valued supply chain. A deeper conceptual discussion on the definition of term "waste" and its relation to supply chain theory can be found in Hicks et al. [21].

Many studies analyzed reverse logistics experiences in different countries [12, 19, 22, 23] which explicitly highlighted differences in motivation in several take-back programs (environmental, economical, and legal motivations). These different motivations have direct influence in the management strategy of reverse logistics process flow.

Similarly to PNRS, many regulatory systems have already incorporate reverse logistics in their environmental system. The different motivations for returning consumed or after-used goods could vary from environmental, economical, and legal aspects. Each real world situation should weight and balance these different issues [12, 19].

Reverse logistics in the PNRS is legislation-driven strategy; however, the economic aspects are important for the overall success. Legal compliance could be costly and require stakeholders finding viable alternatives for final disposal, which sometimes implies economical losses. However, high logistics costs should not be an excuse for non-complying with legal requirements [12, 19].

The strategy used in any logistic system can have a great impact on its economical, legal, and environmental efficiency. Outcomes in reverse logistics channels for recycling are connected to logistics costs (collection costs and recyclers services). Logistics costs are a large part of total recycling costs, reported as much as 95%. One strategy commonly used by decision makers for saving logistic costs is postponement [24, 25].

The postponement principle was originally introduced in the 50s as a strategy for structuring Marketing Distribution Channels involving inventories delays on forward logistics theory [26]. However, recent theory on postponement also included reverse logistics activities, specially relating to differentiation of goods.

This "improved" postponement theory incorporated diverse strategy aspects like collection versus sorting complexity, and segregation versus co-collection. In reverse channels, postponement of transformation activities (separation) might have greater importance than postponement of transfer activities (transport), [24].

The logic behind postponement is that the costs associated to risks and uncertainties are related to goods differentiation that occurs during the logistic process. The postponement/speculation strategy indicates that speculative inventories will be created in the logistic process "if the costs of such inventories are less than the savings from postponement". Postponing to final stages might entail savings in transportation and inventory costs by sorting products in "large lots" and in "undifferentiated states" [26, 27].

In forward logistics channels, smaller volumes of different products are transported together to reduce cost. In reverse channels, materials can be co-collected by using compartmentalized vehicles; by alternate scheduling; or by bagging different materials. In case of toxic products, like pesticide and lubricants containers, postponement can increase risk of contamination [24, 25].

Postponement and speculation principle can also affect the length of the reverse logistic channel. If speculation takes place and materials are co-collected, transfer levels (intermediary disposal units) are often introduced to sort and store some of the fractions. In reverse channels, speculation leads to smaller volumes of each fraction being transported, resulting in higher transportation costs and low capacity utilization [24, 25].

Therefore, differentiation is a keyword for efficiently applying postponement and speculation strategy in reverse logistic channels. Speculation in reverse channels leads to smaller volumes of each fraction being transported and thus resulted in higher transportation costs. Many fractions separated (segregation) early in the collection level can be considered speculation. The more fractions sorted at collection level, improve recyclable quality, but are more challenging for collecting and transporting activities.

4 Discussion

It is a hard task to implement an economically viable reverse logistics program in such a large country like Brazil. The recyclable materials market is still developing and is also widely disperse. There are just a few buyers, mostly concentrated in large cities, and numerous sellers spread all over the country. Transportation costs make most of recyclable materials transactions unbeneficial compared to the equivalent price of raw materials.

The recyclable market has a lot of uncertainties, especially those related to seasonality and quality of recyclable materials. These variables increase industrial costs of using recyclable materials in most products that have a higher aggregate value associated. For that reason, in order to make recyclables competitive, there is a market force to drop the price for these seasonable, mixed, and poor in quality recyclable materials. Most recycled materials (e.g. plastics) are used in low value-added products.

In large communities, economy of scale can be applied [28]. In these cases, speculation and segregation should be considered in order to increase the quality and the homogeneity (reduction of mix) of recyclable materials. These actions would increase the recyclable value, make it feasible for most industries, and turn the reverse chain profitable. The Brazilian aluminum cans reverse chain is a good example of this profitable market. Brazil recycles around 97% of aluminum cans, without any legislation to enforce it.

However, most of recyclable markets in Brazil are not profitable and need some coercive and enforcement power to change industry behavior in using low quality recyclable materials. The legislative strategy is that by enforcing industry to use recyclable materials, it will create a recycling market, which would lead to improvements in the efficiency of this reverse chain. If they are required to use, industry would also organize this reverse supply chain in order to receive better quality recyclable materials.

Nevertheless, this industry requirement for using low quality recyclable materials in their production line should be gradually introduced. This action would stimulate industrial intervention on chaotic reverse supplies, creating a great opportunity for innovation. Market creation is a requirement for reverse chain to operate efficiently.

On the other hand, small markets tend to be unprofitable no matter what. It is almost impossible for them to operate in economy of scale or in economy of scope. Postponement and storage centers might be an alternative to make these small markets viable.

In order to reduce transportation costs, some products collected from different sites might need to be mixed in temporary storages; there should be a segregation stage before final processing the recycled material. In order to increase the amount recovered from each material; there should be incentives for end users to return products into the reverse chain.

Another alternative for collecting small quantities is using compartmentalized vehicles or bagging the products. This type of collection requires intermediate storage space for each different product and postponing segregation phase making it more complex and costly. For sanitary reasons, it is not viable to mix in the same trucks toxic and non toxic products.

Finally, legal requirements such as the ones present in the PNRS are still necessary to boost and to implement most reverse chains. The EPR concept makes liable any stakeholders in the supply chain (forward and reverse). It is still under negotiation the Sectoral Agreements from each industry. These agreements will guide enforcement of EPR in the PNRS.

However, many industries have already started to develop their reverse logistics programs. The postponement and speculation strategy should be combined depending on the type and the amount of material. There is still pending further studies for the best alternative of reverse logistics for each industry, which will depend on the result of the sectoral agreement negotiation. Different industries should use different strategies.

5 Conclusion

The main objective of this study was to analyze reverse logistics in the Brazilian National Waste Management (PNRS). The shared liability (EPR) enables the creation of reverse chain by making all stakeholders responsible for products life cycle. In Brazil, the current reverse logistics programs are incipient and need to be boosted.

However, reverse logistics strategy should not be simplified as just a "shared responsibility" implementation. Public policy should stimulate innovation and enforce law compliance. The way EPR was introduced in the PNRS does not seem to promote innovation, especially on primary and secondary prevention activities. Also, PNRS do not require life cycle analysis and product reengineering. The success of PNRS relies on negotiation (sectoral agreement), which might be considered a battle between environmental protectors and economic developers.

The shared liability among all stakeholders stimulates incorporating environmental costs in the decision making process. It would also make possible for producers to innovate by changing their products and processes, associating the concept of designing for recycling or designing for the environment.

However, the industry might not improve reverse supply chain without compulsory demand for innovation. It is most likely that industry will advocate for "business as usual" strategy. This strategy will not stimulate recyclable markets or reuse products. It could create incentives for less desirable disposable alternatives, such as incineration.

There are some weaknesses on the PNRS that could jeopardize its intent to promote innovative initiatives. In the PNRS, the economic incentives are mostly facultative and there is no instrument to stimulate cooperation. Depending on the sectoral agreements outcome, it is still uncertainty if the required reverse supply chain development will be feasible.

The PNRS tries to improve reverse logistics chain by providing economic incentives, such as: prioritizing recyclables; subsidizing selective collection; and financing recycling and reusing industries. The main PNRS targets should be: avoid and/or reduce waste generation; reuse whenever possible; create a recyclable market; treat and dispose properly. In order to improve reverse supply chain efficiency is mandatory to create a recyclable market.

An alternative to improve waste management efficiency is to increase recycling and composting ratio. An efficient policy should incorporation action to reduce waste generation. The public policy should stimulate recycling market by setting proper economic incentives. Producers should be required to increase gradually their use of recyclable materials in their product line. Strategic policies to reduce waste generation should focus on producers and consumers. Producers should be stimulated to innovate and to change their processes. Consumers should be stimulated to alter their consumption patterns.

In order to make supply chain operational, in products with higher value added, speculation can be applied because transportation costs do not represent a major barrier. In this case centralized storage could be used. In low value products, transporting long distances could make the reverse chain unprofitable. Therefore, there is a need for a more decentralized system, with smaller storage centers. In this case, postponement could be applied efficiently.

Public policies, like the National Waste Management Policy (PNRS) played an important role in implementing reverse logistics chains. In order to make PNRS more operational, the shared responsibility (EPR) should be enforced by using coercive power to change stakeholders' behavior. This public enforcement power is associated to the sectoral agreement, which is, currently being negotiated.

Acknowledgement

Thanks go to FAPERJ, Capes, and CNPq for the financial support.

References

[1] IBGE. Pesquisa nacional de saneamento básico. Rio de Janeiro: IBGE, 1989.
[2] IBGE. Pesquisa nacional de saneamento básico. Rio de Janeiro: IBGE, 2008.
[3] Günther, W.M.R. Resíduos sólidos no contexto da saúde ambiental. São Paulo: Universidade de São Paulo. Departamento de Saúde Ambiental da Faculdade de Saúde Pública, 148p. 2008.
[4] Denison, R.A. Environmental life-cycle comparisons of recycling, landfilling and incineration: a review of recent studies. Annual Review of Energy and the Environment, v. 21, p. 191–237, 1996.
[5] Valerio, F. Environmental impacts of post-consumer material managements: Recycling, biological treatments, incineration. Waste Management, v. 30, p. 2354–2361, 2010.
[6] Meneses, M.; Schuhmachera, M.; Domingo, J.L. Health risk assessment of emissions of dioxins and furans from a municipal waste incinerator: comparison with other emission sources. Environment International, v. 30, p. 481–489, 2004.
[7] Morselli, L.; Robertis, C.; Luzi, J.; Passarini, F.; Vassura, I. Environmental impacts of waste incineration in a regional system (Emilia Romagna, Italy) evaluated from a life cycle perspective. Journal of Hazardous Materials, v. 159, p. 505–511, 2008.
[8] Bohm, RA; Folz, DH; Kinnaman, TC; Podolsky, M.J. The costs of municipal waste and recycling programs. Resources, Conservation and Recycling, v. 54, p. 864–871, 2010.
[9] Zhuang, Y.; Wu, S.W.; Wang, Y.L.; Wu, W.X.; Chen, Y.X. Source separation of household waste: A case study in China. Waste Management, v. 28, p. 2022–2030, 2008.
[10] Giusti, L. A review of waste management practices and their impact on human health. Waste Management, v. 29, p. 2227–2239, 2009.

[11] Kinnaman, T. The economics of municipal solid waste management. Editorial. Waste Management, v. 29, p. 2615–2617, 2009.

[12] Fleischmann, M.; Bloemhof-Ruwaard, J.M.; Dekker, R.; Van Der Laan, E.; Van Nunen, J.A.E.E.; Van Wassenhove, L.N. Quantitative models for reverse logistics: a review. European Journal of Operational Research, v. 103, p. 1–17, 1997.

[13] Guide J.R., V.D.R.; Jayaraman, V.; Linton, J.D. Building contingency planning for closed-loop supply chains with product recovery. Journal of Operations Management, v. 21, p. 259–279, 2003.

[14] Kumar, S.; Putnam, V. Cradle to cradle: Reverse logistics strategies and opportunities across three industry sectors. International Journal of Production Economics, v. 115, p. 305–315, 2008.

[15] Brito, M.P.; Dekker, R. A framework for reverse logistics. Rotterdam: ERIM, 2003. 29p.

[16] Organisation for Economic Co-operation and Development (OECD). Analytical Framework for Evaluating the Costs and Benefits of Extended Producer Responsibilities Programmes, 2005.

[17] Organisation for Economic Co-operation and Development. (OECD). Extended Producer Responsibility. Guidance Manual for Govern, 2001.

[18] Walls M. The Role of Economics in Extended Producer Responsibility: Making Policy Choices and Setting Policy Goals. Resources for the Future. 2003.

[19] Tibben-Lembke R.S, Rogers D.S. Differences between forward and reverse logistics in a retail environment. Supply Chain Management; 7; 2002, p. 271–282.

[20] Stock, James R., "Reverse Logistics in the Supply Chain," Business Briefing: Global Purchasing & Supply Chain Management. October, pp. 44-48, 2001.

[21] Hicks, C, Heidrich, O. Mcgovern, T. And Donnelly, T., "A Functional Model of Supply Chains and Waste", Intern'l Journal Production Economics. 89: 165–174, 2004.

[22] González-Torre P.L, Adenso-Diaz B., Artiba H. Environmental and reverse logistics policies in European bottling and packing firms. International Journal of Production Economics. 88, 2004. p. 95–104.

[23] Dowlatshahi, S. Developing a theory of reverse logistics. Interfaces, v. 30, n. 3, p. 143–155, 2000.

[24] Jahre, M. Household waste collection as reverse channel – a theoretical perspective. Intern. Journal Physical Distribution and Logistics Management, v. 25, n. 2, p. 39–56, 1995.

[25] Jahre, M. The logic costs of collecting recyclable household waste – modeling systems for cost consequence analysis. International Workshop of Systems Engineering Models for Waste Management, Göteborg, Sweden, 1998 apud VEIGA, 2009.

[26] Bucklin L.P., "Postponement, Speculation and Structure of Distribution Channels", Journal of Marketing Research. Feb. pp. 26–31, 1965.

[27] Pagh J.D., Cooper, M.C., "Supply Chain Postponement and Speculation Strategies: How to Choose the Right Strategy", Journal of Business Logistics, Vol. 19, 2: pp. 13–33. 1998.

[28] Veiga, M.M. Flaws in Brazilian take-back program for pesticide containers in a small rural community. Management Research News, v. 32, n. 1, p. 62–77, 2009.

[29] Krikke, H., Pappis, C. P., Tsoulfas G. T. and Bloemhof-Ruwaard J., "Design Principles for Closed Loop Supply Chains: Optimizing Economic, Logistic and Environmental Performance", ERIM Report Series Reference No. ERS-2001-62-LIS. Working Paper Series. Available at http://papers.ssrn.com, 2001.

Technology fusion for MGP remediation: surfactant-enhanced in situ chemical oxidation, pressure-pulse injections and advanced site investigation

G. E. Hoag, W. Guite, M. Lanoue & B. McAvoy
VeruTEK Technologies, USA

Abstract

An *in situ* treatment that combined VeruTEK Technology's patented surfactant-enhanced in situ chemical oxidation (S-SICO®) technology with Wavefront Technology Solutions US Inc's Primawave technology, a novel pressure-pulsing injection enhancement process, and a patent-pending process to quantify subsurface contamination and measure the effectiveness of full-scale treatment, successfully remediated coal tar-related contamination at a former lumber processing facility in New York City. This remedy overcame standard obstacles to effective in situ remediation: even distribution of the injected chemistry and effective transport at the pore-scale level; solubilization of NAPL contaminant into the aqueous phase where it can be oxidized; and identification of the amount and location of the contaminant mass for targeted treatment. Contamination at this site, the future location of a public library on the shore of a New York City river, included residual NAPL within the pore spaces of the soil matrix. Remediation was required reduce the mass of BTEX, naphthalene and PAHs in soil and reduce groundwater concentrations. The remedial process began with a laboratory treatability study that demonstrated the effectiveness of S-ISCO using VeruSOL and alkaline-activated sodium persulfate to destroy the recalcitrant coal tar contamination from site soils. Next, the three technologies (S-ISCO, Primawave and advanced investigation) were implemented during a one-month pilot test. The full-scale remediation that followed, under approval by the NYSDEC, included 5 months of injections accompanied by comprehensive groundwater monitoring at wells within and outside of the treatment area. Monitoring also included collection of soil samples halfway through the

WIT Transactions on Ecology and The Environment, Vol 173, © 2013 WIT Press
www.witpress.com, ISSN 1743-3541 (on-line)
doi:10.2495/SDP130551

injection process to inform modifications to the final stage of injections. The success of the full-scale remediation will be presented, as well as an evaluation of the advantages to combining S-ISCO, Primawave and advanced site investigation to increase the effectiveness of *in situ* treatment of MGPs.

Keywords: coal tar remediation, in situ oxidation, surfactant enhanced oxidation.

1 Introduction

Manufactured Gas Plants (MGPs) burned coal and provided gas to urban areas from 1850 to 1950. The process resulted in a complex mixture of organic hydrocarbons known as coal tar. While the exact composition of coal tar varies at each plant due to unique processing temperatures and coal supply, the primary contaminants of concern at MGP sites are polyaromatic hydrocarbons (PAHs) specifically PAHs with between four to six rings. Because of their historic role MGP wastes are typically found in highly developed regions where residual coal tar may pose a threat to human and environmental health. The mixtures of PAHs found in coal tar have been shown to be more carcinogenic than an equivalent dose of a single compound (benzo[a]pyrene) in isolation. Weyand *et al.* [2] Persulfate (peroxydisulfate $S_2O_8^{2-}$) can be used to chemically oxidize and destroy MGP related contamination. Heat, peroxide, transition metals, high pH or UV light may be used to activate persulfate and generate the sulfate radical $SO_4^{\cdot-}$. Sulfate radical chemistry is more complex than hydroxyl radical chemistry produced by Fenton's reagents. Unlike hydroxyl radicals which add to C=C bond or abstract hydrogen from C-H, sulfate radicals react with organic contaminants to form organic radical cation intermediaries or may react with water to form hydroxyl radicals (Tsitonaki *et al.* [1]) While persulfate is effective at destroying PAHs upon contact, since PAHs are highly hydrophobic organic contaminants with low solubility in water achieving contact between sulfate radicals and the PAHs compounds is challenging. Concentrations of PAHs at coal tar contaminated sites may exceed concentrations predicted by their poor solubility in the form of colloids (Mackay and Gschwend [3]) but to access the bulk of PAH found at these sites it is necessary to use surfactants, solvents or combinations thereof to effectively solubilize the compounds into the aqueous groundwater phase. Nonionic surfactants have been shown to solubilize these compounds effectively (Yeom *et al.* [4]).

The VeruTEK surfactant enhance in situ chemical oxidation (S-ISCO) processes utilizes persulfate radical chemistry and nonionic surfactants to solubilize and oxidize hydrophobic organic contaminants like those found in MGP coal tar.

2 Project overview

VeruTEK Technologies (VeruTEK) successfully implemented its patented surfactant-enhanced in situ chemical oxidation (S-ISCO®) technology to destroy coal tar contamination at a former roofing products manufacturing site in New

York City (the Site). The urban parcel, surrounded by dense residential and commercial development along the shores of the East River, was contaminated by coal tar repurposed from a nearby Manufactured Gas Plant (MGP) for the roofing manufacturing process. VeruTEK conducted five months of S-ISCO injections that destroyed greater than 90% of the BTEX, PAHs and naphthalene contaminants in the targeted interval. The S-ISCO treatment consisted of injections of VeruSOL®, VeruTEK's patented plant-based surfactant and co-solvent mixture, and alkaline-activated sodium persulfate that used Wavefront Technology Solutions US Inc's (Wavefront) Primawave pressure-pulsing injection enhancement technology (Hoag and Collins [6]). The patent-pending RemMetrik^SM process was used to quantify subsurface contamination, target the treatment and measure its effectiveness. S-ISCO was an integral part of the remedial strategy at the Site that resulted in the New York State Department of Environmental Conservation (NYSDEC) issuing a Certificate of Completion (COC) to confirm the success of the cleanup, and enable the Site's redevelopment as a public library and park ranger station. The successful destruction of MGP-related coal tar at this urban Brownfield site demonstrates the effectiveness of S-ISCO as a remedy for MGP-related contamination.

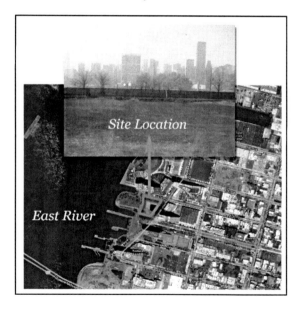

Figure 1:   Site location.

2.1 Site background

Located on the bank of the East River in a densely developed residential and commercial area in New York City, this 0.73-acre parcel is part of an urban revitalization project and will be redeveloped as a public library and park ranger station. During historic roofing products manufacture at the Site, MGP coal tar was brought onto the Site and entered the subsurface, contaminating the soil and groundwater with volatile organic compounds (VOCs) including benzene, toluene, ethylbenzene, total xylenes (BTEX), and semi-volatile organic compounds (SVOCs) including naphthalene, and polycyclic aromatic hydrocarbons (PAHs). Contaminant concentrations in the soil and groundwater exceeded the NYSDEC regulatory limits, including in several groundwater locations by orders of magnitude. SVOCs comprised greater than 95% of the total contaminant mass; naphthalene alone accounted for 65% of the total mass. The majority of contamination was present as residual non-aqueous phase liquid (NAPL) held within the pore spaces of the heterogeneous soil matrix which consisted predominately of sand and silts but which also included lenses of silt and silty clay. Traditionally these NAPL droplets, especially in fine soils such as the silts and clays present at this site, present a challenge to in situ treatment.

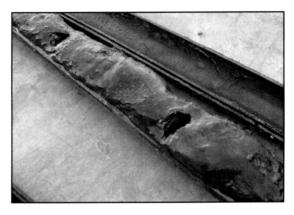

Figure 2: NAPL-stained boring from center of treatment area (11–13 ft bgs), 2008.

2.2 Site challenges

Full-scale excavation is the conventional remedy for sites such as this one which have coal tar-related NAPL contamination. Because of the unique and challenging characteristics of the Site and its location, however, this approach was neither feasible nor practical. A dig-and-haul solution would have involved removal of thousands of truckloads of soil, from depths extending below 22 ft bgs, as well as concomitant de-watering operations. Such a large-scale excavation would have required comprehensive infrastructure to stabilize the subsurface, and may still have compromised the stability of the high-value residences on surrounding parcels especially since this parcel was constructed from landfill brought in over the history of the property. Because of the frequent high-wind conditions associated with the river, a tent or covering would have been necessary to prevent the exposed soil from affecting the humans living, working and traveling in the area. Finally the traffic generated by the continuous stream of construction vehicles to and from the Site would have added congestion to the local roadways and as well as emissions to the air.

2.3 Remedial technologies for in situ treatment

An *in situ* remedy based on VeruTEK's S-ISCO technology was selected to overcome the standard obstacles to effective *in situ* remediation: solubilization of NAPL contaminant into the aqueous phase where it can be oxidized; even distribution of the injected chemistry and effective transport at the pore-scale level; and identification of the magnitude and location of the contaminant mass for targeted treatment. This remedy included S-ISCO with Wavefront Technology Solutions US Inc's (Wavefront) Primawave Pressure-Pulsing Injection Enhancement tool, and the patent-pending RemMetrik[SM] contamination identification and quantification process.

2.3.1 S-ISCO
S-ISCO is one of VeruTEK's patented remedial technologies that use VeruSOL surfactant and co-solvent mixtures to bring NAPL and sorbed contaminants into contact with free radical oxidants. VeruSOL desorbs NAPL contaminants, bringing them into a stable oil-in-water emulsion in the aqueous phase. High-performing activators generate free radicals, including sulfate radicals ($SO_4^{\cdot-}$ or SO_4^{-2}) from sodium persulfate and hydroxyl radicals ($OH\cdot$) from hydrogen peroxide, which then oxidize the aqueous-phase contaminants. Because S-ISCO is able to target the source of contamination, the treatment yields a permanent solution and prevents contaminant rebound.

2.3.2 Primawave™ pressure-pulsing process
The Primawave pressure-pulsing process uses a sidewinder tool attached to the injection well head that generates subsurface pressure waves to open soil pore spaces. Particularly in tight clayey and silty soils, this tool enhances the uniformity of chemical dispersion and affects the treatment's radius of influence.

2.3.3 RemMetrik[SM] contamination investigation and characterization method
The RemMetrik process includes a method and process for calculating the mass and three-dimensional location of subsurface contamination using a grid and random sampling system. The contamination information is used to target the treatment to areas with the most significant impacts. Data collected using this method after treatment, informs an assessment of treatment effectiveness.

2.3.4 Remedial design process
The S-ISCO approach was approved as part of the Brownfield Cleanup strategy for the site after the results of VeruTEK's bench-scale treatability tests and pilot-scale field implementation demonstrated that the S-ISCO process could effectively contact and destroy Site contamination, including sorbed NAPL. The laboratory and field-scale testing, typical components of the S-ISCO design process, indicated that a S-ISCO remedy composed of VeruSOL-3 and alkaline-

activated sodium persulfate (FMC Corporation [5]) was the optimal remedy for site contaminants, while the results of the pilot test indicated that the combination of Primawave pressure-pulsing with S-ISCO injections could affect the radius of influence and dispersion for the injected chemistry. The following sections describe the treatability study and field pilot test.

2.3.5 VeruTEK lab treatability study

Using soil and groundwater from the Site, VeruTEK conducted bench-scale testing to determine the optimal S-ISCO remedy for Site contaminants. The investigation included surfactant-screening tests to identify the optimal VeruSOL blend to maximize contaminant solubilization; aqueous-phase oxidation tests to identity the most effective oxidant and activator system to destroy the solubilized contaminants; and finally, soil column tests to simulate application of the S-ISCO surfactant and oxidant system under field conditions. The results of these tests indicated that an S-ISCO remedy consisting of VeruSOL-3 and alkaline-activated sodium persulfate was optimal for this Site. Figure 3 shows how VeruSOL-3 increased the solubility of VOCs and SVOCs from Site soils by up to 29 times. The column tests demonstrate how the S-ISCO remedy with VeruSOL-3 and alkaline activated persulfate destroyed 96% of SVOCs and 99% of PAHs in 28 days of treatment.

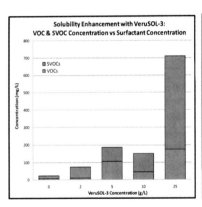 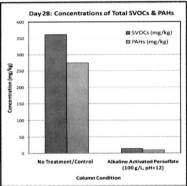

Figure 3:   VeruSOL solubility enhancement (left) column tests (right).

2.3.6 Pilot test

The S-ISCO Pilot Test consisted of ten days of injections into four areas of the Site using the Primawave sidewinder Figure 4 shows these Pilot Test areas (blue circles). Soil analytical data indicated that the S-ISCO chemistry achieved significant contaminant mass removal, including up to 93% in Cell 27. Groundwater data indicated effective chemical transport in the subsurface and also that no NAPL was mobilized beyond the treatment areas – a priority at this Site given its proximity to the East River. In addition the treatment yielded significant reductions in soil gas impacts, including 96% for benzene. The pressure-pulsing sidewinder was used in three of the four areas. By comparison, the pressure-pulsing improved the vertical dispersion and distribution of the injected chemistry, reducing the density-driven tendency of the persulfate chemistry. In addition, it increased the rate at which the chemistry could be injected and appeared to provide more even coverage of the treatment area.

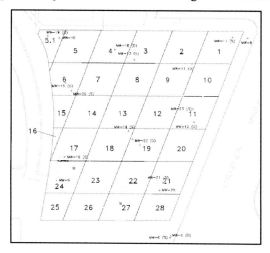

Figure 4:   S-ISCO pilot test areas.

3 Full-scale S-ISCO remediation

Under the approval of the NYSDEC, the full-scale remediation took place between October 2010 and March 2011. During 100 days, the S-ISCO chemistry – VeruSOL-3, sodium persulfate and sodium hydroxide, was injected using the Primawave sidewinder into 34 wells installed in the areas in which the greatest contamination had been identified. These 2-inch wells were variably screened across 6–7 foot lengths within the 10 and 22 ft bgs treatment interval. Injections took place at an average rate of 8 gallons per minute (GPM) per well into 4 wells at a time (32 GPM overall). Table 1 summarizes the injection parameters, including concentrations and total amounts injected all injection system components were housing in a bermed exclusion area that was lined with impermeable plastic and secured with fencing.

Table 1:   Injection summary.

Injection summary		
Chemical	Amount	Injected concentration (g/L)
VeruSOL-3	29,545 kg	5 g/L
Sodium Persulfate	152,000 kg	25 - 50 g/L
Sodium Hydroxide	61,950 kg	20 g/L
Total Fluid	1,201,900 gal	--

3.1 Monitoring

Monitoring was conducted before, during and after S-ISCO injections to track the progress and performance of the injected chemistry in the subsurface and to confirm that the treatment was not negatively impacting sensitive receptors such as the adjacent river. Monitoring was essential to understanding the treatment and informed continuous modification to the process that optimized results. Monitoring included: continuous tracking of water quality parameters including oxidation-reduction potential (ORP), dissolved oxygen (DO), temperature and conductivity using *in situ* data loggers; collection of groundwater samples for analysis of parameters including oxidant concentration, interfacial tension (IFT), total petroleum hydrocarbons (TPH) and pH in VeruTEK's on-site laboratory; observation of all wells on and off-site for indications of NAPL; and collection of soil and groundwater samples for contaminant analysis.

4 Results

4.1 Contamination destruction

Approximately 5 months after the end of injections, when the results of groundwater monitoring indicated that the sodium persulfate reactions had subsided, VeruSOL had largely degraded and pH conditions were approaching pre-injection levels, 114 soil grab samples were collected from the treatment area and analyzed for total VOCs and SVOCs. The RemMetrik process was used to identify sampling locations and intervals. These results were used to calculate the mass of contamination remaining that was then compared to the mass calculated before treatment.

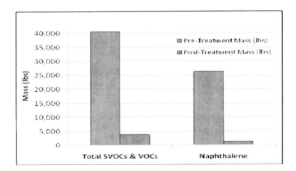

Figure 5:   Contaminant mass reductions.

This analysis indicated that the S-ISCO treatment destroyed 90.3% of the mass of total VOCs and SVOCs present before treatment, including more than 95% of the naphthalene present (Figure 5), and in doing so, exceeded the remedial objective for soil – that is, to destroy 50% of the contaminant mass between 10 and 22 ft bgs. Naphthalene, a principal component of coal tar, was the primary SVOC affecting Site soils and groundwater; it accounted for almost 65% of the total pre-treatment contaminant mass. Table 2 shows additional reductions for priority contaminants, including benzene, toluene, ethylbenzene and total xylenes (BTEX).

Table 2:   Mass reduction for priority contaminants.

Mass reduction for priority contaminants		
Contaminant	Pre-treatment mass (kg)	S-ISCO reduction
Naphthalene	26,389	95 %
Benzene	30	85 %
Toluene	267	81 %
Ethylbenzene	348	75 %
Total Xylenes	1,028	60 %
BTEX	1,674	67 %
Total SVOCs and VOCs	40,621	90.3 %

4.2 Groundwater

4.2.1 Controlled desorption and destruction process
Analysis of groundwater for S-ISCO performance parameters, including IFT, electrolytic conductivity, and concentrations of sodium persulfate and TPH, as well as regular inspection of all on and off-site wells for the presence of either NAPL or the injected chemistry, confirmed that the S-ISCO desorption and destruction process proceeded in a safe, controlled and effective manner. At no time during injections was any indication of either the injected chemistry or the targeted contamination, including NAPL, solubilized NAPL, odours or sheen, observed in off-site groundwater.

4.2.2 Contaminant reductions
Groundwater samples from the nine on-site monitoring wells screened across the treatment interval (10–22 ft bgs) were analyzed before and after treatment. This data indicated that the S-ISCO treatment achieved the groundwater objective – asymptotic decreases in VOCs and naphthalene. VOC reductions included 92% for xylenes; 87% for benzene, the most toxic and mobile VOC at the site; 90% for ethylbenzene; and 91% for BTEX overall. 80% naphthalene reductions were also measured.

4.2.3 Soil gas contamination reductions
Soil vapor samples collected from three areas adjacent to the site were analyzed before (October 2010) and after (April 2011) injections. Because regular measurement of soil gas pressure indicated that the injected oxidant was not causing any measurable increase in pressure, additional rounds of vapor sampling during injections were deemed unnecessary. Reductions in soil gas concentrations are shown in Figure 6, and included 100% for benzene, ethylbenzene, and naphthalene. Improvement in soil gas contamination included

reductions at a sampling location more than 100 feet from the southeastern corner of the injection area, indicating that the effects of the treatment extended far beyond the immediate injection area.

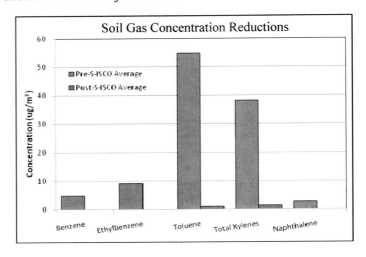

Figure 6:   Soil gas concentration reductions

5 Conclusion

During this project, VeruTEK's largest S-ISCO remediation to date, VeruTEK gained significant insight into the remedial process that will inform future successes. The following section summarizes these lessons.

6 Outcomes

This S-ISCO remediation marks the first time a Green Chemistry solution of this kind has been used to remediate MGP-related contamination in New York City and sets a precedent for the use of innovative technologies to achieve a COC within the state's Brownfield Cleanup Program. S-ISCO provided a low-impact solution that benefits the health and safety of the community and environment. Specifically this treatment:

- Destroyed contamination in place, avoiding digging and hauling thousands of truck-loads of contaminated soil through the community while preserving the stability of the subsurface and high-rise buildings on adjacent parcels;

- Prevented surrounding businesses and residents from exposure to dust and emissions related to large scale excavation, and also reduced soil gas contamination;

- Took place during a short time frame (five months), without disturbing the community; and

- Provided a permanent solution to site contamination, preparing the site for safe and productive reuse as a public library and park ranger station.

References

[1] Aikaterini Tsitonaki, Bejamin Petri, Micelle Crimi, Hans Mosbaek, Robert Siegrist, Poul L Bjerg. "In Situ Chemical Oxidation of Contaminated Soil and Groundwater Using Persulfate: A Review." Critical Reviews in in Environmental Science and Technology (2012): 40:1 55–90.

[2] Eric H. Weyand, Yung-Cheng Chen, Yun Wu, Aruna Kogati, Harold A Dunsford and Lews M. Rodriguez. "Differences in the Tumorogenic Activity of a Pure Hydrocarbon and a Complex Mixture following Ingestion: Benzo [a] pyrene vs. Manufactured Gas Plant Residue." Chem. Res. Toxicol. (1995): 949–954.

[3] Mackay, A. and Gschwend, P. "Enhanced Concentrations of PAHs in Groundwater at a Coal Tar Site." Environmental Science & Technology (2001): 35, 1320–1328.

[4] Ick Tae Yeom, Mriganka M. Ghosh, Chris D. Cox, Kevin G. Robinson. "Micellar Solubilziation of PAHs in Coal-Tar Contaminated Soils." Environmental Science and Technology (1995): 3015–3021.

[5] FMC Corporation, Oxidation of Organic Compounds at High pH., U.S. Patent No. 7,576,254. 18 August 2009.

[6] Hoag, G.E. and Collins, J.B., Soil Remediation Method and Composition. U.S. Patent No. 7,976,241 B2, 12 July 2011.

The scalable solution to recycling of end of life (EOL) printed wiring boards (PWBs)

T. Chen[1], P. Jiang[2], M. A. Harney[1], G. M. L. Lazarus[1], B. Chen[2],
Y. Song[2], H. Chen[2], G. L. Serke[1], G. M. Rose[1] & M. B. Korzenski[1]
[1]*Chief Technology Office, Advanced Technology Materials Inc., USA*
[2]*Chief Technology Office,*
Advanced Technology Materials Inc., P.R. China

Abstract

With <2% of the mass in US landfills, electronic waste (e-waste) accounts for 70% of hazardous materials. Approximately 5% by weight of e-waste consists of valuable secondary resource stock-printed wiring boards (PWBs). Those PWBs with high metal value are sold to overseas smelters and those PWBs with low value are sent to Asia or Africa where the integrated circuits (ICs) are manually desoldered and the trace precious metals are collected either by open burning or from chemical leaching with toxic chemicals such as hot aqua-regia and cyanide, which lead to environmental pollution and human exposure to hazardous chemicals. This paper reports novel cradle-to-cradle PWBs recycling processes and enhanced process efficiencies based on green chemistry and green engineering methodologies for the complete recycling of PWBs. We will describe that one can recover metals and valuable components from end-of-life (EOL) PWBs using cost effective, sustainable, and scalable methods. This includes both chemical desoldering and precious metal reclaim on ATMI's eVOLV™ PWBs recycling line.
Keywords: WEEE, e-waste, EOL, PWBs, green chemistry, green engineering, desoldering, gold leaching, ICs, recycling, valuable metals.

1 Introduction

Globally more than 50 million metric tons of waste from electrical and electronic equipment (WEEE), also known as electronic waste (e-waste) was disposed of in 2009 according to Zeller's [1] and Cobbing's reports [2]. This is expected to

WIT Transactions on Ecology and The Environment, Vol 173, © 2013 WIT Press
www.witpress.com, ISSN 1743-3541 (on-line)
doi:10.2495/SDP130561

grow to over 72 million metric tons by 2014. However less than 20% of all e-waste is recycled with the majority ending up in developing countries such as China, India, and Brazil. For example, a study by Bastiann *et al.* [3] in 2005 shows that the total supply of e-waste in the US was up to 6.6 million metric tons of which 20% was exported to Asia. Among all ten categories of WEEE listed in the Directive 2002/96/EC of the European Union (EU) [4], the volume of the end of life (EOL) printed wiring boards (PWBs) in electronics such as personal computers, mobile devices etc. grows exponentially due to the accelerated replacement of these IT and telecommunication equipment driven by the technical innovation and market expansion. As a matter of fact, the number of personal computer in use around the world, which is a major source of scrapped PWBs, has surpassed 1 billion in 2008, and they would become obsolete by 2013. Thus how to deal with EOL PWBs presents an ever growing waste management problem to the governments, the general public and companies.

Currently the main options for hierarchy management of e-waste including highly valuable EOL PWBs are reuse, remanufacturing and recycling as well as incineration and landfilling. However the incineration of EOL PWBs by traditional methods for municipal solid waste is dangerous. For example, copper in the laminated fiber glass composites based substrates of PWBs with embed flame-retardants is a catalyst for dioxin formation when they are incinerated. This is of particular concern for the incineration of brominated flame retardants such as polybrominated diphenyl ethers (PBDEs) at low temperature. To make things worse, it was estimated that emissions from incineration of certain components in e-waste such as integrated circuits (ICs), capacitors, liquid crystal displays and batteries on EOL PWBs, accounts for 36 metric tons per year of mercury and 16 metric tons per year of cadmium in the EU Community [5].

In the meantime, the last place for these EOL PWBs is a landfill because of the valuable resources in them such as metals (copper, nickel, lead, tin, gold, silver, platinum, and palladium) that could be recycled and reused. For example, it has been reported by Cui *et al.* that the values of copper, silver, and gold alone make up >80% of the total value for most EOL PWBs, which is also confirmed by our own assay analyses. Sulliven [7] reported one ton of used mobile phones (~6000 handsets – a small fraction of the nearly 1 billion annual production) contains 340 g of gold, ~3.5 kg of silver, 140 g of palladium and 130 kg of copper with a combined value of $28,000 (~$2.5 billion total). Global revenues for e-waste recovery are expected to grow to $14.6 billion by 2014 according to Zeller [1]. In addition, while <2% of the mass in US landfills, e-waste accounts for 70% of the heavy metals pollution [8]. And there are adverse environmental impacts of those heavy metals such as lead and mercury in landfills. As a result, a national e-waste strategy was unveiled in US this year that promotes environmentally friendly management of used electronics [9].

There is a general three-step process of recovering the valuable metals in PWBs described by Cui and Roven [6], step 1 – disassembly: a selective disassembly by sorting out both hazardous and valuable components is performed here, step 2 – upgrading: either mechanical processing and/or metallurgical processing is applied to prepare the sorted PWBs for the final refining processes. Step 3 – refining: recovered metals from steps 1 and 2 are melted or dissolved and separated by using metallurgical and chemical techniques, including pyrometallurgical and hydrometallurgical processing. In step 2, mechanical processing such as comminution of EOL PWBs is environmentally friendly except for the potential particular hazards. However its major drawback is the poor recovery of valuable metals in a later refining process (step 3) due to the loss of them during the size reduction step in such a comminution step reported by Ogunniyi and Vermaak [10]. While in step 3, pyrometallurgical process including incineration, smelting in a plasma arc furnace or blast furnace, dross formation, sintering, melting, and reactions in a gas phase at high temperatures arc are commonly applied to both the whole feed stream undergoing minimum mechanical processing or crushed EOL PWBs. However the hazard of releasing toxic furans, dioxins, and noxious gases to the environment is severe and the handling/abatement of the gaseous pollutants is expensive. As compared with pyrometallurgical processing, the hydrometallurgical method is more exact, more predictable, and more easily controlled. As a result, hydrometallurgical processes have been developed in the past two decades and become a very attractive process for recovery of metals from EOL PWBs as reported by Gloe et al. [11] and Ogata and Nakano [12]. However, standard hydrometallurgical processes dissolve all components in, for example, a strong acid and then selectively remove the specific elements of interest. While the dissolution step is simple, selectively removing each component from the mixture in high yield is a complex and time consuming challenge. In addition, numerous studies have been carried out to evaluate the exposure of toxic substances from some informal recycling activities in developing countries, such as China, India, and Nigeria. The level of toxins such as acids released using environmentally unfriendly chemicals in such a hydrometallurgical process is very high in some informal recycling activities. For example, e-waste recycling in Guiyu, China, has been reported by Guo et al. [13] to result in the contamination of the entire region, pervading the water, air, soil, and biota of the region.

Alternatively in a hydrometallurgical process, one may use more complex chemical formulations to selectively dissolve individual metals from EOL PWBs and ICs thereby simplifying the overall recycling process in both steps 2 and 3 mentioned above. Building on its 25-year knowledge-base of developing chemistries for the fabrication of semiconductors, ATMI has been using the principles of Green Chemistry and Green Engineering pioneered by Anastas and Warner [14] and Anastas and Zimmerman [15] on both silicon wafer reclaim reported by Korzenski and Jiang [16] and in-line cleaning of immersion lithography tools reported by Chen et al. [17]. We recently have demonstrated a proprietary all wet cleantech solution – eVOLV^{TM} [18] to retrieve ICs that could be reused or further recycled and to extract surface gold from selectively dissembled EOL PWBs in a safe, environmentally sound and economic manner. A schematic diagram of the process is shown in fig. 1. EOL PWBs pass on a conveyer system from a desoldering module to a gold leaching module or vice versa. ICs are collected and clean boards emerge at the end of process line. In the meantime, all of the chemistry and the rinse water are recycled for reuse in the process. Note that no mechanical processing such as commonly used shredding or grinding is required in ATMI's PWBs recycling process which may lead to the loss of up to 40% of precious metals and/or to the formation of dangerous metal fines, dust containing brominated flame retardants, and dioxins.

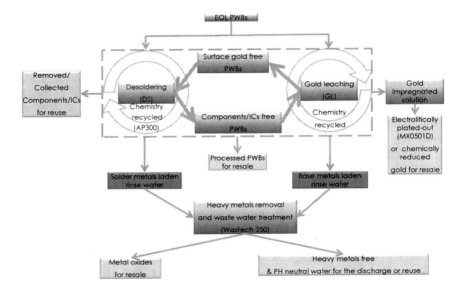

Figure 1: The process flow of ATMI's PWBs recycling technology (the process flow on eVOLV™ PWBs recycling line is in the dotted-line box, all outputs/value streams are in green).

2 Experimental section

2.1 Materials and chemicals

The EOL PWBs samples were purchased or collected from certified e-waste recyclers in the US. Nitric acid, hydrochloric acid were purchased from Aldrich and used as received. All the EOL PWBs were processed either on the ATMI's eVOLV™ PWBs recycling line (fig. 2) or in beakers.

The gold impregnated gold leaching (GL) solution was electrolytically deposited on a 3D carbon cathode on a MX0501D plating tool from Renovare international Inc. (fig. 3). The free acids in ATMI's proprietary desoldering (DS) chemistry can be reclaimed on AP300 from MechChem associates Inc. (fig. 3). The solder/heavy metals laden solutions were treated on WasTech250 system from WasTech Controls and Engineering Inc. (fig. 3).

Figure 2:   The front view of ATMI's eVOLV™ PWBs recycling line.

2.2 Samples preparations and metrologies

To prepare powder samples for the assay experiments, components such as capacitors, liquid crystal displays, and batteries on PWBs which are usually rich in hazardous substances were first removed from the boards before comminution in SM 200 and ZM 300 from Retsch consecutively.

The thickness of immersion gold layers on the surface of EOL PWBs was measured on a Rigaku ZSX 400 WDXRF (Wavelength dispersive X-ray fluorescence) spectrometer. The concentrations of metals ions (Ag, Au, Cu, Ni, Pb, Sn, Pd, Pt, Fe and Zn) in solution were measured on a PerkinElmer Optima 5300DV ICP-OES (Inductively coupled plasma atomic emission spectroscopy) instrument. The concentrations of anions in ATMI's proprietary DS and GL formulations were measured either on a Dionex ICS-2100 ion chromatography instrument or a CARY 50 UV-Vis spectrometer from Varian.

Figure 3:   From left to right: the front view of the electroplating tool – MX0501D, the front view of 2 modules of the acids reclaim tool – AP300 and the front view a module of the heavy metals removal and waste water treatment tool – WasTech 250.

3   Results and discussion

3.1 Desoldering step of ATMI's EOL PWBs recycling process

All ICs and components (capacitors, resistors, heat sinks, connectors, etc.) on as-received PWBs are chemically desoldered in two consecutive desolder modules on ATMI's eVOLV™ PWBs recycling line. This step requires less than 20 minutes immersion of EOL PWBs such as RAM (random access memory) boards, PCI (peripheral component interconnect) video cards, hard drives in an acidic solution at a temperature between 30 and 40 °C. The solid outputs of this step are components free PWBs and removed components including fully functional ICs.

ATMI's proprietary DS chemistry is highly selective towards both Pb/Sn and Sn/Ag solders while leaving copper, gold, etc. on the board and other base metal components intact. Note in fig. 4 that the gold connectors and even the stickers on sample B after the DS step remain intact on the board visually. Further comparison between the measured thickness of gold layers between as-received sample A and desoldered sample B using XRF in fig. 5 shows no measurable difference, demonstrating the good selectivity of the DS chemistry towards different valuable metals. This is highly advantageous as compared to commonly used hot aqua regia in traditional hydrometallurgical processes because the absence of solder metals after ATMI's DS process (fig. 1) in the previous metals refining process simplifies the recovery efforts and increases the resale values of processed components and solders free PWBs. At the same time, ATMI's DS process also reduces any potential human exposure towards toxic Pb containing

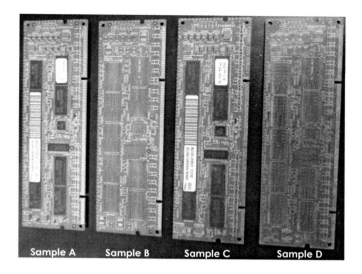

Figure 4:   Pictures of RAM boards processed on ATMI's eVOLV™ PWBs recycling line: A. As-received boards, B. desoldered boards (the removed components are not included), C. surface gold leached boards, D. desoldered and surface gold leached boards (the removed components are not included).

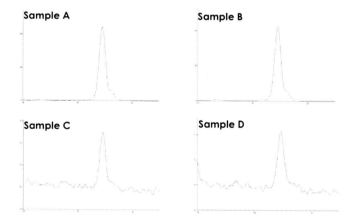

Figure 5:   The XRF spectra of surface gold on RAM boards processed on ATMI's eVOLV™ PWBs recycling line (Au peak intensities in counts vs. 2θ in degree): A. As-received boards, B. desoldered boards, C. surface gold leached boards, D. desoldered and surface gold leached boards.

species during processing as compared to pyrometallurgical approaches in traditional refining process. The removed solder materials, mainly Pb/Sn alloys, is dissolved in ATMI's proprietary DS chemistry first before being converted and collected as a metal oxide salt on the heavy metals removal and waste water treatment tool WasTech 250 and resold.

The bath of ATMI's proprietary DS chemistry can be monitored using both ICP-OES and IC techniques in real time until it is loaded to over 250 g per liter. Furthermore, both DS chemistry and the rinse water are recycled multiple times (fig. 1). The electrical tests of the desoldered chips by a third party institute show that they are still operational and thus may be reused. Given that manufacturing a single 2 g chip uses 1.6 kg of fossil fuels, 72 g of chemicals, 32 kg of water and 700 g of gases reported by Williams *et al.* [19], this is a tremendous environmental and economic savings.

3.2 Gold leaching step of ATMI's EOL PWBs recycling process

The now solder-free components-free PWBs after the desoldering process are subjected to a non-toxic, environmentally benign ATMI's proprietary GL chemistry in the GL module on ATMI's eVOLV^{TM} PWBs recycling line at 30 °C for approximately 5-10 min (depending on composition and thickness of surface gold), which selectively removes all gold together with other precious metals such as silver, palladium, etc. Visually sample D in fig 4 is a components/ICs free, surface gold free bare board. The >98% leaching efficiency of gold in this gold leaching step is further verified by the dramatic difference between the measured thickness of gold layers between as-received sample A and gold leached samples C and D using XRF shown in fig. 5. It is clear that there is little to no gold residue on the surface of PWBs after the gold leaching process on ATMI's eVOLV^{TM} PWBs recycling line, which is further confirmed by little detected gold in ICP-OES measurements of the same type of gold leached PWBs digested in hot aqua regia. Furthermore, the good selectivity of ATMI's proprietary GL chemistry over solder and other base metals is manifested by the components/ICs intact sample C that underwent gold leaching process only and visible nickel/copper underlayers on both samples C and D in fig. 4. This merit of GL chemistry allows flexible and modulated desoldering and gold leaching process flows on ATMI's eVOLV^{TM} PWBs recycling line despite of the process sequence shown in fig. 1. The bath life of this chemistry can also be monitored by UV-Vis technique while the dissolved gold in ATMI's proprietary GL chemistry can be monitored by ICP-OES technique in real time and eventually be reclaimed electrolytically on MX0501D (fig. 3) or hydrometallurgically via a chemical reduction process demonstrated at a bench scale before being sold for its value.

Alternatively, the ICs collected after ATMI's desoldering process may be ground and the trace precious metals, mainly gold, are extracted using ATMI's proprietary GL chemistry in the GL module on ATMI's eVOLV^{TM} PWBs recycling line mentioned above.

After rinsing, the clean printed wiring boards may be chopped and the copper collected and sold. We have demonstrated >99% copper recovery with >99.5%

purity, which have also been confirmed by an independent testing laboratory. Because no solder or base metals are present, the value of these processed PWBs is very high. The remaining chopped fiberglass may be used as filler in, for example, cement.

4 Summary

The entire PWBs recycling process flow in fig. 1 has been validated by reclaiming metals and components/ICs from several tons of EOL PWBs (TV, computer, cell phone, etc.) on ATMI's eVOLV^{TM} PWBs recycling line that is closed so that no volatiles escape (fig. 2). This pilot system has been scaled to handle up to 250 lbs per hour of high value PWBs (RAM boards, PCI video cards, hard drives, CPUs (central processing units)) and all of the chemistry is recycled for reuse in the process. This system is being used to further optimize both the chemistry and the process flow for a wider range of PWBs and to refine the process economic models. Water discharged from ATMI's eVOLV^{TM} PWBs recycling line is treated on WasTech 250, has less than part-per-million trace metals and no organics. It fully meets the discharge criteria from Connecticut department of energy and environment protection in the US (table 1) and can potentially be reused in the PWBs recycling process.

Table 1:   The PHs and trace metal concentrations in two different streams of rinse water from ATMI's eVOLV^{TM} PWBs recycling line before and after the treatment on WasTech 250.

The type of the waste water	The volume of the waste water (gallons)	Before the treatment								Before the final discharge							
		PH	Trace metals (ppm)							PH	Trace metals (ppm)						
			Ag	Cu	Fe	Ni	Pb	Sn	Zn		Ag	Cu	Fe	Ni	Pb	Sn	Zn
DS rinse water	200	2.6	0	0.3	1.4	0.6	1.3	0.1	0.1	8.6	0	0	0.2	0	0	0	0
GL rinse water	200	1.44	0.09	2.3	18	80	2.8	2.5	1.3	9	0.1	0	0	0.8	0	0	0

Acknowledgements

We thank Dr Larry Dubois at ATMI for useful discussions, Guangcai Mark Wang at ATMI for the assistance of the procurement of EOL PWBs, Jessica Broccoli for the build-up of formulation scale-up unit/transfer pumps and Dr Jun-fei Zheng at ATMI for XRF measurements.

References

[1] Zeller, T., *A Program to Certify Electronic Waste Recycling Rivals an Industry – U.S. Plan*, New York Times, April 15, 2010.

[2] Cobbing, M., *Not in Our Backyard. Uncovering the Hidden Flows of e-Waste*, Report from Greenpeace International, http://www.greenpeace.org/international/en/publications/reports, 2008.

[3]   Bastiaan, C., Zoeteman, J., Krikke, H.R. and Venselaar, J., *Handling WEEE waste flows: on the effectiveness of producer responsibility in a globalizing world*, International Journal of Advanced Manufacturing Technology 47, 415–436, 2010.

[4]   European Parliament and the Council of the European Union, *Directive 2002/96/EC of the European Parliament and of the Council of 27 January 2003 on waste electrical and electronic equipment (WEEE)*, Official Journal of the European Union, L37, 24–38, 2003.

[5]   Draft proposal for a European Parliament and Council directive on waste electrical and electronic equipment, European Commission Report Brussels, 2000.

[6]   Cui, J., and Roven, H. J. *Electronic waste*, From Waste: A Handbook for Management, eds. Letcher, T. M., Vallero, D. A., pp. 281–296, 2011.

[7]   Sullivan, D.E., *Recycled Cell Phones – A Treasure Trove of Valuable Metals*, http://pubs.usgs.gov/fs/2006/3097/fs2006-3097.pdf.

[8]   *Computers, E-Waste, and Product Stewardship: Is California Ready for the Challenge*, Report for the US Environmental Protection Agency, Region IX, pp. 13, May 11, 2001.

[9]   Mukhopadhyay, R., *National e-waste strategy unveiled*, Chemical and Engineering News, 89, pp. 28, 2011.

[10] Ogunniyi, I.O., and Vermaak, M.K.G., 2007. *Improving printed circuit board physical processing – an overview*, Proceedings of European Metallurgical Conference, Dusseldorf, Germany, pp. 1645–1656, June 11–14, 2007.

[11] Gloe, K., Muhl, P. and Knothe, M., *Recovery of Precious Metals from Electronic Scrap, in Particular from Waste Products of the Thick-Layer Technique*, Hydrometallurgy 25, 99–110, 1990.

[12] Ogata, T., and Nakano, Y., *Mechanisms of gold recovery from aqueous solutions using a novel tannin gel adsorbent synthesized from natural condensed tannin*, Water Research, 39, 4281–4286, 2005.

[13] Guo, Y., Huang, C.J., Zhang, H., and Dong, Q. X., *Heavy Metal Contamination from Electronic Waste Recycling at Guiyu Southeastern China*, Journal of Environmental Quality, 2009.

[14] Anastas, P., and Warner, J. C., *Green Chemistry: Theory and Practice;* Oxford University Press Inc., New York 1998.

[15] Anastas, P., and Zimmerman, J., Env. Sci. and Tech. 37, 94, 2003.

[16] Korzenski, M., and Jiang, P., *Wafer reclaim*, Handbook of cleaning for semiconductor manufacturing, eds. Reinhardt, K. A., and Reidy, R. F., pp. 473–499, 2011.

[17] Chen, T., Korzenski, M. B., Bilodeau, S., Zhang, P., Hogan, T., van Berkel, K., Mirth, G., Mih, R., Hoekerd, K., Jansen, B., Vangheluwe, R., and Schuh, N, *Environmentally benign in-line cleaning solutions for immersion lithography tools*, Solid State Phenomena, 187, pp. 307–310, 2012.

[18] Korzenski, M. B., Jiang, P., Norman, J., Warner, J., Ingalls, L., Gnanamgari, D., Strickler, F., and Mendum, T., *Sustainable process for*

reclaiming precious metals and base metals from electronic waste, PCT Int. Appl. WO2012024603, 2012.

[19] Williams, E. D., Ayres, R. U. and Heller, M., *The 1.7 Kilogram Microchip: Energy and Material Use in the Production of Semiconductor Devices*, Environ. Sci. Technol. 36, pp. 5504–5510, 2002.

Cause analysis of low collection rate of Chinese waste paper

H. Feng & S. Tomonari
Graduate School of Environment and Energy Engineering,
Waseda University, Japan

Abstract

As waste paper is gradually becoming an important material in paper making with the calling for promoting a sustainable society, waste paper reuse comes to be an important issue nowadays. The collection rate is an index to measure the effectiveness of the domestic collection of waste paper resources used for recycling. Countries likes Germany, Korean, Japan, lead in this field. However, the Chinese collection rate is very low compared with these developed countries. This paper tries to figure out the real reasons behind such phenomenon by analyzing a case of Xishui County in Central China based on a series of field research and interviews. It is found that the recycling behaviours of households are driven by money, and the main reason for none-recycling is the inconvenience of the recycling service and facilities. Also it appears that age is significantly correlated with recycling frequency, and old people tend to more actively engage in paper recycling. Subsequently, related plans are proposed and finally evaluated.
Keywords: waste paper, collection rate, paper recycling, cause analysis, China, case study.

1 Introduction

Paper recycling is gradually becoming a hot issue in developing countries nowadays and greatly helps in building a circular economy to promote a sustainable society. It will reduce energy consumption by 40% (Energy information administration claims) [1] or by 64% (Bureau of International Recycling claims) [2] and drawdown the use of landfill (Recycling 1 ton of

WIT Transactions on Ecology and The Environment, Vol 173, © 2013 WIT Press
www.witpress.com, ISSN 1743-3541 (on-line)
doi:10.2495/SDP130571

newspaper eliminates 3 cubic meters of landfill) [3], and lessens 35% water pollution and 74% air pollution [4].

In recycling, the collection rate is an important index to circulate the actual effectiveness of resource collection before running into utilization procedure. Currently, collection rates of waste paper differ among countries, varying between 21% and 91% in 2009 [5]. Generally speaking, the rate is relatively lower in developing countries. The Chinese waste paper collection rate is low, compared with South Korea, Germany, and the UK. The rate in China was 45.74% in 2010 (by the end of 2010) [6]. However, situations differ in areas. In the eastern part of China, the economy is more developed and the collection rate is higher than other regions. In contrast, the western region is relatively poor in economy as well as collection rate, especially in the rural villages, and the situation in central areas is moderate [7].

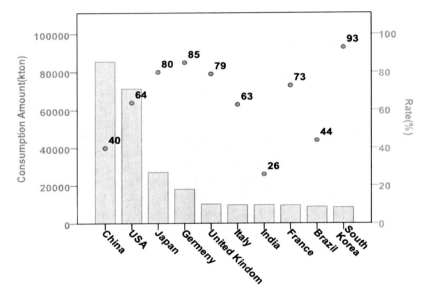

Figure 1: Collection rate of waste paper in countries (year 2009) [8].

This paper is a part from one chapter of one of the author's doctoral thesis – *"Analysis of Low Collection Rate of China's Waste Paper Resources from Policy Aspect"*. The idea is to find three different cases – Eastern Metropolis, Central County, Western village – in China to analyse the collection rate situation and the reasons for low collection according to the "Three Region" view, which was first proposed in the nation's seventh five-year plan to demarcate economic regions in China in 1985 [9], and is still commonly used now. The division is at the most advanced region; the east coast, and followed by the central region and the poorest; the western region. As far as waste paper collection is concerned, the situation is different in regions. Not only is there a huge economical gap between the eastern and western parts of China, but also there is a great difference of income between the rural and urban areas inside each region. This calls for further dividing into the metropolis in the eastern region, county in the central region and village in the western region for the research.

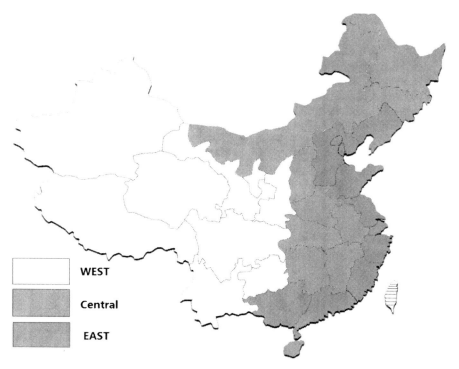

WEST

Central

EAST

Figure 2:   "Three Regions" divisions of China.

Xishui is the selected case representing counties in the central part of China, firstly because it is the central area in the central region. It is called the "Water and Land Hub" of eastern Hubei Province, and has location superiority. Secondly, because its economical level is, on average, far away behind big cities but better than small villages in the central region. It is strong for its agriculture and the primary industry takes up to 37.13% of the whole county's economy. Nowadays, the secondary industry is experiencing a rapid development. The gross domestic production per capita is 8,226 RMB in 2008. The permanent population was 872,650 in November 2010.

2   Waste paper recycling situations

Interviews were taken at local government administrations, companies, former industry associations and schools in February 2012, sponsored by the International Environment Leader program of Waseda University [10].

Unlike developed countries, there are no special statistics about waste paper recycling situation in China. To find the Chinese waste paper collection rate, especially in inland counties, it's more difficult. The waste paper collection rate in the county is estimated at 45% by professionals.

2.1 Recycling cultures

In Xishui County, most household recyclable paper is thrown away sporadically. Recycling only occurs among people who want to sell waste paper and waste paper trade agencies. Waste paper becomes tradable merchandise and recycling turns out to be an economic behaviour in the local area. Lack of knowledge of waste recycling results in a lot of waste paper being mixed with other refuse and dumped outside. This is consistent with the local waste disposal channel. Large proportions of waste mixed with household waste paper are discarded on the street. Sanitation workers are generally divided into 2 people a team. One street has two teams. Teams have two shifts in one day. The garbage truck will come to the working street four times a day, deliver waste to the nearly mid-point (in total 7). Waste is gathered there and is transport to the only landfill site in the county.

Figure 3:   Waste disposal network in Xishui County [11].

Local government has no awareness of paper recycling; there is no requirement for local paper recycling; there are no statistics of waste paper collection, no regulations, and no public recycling facilities. In fact, there is a resource reuse association in the county, but it is established by a local supply agency (collectively owned company), and huge attention is paid to metals rather than paper.

2.2 Waste paper flow

Waste paper generates from offices, schools, households, department stores and streets. Waste paper in offices, schools, and stores is collected by collecting companies. As far as household waste paper is concerned, some is collected by companies, but a large proportion is discarded on curb sides. Other street waste paper is mainly paper packages, and leaflets thrown by pedestrians.

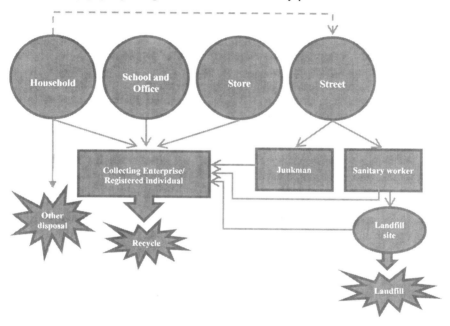

Figure 4: Waste paper flow in Xishui county.

The local waste paper collection presents a "pull–push" model. Waste paper principally generates from houses, schools, offices and department stores. Waste paper in schools, offices, stores are in a huge amount, of good quality and the collection is more intensive and convenient. Benefit drives collecting companies and individuals wild about onsite acquisition. However, collecting from households is more sporadic, costly, lower quality, so it is less attractive to collecting companies. Although local households are willing to have their waste to be sold, a lot is dumped on curb sides, seldom recycled, and are mainly mixed in with the other rubbish and go to landfill as there are no incineration facilities in the county.

2.3 Waste paper businesses

There are 6,872 tons of recovered paper resources amounting to 4.81 million RMB (estimated in 2005) according to the *"Report of Renewable Resource Industry in Xishui County (Aug. 2006)"* [12].

No company specializes in paper collecting. According to the data given by the Registration Branch, Xishui County, there are 248 privately owned enterprises and 100 self-employed individuals registered to run recycling businesses in Xishui County. However, there is no classified information on each field, like paper, metal, etc. No companies specialize in paper collecting; they all have a comprehensive collecting range, usually including metals, machinery, electronics and plastics [13].

In addition, it is easy to enter into the business, because low knowledge and start up capital is required. There are two kinds of people engaging in the waste paper collecting business; one is the people who have no business license, and are mostly lowly-educated. The other is the enterprise scale. Normally, it is cheap to start the business; only 10,000 to 20,000 RMB are needed for the capital turnover at the initial stage, according to Mr Qiushi Chai, the president of Xinfa Renewable Resources Company and former chairman of Resources Recycling Association of Xishui County.

There is a strong necessity of improving the governmental service. One can hardly tell who is running a waste paper collection business from the information on the registration database and a lot of information is missing. Registration items required in the form are, for a privately owned enterprise: registration level, name of enterprise, address, registration capital, scope of business, registration authority, jurisdiction authority, legal representative, establishment date; for the individual, a telephone number, bank account, fixed capital, working capital, employee, nationality and political status are added. But almost all of these detailed items are left blank. 61.39% of the self-employed are currently in the term of validity, which implies the data still needs updating. The validity date shows that privately own companies last longer than self-employed individuals.

Collecting companies are mostly small scale; since for both privately owned enterprises and individuals, registration capital is not a must. 10.08% of privately owned enterprises, their registration capital (although 22.98% of the companies' information is missing) is more than 0.5 million RMB, which is a big scale by county level, for 18.81% of individuals, the fixed assets are greater than 0.1 million.

2.4 Summary

Waste paper collecting is neither a spontaneous obligated activity nor a mandatory activity regulated by the local administrations. High cost, and inconvenient channel leads household recyclable paper to become mixed with garbage dumped on the street, finally going to landfill. There are no companies specializing in paper recycling. It is easy to enter the local recycling business; people running these businesses are mostly self-employed; enterprise scales are small. Awareness should be aroused to improve the administrative service and enhance paper recycling related regulation.

3 Questionnaire survey of household waste paper collection

The questionnaires were designed to survey local households on waste paper collection in Xishui County. The questions were mainly about the residents' attitude towards waste paper collection and their collection activities, and were taken among the local residents living in downtown of Xishui County.

Among 50 questionnaires (one is invalid), there were 28 men (57.14%) and 21 women (42.86%). Age range was from 10 to 81; the median age being 39. The level of education was divided into 4 levels: primary school or below (6); middle school (5); senior high (11); college or above (27), which were 12.24%, 10.20%, 22.45%, and 55.10% respectively.

3.1 Awareness

When asking the question "Do you think waste paper is a kind of resource and can be reused?" 79.59% of people answered "yes", while 21.41% of people said they don't have such kind of awareness. However, when combining it with the previous question, there are actually 65.31% of people who have recycling activities (including 4.08% of people who either mix throw or wait for home acquisition). So why do 14.28% have consciousness to recycle but end up with non-recycling activities? Do they cheat on the question or just have another reason behind the situation?

3.2 Behaviours

When answering the question, "How often do you usually do paper recycling?" 46.94% people answered "sometimes", 24.49% said "always", 16.33% replied "seldom", and 12.24% answered "never". This shows that a large proportion of people say they are engaging in waste paper recycling "sometimes" or "always", and it seems a relatively high frequency.

When asked "Which ways of disposal do you choose for waste paper?" 55.10% of people said they wait for scrap collectors to have a door to door collection. However, 36.73% of people just mix waste paper with other garbage like food residue, plastic packages, and then throw it away. Minorities choose to directly sell to the waste product collecting station (12.24%) or for incineration (4.08%).

3.3 Motivations

With the question "What facilitates you to recycle paper?", the largest proportion (52.02%) gave the reason for recycling as being motivated by money – "sell for money and make profit" – followed by 48.98% of people give environmental concerns, and 34.65% are for saving resources. Still 6.12% of people replied that there is nowhere for them to throw, so they recycle, and 4.08% of people gave no answer.

People of no awareness who said that "waste paper are resources and can be reused" have recycling activities which are mostly economically motivated. Six out of 10 who don't recycle paper said they do it for money (60%). And other reasons are environmental protection (30%), saving resources (10%), nowhere to throw (10%), no answer (10%).

The main reason that people don't achieve their recycling behaviours is that "they couldn't wait for the home acquisition collectors to arrive" (26.53%); "the process of assortment is very troublesome" (24.49%); "the acquisition price is low" (15.38%); and "waste paper is garbage" (15.38%).

The reason why people who have an awareness that "waste paper is a resource and can be reused" but who end up not pursing recycling is mainly because they "they couldn't wait for the home acquisition collectors to arrive" (30.77%); "the process of assortment is very troublesome" (23.08%). Other reasons are "the acquisition price is low" (7.69%), and "waste paper is garbage" (10.26%). In addition, 12 people didn't reply to this question (comprising 30.77%). By segmenting by frequency of recycling, among them, 41.67% are "sometimes" and 41.67% are "always". So it may be that the reason they are actually recycling frequently is there is no reason for them not to recycle.

3.4 Influencing variables testing

Taking "frequency" as the dependent variable y, "age", "gender", "education level" and "consciousness" as the independent variable x, we found a strong correlation between "age" and "frequency", but no significant correlation between "gender" and "frequency", "education" and "frequency", and "conscious" and "frequency".

Table 1:   Definition of variables.

Variables	Definition	Description
Frequency (y)	Numerical variable	X=1,2,3,4
Age (x_1)	Numerical variable	X=1,2,3...
Gender (x_2)	Dummy variables	X=0,1 (0-"female", 1-"male")
Education level (x_3)	Numerical variable	X=1,2,3,4
Consciousness (x_4)	Dummy variables	X=0,1 (0-"not have", 1-"have")

Table 2:   Regression of coefficient.

	Coefficients	Standard Error	t Stat	P-value
Intercept	1.177128	0.659507493	1.784859	0.081179
Age	0.0307588	0.011805094	2.605554	0.012468
Gender	-0.302278	0.283012712	-1.06807	0.291313
Education level	0.0690172	0.133761604	0.515972	0.608457
Consciousness	0.3871775	0.347453295	1.11433	0.271188

4 Proposal

The main obstacle to paper recycling in the county is the problem of the inconvenience of waste paper acquisition from households. To solve this problem the motivations of collecting companies should be stimulated; that is to promote an intensive collection service. Not only will it help to improve paper quality, but also it might reduce inconvenience for households. Thus three plans are made based on the previous analysis and the pros and cons are given as follows.

4.1 Plan A: government monopoly

This refers to the local government enforcing a strict intensive collecting scheme. Drawing an example from Japan – specific acquisition in a fixed period. The Government unifies the whole collection. No money will be paid to households.

Advantage: extreme time and cost-saving; also effective. It will work well especially in the long run as the waste paper recycling reward gradually disappears.

Disadvantage: less effective in the short term because a lot of households are motivated by money No competition through the market may lead to inefficiency. It will also cause unemployment of most self-employed people in the business.

4.2 Plan B: collecting company bidding

This refers to adopting a contracting system, that is, a collection enterprise can bid a selected area to provide an intensive collection service under governmental control.

Advantage: good for collecting companies; they are more efficient and effective because of the possibility of launching an intensive collection in which they won the bidding.

Disadvantage: regional monopoly will lead to a loss of consumer surplus, and it will finally lead to fewer collections in the long run. It will cause unemployment of most self-employed people who are currently engaged in the business.

4.3 Plan C: government accommodation

Make accommodative policy for enterprises to establish a door-to-door acquisition or other convenient recycling logistics and facilities by giving subsidies or making them tax free and so on. Then, after a certain time, back to normal, and let the market regulate itself.

Advantage: good for development of the industry and also employment and the livelihood of rag pickers; sustainable in the long run.

Disadvantage: seldom has an effect in the short run.

4.4 Other policies

Policies that should accompany the proposed plan, such as prohibiting illegal dumping, implementing a waste paper grade and recycling classified standard, improving recycling facilities, like a Recycle Bin, creating a household recycle training program, increasing knowledge of recycling to the public, enhancing environment education since formative education period. Above all, local authorities should target younger generations as old people are actually the active paper recycling group.

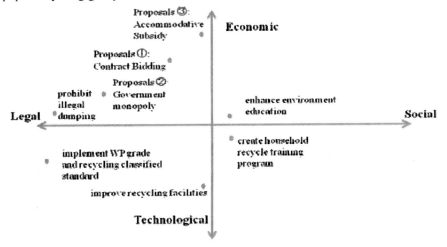

Figure 5:   Proposals and policies.

References

[1]   Energy Information Administration, Saving Energy Recycling Paper and Glass. Recycling Paper and Glass 2006(9).
[2]   Bureau of International Recycling. Information about Recycling. September 27, 2007.
[3]   Sudbury, Jodi B. *50 Simple Things You Can Do to Save the Earth. Berkeley* CA: Earthworks Press 1989.
[4]   US Environmental Protection Agency. Recycle on the Go: Basic Information. October 18, 2007.
[5]   Paper Recycling Promotion Center. International recycling paper situation working papers 2010.March.
[6]   China Paper Association (2011): *Annual report of China Papermaking Industry in Year 2010*, http://www.chinappi.org/.
[7]   Weiliang Li, Measures toward paper recycle in Zhejiang Province. Chinese and Japanese Recovered Paper Seminar, October 11, 2011.
[8]   Feng Hua, Tomonari Shinichi, *Analysis of China's Current Waste Paper Collection Rate*. ECO Design 2011 proceeding, pp. 852-855, 2011.

[9]   China State Council, Seventh Five-year Plan, October, 1985.
[10] Japan Science and Technology Agency, International Environment Leader program, http://www.jst.go.jp/shincho/en/program/kankyou.html
[11] Google Earth, 2012 Kingway Ltd, 2012 Mapabc.com, 2012 Cnes/Spot Image.
[12] Resources Recycling Association of Xishui County, *Report of Renewable Resource Industry in Xishui County,* August. 2016.
[13] Registration Branch of Industry and Commerce Administration Bureau of Xishui county, Information Inquiry System.

Potential of crude oil-degrading bacteria to co-resist heavy metals in soil

S. Mustafa, A. Al-Douseri, K. Majki & E. Al-Saleh
Department of Biological Sciences, Faculty of Science, Kuwait University, Kuwait

Abstract

The toxicity and adverse effects of crude oil pollution entail a quick clean-up using available competent technologies such as bioremediation. One factor affecting the bioremediation of crude oil is the presence of stressors such as heavy metals that halt the biodegradative potentials of the indigenous microbiota resulting in prolonged bioremediation and the accumulation of toxic hydrocarbons in the environment. Thus, it was considered sensible to investigate the potentials of the indigenous microbiota to resist the inhibitory effects of heavy metals (Al, Cd, Co, Hg and Ni) in soil. For this purpose, the tolerance of crude oil-degrading bacteria isolated from three different soils to heavy metals was investigated. Results demonstrated that bacteria isolated from the old crude oil-contaminated site and the recently heavy metal-contaminated construction sites that harbored high concentrations of heavy metals showed significantly ($P<0.05$) higher tolerance to heavy metals compared to those isolated from pristine soil. Furthermore, longer co-existence of bacteria with heavy metals resulted in higher bacterial potentials to tolerate the inhibitory effects of heavy metals where the majority of the isolates exhibited multiple resistances to heavy metals especially to Co and Ni. However, all heavy metals tested, in particular, Hg, Co and Ni showed lethal effects at elevated concentrations.
Keywords: pollution, crude oil-degrading bacteria, crude oil, heavy metals, bioremediation, minimum inhibitory concentration.

1 Introduction

Pollution of soil environment has become a serious problem in many countries; heavy metals (HM) and crude oil are two of the most abundant and potentially

WIT Transactions on Ecology and The Environment, Vol 173, © 2013 WIT Press
www.witpress.com, ISSN 1743-3541 (on-line)
doi:10.2495/SDP130581

harmful pollutants [1]. They are frequently found together as co-contaminants in soils [2]. Heavy metals occur in crude oil partly as organo-metallic compounds [3]. Beside their natural occurrence, they may enter the ecological environment through anthropogenic activities [1]. These pollutants affect the activity of soil enzymes, which can be used to evaluate the soil microbial properties [2], such as Dehydrogenase and urease [1]. A variety of technologies are currently available to treat soil contaminated with hazardous materials [4]. However, bioremediation is the process whereby organic wastes are biologically degraded under controlled conditions to an innocuous state, or to levels below concentration limits [5]. Crude oil and heavy metals are often inhibitory to bioremediative processes [6]. Microorganisms including bacteria are the chief agents for the biodegradation of molecule of environmental concern [4]. Metals may inhibit pollutant biodegradation through interaction with enzymes directly involved in biodegradation or through interaction with enzymes involved in general metabolism [7]. Some bacteria sense the presence of toxic compounds and produce proteins that either convert the toxic compounds into non-harmful products, or extrude them out of the cell through methods such as extracellular precipitation, sequestration by cell envelops, intracellular accumulation, redux transformations, and membrane efflux system. Since certain metals are essential micronutrients, bacteria must adjust their resistance mechanisms to maintain appropriate levels of such compounds [8]. Bacteria which survive in such environments have developed or acquired genetic systems that counteract the effects of high metal ion concentrations [9]. Therefore, the current study was achieved to investigate the potential of the indigenous crude oil-degrading microbiota to resist the inhibitory effects of the heavy metals (Al, Cd, Co, Hg, and Ni) in soil.

2 Materials and methods

2.1 Collection of soil samples

Crude oil contaminated and uncontaminated soils were collected from Al-Ahmadi north of Kuwait, while the garden soil was collected from Kuwait University garden. Six samples of surface soils (10cm) were collected in sterile plastic containers, kept at 4°C and transported immediately to the lab for analyses. Soil samples were sieved (2mm) and stored for two weeks at 4°C for stabilization [10].

2.2 Determination of heavy metals concentration in soils

The method of Rowell [11] was employed for the determination of the total metal content in soil. This method consists of acid digestion of soil samples followed by analysis of the digest by flame atomic absorption spectrometer (FAAS).

2.3 Isolation and molecular identification of the isolated crude oil-degrading bacteria

Soil samples were sieved and (10 grams) were suspended in 40 ml distilled water and kept overnight. Aliquots (0.1 ml) of clear supernatant of soil suspension, indirect and its dilutions (10^{-1}–10^{-4}) were spread on minimal media plates containing droplets of crude oil which are then incubated at 30°C for up to 24 hours, and the grown crude oil-degrading bacterial colonies (CODB) were isolated [12]. Bacterial genomic DNA was extracted, purified, quantified and used for the amplification of the 16S rDNA gene, followed by DNA sequencing and Sequencing Analysis v5.2 Software (Applied Bisystem, USA) was used to analyze the sequences that were compared to other sequences in the GeneBank database using BLAST [13].

2.4 Effect of heavy metals on the growth of isolated bacteria

The potential inhibitory effects of heavy metals (aluminum, cadmium, cobalt, mercury and nickel) on the growth of crude oil degrading bacteria were determined using the agar well diffusion method and optical density measurements.

2.4.1 Agar well diffusion method
The method of Lertcanawanichakul and Sawangnop [14] was adopted. Stocked bacterial cultures were streaked on NA plates and incubated at 30°C for 24 hours. Grown bacterial cultures were transferred into sterile 15 ml Falcon tubes containing sterile 0.85% NaCl solution followed by adjusting the number of bacterial cells to 1.2 x 10^9 cells^{-1} ml using McFarland No. 0.5 as a standard solution. Then, aliquots (100 µl) of the prepared bacterial suspension were spread on the surface of NA plates, spread evenly and left for 30 min at room temperature. Then, wells (10 mm in diameter) were punched using sterile stainless steel cork borer. Prepared metal (Al, 50 mg^{-1} ml; Cd, 50 mg^{-1} ml; Co, 10 mg^{-1} ml; Hg, 10 mg^{-1} ml; Ni, 50 mg^{-1} ml) solutions were directly filled (50 µl) into the wells, plates incubated at 30°C for 24 hours and the diameter of the inhibition zones were measured in millimeters [14].

2.4.2 Optical density measurements of bacterial growth
Prepared bacterial suspensions used for the well diffusion method mentioned previously were used simultaneously for the optical density measurement method. For this purpose, bacterial suspension (50µl), sterile nutrient broth (50µl) and different concentrations of metal solutions (300 µl) were transferred to 100-well Honeycomb plates. Then, plates were incubated shaking at 30°C for 24 hours in automated optical density reader (600 nm). Determined optical density values were plotted against time followed by calculation of bacterial growth rates. Bacterial growth rates were used to determine the minimum inhibitory concentrations (MIC) for tested metals. MIC values were defined as the lowest concentration of tested metals that inhibited the growth of bacteria after 24 hours of incubation.

3 Results

3.1 Heavy metal content in soils

The concentrations of heavy metals in the crude oil-contaminated and construction sites were significantly higher than those in the pristine soil (Table 1). The highest concentration of metals was recorded for Ni followed by that of Co while the lowest concentration determined was that of Cd and Hg (Table 1). Also, the construction site harboured the highest concentrations of metals detected.

Table 1: Heavy metals content in soils.

Heavy metal	Heavy metal concentration (mg kg^{-1})		
	Crude oil-contaminated soil	Construction -site soil	Pristine soil
Cd	0.0142	0.0162	0.0023
Co	2.0113	4.8154	1.6767
Hg	0.0451	0.0621	0.0236
Ni	15.293	38.562	12.445
Al	5069	3967	1332

3.2 Identification of the isolated bacteria

A total of 76 crude oil-degrading bacteria were isolated from all soils. Isolated bacteria were identified by sequencing of the 16S rDNA gene. Four different bacteria genera were identified in the pristine soil compared to two genera identified in the crude oil-contaminated and the construction sites (Table 2).

Table 2: Identities of isolated crude oil-degrading bacteria.

Soil source	Identified bacteria	Number of bacteria found
Construction-site	Streptomyces scabiei strain	8
	Streptomyces sp.	8
	Streptomyces bellus strain	8
	Streptomyces lavendulocolor strain	1
	Arthrobacter oxydans strain	1
	Streptomyces glomeroaurantiacus strain	1
	Streptomyces rochei strain	1
	Streptomyces tumescens strain	1
	Streptomyces ghanaensis strain	1
	Total number of isolated strains = 30	
Crude oil-contaminated	Microbacterium sp.	11
	Staphylococcus sp	1
	Total number of isolated strains = 12	
Pristine soil	Microbacterium sp.	31
	Bacillus pumilus strain	1
	Streptomyces pseudogriseolus	1
	Mycobacterium goodii strain	1
	Total number of isolated strains = 34	

3.3 Effect of heavy metals on the growth of isolated bacteria

3.3.1 Agar well diffusion method

Bacterial tolerance to heavy metals was divided into three ranges based on the size of inhibition zone that is formed due to the reaction of the tested bacteria with heavy metals. Results showed that mercury exerted the highest toxic inhibitory effect on the growth of tested bacteria compared to other metals. On the other hand, aluminum showed the least toxic inhibitory effect (Table 3).

Table 3:   Effects of heavy metals on the growth of crude oil-degrading bacteria.

Number of bacteria tested (%)	Diameter of inhibition zone (cm)								
	Crude oil contaminated soil			Construction site soil			Pristine soil		
	0–0.5	> 0.5–2	> 2	0–0.5	> 0.5–2	> 2	0–0.5	> 0.5–2	> 2
Al	100	Nil	Nil	89.29	10.71	Nil	66	34	Nil
Cd	33.33	50	16.6	Nil	42.86	57.1	12	44	44
Co	91.67	8.33	Nil	75	25	Nil	38	60	2
Hg	25	16.67	58.3	Nil	35.71	64.3	8	42	50
Ni	91.67	8.33	nil	nil	100	nil	14	82	4

3.3.2 Optical density measurements of bacterial growth

Bacterial growth rates were calculated and used to determine the minimum inhibitory concentrations (MIC) for tested metals (Tables 4, 5 and 6). Results

Table 4:   The minimum inhibitory concentrations (MIC) of heavy metals for the crude oil- degrading bacteria isolated from the construction site soil.

MIC (mg ml^{-1})	Percentage of tested bacteria (%)				
	Al	Cd	Co	Ni	Hg
*Nil	10	25	35	45	15
12.5	25	20	Nil	Nil	Nil
5	10	Nil	Nil	Nil	Nil
2.5	Nil	Nil	10	Nil	Nil
0.5	10	10	Nil	25	Nil
0.2	Nil	5	20	5	Nil
0.1	5	10	5	5	Nil
0.05	10	10	Nil	10	Nil
0.04	Nil	Nil	5	Nil	Nil
0.033	30	20	Nil	10	Nil
0.02	Nil	Nil	25	Nil	Nil
0.00667	Nil	Nil	Nil	Nil	5
0.00333	Nil	Nil	Nil	Nil	20
0.002	Nil	Nil	Nil	Nil	15
0.001	Nil	Nil	Nil	Nil	45

showed that, the highest toxicity on tested bacteria was exerted by mercury. On the contrary, aluminium demonstrated to be the least toxic metal tested. Moreover, it was observed that the different bacteria showed different levels of heavy metal resistance expressed as different MIC values. Also, some bacteria demonstrated the potential to resist the high concentrations of different metals (Table 7). In fact, the bacteria ability to resist four, three, two and a single heavy metals is shown (Table 7).

Table 5: The minimum inhibitory concentrations (MIC) of heavy metals for the crude oil-degrading bacteria isolated from the crude oil-contaminated soil.

MIC (mg ml^{-1})	Percentage of tested bacteria (%)				
	Al	Cd	Co	Ni	Hg
*Nil	100	0	66.67	66.67	33.34
12.5	Nil	100	Nil	Nil	Nil
5	Nil	Nil	Nil	Nil	Nil
2.5	Nil	Nil	Nil	Nil	Nil
0.5	Nil	Nil	Nil	33.33	Nil
0.2	Nil	Nil	Nil	Nil	Nil
0.1	Nil	Nil	33.33	Nil	Nil
0.05	Nil	Nil	Nil	Nil	Nil
0.04	Nil	Nil	Nil	Nil	Nil
0.033	Nil	Nil	Nil	Nil	Nil
0.02	Nil	Nil	Nil	Nil	Nil
0.00667	Nil	Nil	Nil	Nil	Nil
0.00333	Nil	Nil	Nil	Nil	Nil
0.002	Nil	Nil	Nil	Nil	33.33
0.001	Nil	Nil	Nil	Nil	33.33

Table 6: The minimum inhibitory concentrations (MIC) of heavy metals for the crude oil-degrading bacteria isolated from pristine soil.

MIC (mg ml^{-1})	Percentage of tested bacteria (%)				
	Al	Cd	Co	Ni	Hg
*Nil	66.68	25.01	41.69	66.68	33.35
12.5	16.66	58.33	Nil	Nil	Nil
5	Nil	Nil	Nil	Nil	Nil
2.5	Nil	Nil	16.66	Nil	Nil
0.5	Nil	2.8	Nil	8.33	Nil
0.2	Nil	Nil	16.66	16.66	Nil
0.1	Nil	Nil	Nil	Nil	Nil
0.05	16.66	8.33	Nil	Nil	Nil
0.04	Nil	8.33	8.33	Nil	Nil
0.033	Nil	Nil	Nil	8.33	Nil
0.02	Nil	Nil	16.66	Nil	Nil
0.00667	Nil	Nil	Nil	Nil	8.33
0.00333	Nil	Nil	Nil	Nil	33.33
0.002	Nil	Nil	Nil	Nil	8.33
0.001	Nil	Nil	Nil	Nil	16.66

Table 7:   Heavy metal resistance phenotypes determined for isolated crude oil-degrading bacteria.

Phenotype (metals resisted)	Number of metals resisted	Number of bacteria tested (%)		
		Crude oil-contaminated soil	Construction site soil	Pristine soil
Al/Cd/Co/Ni	4	-	5	8.33
Cd/Co/Ni/Hg		-	-	8.33
Al/Cd/Co		-	-	8.33
Al/Cd/Ni		-	5	8.33
Al/Co/Ni	3	-	5	8.33
Cd/Co/Hg		-	5	8.33
Cd/Co/Ni		-	5	16.66
Cd/Ni/Hg		-	-	8.33
Co/Ni/Hg		-	-	25
Al/Cd		66.66	-	25
Al/Co		33.33	-	41.66
Al/Hg		33.33	-	16.66
Al/Ni		33.33	10	16.66
Cd/Co		-	5	16.66
Cd/Hg	2	-	5	16.66
Cd/Ni		-	15	16.66
Co/Hg		-	10	8.33
Co/Ni		-	25	41.6
Ni/Hg		-	10	8.33
Al		100	10	66.66
Cd		66.66	35	41.6
Co	1	-	25	25
Hg		33.33	49	66.6
Ni		33.33	15	33.33

4   Discussion

Higher concentrations of heavy metals in crude oil-contaminated and construction site soils were determined compared to those in the pristine soil (Table 1). The sources of these metals could be the crude oil contaminated and the spilled materials used during construction work [1, 2, 4, 15]. In addition, diverse bacterial populations at the genus level were found in the pristine soil compared to other soils (Table 2). The lower bacterial diversity in the contaminated soils could be due the presence of stressors such as high metal and crude oil that are known to reduce bacteria diversity [16]. Also, the inhibition of bacterial growth by high concentrations of heavy metals was expected because it is documented that all metals demonstrate toxicity to living cells at certain concentration [7]. The highest toxicities demonstrated in all soil types were shown by mercury and cadmium, which usually needed, if at all, in very low concentrations thus it was expected for these metals to demonstrate higher toxicity than other metals [7, 17].

5 Conclusions

Data analysis showed that the higher bacterial potential to tolerate heavy metals in the contaminated soils compared to the pristine soil could indicate that bacteria have the potential to develop resistance to stressors such as heavy metals found in their immediate environment. Also, the potential of crude oil-degrading bacteria to resist various concentrations of heavy metals indicated the effectiveness of the indigenous bacteria to utilize crude oil contamination in the presence of heavy metals leading to successful crude oil bioremediation. Thus, it can be concluded that no efforts are need to remediate heavy metals in the crude oil contaminated sites. However, successful biological treatment of contaminated soils is challenging due to factors such as heterogeneity of the contaminants, extreme concentrations of hydrocarbons, variable site conditions and the influence of regulatory constrains in bioremediation process. In addition, crude oil-degrading bacteria were detected in contamination-free soils which showed that, the hydrocarbon degradation trait in bacteria is common among bacteria in different soils.

Acknowledgements

We would like to thank the College of Graduate Studies, Kuwait University and sincerely acknowledge the Research Administration, Kuwait University grant number YS04/11 for supporting our work.

References

[1] Shen, G., Lu, Y., Zhou, Q., and Hong, J., Interaction of polycyclic aromatic hydrocarbons and heavy metals on soil enzyme. *Chemosphere*, **61**, pp. 1175–1182, 2005.

[2] Shen, G., Lu, Y., and Hong, J., Combined effect of heavy metals and polycyclic aromatic hydrocarbons on urease activity in soil. *Ecotoxicology and Environmental Safety*, **63**, pp. 474–480, 2006.

[3] Gondal, M., A., Hussain, T., Yamani, Z., H., and Baig, M., A., Detection of heavy metals in Arabian crude oil residue using laser induced breakdown spectroscopy. *Talanta*, **69**, pp. 1072–1078, 2006.

[4] Balba, M., T., Al-Awadhi, N., and Al-Daher, R., Bioremediation of oil-contaminated soil: microbiological methods for feasibility assessment and field evaluation. *Journal of Microbiological Methods*, **32**, pp. 155–164, 1998.

[5] Vidali, M., Bioremediation. An overview. *Pure Appl. Chem.*, Vol. 73, No. 7, pp. 1163–1172, 2001.

[6] Stephen, J., R., Chang, Y., Macnaughton, S., J., Kowalchuk, G., A., Leung, K., T., Flemming, C., A., and White, D., C., Effect of toxic metals on Indigenous Soil β-Subgroup Proteobacterium Ammonia Oxidizer Community Structure and Protection against Toxicity by Inoculated Metal-

Resistance Bacteria. *Applied and Environmental Microbiology*, Vol. **65**, No. 1, pp. 95–101, 1999.

[7] Sandrin, T., and Maier, R., Impact of Metals on the Biodegradation of Organic Pollutants. *Environmental Health Perspectives*, Vol. **111**, No. 8, pp. 1093–1101, 2003.

[8] Shetty, R., S., Deo, S., K., Shah, P., Sun, Y., Rosen, B., P., Daunert, S., Luminescence-based whole-cell-sensing systems for cadmium and lead using genetically engineered bacteria. *Anal Bioanal Chem.*, **376**, pp. 11–17, 2003.

[9] Trajanovska, S., Britz, M., L., and Bhave, M., Detection of heavy metal ion resistance genes in Gram-positive and Gram-negative bacteria isolated from a lead-contaminated site. *Biodegradation*, **8**, pp. 113–124, 1997.

[10] AL-Saleh, E.S. and Obuekwe, C., Inhibition of hydrocarbon bioremediation by lead in a crude oil-contaminated soil. *International Biodeterioration and Biodegradation*, **56**, pp. 1–7, 2005.

[11] Rowell D.L. (ed). *Soil science*, Pesticides and Metals. Publications: Addison Wesley Longman Limited, Essex, 1994.

[12] Cohen-Bazire G., Sistrom W.R., and Stainer R.Y., Kinetic studies of pigment synthesis by non-sulfur purple bacteria. *Journal of Cellular Physiology*, **49**, pp. 25–68, 1957.

[13] Altschul, S.F., Madden, T.L., Schäffer, A.A, Zhang, J., Zhang, Z., Miller, W. and Lipman, D.J., Gapped BLAST and PSI-BLAST: a new generation of protein database search programs. *Nucleic Acids Research*, **25(17)**, pp. 3389–3402, 1997.

[14] Lertcanawanichakul, M. and Sawangnop, S., A comparison of two methods used for measuring the antagonistic activity of *Bacillus* species. *Walailak Journal of Science and Technology*, **5**, pp. 161–171, 2008.

[15] Alloway, B., J., Contamination of soils in domestic gardens and allotments: a brief overview. *Land Contamination and Reclamation*, **12 (3)**, 2004.

[16] Margesin, R., and Schinner, F., Biodegradation and bioremediation of hydrocarbons in extreme environments. *Appl Microbial Biotechnol*, **56**, pp. 650–663, 2001.

[17] Nies, D., H., Microbial heavy-metal resistance. *Appl Microbial Biotechnol*, **51**, pp. 730–750, 1999.

Variant effects of arsenic compounds on crude oil bioremediation by crude oil-degrading bacteria in Kuwait

K. Majki, S. Moustafa, A. S. Al-Dousari & E. Al-Saleh
Microbiology Program, Department of Biological Sciences,
Faculty of Science, Kuwait University, Kuwait

Abstract

Crude oil spills into the environment such as that of Kuwait cause health and ecological problems which necessitates the cleanup of such pollution by efficient methods such as bioremediation. However, the associated heavy metals such as arsenic with crude oil pollution exert inhibitory effects on bioremediating agents for instance soil microbiota leading to hindered bioremediation. In the current study, the tolerance of two dominant crude oil-degrading bacteria in Kuwaiti soil, *Acinetobacter spp.* a Gram-negative bacteria and *Nocardia spp.* a Gram-positive bacteria, to varying concentrations of arsenate and arsenite was investigated. Results showed the higher potentials of *Nocardia spp.* to resist the inhibitory effects of added arsenic compounds. Also, arsenite demonstrated significantly higher inhibitory effects on bacterial growth and activity compared to those of arsenate. Additionally, determination of the crude oil mineralization potentials of isolated bacteria demonstrated the significantly higher potentials of *Nocardia spp.* to mineralize crude oil in presence of arsenic compounds. Moreover, the phylogenetic assessment of isolated strains of *Acinetobacter* and *Nocardia* using 16S-RFLP analyses showed the higher diversity of *Nocardia* strains compared to *Acinetobacter*. Thus, this study demonstrated the variant effects of arsenic species on the growth and activity of different crude oil-degrading bacteria. Also, results indicated that, the potential of crude oil-degrading bacteria to tolerate the inhibitory effects of heavy metals, such as arsenic, could accelerate the bioremediation of crude oil pollution.
Keywords: Crude oil-degrading bacteria, Gram-negative bacteria, Gram-positive bacteria, Acinetobacter spp., Nocardia spp., arsenite, arsenate.

WIT Transactions on Ecology and The Environment, Vol 173, © 2013 WIT Press
www.witpress.com, ISSN 1743-3541 (on-line)
doi:10.2495/SDP130591

1 Introduction

Crude oil contamination is a worldwide continuous problem especially to oil-exporting countries such as Kuwait. Oil spills both deliberate and accidental [1] have the tendency to affect human health [2] and ecological niches [3]. Thus, bioremediation is highly required for such polluted environments and considered an excellent approach for cleaning-up crude oil pollution [4] via the indigenous microbiota that in general are sequentially exposed to a variety of pollutants [5]. Usually crude oil pollution is associated with heavy metals contamination, in particular arsenic [6–8]. In nature arsenic occurs in four oxidation states: (-3) in the form of arsenides, arsine (AsH_3) and arsenic chloride ($AsCl_3$); (0) in the form of native arsenic; (+3) in the form of oxides, sulfides, sulfo-salts, and arsenite, and (+5) in the form of arsenate [9]. Arsenic exerts severe toxic effects to all forms of organisms [10], and as a result it was ranked as number one on the Environmental Protection Agency (EPA) list of toxic metals [11]. However, scarce studies are available on the effects of arsenic compounds on hydrocarbon biodegradation potentials of the soil microbiota [12]. Therefore, the growth, activity, diversity and tolerance of two dominant crude oil-degrading bacteria (CODB) in Kuwaiti soil, *Acinetobacter spp.* [13, 14] a Gram-negative bacteria and *Nocardia spp.* [15, 16] a Gram-positive bacteria to varying concentrations of arsenate and arsenite were investigated in the current study.

2 Materials and methods

2.1 Effect of arsenate and arsenite on the growth of the CODB *Acinetobacter spp.* and *Nocardia spp.*

The potential inhibitory effects of arsenic compounds (arsenate and arsenite) on the growth of the CODB *Acinetobacter spp.* and *Nocardia spp.* were determined using the well diffusion method and optical density measurements.

2.1.1 Agar well diffusion method

The method of (Lertcanawanichakul and Sawangnop [17]) was adopted. Stocked bacterial cultures were streaked on NA plates and incubated at 30°C for 24 hours. Grown bacterial cultures were transferred into sterile 15 ml Falcon tubes containing sterile 0.85% NaCl solution followed by adjusting the number of bacterial cells to 1.2×10^9 cells^{-1} ml using McFarland No.0.5 as a standard solution. Then, aliquots (100 µl) of the prepared bacterial suspension were spread on the surface of NA plates, spread evenly and left for 30 min at room temperature. Then, wells (10 mm in diameter) were punched using sterile stainless steel cork borer. Prepared metal (As^{+5}, 50 mg^{-1} ml and As^{+3}, 5 mg^{-1} ml) solutions were directly filled (50 µl) into the wells, plates incubated at 30°C for 24 hours and the diameter of the inhibition zones were measured in millimeter [17].

2.1.2 Optical density measurements

Prepared bacterial suspensions used for the well diffusion method mentioned previously were used simultaneously for the optical density measurement method. For this purpose, bacterial suspension (50μl), sterile nutrient broth (50μl) and different concentrations of arsenate and arsenite solutions (300 μl) were transferred to 100-well Honeycomb plates. Then, plates were incubated shaking at 30°C for 24 hours in automated optical density reader (600 nm). Determined optical density values were plotted against time followed by calculation of bacterial growth rates. Bacterial growth rates were used to determine the minimum inhibitory concentrations (MIC) for tested metals. MIC values were defined as the lowest concentration of tested metals that inhibited the growth of bacteria after 24 hours of incubation.

2.2 Effect of arsenic compounds on the activity of the CODB *Acinetobacter spp.* and *Nocardia spp.*

The inhibitory effects of arsenate and arsenic on the activities of the CODB *Acinetobacter spp.* and *Nocardia spp.* were determined. For this purpose, the activity of the dehydrogenase and the rate of carbon dioxide evolution were used as indicators for bacteria activity under different carbon sources and metal concentrations.

2.2.1 Determination of dehydrogenase activity

The method of (Alef [18]) was adopted. Overnight grown bacterial cultures on nutrient broth were harvested at 4200 xg in sterile 50 ml falcon tubes. Pellets were suspended in 0.85% NaCl and the optical density of the cultures was adjusted to 1.0 OD (620 nm). Then, bacterial suspension (1.5 ml), carbon source (crude oil, 100μl and 20 mM; nutrient broth as control) and metal solution (0.5 ml of arsenate and arsenite) were transferred into 50 ml sterile Falcon tubes followed by the addition of triphenyltetrazolium chloride (TTC) solution (5 ml) solution, contents mixed well and incubated shaking (200 rpm) at 30°C for 24 hours. Solution of TTC was prepared by dissolving 0.1 g TTC in 100 ml 100 mM Tris HCl buffer (pH 7.6). Following incubation, the reduction product of TTC, triphenyl formazan (TPF), was extracted with acetone (40 ml) by agitation in the dark. The extracts were membrane filtered (0.45 mm) and the presence of the red-coloured TPF was detected in the filtrate by a spectrophotometer (Genesis 5) at 546 nm. Concentration of formed TPF was determined using TPF calibration curve.

2.2.2 Mineralization of crude oil

The effects of the addition of different concentrations of arsenate (5, 10 and 20 mg^{-1} ml) and arsenite (0.6, and 1.2 mg^{-1} ml) in on the utilization of crude oil by crude oil-degrading bacteria were determined using respirometry. The amounts of carbon dioxide evolved were measured using a Micro-oxymax respirometer (Columbus Instruments, USA). The reaction vessels contained 1 ml of overnight bacterial cultures with optical density adjusted to 1.0 (600 nm) as mentioned previously, Hutner's minimal media (45 ml), crude oil (100μl), and desired metal concentration (4 ml). Reaction vessels were incubated in a shaking water bath at 30°C for 24 hours. Three sets of controls were used. One set of controls constituted vessels contained sterile Hutner's minimal media and crude oil. Another set of controls included vessels contained Hutner's minimal media, crude oil and bacterial cultures. In addition, one set of controls constituted vessels contained sterile Hutner's minimal media and bacterial cultures. The amounts of evolved carbon dioxide determined were used as indicator of bacterial activity.

2.3 Fingerprinting of the CODB *Acinetobacter spp.* and *Nocardia spp.* using restriction fragment length polymorphism (RFLP) of 16S rRNA

Sequences of 16S rDNA genes of the CODB *Acinetobacter spp.* and *Nocardia spp.* strains were amplified from extracted DNA. Following PCR amplification, 10 µl of amplified 16S rDNA from each of isolates were digested separately with *BstUI* restriction endonuclease (New England Biolabs) in 15 µl reaction mixtures as recommended by the manufacturer. Digests were electrophoresed in 2% agarose gels, with TBE buffer. Gels were stained with ethidium bromide and then photographed under UV light. DNA fragment sizes were determined using Kodak Digital Image analysis software (Kodak, Rochester). The quality of the numerical data was checked by comparing the sum of fragment sizes in each restriction pattern with the original product size (approximately 1,499 bp). Cluster analyses of band patterns were carried out using GelCompar II software (Applied Maths). Profiles of isolated bacteria were compared based on Pearson coefficient with an optimization of 1.0% and a tolerance of 1.0%. Dendrograms were obtained using the hierarchical Dice correlation/unweighted pair group method with arithmetic mean (UPGMA) algorithm. Fragments smaller than 48.5 bp in length were not used in the analyses [19]. Each phylotype was defined as a group of sequences that have indistinguishable *BstUI* restriction patterns [20].

3 Results

3.1 3.1 Effects of Arsenic compounds on the growth of the CODB *Acinetobacter spp.* and *Nocardia spp.*

The effects of arsenate and arsenite on the growth of *Acinetobacter spp.* and *Nocardia spp.* strains were determined by the well diffusion method and by optical density measurements (Tables 1–3). Based on the values of diameter of inhibition zones, it was considered convenient to group the tested bacteria into three groups (Table 1). All tested bacteria showed zone of inhibition of ≤ 0.5 cm when reacted with arsenate. On the other hand, 38.1%, 19% and 42% of tested *Acinetobacter* strains showed zones of inhibition of 0.5, $> 0.5 < 1$, and ≥ 1cm, respectively, also, 55.6% and 44.4% of tested *Nocardia spp.* showed zones of inhibition of 0.5 and $> 0.5 < 1$ when reacted with arsenite (Table 1). Moreover the MIC values of arsenic compounds determined from the optical density measurements showed the varying reactions of tested bacteria against arsenic compounds (Tables 2). Higher MIC value was recorded for arsenate (30 mg ml^{-1}) compared to arsenite (1.5 mg ml^{-1}) among *Acinetobacter spp.* and *Nocardia spp.* strains, respectively.

Table 1:   Effects of arsenate and arsenite on the growth of *Acinetobacter spp.* and *Nocardia spp.*

Bacteria	Number of tested bacteria	Inhibition zone (cm)		
		≤ 0.5	$> 0.5 < 1$	≥ 1
Arsenate (As^{+5})				
Acinetobacter spp.	24	24	Nil	Nil
Nocardia ssp.	34	34	Nil	Nil
Arsenite (As^{+3})				
Acinetobacter spp.	42	16	8	18
Nocardia ssp.	27	15	12	Nil

Table 2:   MIC values of arsenate and arsenite of *Acinetobacter spp.* and *Nocardia spp.*

Serial No.	Bacteria	MIC (mg ml^{-1})	
		Arsenate	Arsenite
1	*Acinetobacter schindleri*	Nil*	1.5
2	*Acinetobacter schindleri*	30	1.5
3	*Acinetobacter schindleri*	30	1.5
4	*Acinetobacter schindleri*	Nil*	1.5
5	*Nocardia cummidelens*	30	1.5
6	*Nocardia fluminea*	Nil*	Nil*
7	*Nocardia ignorata*	Nil*	1.5
8	*Nocardia ignorata*	Nil*	1.5
9	*Nocardia sp.*	30	1.5
10	*Nocardia sp.*	30	Nil*
11	*Nocardia sp.*	30	1.5
12	*Nocardia cummidelens*	Nil*	1.5
13	*Nocardia cummidelens*	Nil*	Nil*
14	*Nocardia sp.*	Nil*	0.15

*No MIC values were determined due to the ability of bacteria to grow at high concentrations of the arsenic compounds.

In addition, the abilities of these bacterial strains to grow at high concentrations of arsenic compounds were used to demonstrate the arsenic resistance phenotypes (Table 3). Results revealed that while 50% of *Acinetobacter spp.* strains showed resistance to arsenate, none of them were resistant to arsenite. In contrast, 60% and 30% of *Nocardia spp.* strains showed resistance to arsenate and arsenite respectively. Also, 20% of *Nocardia spp.* strains demonstrated resistance against both arsenate and arsenite (Table 3).

Table 3:   Resistance phenotypes of *Acinetobacter spp.* and *Nocardia spp.* reacted with arsenic compounds.

Serial No.	Bacteria	Resistant
1	*Acinetobacter schindleri*	As^{+5}
2	*Acinetobacter schindleri*	Nil*
3	*Acinetobacter schindleri*	Nil*
4	*Acinetobacter schindleri*	As^{+5}
5	*Nocardia cummidelens*	Nil*
6	*Nocardia fluminea*	As^{+5}/As^{+3}
7	*Nocardia ignorata*	As^{+5}
8	*Nocardia ignorata*	As^{+5}
9	*Nocardia sp.*	Nil*
10	*Nocardia sp.*	As^{+3}
11	*Nocardia sp.*	Nil*
12	*Nocardia cummidelens*	As^{+5}
13	*Nocardia cummidelens*	As^{+5}/As^{+3}
14	*Nocardia sp.*	As^{+5}

*No phenotypes were determined due to the un-ability of bacteria to grow at high concentrations of arsenic compounds.

3.2 Effects of arsenic compounds on the dehydrogenase activity of isolated strains of *Acinetobacter spp.* and *Nocardia spp.*

The affects of arsenate and arsenite on the dehydrogenase activity in the presence of crude oil were investigated. Both *Acinetobacter spp.* and *Nocardia spp.* strains showed significantly low dehydrogenase activity when supplied with crude oil compared to that of nutrient broth. Moreover the dehydrogenase activity of tested strains was more labile to arsenite compared to that in the presence of arsenate (Table 4).

3.3 Effects of arsenate and arsenite on crude oil mineralization by the *Acinetobacter spp.* and *Nocardia spp.*

Crude oil mineralization was determined by respirometry. Higher amounts of crude oil mineralization were determined for *Nocardia spp.* strains compared to that of *Acinetobacter spp.* strains (Table 5).

Table 4:   Effects of arsenate and arsenite on the dehydrogenase activity of *Acinetobacter spp.* and *Nocardia ssp. bacteria* supplied with crude oil.

Bacteria	Nutrient Broth (Control)			Crude oil		
Arsenate (mg ml^{-1})	5	10	20	5	10	20
Acinetobacter spp.	96-3.8	91-1.7	83.3-0.64	33.3-0	25-0	5.5-0
Nocardia spp.	82-7.5	78-3.3	62-2.1	96-60	91-40	79-5
Arsenite (mg ml^{-1})	0.6		1.2		0.6	1.2
Acinetobacter spp.	66.6-0.5		50.8-0.2		25-0	20-0
Nocardia spp.	62-31		60-26		67-30	51-25

Table 5:   Effects of arsenate and arsenite on crude oil mineralization by *Acinetobacter spp.* and *Nocardia spp.* bacteria.

Bacteria	Arsenic compounds (mg ml^{-1})				
	Arsenate (As^{+5})			Arsenite (As^{+3})	
	5	10	20	0.6	1.2
	Amount of carbon dioxide evolved (%)				
Acinetobacter spp.	60	55.6	5.8	68.3	6.6
Nocardia spp.	98	64.9	9.3	8.2	68.5

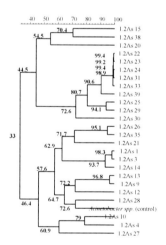

Figure 1:   Dendrogram constructed by UPGMA cluster analysis of similarity coefficients derived from RFLP analysis of 16S rDNA of crude oil-degrading *Acinetobacter spp.*, isolated from soil amended with arsenite (1.2 mg^{-1} ml) obtained with BstUI restriction enzyme. The levels of linkage representing the Dice correlation/UPGMA are expressed as percentages shown at each node.

3.4 Phylogenetic analysis of the CODB strains of *Acinetobacter spp.* and *Nocardia spp.* by RFLP

In order to evaluate the diversity of the *Acinetobacter spp.* and *Nocardia spp.* in the presence of arsenic compounds, the 16S rDNA sequences of different strains isolated from soil amended with 1.2 mg ml^{-1} of arsenite were compared using the 16S-RFLP method. The assessment of the diversity of the *Nocardia* isolates by 16S-RFLP analysis demonstrated the presence of sixteen different phylogroups at similarity coefficient of 90% (Figure 2). Moreover, four different species belonging to the genus *Nocardia* were identified. On the other hand, 16S-RFLP analyses of *Acinetobacter* isolates showed the presence of fifteen different phylogroups at similarity coefficient of 90% (Figure 1). Also only two different species belonging to the genus *Acinetobacter* were identified.

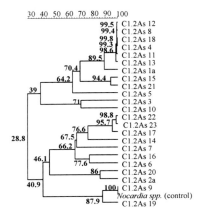

Figure 2:   Dendrogram constructed by UPGMA cluster analysis of similarity coefficients derived from RFLP analysis of 16S rDNA of crude oil-degrading *Nocardia spp.*, isolated from soil amended with arsenite (1.2 mg^{-1} ml) obtained with BstUI restriction enzyme. The levels of linkage representing the Dice correlation/UPGMA are expressed as percentages shown at each node.

4 Discussion

Differences in bacteria growth determined by well diffusion method were insignificant in the presence of arsenate which could be due to nature of the method or the potential of bacterial biofilms to resist heavy metals [21]. However, the addition of arsenite showed significant differences in bacterial growth (Table 1). This indicated the higher potentials of arsenite to inhibit bacterial growth which was further investigated by the optical-density measurement experiments that confirmed previous results (Tables 2 and 3). In addition, higher MIC values were recorded for arsenate (30 mg ml^{-1}) compared to arsenite (1.5 mg ml^{-1}). Thus, based on well diffusion and optical density measurement experiments, it was concluded that arsenite possessed higher toxicity on bacterial growth compared to arsenate which was in agreement with previous studies [22, 23]. The effects of arsenic compounds on bacterial activity were further studied and results showed the higher inhibitory effects of arsenite on bacterial dehydrogenase activity compared to that of arsenate (Table 4). Also, the higher dehydrogenase activity determined in the presence of nutrient broth compared to that in the presence of crude oil indicated the bacterial preference to nutrient broth over that to crude oil. These results were in agreement with previous reports indicating that crude oil is typically non-preferred substrates for bacteria [24]. Furthermore, higher crude oil mineralization determined for the Gram-positive bacterium *Nocardia spp.* compared to that of the *Acinetobacter spp.* a Gram-negative bacterium. The potential of these bacteria to degrade hydrocarbons was documented previously [25–28] and have been isolated previously from Kuwait environment [13–16]. Thus, it was unsurprising to isolate them from crude oil-contaminated soils in Kuwait. Moreover, 16S-RFLP analyses showed the higher diversity of *Nocardia spp.* compared to *Acinetobacter spp.* strains which reflected the high adaptable nature of *Nocardia spp.* to the harsh environment of contaminated sites in Kuwait harboring high concentrations of hydrocarbons and heavy metals that reduced the diversity of less adaptable strains of *Acinetobacter spp.* These finding were in agreement with previous reports demonstrating the effects of hydrocarbons and heavy metals on bacterial diversity in soil [29, 30].

5 Conclusions

The bioremediation of crude oil in soil is a complex process that is affected by several factors explicitly the characteristics of soil indigenous microbiota and chemical composition of soil. Thus the assessment of the effects of arsenic compounds on crude oil bioremediation in soil for the predominant CODB in Kuwait *Acinetobacter spp.* a Gram-negative bacterium and *Nocardia spp.* a Gram-positive bacterium were determined. The potential inhibitory effects of arsenic compound on bacterial growth and activities showed higher toxicity of arsenite over that of arsenate. Moreover it was concluded that *Nocardia spp.* strains possessed higher adaptation potentials to the presence of arsenic compounds and crude oil compared to *Acinetobacter spp.* strains which most probably affected their diversity in soil. The current study was one of the first efforts to investigate the effects of arsenic compounds on soil microbiota in Kuwait, thus, more studies are required on more soil samples from other areas of Kuwait to investigate effects of arsenic compounds on crude oil bioremediation.

Acknowledgements

We would like to acknowledge the Research Administration and College of Graduated Studies in Kuwait University for funding this project. The efforts of the sequencing facility of the Biotechnology Center in Kuwait University are highly appreciated.

References

[1] Zarba, M. A., Mohammad, O. S., Anderlini, V. C., Literathy, P. and Shunbo, F. Petroleum residues in surface sediments of Kuwait. *Marine Pollution Bulletin*, **16(5)**, 209-211, 1985.

[2] Mahmoud, F. F., Al-Harbi, S. A., McCabe, M., Haines, D. D., Burleson, J. A. and Kreutzer, D. L. Abnormal lymphocyte surface antigen expression in peripheral blood of a Kuwaiti population. *Annals of the New York Academy of Sciences*, **793(1)**, 498-503, 1996.

[3] Durako, M. J., Kenworthy, W. J., Fatemy, S. M. R., Valavi, H. and Thayer, G. W. Assessment of the toxicity of Kuwait crude oil on the photosynthesis and respiration of seagrasses of the northern Gulf. Marine Pollution Bulletin, **27**(2), 223-227, 1993.

[4] Obuekwe, C. O. and Al-Zarban, S. S. Bioremediation of crude oil pollution in Kuwaiti Dessert: the role of adherent microorganisms. *Environment international*, **24(8)**, 823-834, 1998.

[5] Shen, G., Y. Lu and J. Hong. Combined effect of heavy metals and polycyclic aromatic hydrocarbons on urease activity in soil. *Ecotoxicology and environmental safety*, **63(3)**, 474-480, 2006.

[6] Christensen, L. H. and Agerbo, A. Determination of sulfur and heavy metals in crude oil and petroleum products by energy-dispersive X-ray fluorescence spectrometry and fundamental parameter approach. *Analytical Chemistry*, **53(12)**, 1788-1792, 1981.

[7] Puri, B. K. and Irgolic, K. J. Determination of arsenic in crude petroleum and liquid hydrocarbons. *Environmental Geochemistry and Health*, **11(3-4)**, 95-99, 1989.

[8] Stigter, J. B., De Haan, H. P. M., Guicherit, R., Dekkers, C. P. A. and Daane, M. L. Determination of cadmium, zinc, copper, chromium and arsenic in crude oil cargoes. *Environmental Pollution*, **107(3)**, 451-64, 2000.

[9] Matera, V. and Hecho, I. L. Arsenic behavior in contaminated soils: mobility and speciation. Lewis Publishers: Washington, DC, 2001.

[10] Hughes, M. F. Arsenic toxicity and potential mechanisms of action. *Toxicology letters*, **13(1)**, 1-16, 2002.

[11] Tsai, S. L., Singh, S., and Chen, W. Arsenic metabolism by microbes in nature and the impact on arsenic remediation. *Current opinion in biotechnology*, **20(6)**, 659-667, 2009.

[12] Gogolev, A. and Wilke, B. M. Combination effects of heavy metals and fluoranthene on soil bacteria. *Biology and fertility of soils*, **25(3)**, 274-278, 1997.

[13] AL-Saleh, E., Drobiova, H. and Obuekwe, C. (2009). Predominant culturable crude oil-degrading bacteria in the cost of Kuwait. *Inter. Biodeg. Biodeter.*, **63**: 400-406.

[14] Radwan, S. S., Al-Hasan, R. H., Al-Awadhi, H., Salamah, S. and Abdullah, H. M. Higher oil biodegradation potential at the Arabian Gulf coast than in the water body. *Marine Biology*, **135(4)**, 741-745, 1999.

[15] Sarkhoh, N. A., Ghannoum, M. A., Ibrahim, A. S., Stretton, R. J. and Radwan, S. S. Crude oil and hydrocarbon degrading strains of *Rhodococcus*: *Rhodococcus* strains isolated from soil and marine environments in Kuwait. *Environmental Pollution*, **65(1)**, 1-17, 1990.

[16] Khan, Z. U., Neil, R., Chandy, T. D., Al-Sayer, H., Provost, F. and Boiron, P. *Nocardia asteroides* in the soil of Kuwait. *Mycopathologia*, **137(3)**, 159-163, 1997.

[17] Lertcanawanichakul, M. and Sawangnop, S. A comparison of two methods used for measuring the antagonistic activity of *Bacillus* species. *Walailak Journal of Science and Technology*, **5(2)**, 161-171, 2008.

[18] Alef, K. Dehydrogenase activity. Academic Press, Inc: London, 1995.

[19] Tenover, F. C., Arbit, R. D., Goering, R. V., Mickelsen, P. A., Murray, B. E., Persing, D. H. and Swaminathan, B. Interpreting chromosomal DNA restriction patterns produced by pulsed-field gel electrophoresis: criteria for bacterial strain typing. *Journal of clinical Microbiology*, **33(9)**, 2233-2239, 1995.

[20] Dunbar, D., Wormsley, S., Lowe, T. and Baserga, S. Fibrillarin-associated box C/D snoRNAs in *Trypanosoma brucei*: sequence conservation and implication for 2'-O-ribose methylation of rRNA. *The Journal of Biological Chemistry*, **65(16)**, 1662-1669, 1999.

[21] Jackson, C. R., Harrison, K. G. and Dugas, S. L. Enumeration and characterization of culturable arsenate resistant bacteria in a large estuary. *Systematic and Applied Microbiology*, **28(8)**, 727-734, 2005.

[22] Turpeinen, R., Kairesalo, T. and Haeggblom, M. M. Microbial community structure and activity in arsenic, chromium, and copper contaminated soils. *FEMS microbiology Ecology*, **47(1)**, 39-50, 2004.

[23] Achour, A. R., Bauda, P. and Billard, P. Diversity of arsenite transporter genes from arsenic-resistant soil bacteria. *Research in microbiology*, **158(2)**, 128-137, 2007.

[24] Ma, D., D. N. Cook, J. E. Hearst, and H. Nikaido. Efflux pumps and drug resistance in Gram-negative bacteria. *Trends in Microbiology*. **2(12)**, 489-493, 1994.

[25] Ramos, J. L., Duque, E., Gallegos, M. T., Godoy, P., Ramos-Gonzalez, M. I., Rojas, N., Terán, W. and Segura, A. Mechanisms of solvent tolerance in gram-negative bacteria. *Annual Review of Microbiology*, **56(7)**, 743-68, 2002.

[26] Hanson, K. G., Nigam, A., Kapadia, M. and Desai, A. Bioremediation of crude oil contamination with *Acinetobacter* sp. A3. *Current Microbiology*, **35(3)**, 191-193, 1997.

[27] Davis, J. B. and Raymond, R. L. Oxidation of alkyl-substituted cyclic hydrocarbons by a *Nocardia* during growth on *n*- alkanes. *Applied Microbiology*, **9(5)**, 383-388, 1961.

[28] Gebhardt, H., Meniche, X., Tropis, M., Krämer, R., Daffe, M. and Morbach, S. The key role of the mycolic acid content in the functionality of the cell wall permeability barrier in Corynebacterineae. Microbiology. **153(5)**, 1424-34, 2007.

[29] Juck, D., Charles, T., Whyte, L. G. and Greer, C. W. Polyphasic microbial community analysis of petroleum hydrocarbon-contaminated soils from two northern Canadian communities. *FEMS Microbiology Ecology,* **33(3)**, 241-249, 2000.

[30] Kozdrój, J and Van Elsasb, J. D. Structural diversity of microorganisms in chemically perturbed soil assessed by molecular and cytochemical approaches. *Journal of Microbiological Methods*, **43(3)**, 197-212, 2001.

Photodegradation of photodynamic therapy agents in aqueous TiO$_2$ suspensions

A. S. Oliveira[1,2], C. G. Maia[1], P. Brito[1], R. Boscencu[3],
R. Socoteanu[4], M. Ilie[3] & L. F. V. Ferreira[2]
[1]Centro Interdisciplinar de Investigação e Inovação, C3I,
Escola Superior de Tecnologia e Gestão,
Instituto Politécnico de Portalegre, Portugal
[2]Centro de Química-Física Molecular e Instituto de Nanociencias e
Nanotecnologia, Instituto Superior Técnico,
Universidade Técnica de Lisboa, Portugal
[3]Faculty of Pharmacy, "Carol Davila" University of Medicine
and Pharmacy, Romania
[4]"Ilie Murgulescu" Institute, Romanian Academy, Romania

Abstract

The presence of emergent pollutants in waters and wastewaters are an issue of increasing concern due to the risk they pose to human and environmental health. Cancer Photodynamic Therapy photosensitizers and their metabolites and photodegradation products are pharmaceutical substances that after treatment will be eliminated from the human body and will eventually reach water bodies. Porphyrins are well established PDT sensitizers and cyanine dyes are promising candidates for the same use. In that way it is important to know how those compounds degrade once they reach water bodies and to find efficient treatment methodologies in case they are persistent. In this paper the simulated solar light photodegradation of a porphyrin (Zinctetraphenylporphyrin) and of a cyanine dye (3,3'-diethylindocarbocyanine iodide) in water was investigated, in the absence and in the presence of the most used photocatalyst for semiconductor photocatalysis: Titanium dioxide (TiO$_2$). We observed that the porphyrin (1×10^{-3}M) did not undergo photodegradation in the absence of photocatalyst and that in its presence the photodegradation process was strongly promoted (60% photodegradation reached after 1 hour of irradiation with 0,01g of TiO$_2$). The

WIT Transactions on Ecology and The Environment, Vol 173, © 2013 WIT Press
www.witpress.com, ISSN 1743-3541 (on-line)
doi:10.2495/SDP130601

cyanine dye $(1 \times 10^{-3} M)$ suffered a photodegradation of about 20% even in the absence of TiO_2 and reached 100% photodegradation in its presence.

Keywords: emergent pollutants, wastewater treatments, Porphyrins, cyanine dyes, photodynamic therapy sensitizers (PDT), advanced oxidation processes (AOPs), heterogeneous photocatalysis, TiO_2, solar photocatalysis.

1 Introduction

Nowadays wastewater may contain several different pharmaceuticals including antibiotics, hormones and other endocrine disruptors, chemotherapy and photodynamic therapy medicines, antipyretics, etc. Those are present in municipal sewage, largely as a result of human use and/or excretion. Much of the concern regarding the presence of these substances in wastewater and their persistence to wastewater treatment processes is because they may contribute to directly or indirectly affect the environmental and human health [1, 2]. For most of these substances their potential highly harmful effect on environmental and human health is just starting to be perceived, and the correct extension of their impacts is still far from being fully understood; reason why these substances are generically referred as emerging pollutants. Conventional water and wastewater treatment are inefficient for substantially removing many of them [1–3].

The photodegradation and mineralization of several emerging pollutants, namely different pharmaceuticals is currently been widely studied because of the danger their present or that of their residues in water bodies represent to the environment and also due to their highly recalcitrant character. Research has show that advanced oxidative processes, which generate very active oxidative species such as the hydroxyl radicals, are promising tools for the destruction of pharmaceuticals compounds [3–5]. While there appears to be no standard treatment for removal of all residual pharmaceuticals under conventional treatment processes, there is a strong opinion that advanced oxidation processes can be used for their effective removal [3–5].

The advanced oxidative processes (AOP's) are an alternative treatment for wastewater containing persistent and biorecalcitrant pollutants [3 and references quoted there]. Fujitsu and Honda [6] discovery of the photoinduced water cleavage by titanium dioxide (TiO_2) heterogeneous photocatalytic oxidation using the semiconductor as catalytic. The semiconductor TiO_2 presented advantageous such as simplicity, low cost, high photochemical reactive, stability in aqueous systems and low environmental toxicity, while promoting efficiently the degradation of very persistent target organic compounds and industrial effluents [7, 8].

In recent few years the use of Porphyrins in biomedical applications increased exponentially. Porphyrins are structures that mimic naturally occurring compounds and promising candidates as fluorescent markers. This new field of use for porphyrins was partially steamed by their application as sensitizers in photodynamic therapy (PDT), exhibiting convenient absorption in the phototherapeutic window (~670 to 1100nm). Focus on all classes of NIR probes was mostly triggered by the development of reliable and inexpensive NIR emitting laser diodes. The gallium-arsenic semiconductor laser (780–830nm) made these probes highly efficient absorbers, mainly for medical applications, as fluorescent NIR probes avoid interference with background fluorescence of biomolecules. NIR probes are also suitable for biological applications, since light of longer wavelengths penetrates the tissue more easily and without interferences, making them more attractive for in vivo measurements [9–12]. Although less used in PDT than porphyrins, several cyanine dyes emitting in the same region have been also recently reported as promising candidates for use as PDT sensitizers [13–15].

The aim of this work is to know how near infrared porphyrin and cyanine dyes fade after being discharged in wastewaters following their biomedical uses and investigate if advanced oxidative processes can be useful on promoting and accelerate their photodegradation on wastewaters. Titanium dioxide (TiO_2) heterogeneous photocatalysis was the AOP treatment selected. Semiconductor photocatalysis by is an alternative method for conventional water and wastewater treatment technologies being able to mineralise to CO_2 and H_2O the most recalcitrant compounds. This methodology has the advantage that it can be sensitized by solar light what represents a major energy cost saving when developing a water and wastewater remediation treatment. TiO_2 is a photostable, inexpensive and non toxic material. The most popular titanium dioxide used is P25 produced by Degussa Company [3].

2 Experimental section

2.1 Reagents and materials

Zinctetraphenylporphyrin (ZnTPP) and 3,3'-diethylindocarbocyanine iodide were purchased from Aldrich in the highest purity available.

The photocatalyst used was titanium dioxide, Degussa P25 (80% anatase), is the most commonly used due to its high photoactivity when compared to other sources. This is due to its high surface area about 50 m^2 to its crystalline complex microstructure and promotes better separation of inhibiting the loads recombination. All the other chemicals used in this study were obtained from Aldrich. We used bidistilled water prepared in the laboratory.

2.2 Experimental procedure

Fresh solutions were always prepared before used and diluted according to the requirements of the experiments. Photodegradations were performed with 50 ml of solutions prepared with the porphyrin and the cyanine in distilled water. Before irradiation each sample was placed in a static mixer, in the dark for 40 minutes. Then the solutions were placed under irradiation, in static mixer, to keep the solution homogeneous.

For the study of the influence of TiO_2 photocatalyst concentration of the photodegradation efficiency 50 ml of a 0,01 gL^{-1} dye solution of each of the studied dyes containing different concentrations of TiO_2 (0, 1×10^{-3} and

$1 \times 10^{-2} gL^{-1}$) were irradiated in the photoreactor described below for 300 min. Samples were collected at the times, 0, 15, 30, 45, 60, 90,120, 180 and 300 minutes for analysis in UV-Visible.

The photodegradation of the samples of the porphyrins and cyanine dyes were evaluated spectrophotometrically measuring the maximum absorption at the corresponding wavelength of each dye (respectively λ_{max}= 422nm for ZnTPP and λ_{max}= 477nm for 3,3'-diethylindocarbocyanine iodide). A double beam UV-Visible spectrophotometer (Cary 100 Bio) was used for spectrophotometric determinations of the absorption spectra of the dyes from 200-800 nm. Spectra of the dyes in water were recorded with 1 cm or 1 mm quartz cuvettes.

The samples were irradiated with a 125 Watts mercury vapour lamp (from Osram). In this type of commercial lamps, the filament is protected by a glass bulb that cuts all UV-A and UV-B radiation. The glass bulb presents a white colour due to the internal phosphor coating that improves the radiation of the lamp on the visible region. This type of lamps with glass bulb is appropriated to selectively illuminate and exclusively excite TiO_2 band gap, avoiding direct photolysis of the dye molecules that could be simultaneously promoted if all the lamp emission profile was available.

The photoreactor were the samples undergo irradiation is composed by an elliptical cover that supports the irradiation source described above and of a base containing a magnetic stirrer, where the samples to be irradiated are placed in 100 mL beakers. The light arising from the mercury lamp was measured at 366 nm (the wavelength of TiO_2 bandgap [3]) with the help of a Cole Parmer radiometer (series 9811-50) placed above the beaker with the sample to be irradiated. All samples were illuminated with an average irradiation power of $2.7 mW/cm^2$.

3 Results and discussion

3.1 Effect of TiO₂ photocatalyst concentration on Porphyrin photodegradation

Figure 1 displays the results of the photodegradation of ZnTPP in water. Figure 1a) present the results of the porphyrin irradiation in the absence of TiO_2 while Figure 1b) presents the results of the porphyrin irradiated with 0,01g of TiO_2.

In Figure 1a) we can observe that ZnTPP in water doesn't experiment any significant photodegradation during the 5hours irradiation period in the absence of the photocatalyst while in part b) of the same figure we see the porphyrin undergo a significant photodegradation in the same period. For a smaller amount of TiO_2 added the photodegradation observed was much smaller.

Figure 2 displays the percentage photodegradation of the compound calculated as

$$Photodegradation = \left(\frac{Absi-Absf}{Absi}\right) * 100.$$

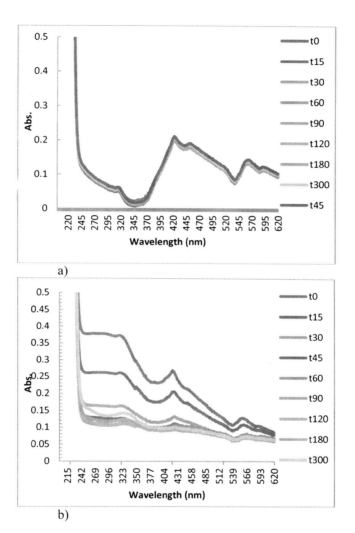

Figure 1: Ground state absorption spectra for Zinctetraphenylporphyrin in water (1×10^{-3}M) under a 125 watt mercury vapour lamp irradiation over time. Spectra were register after 0, 14, 30, 45, 60, 90, 120, 180 and 300 minutes of irradiation in a) without and b) with TiO$_2$.

Contrarily to the commonly observed to several dyes [8] for this porphyrin in water the total photodegradation of the dye wasn't reached in the total irradiation time. This is probably due to the fact that porphyrins are mostly insoluble in water. Even though it was possible to conclude that the efficiency of photocatalytic degradation of ZnTPP in water was clearly increased by the addition of photocatalyst and by increasing its amount.

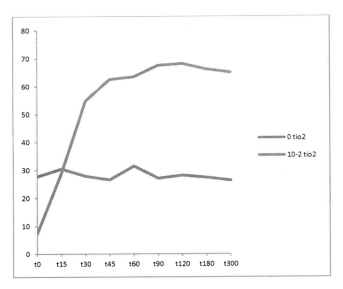

Figure 2:   Percentage photodegradation obtained for Zinctetraphenyl-porphyrin in water (1×10^{-3}M) under a 125 watts mercury vapour lamp irradiation over time (respectively 0, 14, 30, 45, 60, 90, 120, 180 and 300 minutes of irradiation without and with TiO_2.

3.2 Effect of TiO_2 photocatalyst concentration on cyanine photodegradation

Figure 3 displays the results of the photodegradation of 3,3'-diethyl-indocarbocyanine iodide in water. Figure 3a) presents the results of the cyanine irradiation in the absence of TiO_2 while Figure 3b) presents the results of the cyanine irradiated with 0,01g of TiO_2.

As can be seen from Figure 3a) this cyanine dye in water experiments some photodegradation even in the absence of titanium dioxide. The dye slowly loses its colour during the time of the experiment as shows the neat decrease of the maximum of the absorption spectrum of the cyanine in water after 5 hours of irradiation. When 1×10^{-2} gL^{-1} of TiO_2 were added to the solution to be remediated, a much consistent and quick lost of colour can be observed. By the end of 300 minutes of irradiation, the typical visible absorption band of the cyanine dye disappeared completely. After treatment with the photocatalysts only their absorption bands in the UV region on the absorption spectra are still present.

Figure 4 displays the percentage photodegradation of the cyanine dye in water in the presence and in the absence of the photocatalyst.

From Figure 4 it can be observed that cyanine dye alone degraded around 20% while in the presence of 0,01 g of TiO_2 the degradation reached 100% in the 300 minutes of degradation. In the remaining smaller concentrations of TiO_2 studied, it was found that the degradation was less efficient.

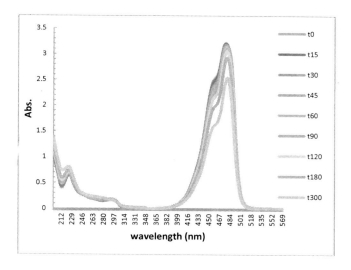

a)

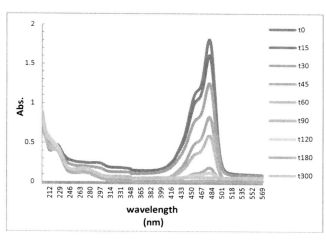

b)

Figure 3:   Ground state absorption spectra for 3,3'-diethylindocarbocyanine iodide in water (1×10^{-3}M) under 125 watt mercury vapour lamp irradiation over time. Spectra were register after 0, 14, 30, 45, 60, 90, 120, 180 and 300 minutes of irradiation in a) without and b) with TiO_2.

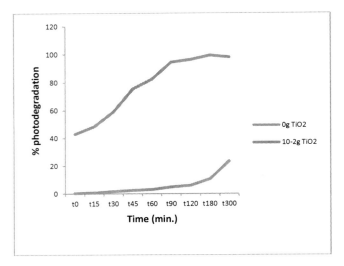

Figure 4:   Percentage   photodegradation   obtained   for   3,3'-diethylindocarbocyanine iodide in water (1×10^{-3}M) under a 125 watts mercury vapour lamp irradiation over time (respectively 0, 14, 30, 45, 60, 90, 120, 180 and 300 minutes of irradiation without and with TiO_2.

4   Conclusions

In this study it was concluded that is possible to promote and increase the photodegradation rate of porphyrins and cyanine dyes in water through heterogeneous semiconductor photocatalysis. These two classes of dyes are sensitizers for photodynamic therapy of cancer and so after PDT cancer treatment these sensitizers and their photodegradation probes can reach water bodies. Zinctetraphenylphorpyrin did suffer significant photodegradation in the absence of a photocatalyst, but its presence definitely and efficiently promoted its substantial photodegradation. The studied cyanine dye experienced some photodegradation in the absence of photocatalyst and reached complete photodegradation in its presence during the time of the experiment. We can conclude that we successfully achieved the photodegradation of these two potential PDT agents in water and that the efficiency of the process is dependent of the irradiation time and on the amount of the photocatalyst used. This work demonstrates the possibility of using heterogeneous photocatalysis on the remediation of waste waters containing medicine residues from cancer PDT treatment.

Acknowledgements

The authors gratefully acknowledge the Fundação para a Ciência e Tecnologia (FCT), Portugal through projects PTDC/QUI/70123/2006, ERA-MNT/0003/2009 and ERA-MNT/0004/2009.

References

[1] Exall, K. A review of water reuse and recycling, with reference to Canadian practice and potential: 2. Applications. *Water Research Journal of Canada*, **39**(1), pp. 13-28, 2004.

[2] Vigneswaran, S., Sundaravadiel, M. Recycle and Reuse of domestic wastewater. *Wastewater recycle, reuse and reclamation*, ed. Saravanamuthu, V., Eolss Publishers, Oxford, UK, 2004.

[3] Oliveira A. S., Saggioro E. M., Pavesi T., Moreira J. C., Vieira Ferreira L. F. Solar Photochemistry for Environmental Remediation – Advanced Oxidation Processes for Industrial Wastewater Treatment (Chapter 15), *Molecular Photochemistry – Various Aspects*, ed. Satyen Saha pp. 355–380, 2012. ISBN: 978-953-51-0446-9.

[4] Güitekin, I., Ince, N.H., Synthetic endocrine disruptors in the environment and water remediation by advanced oxidation processes. *Journal of Environmental Management*, **85**, pp. 816–832, 2007.

[5] Le-Minh, N., Khan, S.J., Drewes. J.E., Stuetz, R.M., Fate of antibiotics during municipal water recycling treatment processes. *Water Research*, **44**, pp. 4295–4323, 2010.

[6] Fujishima A., Honda K., Electrochemical Photolysis of Water at a Semiconductor Electrode. *Nature*, **238**, pp. 37, 1937.

[7] Oliveira A.S., Saggioro E.M., Barbosa N., Mazzei A., Vieira Ferreira L. F., Moreira J., Surface Photocatalysis: A Study of the Thickness of TiO_2 Layers on the Photocatalytic Decomposition of Soluble Indigo Blue Dye. *Rev. Chim.*, **62**(4), pp. 462–468, 2011.

[8] Saggioro E., Oliveira A.S., Pavesi T., Maia C., Vieira Ferreira L. F., Moreira J., Use of Titanium Dioxide Photocatalysis on the Remediation of model textile wastewaters containing azo dyes. *Molecules*, **16**, 10370-10386, 2011.

[9] Socoteanu R., Boscencu R., Hirtopeanu A., Manda G., Oliveira A. S., Ilie M., Vieira Ferreira L. F., Trends in Interdisciplinary Studies Revealing Porphyrinic Compounds Multivalency Towards Biomedical Application, *Biomedical Engineering – From Theory to Applications*, ed. Reza Fazel-Rezai, 2011. ISBN: 978-953-307-637-9.

[10] Boscencu R., Ilie M., Socoteanu R., Oliveira A.S., Constantin C., Neagu , M., Manda G., Vieira Ferreira L.F., Microwave Synthesis, Basic Spectral and Biological Evaluation of Some Copper (II) Mesoporphyrinic Complexes, *Molecules*, **15**, pp. 3731–3743, 2010.

[11] Constantin, C, Neagu, M, Boscencu R., Hinescu, M. E., Oliveira, A. S.. Potential intracellular tracker capacity of novel synthetic metalloporphyrins, *Toxicology Letters*, **205**, S61-S61, 2011.

[12] Vieira Ferreira L. F., Ferreira D. P., Oliveira A. S., Boscencu R., Socoteanu R., Ilie M., Constantin C., Neagu M., Synthesis, photophysical and cytotoxicity evaluation of A3B type mesoporphyrinic compounds. *Dyes and Pigments*, 95, pp. 296–303, 2012.

[13] Santos P.F., Reis L.V., Almeida P., Oliveira A.S., Vieira Ferreira L.F., Efficiency of Singlet Oxygen Generation of Aminosquarylium Cyanines. *J. Photochem. Photobiol.*, **163**, pp. 267–269, 2004.

[14] Santos P.F., Reis L.V., Duarte I., Serrano J. P., Almeida P., Oliveira A.S., Vieira Ferreira L.F., Synthesis and photochemical evaluation of iodinated squarylium cyanine dyes. *Helv. Chim. Acta*, **88**, pp. 1135, 2005.

[15] Vieira Ferreira L. F., Ferreira D. P., Duarte P., *et al.*, Surface Photochemistry: 3,3'-Dialkylthia and Selenocarbocyanine Dyes Adsorbed onto Microcrystalline Cellulose, *International Journal of Molecular Sciences*, **13** (1), pp. 596–611, 2012.

Analysis of sustainability aspects of the packaging deposit-refund system in Latvia

E. Dāce. I. Pakere & D. Blumberga
Institute of Energy Systems and Environment,
Riga Technical University, Latvia

Abstract

In Latvia, for more than a decade, a container system for packaging waste segregation has been in a continuous process of development – starting with the first containers in the beginning of 2000s until now, when there are efforts made to provide containers to people living in rural areas. Although the regeneration targets set by EU are fulfilled by the existing system, it is still considered as not effective enough. In many cases the existing system is considered as economically and even environmentally unsustainable, but it is still maintained due to governmental pressure. At the same time, for about last five years hot discussions are held on implementation of packaging deposit system which would operate in parallel with the existing containers' system. Since there are too many controversial arguments from the stakeholders involved, an analysis is necessary to assess the sustainability aspects of implementation of the deposit-refund system in Latvia. The paper presents the results of an analysis of the social, economic and environmental aspects. The results show that the deposit-refund system has a positive influence on the environmental aspects, however the benefits gained have to be balanced with the system's costs and efficiency, which is hard to reach in Latvia because of small beverage drinks' consumption. Therefore, solutions have to be found to enhance the existing curbside containers' system rather than to introduce the deposit-refund system.
Keywords: deposit-refund system, packaging waste, sustainability, deposit fee, beverage drinks.

1 Introduction

Reduction of municipal waste has been an important issue in Latvia as large part of waste is deposited in landfills. Even if sorting rate of different waste materials

WIT Transactions on Ecology and The Environment, Vol 173, © 2013 WIT Press
www.witpress.com, ISSN 1743-3541 (on-line)
doi:10.2495/SDP130611

increases with every year, still, according to Central Statistical Bureau of Latvia (CSB) [1] 46% of municipal waste was landfilled in 2010. Up to 20% of municipal solid waste is compiled of used packaging materials. Different experiences from other countries show the way to increase recovery rates for packaging materials by introducing deposit-refund system (DRS). DRS means an extra payment for product which would be refunded after giving back the empty packaging unit. This system is mainly used for beverage drinks filled in different polyethylene terephthalate (PET) or glass bottles, as well as in aluminum cans. Packaging involved in DRS constitute on average 20% of all packaging waste.

In Latvia, the first curbside containers for separate waste collection system were set up in 2001, as reported by one of the operating producer responsibility organizations – Latvian Green dot [2]. Since then the regeneration rates for packaging waste have increased from about 28% in 2003 up to 47% in 2010, fig.1. As it can be seen, there are inconsistencies in the data of regenerated waste amounts. Until 2006, the regulations No. 139 issued by the Cabinet of Ministers of the Republic of Latvia [3] were applied, however definitions and explanations on the terms 'recycling' and 'regeneration' were lacking, thus the enterprises submitted the data by their understanding. From 2006, European Parliament and Council Directive 94/62/EC on packaging and packaging waste [4] came into force, defining the terms and setting the regeneration targets binding to Latvia. Thus the data until 2006 are unlikely and inconsistent, whereas data from 2007 onwards are more believable.

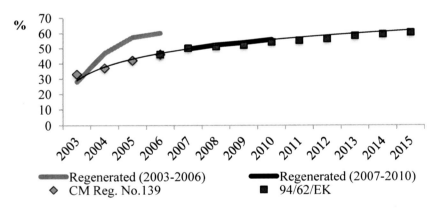

Figure 1:   Targets of regeneration rates of the packaging waste according to regulations issued by the cabinet of ministers of the republic of Latvia (2003-2006) [3] and European parliament and council directive 94/62/EC on packaging and packaging waste (2006-2015) [4] and their performance in Latvia according to statistical reports on regenerated packaging materials [5].

It can be seen from Figure 1 that in 2010 percentage of regenerated packaging waste has exceeded 55%. Nevertheless, the landfilled amount of waste is still very high.

European Parliament and Council Directive 94/62/EC on packaging and packaging waste [4] requires 60% regeneration rate for packaging waste in 2015. From the Figure 1 it seems that it would not cause difficulties to reach this level, however directive sets also fixed targets for recovery of different packaging materials, and until now Latvia is step behind these rates.

In order to assess whether an increase of the level of recycling is possible by using DRS in Latvia, a study by a company Price Waterhouse Cooper was conducted in 2008 [6]. Necessity of DRS, details on how the system will work and the costs and profits of the system were analyzed in the study. Until now this is the widest study on the implementation of the DRS in Latvia. Nevertheless, the study does not include an analysis of all sustainability aspects, i.e. social, environmental and economic.

As DRS has been applied in different countries, number of studies can be found on targets achieved for the waste reduction possibilities. However, the situation in other countries cannot be directly applied for analyzing the situation in Latvia, since waste management policy, as well as social, economic and environmental aspects for Latvia differ from other European countries.

According to the latest announcements from the government's representative Vesere [7] it is expected that in Latvia the implementation of the DRS could be started in 2015, therefore the aim of the present paper is to analyze the social and environmental aspects, as well as to estimate the costs of implementation of the DRS in Latvia.

2 Methodology

There are several parties involved in the DRS (producers, retailers, consumers, government and other), which make the system more complicated since every participant has different interests and needs. The DRS can gain the optimal result only in the case when all the parties are economically or emotionally motivated to take part in the DRS.

The basic aim of the system is to increase the level of recovery of packaging waste. As deposit added to the products has been paid by customers, they are interested to return the empty bottles and cans in order to get back the money spent. Producers are participating in the system as otherwise they are obliged to pay the natural resource tax per every packaging unit. If the tax is higher than costs of participation in the DRS, producers have a strong motivation to involve. Retailers can use the DRS as a marketing resource to attract customers. Whereas for government the DRS is an instrument to fulfill the binding targets set by EU.

Since there are so many stakeholders involved in the DRS, it is necessary to find a balance among interests and needs of all the interested parties from economic, social and environmental points of view.

2.1 Social aspects

In order to analyze the social aspects of the implementation of the DRS a couple of surveys were conducted at the beginning of 2012 – for consumers and municipalities. Consumers were surveyed in Riga (capital of Latvia) in four supermarkets of a company Rimi Latvia which has the largest food market network in Latvia. The supermarkets included in the study are located in different parts of the city. 125 valid answers given by both male and female of age between 18 and 62 were collected and analyzed. The questionnaire included items about packaging from consumer perspective (does it influence their choice, what happens when the product is unpacked etc.) to find out their viewpoint about implementation of deposit packaging and DRS.

In Latvia, municipalities are responsible for managing waste in their administrative territory, therefore municipalities are an important stakeholder of the DRS. At the beginning of 2012, a survey was conducted in order to find out the opinion of municipalities. The survey was conducted by preparing an online questionnaire sent out to all 119 municipalities of Latvia. Eighty-eight valid answers were received from municipalities of 7 major cities and 81 districts. The questionnaire included items about waste management system and its efficiency in municipalities, as well as factors preventing and motivating population to involve in the waste management system and waste sorting.

2.2 Economic aspects

The costs of the implementation of the DRS were determined by estimating the amount of beverage drinks (i.e. bottled water, soft drinks, beer and light-alcoholic cocktails) placed in the market. The existing and future consumption of beverage drinks was determined by assuming that it changes with the changes of gross domestic product (GDP). By using the projected data of products' consumption, as well as fraction of different packaging materials, an approximate amount of units of the deposit packaging placed in the market in 2015 onwards was estimated. Further, the estimated amounts of packaging units were used to assess the collection costs, which make the basis for payment's quantification to retailers.

When the packaging is collected, the refillable units are delivered to producers of beverage drinks, whereas one-way packaging is sold to recyclers. That forms the income of the operator. Besides the income from material sales, the operator also has income from the unredeemed deposits (sum of deposit fees for packaging that has not been returned by customer). However, the operator has also to cover the costs of retailers for collection of one-way packaging. In case of one way packaging, the balance between profit and costs of the operator is very important for optimal result. The deficit is covered by service charges made by producers. Operation costs of the operator are composed of a loan and interest payments, labor, transportation, maintenance, production and administrative costs.

The service charge shows the costs of packaging waste management that have to be covered by producers. The service charge can be compared to other alternative waste management systems to find the cheapest solution for producers.

2.3 Environmental aspects

The environmental aspects were evaluated in terms of decreased energy consumption and related CO_2 emissions, as well as diminishing waste littered in the surrounding environment. It was assumed that the energy savings would arise from recycling and reuse of the collected packaging material and utilizing it instead of the virgin material. Consumers' purchasing power would lower due to application of the deposit fee, thus decreasing the consumption of beverage drinks and the amount of packaging used with it. Thereby, also here the energy consumption and CO_2 emissions would be decreased.

In order to estimate an influence on littering, a test was conducted to determine the composition of waste littered in Latvia. Starting from 2008, an environmental clean-up campaign is held once a year. During the campaign the litter is being collected in special garbage bags and delivered to the sanitary landfill sites. In this study, one landfill site was chosen, were the test was conducted. The composition of the collected garbage bags was analyzed by sorting their content into deposit packaging and other waste.

3   Results and discussion

3.1 Social aspects

Although in Latvia a curbside container system for segregated waste was started in 2001 [2], the results of the municipalities' survey have shown that more than fifth of municipalities (22%) does not have any elements of the waste sorting system, 9% have just a few containers in a whole municipality, but 7% have only a drop-off point, fig. 2.

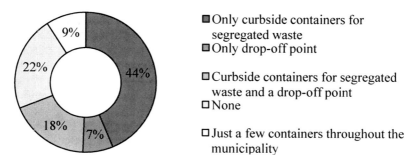

Figure 2:   Level of provided waste sorting system in municipalities of Latvia in 2012.

The results also show that only 9% of municipalities consider the existing curbside container system to be effective to increase the packaging recovery rates. The rest hold a view that the DRS would possibly (56%) or definitely (31%) be more effective for their municipality. This is also proved by the consumer survey, results of which show that lack of curbside containers and large distances to reach the containers are fairly important factors, which hinder from sorting the packaging waste. However inconvenience of sorting waste in the households is rather significant factor, thus stronger motivating instruments are necessary.

The results show that the strongest factors that would motivate the population to sort their packaging waste are convenient access to curbside containers and/or take-back points of DRS. Also an increase of waste management costs of unsorted waste would be a strong motivating factor.

According to the results of Eurobarometer survey conducted in 2011 [8], about 28% of the population in Latvia sort most of their waste for recycling. Whereas, the analysis of the results of consumers' survey show that in case if the DRS would be implemented the percentage of population sorting their packaging waste for recycling might increase up to about 80%. Fifth of the consumers would be motivated to sort by the possibility to receive back the money spent, i.e. the deposit fee, whereas only 7% would sort for cleaner surrounding environment. 6% of the respondents would be motivated to sort only if it would not cause inconvenience, i.e. the take-back points of the deposit packaging would be easy accessible. However, all of the factors mentioned above are equally important for the majority of respondents (66%). That confirms the necessity to find a balance among all the influencing factors – determination of an optimal amount of the deposit fee, providing convenient sorting facilities, as well as informing the society of the systems' positive influence on the environment.

The idea of DRS is that the deposit fee is added to the product packed in the deposit packaging and received back later when the packaging is delivered to the take-back point. That is, it used as an instrument motivating the consumer to return the packaging for recycling. However, it can also influence the consumers' purchasing power; thus, the choice of products.

As the results of the consumers' survey show, when choice is made between similar products, packaging can always (17%) or sometimes (58%) be a decisive factor for 75% of respondents. This is important, if deposit packaging is considered. The results show that 76% of respondents would prefer a product in the deposit packaging. However, for now there is a lack of information that would explain to the society that the DRS might cause also economic burden related to rise of the price of products.

Regarding the waste management costs, Eurobarometer [9] has reported results, which state that in Latvia 45% of population would prefer to include the cost of waste management in the price of products they buy. In order to assess the influence of the increased price of products, elasticity of demand of beverage drinks was considered, which shows the percentage of the demand's changes, if the price of the product changes by 1% (Andreyeva *et al.* [10]). The elasticity of demand for bottled water is 0.36 (Reizina [11]), for soft drinks – 0.79 (Andreyeva *et al.* [10]), whereas for alcoholic drinks – 0.38 (Fogarty [12]). It can be seen that elasticity of demand is lower for bottled water and alcoholic drinks than that of soft drinks. It means that changes of consumer prices have larger influence on the consumption of the soft drinks than on other drinks mentioned. It was found that depending on the amount of deposit fee, the price per 1l of alcoholic drinks will increase by 2.4 – 5.6%, soft drinks – by 5.6 – 13%, whereas bottled water – by 10% up to 25%. That will cause the drop of consumption of the beverage drinks by 1.5 – 5%, which will affect producers of the beverage drinks, since their income will decrease. It also explains why in Latvia producers strongly oppose the implementation of DRS. Besides, according to a study by Price Waterhouse Coopers [13] the producers' costs for packaging waste management would increase by 62% if compared to the existing system. Moreover, the Association of Small Breweries states that extra costs for breweries will reduce the ability to compete with other products that will not join the DRS.

The largest food retailers, on their side, support the DRS as it can attract new customers. The experience of other countries shows that in case if a retailer chooses to use reverse vending machine (RVM) for collection of the deposit packaging, then the deposit fee refunded for the empty packaging is mainly paid as a receipt that later can be used as a discount when purchasing products from the same retailer. If traders use such payment system, then DRS can be considered as a positive marketing activity.

However, the implementation of the DRS is more complicated for small retailers. As pointed out by the Latvian Traders' Association, DRS will significantly increase the retailers' costs. It will be necessary to install take-back points for empty packaging with extra employees. Also strict documentation will be necessary.

3.2 Economic aspects

There are several studies reporting the assessment of economic aspects of DRS [14–17], besides a few studies deal with analysis of impact from packaging DRS on consumers and producers [18–20].

The economic estimates show that large investments will be necessary to implement the DRS in Latvia – more than 20 million EUR will be required in the first three years. The annual costs of DRS are determined by the amount of deposit packaging placed on the market. The costs of retailers differ for manual and automatic collection. In case of automatic collection reverse vending machines (RVM) are used. In order to cover the costs of purchase, adjustment and maintenance each RVM needs to collect at least 1200 units of packaging per day. The retailers' costs of packaging collection are covered by producers in case of refillable bottles or by the operator in case of one-way packaging. The money paid to retailers for covering the collection costs of the packaging ranges between 27.6 and 29.6 EUR per thousand units of packaging for manual collection, and between 44.4 and 45.7 EUR per thousand units of packaging for collection with RVMs.

When the packaging is collected, the refillable units are delivered to producers of beverage drinks, whereas one-way packaging is sold to recyclers. Nevertheless aluminum composes the smallest part of deposit packaging both, by units and weight, it ensures the largest profit from sales to recyclers. This profit is one of the income sources for the operator of the DRS. Another source is from unredeemed deposits, i.e. the deposit fees of the packaging that has not been returned to the system. The balance between the operator's profit and costs is very important for optimal result. The service charges were estimated to find the amount of money producers have to pay per kg of packaging to cover the operator's deficit.

Now, when the curbside system is in operation, the producers of beverage drinks can choose to pay for the collection of their packaging by a natural resource tax to the government or by a contract price to a producer's responsibility organization (PRO), which ensures collection of packaging waste and exempts the contractor (producer) from the natural resource tax. Currently the most of the market (91.7% of producers' generated packaging volumes in 2008) is covered by two PROs – Zaļais punkts (Green Dot Latvia) and Zaļā josta (Green Belt) (Hogg et al. [15]).

For some materials the difference between the natural resource tax and the contract price is even tenfold, fig. 3. Since producers have two possible options, they mostly choose the cheapest one, i.e. to sign a contract with a PRO and pay the contract price (tariff) per each kilogram of used packaging material. Thus, in reality only minor part of producers pay the natural resource tax.

The estimates show that in case of operator's service charge (DRS), producers will have to pay more for PET and aluminum packaging than they do by having a contract with PRO. However, in case of glass packaging it would be more advantageous to pay the service charge since it is lower than any of PROs' contract prices. Thus the DRS can be considered economically feasible for producers only in case of glass packaging.

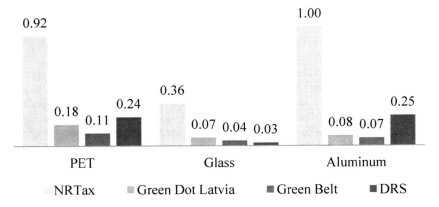

Figure 3: Charges for the packaging in Latvia in 2012, and the average service charges for deposit packaging in 2015–2020, in EUR/kg [21–23].

3.3 Environmental aspects

There are several environmental advantages that can be gained by implementation of the DRS. The most frequently mentioned is reduction of landfilled municipal waste, as well as reduction of littering which has been discussed in a number of studies [14, 24, 25]. Littering has been mentioned as one of the environmental problems that can be reduced by implementation of the DRS. In Latvia, littering is common along the roads, in parks and forests, in bus stops, as well as in territories of abandoned allotments. According to Yeh and Vaughn [26] the packaging of beverage drinks is often left on the roadways, parks and beaches, because people find it convenient to do so. DRS can help to solve the problem of littering by offering a motivational tool for consumers to bring the packaging to the collection point. The importance of the littering's reduction that results in cleaner surrounding environment has been pointed out by Hogg *et al.* [24]. Nevertheless, a report by Europen [25] argues that beverage containers make only 5 – 15% of littering in Europe. That was also confirmed by analyzing the composition data of littering collected during the clean-up campaign in Latvia. The results of the analysis show that the deposit packaging compiles only 11% of the total waste mass collected, or 28% of the total volume collected. Thus, by implementing the DRS the littering problem can be solved only partly.

The main aim of the DRS is to enhance the material recycling rates, thus saving energy and resources. Aluminum and PET are among the most required materials. According to Holmgren and Henning [27], it is possible to save up to 97% of energy by producing cans from secondary materials compared to production from bauxite ore. Production of PET from secondary materials saves 96%, but glass – about 30% of energy. Depending on the recovery rates it is possible to save a considerable amount of energy by recycling the packaging waste (fig. 4).

As the figure shows, the largest amount of energy can be saved by recycling the PET packaging since the amounts produced and energy saved are higher than for aluminum and glass. The lowest energy savings can be achieved by recycling glass; therefore, more attempts should be driven towards reuse.

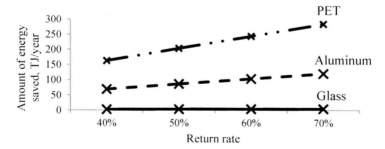

Figure 4:   Amount of energy that can be saved depending on the material return rates (based on the packaging waste amount generated in Latvia in 2010).

It has been estimated that by implementing the DRS the average fraction of packaging materials recycled would increase by 10% if the fraction of packaging returned would be at least 70%. In that case almost 60TJ of energy could be saved annually (corresponding to the amount of deposit packaging in Latvia). Depending on the energy resource and efficiency of the equipment used it is possible to estimate the amount of CO_2 emissions prevented. The experience of other countries [28–30] shows that the fraction returned can exceed 70%, thus giving even greater energy savings.

4 Conclusion and recommendations

In Latvia, a curbside container system is in operation for packaging waste, however most of the municipalities are not satisfied with the existing system, since it develops too slowly. Besides the curbside container system does not motivate most of the population to sort their waste due to inconvenience caused by waste sorting in households and the distances they have to make to reach the containers. Since the EU's regeneration targets are binding to Latvia, solutions have to be found to enhance the existing curbside containers' system or to introduce a new system for packaging waste management. A deposit-refund system (DRS) to be started in 2015 is in consideration at the government level. However, also DRS has several disadvantages: (i) implementation of packaging DRS requires high costs and results with higher prices of products; (ii) deposit packaging contributes only about 20% to all packaging materials placed in the market, thus curbside collection system still needs to work together with DRS, which means maintaining two systems in parallel (including double transportation and higher CO_2 emissions in the air).

There are also other aspects to be taken into account when considering the implementation of DRS. In order to ensure the systems' equal availability to all consumers, location of the take-back points has to be planned properly since it has a large influence on the systems' costs and efficiency. Proper decisions have also to be made on the types of packaging to be included in the system. The initial estimates show that the recovery rates will be larger than with the existing system, however it will also increase the producers' costs of packaging waste management. It is estimated that the DRS in Latvia will be feasible for beverage drink producers only in case of glass packaging.

The advantages provided by the DRS are the considerable increase of recovery rates of the materials included in the system and the amount of energy saved by recycling the materials instead of producing them from virgin raw materials. It has been estimated that even a slight increase in recovery rates can give a considerable decrease in the energy consumed, thus the CO_2 emitted into the air. Also littering problems can be lessened. It was estimated that in Latvia PET and glass bottles and aluminum cans compile about 11% of the total litter.

The potential benefits have to be evaluated in relation to the costs of the system. It can be concluded that DRS can be feasible and sustainable in countries with large consumption of beverage drinks, where the 'per unit' costs are low. However, in order to find the optimal solution for Latvian conditions (improvements of the existing system, the existing system combined with the deposit system, or deposit system alone) it is necessary to develop a model that includes all sustainability aspects presented in a dynamic manner. In order to do that thorough sociological study is suggested to understand the human behavior, as well as analysis of the results of existing experience of DRS' implementation in other countries.

References

[1] Central Statistical Bureau of Latvia, database No. VIG04. Municipal and hazardous waste: collection and treatment, http://data.csb.gov.lv/ DATABASEEN/vide/Annual%20statistical%20data/14.%20Natural%20res ources%20and%20environmental%20protection/14.%20Natural%20resour ces%20and%20environmental%20protection.asp

[2] European Environment Agency, Statistical report on generated packaging waste and recovery of resources in the Republic of Latvia in 2003-2011 according to the European Commission Decision 2005/270/EC.

[3] Annual Report of the Latvijas Zalais punkts. Riga, 2009, http://www.zalais.lv/files/2010_09_13_lzp_parskats_eng.pdf

[4] Regulation No.139 of the Cabinet of Ministers of the Republic of Latvia "Regulations regarding volumes and time periods for recovery of packaging waste, procedures for submission reports and model forms of reports". Latvijas Vēstnesis 52 (2627), 05.04.2002.

[5] Directive 2004/12/EC of the European Parliament and of the Council amending Directive 94/62/EC on packaging and packaging waste. Official Journal of the European Union L47/26, 18.2.2004.

[6] Analysis of implementation aspects of the packaging deposit-refund system, and development of preconditions for glass and PET bottles and aluminum cans [in Latvian]. Price Waterhouse Coopers, 2008.

[7] Vesere, R. Personal communication, 15 December 2011, Head of the Department of Environmental Protection, Ministry of Environmental Protection and Regional Development, Latvia.

[8] Attitudes of European citizens towards the environment, Special Eurobarometer 365. Eurobarometer, 2011.

[9] Analytical report: Attitudes of Europeans towards resource efficiency, Flash EB Series #316. Eurobarometer, 2011.

[10] Andreyeva,T., Long, W.M. and Brownell, B.K., The Impact of Food Prices on Consumption: A Systematic Review of Research on the Price Elasticity of Demand for Food. American Journal of Public Health, 100 (2), pp. 216-222, 2010.

[11] Reizina, V., Impact of economic situation on the changes in Latvia's inhabitant consumption expenditures. Scientific Journal of Riga Technical University, Economics and Business. Economy: Theory and Practice, Vol. 20, pp. 100-107.

[12] Fogarty J., The own price elasticity of alcohol: A meta-analysis. The University of Western Australia: Crawley, 2010.

[13] Impact of one-way packaging deposit-refund system on the beverage drink industry in Latvia [in Latvian]. Price Waterhouse Coopers, 2010.

[14] Lavee, D., A cost-benefit analysis of a deposit-refund program for beverage containers in Israel. Waste Management, 30 (5), pp. 338-345, 2010.

[15] Hogg, D., Elliot, T., Croasdell, S., et al., Options and Feasibility of a European Refund System for Metal Beverage Cans. Final report. Eunomia, 2011.

[16] Mrozek, J.R., Revenue Neutral Deposit/Refund Systems. Environmental and Resource Economics, Vol. 17, pp. 183-193, 2000.

[17] Palmer, K., Sigman, H. and Walls, M., The Cost of Reducing Municipal Solid Waste. Resources for the Future, 1996.

[18] Numata, D., Economic analysis of deposit – refund systems with measures for mitigating negative impacts on suppliers. Resources, Conservation and Recycling, Vol. 53, p. 199-207, 2009.

[19] Onuma, A. and Saito, T. Some Effects of Deposit-Refund System on Producers and Consumers. Keio Economics Society Discussion Paper Series (KESDP), 2006.

[20] Kulshreshtha, P., and Sarangi, S., No return, no refund: an analysis of deposit-refund systems. Journal of Economic Behavior and Organization, Vol. 46, pp. 379-394, 2001.

[21] Natural Resource Tax Law. Latvijas Vēstnesis, No 209 (3367), 29 December 2005.

[22] Tariff of Latvijas Zaļais punkts, http://www.zalais.lv/lv/uznemumiem /tarifu-kalkulators/iepakojumu-tarifu-kalkulators/

[23] Tariff of SIA Zaļā josta and other PROs, http://www.zalajosta.lv /lat/jaunumi/?doc=128

[24] Hogg, D., Fletcher, D., Elliot, T. and Eye, M.V., Have We Got the Bottle? Implementing a Deposit Refund Scheme in the UK. Eunomia Report, 2010.

[25] Better rules for a better environment: Modern Beverage Container Policy. Europen, 2009.

[26] Yeh, C.-N. and Vaughn, P.J., Consumer's Behavior under Mandatory Deposit System. International Advances in Economic Research, 14(4), pp. 472, 2008.

[27] Holmgren, K. and Henning, D., Comparison between material and energy recovery of municipal waste from an energy perspective. Resources, Conservation and Recycling, Vol. 43, pp. 51-73, 2004.

[28] Dansk Reursystem, http://www.dansk-retursystem.dk/content/us/

[29] Eesti Pandipakend, http://www.eestipandipakend.ee/

[30] Returpack, http://www.returpack.se/en/ownership-structure/

Section 13
Improving safety of users in evacuation
(Special session organised by F. Russo)

A prototypal test using stated preferences data to model evacuation decisions

F. Russo & G. Chilà
Dipartimento di Ingegneria dell'Informazione delle Infrastrutture e dell'Energia Sostenibile, DIIES, Università degli Studi Mediterranea di Reggio Calabria, Italy

Abstract

An experiment carried out on stated preferences (SP) data highlights the role of the informer in the user choice process during evacuation conditions. Starting from the SP data, in this paper we propose a prototypal experimentation of choice models simulating the choice to evacuate or not in different evacuation conditions: calibrated models focus on the role of the informer that determine different responses of users, given a particular kind of dangerous event.
Keywords: evacuation conditions, hypothetical scenarios, calibrated parameters.

1 Introduction

The simulation of user behaviour during an evacuation is a very complex problem, as the behaviour depends on different factors, such as kind and entity of the dangerous event, the socio-economic characteristics of users, and panic. Different demand models have to be specified in relation to the kind of event, which can be classified according to its effects in the space and in the time [1, 2]. With respect to the effect in time, in demand analysis we consider a delayed or immediate approach, in relation to the time gap available between the time at which the dangerous event actually occurs and the time when the event starts its effects on the population.

The international literature relating to evacuation conditions proposes many studies which focus on the hurricane emergency case, by estimating demand models based on revealed preference (RP) surveys. These are inferred from observations of the decision maker's actual choices, in relation to real contexts [3–5]. As RP data are not available for all dangerous events, such models cannot be directly applied to other dangerous events [1, 6]. The prediction of user behaviour becomes essential. For this purpose, evacuation trials and stated preference (SP) surveys may be conducted.

To approach this problem, in previous works we introduce hypothetical scenarios to analyze, in the absence of evacuation trials, the statistical behavioural of the users in evacuation conditions from their statements (SP data) [7].

Obtained results have pointed out the importance of the informer in determining the different responses of users, given a particular kind of dangerous event [8, 9]. The knowledge of the figures that have the better credibility, allow the possibility of organizing an emergency plan with activities adequate to perform clear outcomes and then goals [10, 11]. In order to plan activities, it is necessary to start from a specific demand-supply interaction model [12], introducing the dynamic in terms of qualifying elements [13, 14].

In this work we should propose choice models in considering, for evacuation conditions, the role of the informer in the user choice process.

Below we describe hypothetical scenarios proposed for the sample considered (section 2) and proposed models based on analysis of statements (section 3); we then draw some prototypal conclusions (section 4).

2 Database

In this section we propose a description of data used in the model calibration.

Data are obtained from hypothetical scenarios proposed in an experiment conducted at Mediterranea University of Reggio Calabria, during a planning transport seminar at LAST (Laboratory of Transport System Analysis), which took place in 2011. The experiment was developed as described below. The analyst read aloud the description of hypothetical emergency scenarios, one scenario at a time. Each user in the sample then had to fill out a paper ballot with all information relating to a choice context (traditional method), choosing from a range of alternative options, as in the choice method of SP surveys.

Emergency scenarios proposed to the participants (table 1) are characterized by:

- an anthropogenic kind of dangerous event;
- delayed effect in the time of the dangerous event;
- absence of constrained times to evacuate;

and they are different in respect of:

- effect in the space, which could be punctiform, for scenario 1, or diffused, for scenario 2;
- place of effect for users during the dangerous event, which could be the user's workplace, for scenario 1, or downtown, for scenario 2.

In particular, in scenario 1 we analyze the different responses of users in respect of the informer who communicates the state of emergency to potential stakeholders: a stranger or the head of department. The objective is to determine whether, according to the reliability of the informer who broke the news, different behaviour may be found in users.

Scenario 2 was constructed by considering an environment different from the workplace, within the university campus: the environment is the city centre, and the objective is to test any differences in behaviour under more critical traffic conditions, in an urban rather than a campus context. Also in this scenario, we test differences in respect of the considered informer: a stranger, a representative of the Mayor or a professor.

Table 1:   Scenarios description for dangerous events with delayed effect in the time.

Scenario		Effect in the space	Place of effect for user	Informer
1	You are working at the LAST laboratory of the University of Reggio Calabria on a report to be delivered shortly. Suppose an informer suddenly enters your room and asks you to leave your workplace because a bomb is going to explode in the laboratory. The informer tells you to go and reach Piazza San Brunello. The informer suggests that, to allow faster flow, he/she will open the locked gate to the Agricultural College of the University of Reggio Calabria.	Punctiform	Workplace	Stranger Department head
2	You are in the town hall, in the Hall of Lamps, for a conference on the Euro-Mediterranean area. You have arrived at around 9.20, after parking your car on Via Marina at the Villa Zerbi. Suddenly, an informer breaks into the hall and tells you that you must evacuate the building: a tanker full of flammable liquid is blocked between Via Marina and Corso Garibaldi and is about to explode.	Diffused	Downtown	Stranger Representative of the Mayor Professor

In scenario 1 we consider the effect of two different informers (stranger or department head) when the dangerous event is with punctiform effects in the space and the user is in her/his workplace.

In scenario 2 we consider three different informers (stranger, representative of the Mayor, professor) when the dangerous event is with diffuse effects in the space and the user is downtown. We focus on a different place of the user, in order to assess whether and how this can affect the behaviour found in the workplace.

We consider three prototypal samples:

- Sample A, a focus group of 25 people, aged between 23 and 54 years, characterized by a high cultural level (e.g. professor, researcher, PhD student), useful for testing SP surveys, identifying significant variables not yet included in the survey;
- Sample B, including 51 people, aged between 20 and 31 years, participating in a transport seminar at LAST [9];
- Joint sample A+B, including 76 people, aged between 20 and 54 years.

In tables 2 and 3 a synthesis of characteristics of samples A and B, respectively, is reported. Particularly, for sample A, a percentage of 32% had participated in previous evacuation trials; this percentage is equal to 63% for sample B and, for this sample, 61% of the total had a knowledge of risk field which was at least sufficient. In table 4, a synthesis of characteristics of joint sample A+B is proposed.

Table 2:   Description of sample A.

Data		Value	Percentage
Sex	Male	13	52%
	Female	12	48%
Age	Average	31,36	
Professional status	Workers	25	100%
Socio-economic data	Driving license owner	23	92%
	Car owner	19	76%
Participation in evacuation trials	Yes	8	32%
	No	17	68%

Table 3:   Description of sample B.

Data		Value	Percentage
Sex	Male	22	43%
	Female	29	57%
Age	Average	21,02	
Professional status	Full Time Students	49	96%
	Part Time Students	2	4%
Residence	Resident in Reggio Calabria	29	57%
	Resident outside the province	1	2%
	Resident inside the province	21	41%
Domicile	Domiciled in Reggio Calabria	34	67%
Socio-economic data	Driving license owner	50	98%
	Car owner	35	69%
	Motorvehicle owner	17	33%
Knowledge of risk issues	Good	4	8%
	Sufficient	27	53%
	Poor	20	39%
Participation in evacuation trials	Yes	32	63%
	No	19	37%

Table 4:   Description of joint sample A+B.

Data		Value	Percentage
Sex	Male	42	55%
	Female	34	45%
Age	Average	24,42	
Professional status	Full Time Students	49	65%
	Part Time Students	2	2%
	Worker	25	33%
Socio-economic data	Driving license owner	73	96%
	Car owner	54	71%
Participation in evacuation trials	Yes	8	11%
	No	68	89%

3   Specification, calibration and validation of proposed choice models

In this section we propose different specifications with respect to the simulated scenarios (1, 2).

For all scenarios, we consider a behavioural approach, with random residual ε_j independently and identically distributed according to a Gumbel random variable of zero mean and parameter θ.

We consider a choice including two alternatives:
- to evacuate (e),
- not to evacuate (ne).

We define V_e the systematic utility related to the alternative to evacuate and V_{ne} the systematic utility related to the alternative not to evacuate.

A prototypal experimentation of a choice model simulating the choice to evacuate or not is proposed according to the logit model hypothesis.

It is important to highlight that SP surveys could be characterized by problems related to the realism in the responses of users and to the covariance among different scenarios. Other potential errors relate to: respondent fatigue, policy response bias, self-selectivity bias [7]. Recently, SP-off-RP questions have been introduced in choice modelling [15]. In particular, the alternatives and choice of a respondent in a real-world setting are observed, and the respondent is asked whether s/he would choose the same alternative or switch to another alternative if the attributes of the chosen alternative were less desirable in ways specified by the researcher and/or the attributes of non-chosen alternatives were more desirable in specified ways. This construction, called stated-preference off revealed-preference (SP-off-RP), is intended to increase the realism of the stated-preference task but creates endogeneity.

In this work we have considered standard SP surveys with their potential problems.

Scenario 1

Sample B and sample A + B

$$V_e=\beta_{DHI}\cdot DHI+\beta_{KR}\cdot KR+ \beta_{TRAINING}\cdot TRAINING \tag{1}$$
$$V_{ne}=\beta_{CAR}\cdot CAR+\beta_{RC}\cdot RC \tag{2}$$

where

DHI is a dummy variable equal to 1 if the informer is the department head, to 0 otherwise;

KR is a variable related to knowhow in the risk field, in relation to higher education and/or career of the user and is specified as a dummy variable;

TRAINING is a variable equal to 1 if the users had already participated in evacuation trials, to 0 otherwise;

CAR is a variable equal to 1 if the user owns a car, to 0 otherwise;

RC is a variable equal to 1 if the user's home is in the town centre of Reggio Calabria, to 0 otherwise;

β_i are parameters to be calibrated, being i the linked attribute.

Obtained results from calibration are reported in table 5.

Scenario 2

Sample B

$$V_e=\beta_{PI}\cdot PI+\beta_{Car}\cdot Car+\beta_{FTS}\cdot FTS+\beta_{KR}\cdot KR \tag{3}$$
$$V_{ne}=\beta_{MI}\cdot MI+\beta_{PM}\cdot P \tag{4}$$

where

PI is a dummy variable equal to 1 if the informer is the professor, to 0 otherwise;

CAR is a variable equal to 1 if the user owns a car, to 0 otherwise;

FTS is a dummy variable equal to 1 if the user is a full time student, to 0 otherwise;

KR is a variable related to knowhow in the risk field, in relation to higher education and/or career of the user and is specified as a dummy variable;

MI is a dummy variable equal to 1 if the informer is the Mayor, to 0 otherwise;

PM is a variable equal to 1 if the user utilizes the motorcycle or car to go to school, to 0 otherwise;

β are parameters to be calibrated.

Obtained results from calibration are reported in table 6.

Table 5:   Parameter calibration for scenario 1.

Variable		Alt.	Sample B Value (t-student)	Value (t-student)	Sample A+B Value (t-student)
Department head informer	DHI	e	0,27 (0,50)	0,33 (0,60)	0,41 (0,90)
Car ownership	CAR	ne	-0,17 (-0,20)	-0,42 (-0,60)	-1,75 (-4,20)
Know how risk field	KR	e	0,60 (0,90)		
Home in Reggio Cal.	RC	ne	-1,38 (-2,30)	-1,50 (-2,50)	
Participation at evacuation trials	TRAINING	e	1,18 (1,90)	1,23 (2,20)	1,55 (3,00)
Num. obs.			102,00	102,00	152,00
Initial value			-70,70	-70,70	-105,36
Final value			-33,87	-34,28	-50,72
rho-quadro			0,52	0,52	0,52

Table 6:   Parameter calibration for scenario 2 (sample B).

Variable		Alt.	Value (t-student)	Value (t-student)
Professor informer	PI	e	1,18 (2,20)	1,16 (2,10)
Mayor informer	MI	e	+0,68 (+1,40)	-0,66 (1,40)
Car ownership	CAR	e	0,65 (1,40)	0,59 (1,23)
Full time student	FTS	e	1,23 (2,90)	1,16 (2,60)
Risk know how	KR	e	-1,06 (-2,20)	-1,02 (2,01)
Private mode	PM	ne		-0,32 (-0,70)
Num. obs.			153,00	153,00
Initial value			-106,05	-106,05
Final value			-68,96	-68,74
rho-quadro			0,35	0,35

Sample A+B

$$V_e = \beta_{PI} \cdot PI + \beta_{DL} \cdot DL + \beta_{FTS} \cdot FTS + \beta_{MI} \cdot MI \qquad (5)$$
$$V_{ne} = \beta_{SI} \cdot SI + \beta_{TRAINING} \cdot TRAINING \qquad (6)$$

where

PI is a dummy variable equal to 1 if the informer is the professor, to 0 otherwise;
DL is a variable equal to 1 if the user owns the driving license, to 0 otherwise;
FTS is a dummy variable equal to 1 if the user is a full time student, to 0 otherwise;
MI is a dummy variable equal to 1 if the informer is the Mayor, to 0 otherwise;
TRAINING is a variable equal to 1 if the user has already participated in evacuation trials, to 0 otherwise;
SI is a dummy variable equal to 1 if the informer is the stranger, to 0 otherwise;
β are parameters to be calibrated.

Obtained results from calibration are reported in table 7.

Proposed models were validated by verifying the reasonableness and the significance of estimated coefficients, as well as the model's ability to reproduce the choices made by a sample of users. All these activities can be completed with appropriate tests of hypotheses for a sample of users. In this work, we performed informal and formal tests. Informal tests are based on the expectations on the signs of the coefficient calibrated. Formal tests allow us to verify different assumptions on Maximum Likelihood estimates using asymptotic results. The t-student statistic allows us to verify that all the estimates of the coefficient are significantly different from zero. The rhosquare allow the model's goodness of fit to be ascertained, i.e. its ability to reproduce the choices made by a sample of users.

Table 7:   Parameter calibration for scenario 2 (Sample A+B).

Variable		Alt.	Value (t-student)	Value (t-student)	Value (t-student)
Professor informer	PI	e	0,96 (1,80)	0,66 (1,20)	0,64 (1,20)
Mayor informer	MI	e	+0,48 (+1,00)		
Stranger informer	SI	ne		0,19 (0,40)	0,20 (0,40)
Driving license	DL	e	+0,99 (+2,50)	1,40 (4,10)	1,22 (1,50)
Participation at evacuation trials	Training	ne	-0,15 (-0,40)		
Full Time Student	FTS	e			0,20 (0,20)
Num. obs.			153,00	153,00	153,00
Init al value			-106,05	-106,05	-106,05
Final value			-71,01	-71,30	-71,30
rho-quadro			0,33	0,33	0,33

4 Conclusion

In this paper we have proposed the specification, calibration and validation of demand models able to simulate the choice of a generic user to evacuate or not in emergency conditions, starting from SP data. We have considered two scenarios, defined considering an anthropogenic kind of dangerous event, delayed effect in the time of the dangerous event and absence of constrained times to evacuate.

The scenarios differ in respect of:

- effect in the space, that is punctiform for scenario 1 and diffused for scenario 2;
- place of effect for users during the dangerous event, that is the user's workplace for scenario 1 and downtown, for scenario 2;
- considered informer
  - o stranger or department head, for scenario 1;
  - o stranger, representative of the Mayor, professor, for scenario 2.

Obtained results confirm the role of the informer highlighted in previous papers, based on the statistical analysis of stated preferences data [8, 9]. In particular, this paper shows that higher evacuation percentages are obtained if the informer is the department head or the professor.

Calibrated parameters confirm this result. In fact, for scenario 1, the parameter associated to the head of the department informer is positive and represents the trend to evacuate for every considered specification (Sample B, Sample A+B). In scenario 2, it is possible to compare the obtained parameter for three different types of informer. Other results show that:

- for the professor, the calibrated parameter represents the trend to evacuate and is higher, in comparison with the parameter associated to a representative of the Mayor and stranger;
- for the representative of the Mayor, the calibrated parameter is positive and represents the trend to evacuate, even if the value is lower in comparison with that associated to the professor;
- for the stranger, the calibrated parameter is positive, but it is specified in the alternative not to evacuate, then it represents the trend to not evacuate.

A prototypal result is related to the variable training, specified for scenario 1. This is characterized by a positive sign and then represents the trend to evacuate; moreover, the obtained t-student is very high, for every specification (Sample B, Sample A+B), as training is very significant in the user's choices. These results support psychological studies related to the human behaviour in emergency conditions.

Finally, the trend to evacuate is, moreover, related to car ownership, driving license and the user's home is in the town centre of Reggio Calabria.

Our next objectives are finalized to analyze, in a more in depth approach, the influence of training in the user's choices and to develop a comparison between SP and SP-off-RP approaches.

References

[1] Russo F. and Chilà G., Safety of users in road evacuation: demand models. WIT Transactions on the Built Environment, Volume 96, Urban Transport XIII, Urban Transport and the Environment in the 21st century, Brebbia C. A. (ed.), WIT Press, Southampton, pp. 773-782, 2007.

[2] Russo F. and Vitetta A., Risk evaluation in a transportation system. *International Journal of Sustainable Development and Planning*, 1 (2), pp. 170-191, 2006.

[3] Wilmot C.G. & Fu H., A sequential logit dynamic travel demand model for hurricane evacuation. *Transp. Research Record*, 1882, pp. 19-26, 2004.

[4] Cheng, G., Wilmot C.G., and Baker R.J., A destination choice model for hurricane evacuation. In *Transp. Research Board Annual Meeting 2008*. CD-ROM. Washington, D.C., 2008.

[5] Hasan, S., Hukkussuri, S., Murray-Tuite, P., A Behavioral Model to Understand Household Level Hurricane Evacuation Decision Making. Submitted for Publication in ASCE Journal of Transportation, 2011.

[6] Russo F. and Chilà G., Safety of users in road evacuation: RP vs. SP surveys in demand analysis. WIT Transactions on the Built Environment, Volume 101, Urban Transport XIV, Urban Transport and the Environment in the 21st century, Brebbia C. A. (ed.), WIT Press, Southampton, pp. 703-713, 2008.

[7] Ortuzar, J. and de D. Willumsen, L.G., *Modelling Transport,* John Wiley & Sons Ltd, Chichester, 2006.

[8] Russo F. and Chilà G., A statistical approach to analyse user behaviour in road evacuation. *WIT Transactions on the Built Environment, Volume 117, Safety and Security engineering IV*, Guarascio M., Reiners G. Brebbia C. A. and Garzia F. (ed.), WIT Press, Southampton, pp. 377-390, 2011.

[9] Russo F. and Chilà G., Models in road evacuation: role of the informer in user behaviour. *Proceedings of Sustainable City 2012*, 7th International Conference on Urban Regeneration and Sustainability, Brebbia C. A. (ed.), WIT Press, Southampton, 2012.

[10] Russo, F. and Rindone, C., Safety of users in road evacuation: Modelling and DSS for LFA in the planning process. *WIT Transactions on Ecology and the Environment*, 120, pp. 453-464, 2009.

[11] Russo, F. and Rindone, C., Safety of users in road evacuation: Planning internal processes and guidelines. *WIT Transactions on the Built Environment*, 96, pp. 825-834, 2007.

[12] Vitetta, A., Musolino, G. and Marcianò, F.A., Safety of users in road evacuation: Supply and demand-supply interaction models for users. *WIT Transactions on the Built Environment*, 96, pp. 783-792, 2007.

[13] Polimeni, A. and Vitetta, A., Optimising waiting at nodes in time-dependent networks: cost functions and applications. *Journal of Optimization Theory and Applications*, 156(3), pp. 805-818, 2013.

[14] Polimeni A. and Vitetta A., Dynamic vehicle routing in road evacuation: Route design experimentation, *WIT Transactions on the Built Environment*, 117, pp. 391-402, 2011.
[15] Train K. and Wilson W.W., Monte Carlo analysis of SP-off-RP data. *Journal of Choice Modelling*, 2(1), pp. 101-117, 2009.

Simulation, design and structure of ITS models for supporting evacuation in smart cities

M. L. De Maio, G. Musolino, A. Polimeni & A. Vitetta
Dipartimento di Ingegneria dell'Informazione, delle Infrastrutture e dell'Energia Sostenibile, DIIES, Università degli Studi Mediterranea di Reggio Calabria, Italy

Abstract

Many technologies have been developed to assist mobility in a smart city; however, there is a lack of models to support the technology. In this paper, a framework is proposed to integrate a model system into an Intelligent Transport System (ITS) environment. The framework allows us to integrate the information provided by the technology in order to configure the transport network. Models considered are both simulation models (i.e. assignment) and design models (vehicle routing). This framework could be applied to support managing evacuation operations in a city.
Keywords: smart city, Intelligent Transportation Systems, path choice, vehicle routing, design models.

1 Introduction

A smart city is a city well performing in six characteristics, built on the 'smart' combination of endowments and activities of self-decisive, independent and aware citizens (http://www.smart-cities.eu/model.html). Smart mobility is a relevant element in smart city definition. Although many studies aimed to support mobility are mainly technology-oriented, the modelling system is not enough developed. Technologies able to support the mobility in a smart city are called Intelligent Transportation Systems (ITS): their applicability range from the vehicles survey to information for users.

ITS can be used to improve the mobility in a city; but ITS introduction in a transport system needs a preliminary system analysis to appraisal their effects [1]. The analysis in this paper regards the models applicable into an ITS

WIT Transactions on Ecology and The Environment, Vol 173, © 2013 WIT Press
www.witpress.com, ISSN 1743-3541 (on-line)
doi:10.2495/SDP130631

environment in order to simulate and design an urban traffic network. The aim is to support city managers, municipal authorities [2] and users during an evacuation, it is necessary to guide users toward a safe area. If users move with private motorized modes, information in real time on transport network is crucial to speed up the evacuation. For example, users can get information about the path to follow or about the nearest safe area. Similar considerations can be made considering the case in which users are evacuated using transit modes (i.e. bus) or, if it is necessary, an ambulance. In this case, drivers should receive from ITS system information about paths and user's location. A compact scheme to represent the aim of the simulation of users of a transportation system is reported in Figure 1 that will be detailed in the next sections of the paper. Starting from the current transport system (network topology and costs, signal setting), ITS depicts the current traffic conditions at time t. The behavioural simulation includes all the procedures allowing forecasting the system status after a time slice Δt. If the transport system conditions are surveyed at instant t and the behavioural simulation require a computing interval Δt_0, the approach done the forecasted traffic conditions until the time t + Δt.

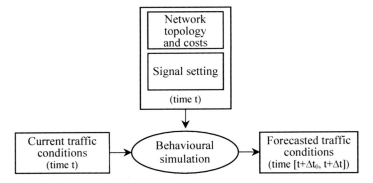

Figure 1:   Compact system simulation.

The paper is structured as follows. Section 2 reports on a literature review on smart mobility and transport system simulation models. In Section 3 the general framework is discussed. In Section 4 the ITS to survey the system conditions are analysed. Section 5 reports on behavioural simulation, considering three subsections: demand and supply, dynamic traffic assignment, reverse assignment. In Section 6, a design procedure (that includes behavioural simulation) is proposed to solve the vehicle routing problem.

2 Literature review

Technologies supporting a smart mobility can be subdivided into devices to survey the transport system and devices to inform users. In first case, the aim is to collect traffic data (i.e. flow, speed, travel time); in second case the aim is to know the network performances and to allow forecasting the transport system over time. To make this possible, simulation models are required in order to anticipate the system evolution. One approach to this problem is the use of the Dynamic Traffic Assignment (DTA) models, which simulate the interactions between the time-varying network and time-varying travel demand (in non steady-state traffic conditions). The aim is to capture transport system evolution when travel demand peaks, temporary capacity variations, queue formation and dispersion occur.

DTA models can be classified into analytical (system optimum or user equilibrium) and simulation-based [3, 4]. The former approximate the problem with a system-wide (system optimum) or individual (user equilibrium) objectives, through mathematical formulations and explicit constraints. Yet they represent user behaviour and traffic dynamics in a simplified way. The latter are able to reproduce via simulation the complex inter-temporal demand-supply interactions between time-varying travel demand and the transport network. However, their outputs depend on a large amount of inputs and parameters that need to be estimated. Simulation-based models are generally grouped according to their level of aggregation of user behaviour into macroscopic, mesoscopic and microscopic.

A large literature describes experiences connected to urban traffic monitoring. The traffic flow measures by means of monitoring techniques belong to two classes [5, 6]:

- measures at fixed points of the network with tools like loop detectors and image processing [7];
- measures with floating cars [8] in the network (individual cars, taxis, transit system vehicles).

In the information field, Maerivoet *et al.* [9] propose a system able to capture the user behavioural giving information related to the travel cost variations, while in [10] is analysed the impact of user information in path choice. In [11] a probe vehicle equipped with a personal digital assistant and GPS antenna provided the link travel time.

3   General framework

Figure 2 depicts a general framework where the simulation and design models are integrated into an ITS environment. It describes the behavioural simulation which is operated by means of the Dynamic Traffic Assignment (DTA) and the Reverse Assignment (RA) models.

The survey is based on *hardware/software* devices [5, 6] able to capture the current traffic conditions on the networks.

The survey is carried out using an automatic monitoring system, which consists on a peripheral survey station close to the traffic scene to be monitored, and a transmission system [12].

The monitoring system provides in real time (*on-line data*) data related to the current traffic conditions that converge into a dataset (*dataset population*). They are stored as historical data (*off-line data*).

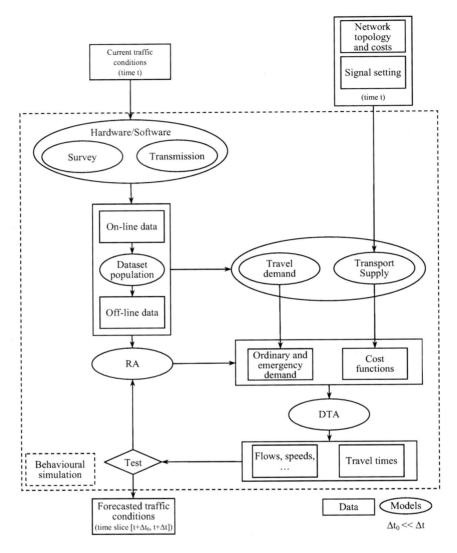

Figure 2:   System simulation and design in an ITS environment.

The collected data (both on-line and off-line) are the input for *travel demand* and *transport supply* models.

The *travel demand* model allows us to estimate the users that travel from origins to destinations, with each available mode. In evacuation conditions, two levels of demand must be considered [13, 14]: the *ordinary demand* (or historical demand), composed by users of the road network that perform systematic trips by motorized modes in the reference time period; the *emergency demand*, composed by users of the road network that perform trips by motorized modes in order to leave from the place where they are in the reference time period and where it is supposed that the catastrophic event will deploy its effects.

The *supply model* allows obtaining the *cost functions*. The time spent in the network by a user depends on the network configuration (in terms of lanes allocation, link direction and junction optimization): fix the network configuration; it is possible to define the link *cost functions*. Generally, the used cost functions, to forecast the link cost, depend both on flow and time [15, 16]. In an ITS system it is possible to update the function, re-calibrating the parameters considering the real time collected data.

The DTA model has input the demand and the supply. DTA simulates the interaction between travel demand flows and the road transport network in order to estimate time-varying travel times and vehicular flows on a network. Among the outputs, are highlighted *flows*, *speed* and *travel time*.

The output of simulation-based DTA are the input for *Reverse Assignment (RA)*. Other input for the RA coming from ITS system in the form of *on-line data* and *off-line data*. Note that the on-line data contribute to populate a database that collect all the observed data.

RA is an approach that makes it possible, starting from the cost and the flow on some links, to obtain the demand and the costs of all links.

The RA models [17] have the following input:
- link flows;
- link performance in terms of costs;

and give as output
- the link cost parameters of the cost-flow functions used in the supply model;
- the value (number of trips) and/or the model parameters of the demand model.

Figure 2 shows the loop existing between the DTA and RA: to correct the link costs and calibrate model parameters, the RA use recursively the output given by the DTA until the convergence.

The output of whole procedure is the *forecasted traffic conditions* in a time interval $[t+\Delta t_0, t+\Delta t]$, where Δt_0 takes into account the computation time to run the DTA model ($\Delta t_0 << \Delta t$).

The procedure works in time according to the concept of rolling horizon, as detailed in [16].

4   Brief overview on survey and transmission systems

In this section, a small overview on survey and transmission systems it is not the core of the paper but a brief description is required to frame the topic.

The survey and transmission system works as follows. Traffic data are detected by sensors and, then, they are stored and transmitted to a remote station. Sensors may be distinguished in relation to the installation procedure (intrusive or non-intrusive) or in relation to the extension of the monitored area (tripwire or vehicle tracking).

Systems able to detect a specific vehicle, called Automatic Vehicle Location systems (AVL), may be based on a GPS technology, GSM modem, Wi-Fi, radio frequencies.

Data acquired through sensors located in the peripheral station are transmitted with off-line or on-line mode. Because of the recent widespread of technologies, several communication systems can be used in order to give information to users like radio, telephone, mobile, internet, SMS, GSM, Wi-Fi and so on. It is worth distinguishing systems providing information to road users and systems providing information supporting logistic fleets.

Intelligent systems used to provide information to users are called Advanced Traveler Information System (ATIS) [18] and may be distinguished in relation to the kind of information provided: pre-trip or en-route.

Application of ITS in the logistic field concerns the Computerised Vehicle Routing and Scheduling (CVRS) systems which optimize vehicles routes and vehicles allocations. Also in this case, some specific systems are available in emergency conditions: for managing emergency vehicles like ambulances and fire trucks, by sending them radio messages (e.g. about path to be followed [19]). GSM technology was used in [20] and a monitor can be used by the ambulance driver to know the path to be followed as indicated by the control center. The importance of this topic has been stressed in the MAGES project (Mature Applications of Galileo for Emergency Scenario), which describes supports for managing emergencies [21].

5 Behavioural simulation

Some models compose the behavioural simulation, to consider some relevant aspects of the transport system. The models considered in this paper, and explained in detail in the next sub-section, are:

- demand and supply models;
- dynamic traffic assignment;
- reverse assignment.

5.1 Demand and supply models

The ordinary demand is usually estimated using a multistep approach, considering the emission, the departure time, the distribution and the modal split levels. The emergency demand, can be estimated with a sequential approach (see [22–24]), by considering that in the presence of an ITS, some choice dimensions (i.e. departure time, path choice) can be influenced by the information provided to users.

The demand (ordinary and evacuation), in a time interval Δt for an origin-destination pair rs, can be expressed per category, as in [22]:

$$d_{rs}(\Delta t) = d^R_{rs}(\Delta t) + d^W_{rs}(\Delta t) + d'_{rs}(\Delta t) + d^S_{rs}(\Delta t) + d^P_{rs}(\Delta t) \qquad (1)$$

where

- R, residents; W, employees; C, occasional customers; S, teachers and pupils; D, weak users;
- $d^R_{rs}(\Delta t)$, demand of people belong to resident category;
- $d^W_{rs}(\Delta t)$, demand of people belong to employee category;
- $d^{\,}_{rs}(\Delta t)$, demand of people belong to occasional customer category;
- $d^S_{rs}(\Delta t)$, demand of people belong to schools;
- $d^D_{rs}(\Delta t)$, demand of people belong to weak users' category.

Each category can be specified with a descriptive or a behavioural model.

Transport supply could change due to effects of emergency conditions. The network configuration could be modified to make easy the evacuation procedures, changing the use of some links or their direction (as in contraflow operations).

Hence, a modified configuration of the network may be currently available. Users cannot have a complete knowledge of the current state of the network. Considering that users' behaviour is influenced by their experience and knowledge of the network, it is clear the important role played by information in this case. Monitoring systems are necessary to survey and detect changes on the network, with must be used to correct the network configuration, in order to obtain results from assignment simulation (which are consistent with the modified network configuration) and to be diffused to users.

5.2 Dynamic Traffic Assignment

Existing within-day DTA models may be employed according to approaches: non-equilibrium or equilibrium. A description of the two approaches is reported in [5, 6, 16, 25]. In the case of an equilibrium approach, an iterative process is necessary to find the dynamic equilibrium solution, based on three algorithms [25]: i) an algorithm which calculates route travel times (network loading); ii) a shortest path algorithm which calculates k shortest path and updates path choice set; iii) an algorithm which provides assignment of vehicles to paths in order to simulate the dynamic equilibrium. After completing the three steps described above, it is necessary to come back to the first one: route choices made in the first iteration changed travel times on the network. The iterative procedure is repeated until convergence (if any).

A specific dynamic non-equilibrium model is proposed in [25] in order to simulate path flows related to each rs pair, $d_{rs}(\Delta t)$, composed by flows on all paths k chosen by users between origin r to destination s. Considering time composed by several decision time instants, τ^*, the travel demand flow on path k in time τ^* will be h_{k,τ^*}. For simplicity's sake here is reported briefly the mathematical formulation for simulation of $d_{rs}(\Delta t)$, which allows obtaining the traffic flow on link a at time instant $t, f_a(t)$:

$$f_a(x) = \sum_{\tau^*=[t0,\ t]} \sum_{(rs)} \sum_{k\ \in lrs:\ a\in k} q_a^k(x|\ \tau^*)\ h_{k,\tau^*} \quad x \in [t+\Delta t_0,\ t+\Delta t] \qquad (2)$$

where

- $q_a{}^k(t|\, \tau^*)$ is the probability of being on link a belonging to path k at the time instant t conditional upon the decision (to choose path k) at time instant τ^*;
- $h_{k,\tau^*} = p_{k,\tau^*}\, d_{rs}(\Delta t)$ is the travel demand flow on path k for each decision time instant τ^*;
- p_{k,τ^*} is the probability to choice the path k at instant τ^*.

5.3 Reverse assignment

The RA was proposed in [17] to re-calibrate link cost functions and update demand values from traffic counts and time measurements on some network links. RA models, starting from observed costs and flows, provide link cost parameters of the cost-flow functions used in the supply model, the value (number of trips) and/or the model parameters of the demand model. A mathematical formulation of RA is provided by [17]:

objective function: $z_1(\mathbf{d}(\Delta t), \mathbf{d}^*(\Delta t)) + z_2(\mathbf{f}(t), \mathbf{f}^*(t)) + z_3(\mathbf{c}(t), \mathbf{c}^*(t))$ (3)

control variables: $\mathbf{d}_t, \mathbf{f}_t, \mathbf{c}_t$

constraints:

$$\mathbf{d}(\Delta t) \geq \mathbf{0}$$
$$\mathbf{f}(t) \geq \mathbf{0}$$
$$\mathbf{c}(t) \geq \mathbf{0}$$
$$t \in [t+\Delta t_0,\ t+\Delta t]$$

user behaviour (as equation (2))

where

- $\mathbf{d}(\Delta t), \mathbf{f}(t), \mathbf{c}(t)$ (demand, flow and cost vector) are time dependent;
- $z(\cdot)$ is a distance function between the observed values and the estimated values for demand (z_1), flow (z_2) and cost(z_3).

6   Routes design

The behavioural simulation is a fundamental component of the approach proposed to design the vehicle routes, which also includes the Network Topology and Signal Setting Design Problem (NTSSDP). Figure 3 shows the recursive procedure that depicts the relationship among the three components. In the design approach, four constraint types are considered:

- *law constraints* (imposed by administration, i.e. restrict the access in an area);
- *technological constraints* (imposed by the limitations in the available instruments);
- *behavioural constraints* (hypothesis on user's behavioural);
- *technical constraints* (imposed by the design problem, i.e. green time, number of lanes).

     The recursive procedure, starting from a system status (i.e. the system status at instant *t*) simulate the system with the behavioural simulation obtaining the *forecasted traffic estimation* data used in NTSSOP to design the *network*

topology and the *signal setting*. Supposing that the current system status is surveyed at instant t, the behavioural simulation done the transport system status for a time slice $t + \Delta t$, considering a time slice Δt_l to solve the behavioural simulation.

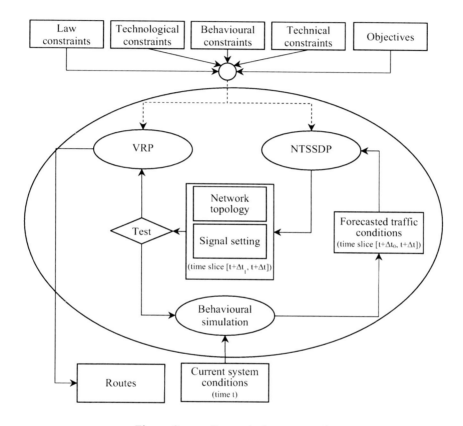

Figure 3:   Route design approach

The lane allocation and the link direction define the network topology; due objectives and constraints, the problem can be formulated as an optimum constrained problem. Generally, the design approach is a heuristic, but can be considered hybrid approaches (i.e. an algorithm for topology design another for node optimization). In the network topology design [26] various objectives can be introduced: for example, the evacuation time for all users can be minimized, the route travel time of emergency vehicles can be minimized and so on [26]. A multi-objective problem can be also formulated.

The signal setting consists on defining, for each junction in the network, the cycle and the green time. The problem can be solved simultaneously or after the network topology design, with a global approach or a local approach.

 WIT Transactions on Ecology and The Environment, Vol 173, © 2013 WIT Press
www.witpress.com, ISSN 1743-3541 (on-line)

The procedure is repeated until a test is satisfied (i.e. the value of objective function, the maximum number of iterations).

The output is the network configuration in term of topology and signal setting (that are the first set of output of the whole procedure), that are also the input of *VRP*. The solution of VRP are the *routes* for a fleet of vehicle that move in the transportation system.

A joint VRP-NTSSDP formulation is proposed in [26]. The general formulation is as follows:

objective function: $z(\mathbf{y}^{(TO)}, \mathbf{y}^{(SG)}, \Omega, \mathbf{f}(t))$ (4)

control variables: $\mathbf{y}^{(TO)}, \mathbf{y}^{(SG)}, \Omega, \mathbf{f}(t)$

constraints:

technical and structural;

network connection;

user behaviour;

VRP classical constraints

where
- $\mathbf{y}^{(TO)}$ and $\mathbf{y}^{(SG)}$ vectors, the first being related to the network topology (lane allocation), and the second being related to the signal setting (intersection regulation, capacity);
- Ω matrix, related to the paths used by the vehicles in VRP;
- $\mathbf{f}(t)$, flow vector.

7 Conclusions

A general framework where simulation and design models are integrated into on an ITS environment was proposed. The framework is suited to support an evacuation in a smart city. The framework components are:
- the transport system in term of network topology and signal setting, at a generic time;
- the ITS, to capture the actual system conditions.;
- a behavioural simulation, consisting on Dynamic Traffic Assignment (DTA) and Reverse Assignment (RA), to forecast the system status in a time slice.

For each framework component, a formulation was proposed. Finally, a vehicle routing problem with topology and signal setting design was formulated in an integrated model.

Acknowledgements

Partially supported by National MIUR under PRIN2009 grants n. 2009EP3S42_001.

References

[1] Cantarella, G.E. Day-to-day dynamic models for Intelligent Transportation Systems design and appraisal. *Transport. Res. Part C*, 2012.

[2] Russo, F. and Rindone, C., Evaluation methods for evacuation planning. *WIT Transactions on the Built Environment*, 111, pp. 335–343, 2010.

[3] Peeta S. and Ziliaskopoulos A.K., Foundations of Dynamic Traffic Assignment: the past, the present and the future, *Net and Spat Econ*, 1(3), pp. 233–265, 2001.

[4] Mahamassani H, Dynamic network traffic assignment and simulation methodology for advanced system management applications. *Networks and Spatial Economics*, 1, 3–4, pp. 267–292, 2001.

[5] Polimeni, A. and Vitetta, A., The role of ITS in evacuation route optimization for emergency vehicles. *WIT Transactions on Information and Communication Technologies*, 44, pp. 517–529, 2012.

[6] De Maio, M.L., Musolino, G. and Vitetta, A., The role of ITS in evacuation route choice. *WIT Transactions on Information and Communication Technologies*, 44, pp. 503–515, 2012.

[7] Chen, A., Pravinvongvuth, S. and Chootinan, P., Scenario-based multi-objective AVI reader location models under different travel demand patterns. *Transportmetrica*, 6(1), pp. 53–78, 2010.

[8] Torday, A. and Dumont, A.G. Probe vehicle based travel time estimation in urban networks. *In*: TRISTAN V, 2004.

[9] Maerivoet, S., Daems, F., Maertens, F., Renckens, K., Van Houtte, P. and Buelens, L., A field trial on smart mobility. *Procedia – Social and Behavioral Sciences*, 54, pp. 926 – 935, 2012.

[10] Dong C. and Paty C. S., Application of adaptive weights to intelligent information systems: an intelligent transportation system as a case study. *Information Sciences*, 181, pp. 5042–5052, 2011.

[11] Ando N. and Taniguchi E., Travel time reliability in vehicle routing and scheduling with time windows. *Netw Spat Econ*, 6, pp. 293–311, 2006.

[12] Iera A., Modafferi A., Musolino G. and Vitetta A. An experimental station for real-time traffic monitoring on an urban road. *The IEEE 5th International Conference on Intelligent Transportation Systems*, 2002.

[13] Vitetta, A., Musolino, G. and Marcianò, F.A., Safety of users in road evacuation: Supply and demand-supply interaction models for users. *WIT Transactions on the Built Environment*, 96, pp. 783–792, 2007.

[14] Vitetta, A., Musolino, G. and Marcianò, F.A., Safety of users in road evacuation: Calibration of cost functions and simulation. *WIT Transactions on the Built Environment*, 101, pp. 715–725, 2008.

[15] Polimeni, A. and Vitetta, A., Optimising waiting at nodes in time-dependent networks: cost functions and applications. *Journal of Optimization Theory and Applications*, 156(3), pp. 805–818, 2013.

[16] Musolino, G. and Vitetta, A., Short-term forecasting in road evacuation: calibration of a travel time function. *WIT Transactions on The Built Environment*, 116, pp. 615–626, 2011.

[17] Russo, F. and Vitetta, A., Reverse assignment: calibrating link cost functions and updating demand from traffic counts and time measurements. *Inverse Problems in Science and Engineering*, 19 (7), pp. 921–950, 2011.

[18] Emmerink R.H.M., Axhausen K.W., Ijkamp P. and Rietveld P., The potential of information provision in a simulated road transport network with non-recurrent congestion. *Transp. Res. C*, 3(5), pp. 293–309, 1995.

[19] Beynon-Davies P., Human error and information systems failure: the case of the London ambulance service computer-aided despatch system project. *Interacting with Computers*, 11, pp. 699–720, 1999.

[20] Derekenaris G., Garofalakis J., Makris C., Prentzas J., Sioutas S. and Tsakalidis A., Integrating GIS, GPS and GSM technologies for the effective management of ambulances. *Comput., Environ. and Urban Systems*, 25, pp. 267–278, 2001.

[21] Dixon C.S. and Haas R., GNSS user requirement in emergency management. *Proc. of* RIN NAV '08 Conference, 2008.

[22] Russo, F. and Chilà G., Safety of users in road evacuation: Modelling and DSS for demand. *WIT Transactions on Ecology and the Environment*, 120, pp. 465–474, 2009.

[23] Russo, F. and Chilà, G., Safety of users in road evacuation: demand models. *WIT Transactions on the Built Environment*, 96, pp. 773–782, 2007.

[24] Russo, F. and Chilà G., Safety of users in road evacuation: RP vs. SP surveys in demand analysis. *WIT Transactions on the Built Environment*, 101, pp. 703–713, 2008.

[25] De Maio, M. L., Musolino, G. and Vitetta, A., Traffic assignment models in road evacuation. *The Sustainable City VII*, pp.1041–1051, 2012.

[26] Polimeni, A. and Vitetta, A., Joint network and route optimization in road evacuation. *WIT Transactions on Ecology and the Environment*, 155, pp. 1053–1065, 2011.

Civil risk manager at European level

F. Russo & C. Rindone
Dipartimento di Ingegneria dell'Informazione delle Infrastrutture e dell'Energia Sostenibile, DIIES, Università degli Studi Mediterranea di Reggio Calabria, Italy

Abstract

The purpose of this paper is to propose a standard process for training and certification to identify at European level a civil risk manager, with a common background.

An analysis of possible training and education activities in emergency planning at an international level is shown. Among preparedness activities, in this paper we consider activities that contribute to reducing the exposure risk components. The dangerous goods transportation risk is considered as a reference case, analyzing standard training and the certification process introduced by the United Nations and adopted at an international level. The experiences of the USA, the EU and Italy, in the context of civil risk training, are reported.

It is possible to reduce the exposure risk component implementing training activity to increase the capability of subjects involved in emergency conditions. Experiences of the USA and the EU relative to training constitute different attempts to certificate training in emergency planning. However, there is a lack of international standards to certificate a professional expert that can manage disaster in a standard way. It is possible to introduce training and certification for an EU civil risk manager adopting the United Nations' model concerning dangerous goods transportation.

In this paper, the necessity to implement training activities at different levels to reduce risk is highlighted. A possible trend of a risk level function depending on training activities' implementation at the time is proposed. However, in further studies, the function could be specified and calibrated referring to a model and specific surveys.

This study, in the context of analysis related to the standardization process in emergency planning, is the first proposal, to the authors' knowledge, into the

WIT Transactions on Ecology and The Environment, Vol 173, © 2013 WIT Press
www.witpress.com, ISSN 1743-3541 (on-line)
doi:10.2495/SDP130641

introduction of standard vocational training and an international certification process for civil risk managers.

Keywords: civil risk, planning, training, certification, standard.

1 Introduction

In recent years, within the sustainable development topic, the United Nations (UN) introduced disasters in relation to their economic and human impacts. The UN's office for disaster risk reduction indicates that *over the last twenty years, it is conservatively estimated that disasters have killed 1.3 million people, affected 4.4 billion and resulted in economic losses of $2 trillion.* These are costs' measures of inaction on climate change and risk reduction [1].

Disaster risk reduction refers to activities that aim to limit the impacts of a dangerous event. United Nation adopts *International Strategy for Disaster Reduction* (ISDR) starting from *systematic efforts to analyse and reduce the causal factors of disasters. Reducing exposure to hazards, lessening vulnerability of people and property, wise management of land and the environment, and improving preparedness for adverse events are all examples of disaster risk reduction.* ISDR is adopted to pursue four objectives: increase public awareness to understand risk; obtain commitment from public authorities to implement disaster risk reduction policies and actions; stimulate interdisciplinary and intersectorial partnership; improve scientific knowledge about disaster reduction [2].

At an international level, disaster risk reduction activities, can be synthetized as defined by four serial activities [3–5]: *mitigation,* comprising activities carried out in advance of an emergency event (e.g. land management and planning; public information campaigns); *preparedness,* comprising activities to ensure, if an emergency occurs, that communities, resources and services are capable of responding to the effects (e.g. evacuation planning; exercising, training and testing of emergency service staff [6, 7]; *response,* including activities to control, limit or modify the emergency and to reduce its consequences (e.g. implementation of emergency plans and procedures in response to emergency incidents and provision [8, 9]; *recovery (community),* including activities to support reconstruction of physical infrastructure after emergency situations (e.g. restoration of essential services, temporary housing; long-term medical care).

Considering a specific event, these activities can be organized respect to the period (time slice, Δ) over which the event evolves; then four main intervals can be defined ($\Delta_0, \Delta_1, \Delta_2, \Delta_3$) [10]:

- $\Delta_0 = (t_0, t_1]$ between the times
  t_0, the time when the study of the evacuation plan is started;
  t_1, the time when the hazardous event is known to happen or supposed forecasted;
  in this interval *mitigation* and *preparedness* activities can be implemented;

- $\Delta_1 = (t_1, t_2]$ between the times t_2 and t_3, the time when the threat occurs and becomes a dangerous event and starts its effects;
  in this interval *response* activities can be implemented;
- $\Delta_2 = (t_2, t_3]$ between times t_2 and t_3, the time when the final effect occurs and people cannot be rescued;
  in this interval *response* activities can be implemented;
- $\Delta_3 = (t_3, t_4]$ between times t_3 and t_4, the time when the hazardous event ceases its effect on the population;
  in this interval *recovery* activities can be implemented.

In recent years, much effort has been spent in preparedness activities at an international level. The USA National Incident Management System (NIMS) considers preparedness as a *continuous cycle of planning, organizing, training, equipping, exercising, evaluating, and taking corrective action in an effort to ensure effective coordination during incident response* [11]. Training activities assume a relevant role in the context of preparedness; for instance United Nation promotes education programs and training on disaster risk reduction in schools and local communities. *The entire community must know about the hazards and risks to which they are exposed if they are to be better prepared and take measures to cope with potential disasters. Awareness, education and capacity building programs on disaster risk and mitigation measures are key for mobilizing citizen participation in the city's disaster risk reduction strategies. This will improve preparedness and help citizens respond to local early warnings* [12].

Among preparedness activities, in this paper we consider activities that contribute to reducing the exposure risk component. We consider the specification in which the risk is obtained from the product of three main components: occurrence of an event; vulnerability involved land system; exposure calculated as the equivalent homogeneous weighted value of people, goods and infrastructures affected during and after the event [13].

For disastrous events with delayed approach, activities to reduce exposure are included in the set of preparedness. These activities can be classified into homogeneous classes in terms of execution time and decision-maker of single activities: activities related to *material infrastructures* (e. g. interventions on physical characteristics); *non-material* activities (e. g. interventions on learning and training or on Intelligent Transportation Systems) ([14, 15]); activities related to *equipment* (e. g. interventions to acquire tools and specific transport means); *management* activities (e.g. interventions to design transportation services) [16–20]; *governance* and *institutional* activities (e.g. interventions to regulate the transportation system).

Training activities are specific of non-material; these activities can be classified in two macro classes [21]:

- discussion-based activities, to discuss between trainer and participants about current plans, policies, agreements, and evacuation procedures;

- operation-based activities, to simulate, in an operational context, a real emergency situation and to implement plans, policies, agreements, and evacuation procedures.

In the context of operation based activities training, European Union has organized in several state members simulation exercises *to accelerate response in major emergencies. These exercises provide a learning opportunity for all actors involved in operations.* Planning, decision-making procedures and provision of information to the public are tested during these exercises to prepare for similar real-life situations. Exercises constitute a support to identify training needs and operational gaps to be improved [22].

In Figure 1 is presented the standard training activities classification in the USA, introduced with Homeland Security Exercise and Evaluation Program (HSEEP) by the National Preparedness Directorate (NPD) [23]. HSEEP is a capabilities and performance-based exercise program that provides a standardized methodology and terminology for exercise design, development, conduct, evaluation, and improvement planning [24].

In literature there are limited researches that analyze how training reduces risk level. Training impacts in the functioning of the organization's emergency operations centre during a crisis are investigated in Sinclair *et al.* [25].

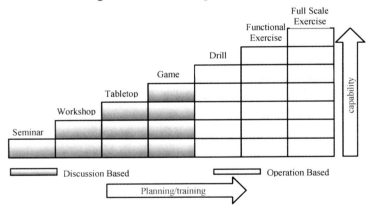

Figure 1:   Training activities classification (source: [24]).

It is possible to suppose that a quantity of risk reduction can be obtained for each training activity.

If we indicate with R_{01} the risk level in the time τ_{01}, inside the time slice Δ_0 we can obtain a reduction of this level developing training activities.

For each activity i, Seminar, Workshop, ..., we can reduce the risk of a quantity Δr_i, where i is the generic training activity.

To simplify with a graphic presentation (Figure 2), we suppose that for each activity i the reduction is constant and it is equal to $\Delta \bar{r}$; then:

$$\Delta r_i = \Delta \bar{r} \qquad \forall \, i$$

If we develop a set I of activities during the time $(\tau_{01}, \tau_{02}]$ the risk reduction is:

$$\Delta R_{12} = \Sigma_{i \in I} \Delta r_i = \Sigma_{i \in I} \Delta \bar{r}$$

If any other activity is conducted, in the considered time period, the risk in the time τ_{02} is:

$$R_{02} = R_{01} - \Delta R_{12}$$

A possible trend of a risk level function, inside the period Δ_0, is presented in Figure 2, where a constant risk reduction for each training activity is hypothesized. Risk level decreases from the value R_{01} to the value R_{02}.

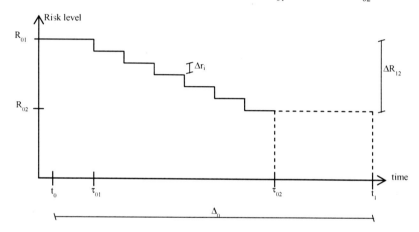

Figure 2:   Risk reduction with preparedness activities.

From these considerations, it emerges the necessity to implement training activities at different level. Two possible reference levels are:

- base level that produces a professional certificate training released at national level;
- university level that produces a master or degree certificate training according to national laws.

Alexander [26] highlights a lack of homogeneity, consistency and quality control in emergency planning. For this reason, a set of criteria needs upon which standard professional in emergency planning might be based. These lacks are complementary to the asked level, then in section 2 we consider, the specific risk for dangerous good transportation: training and certification are analyzed. This case is presented how example of (inter)national professional certification. The USA, EU and Italian experiences are recalled.

In section 3, the current contents of civil risk management training is analyzed. Experiences of basic and university training levels in the USA and EU are recalled. In section 4 a feasible process to introduce training and certification of a civil risk manager is proposed.

2 Dangerous good transportation training and certificate

The United Nations set down recommendations on how dangerous goods should be transported to reduce risk and then to increase safety. The United Nations every two years publish recommendations which are then adopted by the governs for each modal regulation. These recommendations are not mandatory in law until they are adopted in the dangerous goods regulations below *Recommendations on the transport of Dangerous Goods – Model Regulations*, known as *The Orange Book* [27].

In the set of international experiences to certify Dangerous Good Safety Advisor (DGSA), according to United Nation indications, the selected references are USA (section 2.1) and EU (section 2.2).

2.1 The USA experience

The USA Pipeline and Hazardous Materials Safety Administration (PHMSA) provide education and training programs designed to increase expertize in dangerous good transportation. *These programs build on cooperative linkages between industry, academia, professional associations and government at all levels* [28].

The USA *federal hazardous materials transportation law* regulates the transportation of hazardous materials (*hazmat*) in the United States. This law requires the training of all hazmat employees. The purpose is to increase a hazmat employee's safety awareness and be an essential element in reducing hazmat incidents. The Hazardous Materials regulations (HMR) define training requirements that a hazmat employer must have: *on the safe loading, unloading, handling, storing, and transporting of hazardous material and emergency preparedness for responding to an accident or incident involving the transportation of hazardous material. After completing the training, each hazmat employer shall certify, with documentation the Secretary of Transportation may require by regulation, that the hazmat employees of the employer have received training and have been tested on appropriate transportation areas of responsibility* [29].

2.2 The EU and Italian experiences

The European Union requires Member States to implement legislation for introducing DGSA for transport of dangerous goods by road, rail and inland waterways, including the phases of loading and unloading [30, 31]. The regulations prohibit the transport of dangerous goods by road and rail both within the State and internationally in Europe by companies which have not been appointed a DGSA.

A DGSA shall hold a *vocational training certificate* appropriate to the modes of transport and to the dangerous goods classes. The certificate shall be issued by the competent authority after a training course and by passing an examination approved by a competent state authority.

The aim of the training is to provide a *sufficient knowledge of the risks inherent in the carriage of dangerous goods, of the laws, regulations and administrative provisions applicable to the modes of transport.*

The aim of examination is to verify *whether candidates possess the necessary level of knowledge to carry out the duties incumbent upon a safety adviser.*

The examination consists of a written test *which may be supplemented by an oral examination.* The written test consists of two parts: in the first part the candidate has to fill a questionnaire that includes 20 open questions covering subjects' regulation about transportation of dangerous goods; in the second part the candidate shall undertake a case study in order to demonstrate that he has the *necessary qualifications to fulfill the task of adviser.* The certificate is mutually recognized in member States of the European Community. The certificate is valid for five years. The period of the validity is extended passing an examination [32].

In Italy, according to EU requirements, the law that receipted the rules to define and to qualify Italian DGSA, was approved and published in 2000. The Italian DGSA must have a *vocational training certificate* issued by the state Transport Ministry, after passing an examination according to European regulations. Firms, indicated in national law, must appoint one or more advisers. The adviser must prepare an annual report for the firm responsible. In the case of accident during the loading, carriage or unloading of dangerous goods that affects the health or safety of any person or causes damage to the environment, the adviser must prepare a report about the accident for the firm responsible and for the state Transport Ministry [33].

The Italian DGSA certificate, like the European adviser certificate, has to be renewed every five years after passing an examination.

3 Civil risk management training

In the set of international experiences in training to certificate civil risk manager capabilities we consider the USA (section 3.1) and EU (section 3.2) study cases.

3.1 The USA experience

3.1.1 Master and degree programs

In the USA, emergency management degree programs are available in universities and schools.

Federal Management Emergency Agency (FEMA) is a part of DHS that ensures that the single state improves the capability to prepare for, protect against, respond to, recover from, and mitigate all hazards. The FEMA approach [24, 34, 35] defines a continuous cycle process made by five modules:

- *planning* is a process *consisting of logical steps to identify a mission or requirement, develop, analyze, and compare alternate courses of action, select the best practice of action, and produce a plan* [36];

- *training* and education is a process that concerns, how teaching *what* to think and *what* the answers ought to be (*training*) and all about teaching *how* to think and *what* the questions ought to be (*education*);
- *exercise* is a process *to train for, assess, practise and improve performance in prevention, protection. response and recovery capabilities in a risk-free environment* [37]; exercises include *discussion based* exercises and *operations based* exercises;
- *evaluation* is a process *of examining, measuring and/or judging how well an entity, procedure, or action has met or is meeting stated objectives* [38];
- *improvement* is a process *by which the observations and recommendations recorded are resolved through development of corrective actions* [34].

FEMA National Training Program provides training, education and exercises by four institutes: Center for Domestic Preparedness (CDP), Emergency Management Institute (EMI), National Training and Education Division (NTED) and National Fire Academy (NFA). Among these EMI established in 1994 Emergency Management Higher Education Program (EM Hi-Ed) to encourage and support the dissemination of hazard, disaster, and emergency management-related information in colleges and universities across the United States. This program aim to institute emergency management higher education by: doctoral programs; masters programs; bachelors programs; associate programs (community, technical and junior colleges) [35].

For instance, the George Washington University Institute for Crisis, Disaster and Risk Management (ICDRM) propose: a Master of Science (MS) in Engineering Management with a concentration in Crisis, Emergency and Risk Management; a Graduate Certificate in Homeland Security Emergency Preparedness and Response; a Graduate Certificate in Emergency Management and Public Health; a Professional Degree (Engineer or Applied Scientist); Doctorate of Philosophy (PhD) in Engineering Management [39].

3.1.2 Disaster risk manager certification

The International Association of Emergency Managers (IAEM), that is a non-profit educational supported by FEMA, has created two subsequent certification levels to raise and maintain professional standards: the first level is *Associate Emergency Manager Programs* (AEM$_{SM}$); the second and higher level is *Certified Emergency Manager® program* (CEM®).

CEM® and AEM$_{SM}$ certification are obtained in a peer review process administered through the IAEM. Certification is maintained in five-year cycles. The process is followed by a CEM® Commission, *which is composed of emergency management professionals, including representatives from allied fields, education, military and private industry* [40].

The IAEM is a well-known professional and academic organization of Emergency and Disaster Professionals worldwide. The main goals of this organization are to protect human lives, assets, and the environment during disasters. In addition, the organization's principles are to providing information, networking, education, professional opportunities, and to advance the emergency management profession.

The Emergency Management Accreditation Program (EMAP) is a standard-based voluntary accreditation process for US government programs responsible for coordinating prevention, mitigation, preparedness, response, and recovery activities for disasters. Accreditation is based on compliance with collaboratively developed national standards, the *Emergency Management Standard by EMAP*. *The Emergency Management Standard by EMAP is designed as a tool for continuous improvement as part of a voluntary accreditation process for local and State emergency management programs.*

Accreditation is open to all U.S. States, territories, and local government emergency management programs. Anyone can subscribe to receive standards and guidance materials [41].

3.2 The EU and Italy experiences

The European Civil Protection (ECP), by means of the Community Mechanism for Civil Protection (CMCP), has organized: a Monitoring and Information Centre (MIC); a Common Emergency and Information System (CESIS); a Training program.

The EU doesn't have a Federal Agency that gives specific indications to the States. Each State organizes its training and certification. The EU attention is given to define homogeneous knowledge in the case of pan-European risk, or great national risk that involves, in the operative actions, people arriving from different states.

The courses offered by the European Community Civil Protection Mechanism Training Program presents a wide range of opportunities for civil protection experts.

The European training program has been set up with a view to improving the co-ordination of civil protection assistance interventions by ensuring compatibility and complementary between the intervention teams from the participating states.

The program involves training courses, joint simulation exercises and an exchange program, where experts can learn first-hand about similar responsibilities under different national systems [22].

The principal aim of training courses consists in preparing experts *for international civil protection assistance interventions inside as well as outside Europe.* A certificate is handed out at the end of each course providing the participant has attended the entire course.

Candidates conclude their preparation with a certification test, sometime useful to gain admission to the next course.

Every year the course program is updated, with new modules and new specific courses. It is possible, however, to schematize three different levels.

Introduction level. Different courses can be attended. The preliminary is the *Community Mechanism Introduction Course (CMI)* that provides generic information about the EU Civil Protection Mechanism and actors in an international emergency environment inside and outside Europe.

Operational level. A multiplicity of courses are supplied that present main elements from information management to security and assessment mission. The starting one is the *Operational Management Course (OPM)* that provides the basics for graduates *to function as a full member in an On-site Operational Coordination Centre (OSOCC – outside Europe) or coordination setting (inside Europe)*. The OPM course is open to those who are in possession of the CMI certificate and the *Distance Preparation Certificate* for the OPM.

Management level. Two main courses are actually defined. The *High Level Coordination course (HLC)* aims at experts who could be selected as members of a team that can be deployed by the European Commission to facilitate coordination assistance in emergencies. The final course is to obtain a *Head of Team (HoT)* during civil protections, that imply a heavy responsibility: from the internal team management and psychology and leadership to interact effectively with the media in stressful situations. The HLC course is open to those who are in possession of the of CMI, OPM certificates and the *Distance Preparation Certificate* for the HLC.

It is evident that even if the courses have an international finality, the contents can be very useful also in the national context.

Actually, it is not possible for individual national experts to sign up directly for a course.

In Italy, professional and high level training has been realized. Among these:

- the Ministry of Research has instituted safety engineering bachelor programs and master programs *Safety Engineering* master *(LM-26 – safety engineering,* [42]) mainly to industrial risk manager;
- the Centre for Studies E.Di.Ma.S. (Emergency and Disaster Management Studies), in collaboration with several Italian and European Universities, and linked with the IAEM internet platform, has activated two types of master's degrees [43]:
  - master on *Official of Disaster and Emergency Management*[©] (ODEM) that train an *Emergency Junior Manager*;
  - Emergency Management of Civil Protection[©] (EMCP) that train *Emergency Senior Manager*;
- the Disaster Manager National Association releases *Emergency Manager Italian Certification (EMIC)* to certify two professionals profile [44]:
  - *coordinator* that is an expert capable to coordinate activities to support functions of local operations centers in emergency conditions;
  - *planner* that is an expert capable to examine and to draw up emergency plans, to provide consultant activities and to support civil protection authorities.

4 A process for training and certification of civil risk manager

From previous analysis, it emerges the relevance of training in evacuation planning. The USA and EU experiences presented in section 3 show that different attempts to certificate training in emergency planning has been tried. However there is a lack of international standards to certificate a professional expert that can manage disaster in a standard way.

In recent years some proposal of standardization in risk management was introduced. The International Organization for Standardization (ISO) has published *guideline for incident preparedness and operational continuity management* [45], principles and guidelines for risk management [46]. In these guidelines there is not a proposal to certificate a civil risk manager.

It is possible to hypothesize the training and the certification for an EU civil risk manager. The reference model could be United Nations' general provisions concerning dangerous good transportation [32], presented in section 2 of this paper.

In this way a possible civil risk training and certification process can be constituted of the following steps:

- manual adoption to collect standard operations of civil risk manager, the reference is the manual for transportation of dangerous good by road;
- subjects' definition to appoint a civil risk manager (public authorities);
- civil risk manager knowledge, competencies and relative responsibilities definition; the responsibilities can be similar to those of *safety adviser* defined in UN 1.8.3.3; the civil risk manager' activities, testified for instance in an annual report, comprehend:
  - monitoring of risks that affect community and undertaken activities to reduce risk;
  - advising in terms of corrective activities to reduce risk;
- examination procedures definition to obtain a vocational training certificate for civil risk manager; the procedures can be similar to those of *safety adviser* examination procedures defined in UN 1.8.3.11; the examination is intended to verify knowledge about responsibilities defined in previous steps;
- certificate validity and renewal definition; according to dangerous good transportation regulations (ADR) and IAEM provisions, the period of validity can be five years conditioned to passing another examination (validity and renewal of certificate).

References

[1] UN, United Nation's office for Disaster Risk Reduction, http://www.unisdr.org/who-we-are/what-is-drr, 2012 (last access January, 2012).

[2] UN, United Nation's office for Disaster Risk Reduction, 2012, http://www.unisdr.org/campaign/resilientcities/toolkit/essentials/view/7, (last access January, 2012).

[3] Australia Governments, Emergency Management Approaches, 2010, http://www.ema.gov.au/, (last access January, 2011).

[4] USA, DoT, DHS, Department of Transport, Department of Homeland Security, Report to congress on catastrophic hurricane evacuation plan

evaluation, 2006, http://www.fhwa.dot.gov/reports/hurricanevacuation/ (last access January, 2011).

[5] EC, European Commission, European civil protection, 2012, http://ec.europa.eu/echo/civil_protection/civil/prevention_overview.htm (last access November, 2012).

[6] Marcianò F. A, Musolino G., Vitetta A., Within-day traffic assignment and signal setting in road evacuation: a procedure with explicit path enumeration. *WIT Transactions on The Built Environment*, Vol. 117, pp. 403–414, 2011.

[7] Russo, F. and Vitetta, A., Reverse assignment: calibrating link cost functions and updating demand from traffic counts and time measurements. *Inverse Problems in Science and Engineering*, 19 (7), pp. 921–950, 2011.

[8] Russo F. and Trecozzi M. R., Models for humanitarian logistics, *WIT Transactions on Ecology and the Environment*, Vol. 155, WIT Press, Southampton, 2012.

[9] Polimeni, A. and Vitetta A., Optimising waiting at nodes in time-dependent networks: cost functions and applications. *Journal of optimization theory and applications*, 156 (3), pp. 805–818, 2013.

[10] Russo F. and Chilà A., Dynamic approaches to demand model in evacuation conditions, *WIT Transactions on The Built Environment*, Vol. 111, Pratelli A. and Brebbia C. A. (ed.), WIT Press, Southampton, 2010.

[11] USA, FEMA, Federal Emergency Management Agency, 2012, http://www.fema.gov/national-incident-management-system (last access November, 2012).

[12] UN, United Nation's office for Disaster Risk Reduction, Essential Seven: Training, Education and Public Awareness, 2011, http://www.unisdr.org /campaign/resilientcities/toolkit/essentials/view/7 (last access January, 2011).

[13] Russo F. and Vitetta A., Risk evaluation in a transportation system. *International Journal of Sustainable Development and Planning*, 1 (2), pp. 170–191, WIT Press, Southampton, 2006.

[14] Polimeni, A. and Vitetta, A., The role of ITS in evacuation route optimization for emergency vehicles. *WIT Transactions on Information and Communication Technologies*, Vol. 44, pp. 517–529, WIT Press, Southampton, 2012.

[15] De Maio, M.L., Musolino, G. and Vitetta, A., The role of ITS in evacuation route choice. *WIT Transactions on Information and Communication Technologies*, Vol. 44, pp. 503–515, 2012.

[16] Russo, F. and Chilà G., A sequential dynamic choice model to simulate demand in evacuation conditions. *WIT Transactions on Information and Communication Technologies*, Vol. 43, pp. 431–442, 2010.

[17] Russo, F. and Chilà, G., Safety of users in road evacuation: demand models. *WIT Transactions on the Built Environment*, Vol. 96, pp. 773–782, 2007.

[18] Russo, F. and Chilà G., Safety of users in road evacuation: RP vs. SP surveys in demand analysis. *WIT Transactions on the Built Environment,* Vol. 101, pp. 703–713, 2008.

[19] De Maio, M. L., Musolino, G. and Vitetta, A., Traffic assignment models in road evacuation. *WIT Transactions on Ecology and the Environment,* Vol. 155, pp.1041–1051, 2012.

[20] Polimeni, A. and Vitetta, A., A procedure for an integrated network and vehicle routing optimisation problem. *Procedia – Social and Behavioral Sciences,* 54, pp. 65–74, 2012.

[21] Russo F., Rindone C., Trecozzi M.R., The role of training in evacuation. *WIT transactions on information and communication technologies,* Vol. 44, pp. 491–502, 2012.

[22] EC, European Commission, The European civil protection training programme, 2012. http://ec.europa.eu/echo/civil_protection/civil/prote/ pdfdocs/Training%20brochure.pdf, (last access December, 2012).

[23] USA, FEMA, Federal Emergency Management Agency, 2012 http://training.fema.gov/, (last access December, 2012).

[24] USA, DHS, Department of Homeland Security, Homeland Security Exercise and Evaluation Program (HSEEP), 2007, https:// hseep.dhs.gov/ pages/ 1001_HSEEP7.aspx, (last access December, 2012).

[25] Sinclair H., Doyle E. E., Johnston D. M., Paton D., Assessing emergency management training and exercises, *Disaster Prevention and Management,* Vol. 21 Iss: 4 pp. 507– 521, 2012.

[26] Alexander D., Towards the development of standards in emergency management training and education, *Disaster Prevention and Management,* Vol. 14, No. 2, Emerald, pp. 158–175, 2005.

[27] UN, United Nation, UN Recommendations on the Transport of Dangerous Goods – Model Regulations, Seventeenth revised edition, 2011 http://www.unece.org/trans/danger/publi/unrec/rev17/17files_e.html (last access December, 2012).

[28] USA, DoT, PHMSA, Department Of Transportation (DoT), Pipeline and Hazardous Materials Safety Administration, Training Resources, 2012 http://www.phmsa.dot.gov/training, (last access December, 2012).

[29] USA, DoT, Department of Transportation, Federal hazardous materials transportation law, 1994 http://www.law.cornell.edu/uscode/text/49 /subtitle-III/chapter-51, (last access December, 2012).

[30] EC, European Commission, Directive 96/35/EC of the European parliament and of the council of 3 June 1996 on the appointment and vocational qualification of safety advisers for the transport of dangerous goods by road, rail and inland waterway, 1996.

[31] EC, European Commission, Directive 2008/68/EC of the European parliament and of the council of 24 September 2008 on the inland transport of dangerous goods, http://eur-lex.europa.eu/LexUriServ/LexUriServ.do? uri=OJ:L:2008:260:0013:0059:en:PDF, 2008.

[32] UN, United Nation, *European Agreement concerning the International Carriage of Dangerous Goods by Road – ADR 2011,* 2010

http://www.unece.org/trans/danger/publi/adr/adr2011/11contentse.html, (last access December, 2012).

[33] Italian Government, Italian Law 40/2000, Attuazione della direttiva 96/35/CE relativa alla designazione e alla qualificazione professionale dei consulenti per la sicurezza dei trasporti su strada, per ferrovia o per via navigabile di merci pericolose, 2000, http://www.camera.it/ parlam/ leggi/ deleghe/ 00040dl.htm, (last access December, 2012).

[34] USA, FEMA, Federal Emergency Management Agency, National Preparedness Guidelines, 2007, http://www.fema.gov/pdf/emergency/nrf/ National_Preparedness_Guidelines.pdf, (last access January, 2011).

[35] USA, FEMA, Federal Emergency Management Agency, National Training Program, 2012, http:// www.fema.gov/ prepared/ train.shtm#1 (last access December, 2012).

[36] USA, FEMA, Federal Emergency Management Agency, Developing and Maintaining Emergency Operations Plans, 2010, http://www.fema.gov /sites/default/files/orig/fema_pdfs/pdf/about/divisions/npd/CPG_101_V2.pdf (last access December, 2012).

[37] USA, FEMA, Federal Emergency Management Agency, HSEEP glossary, 2012, https://hseep.dhs.gov/DHSResource/Glossary.aspx#E (last access December, 2012).

[38] USA, DHS, Department of Homeland Security, DHS risk lexicon, 2008, http://www.dhs.gov/xlibrary/assets/dhs_risk_lexicon.pdf (last access December, 2012).

[39] GWU, George Washington University, 2012, http://www.gwu.edu/~icdrm/

[40] IAEM, International Association of Emergency Managers, 2012, http://www.iaem.com/certification/generalinfo/intro.htm

[41] EMAP, Emergency Management Assessment Program, 2012 http://www.emaponline.org/index.php?option=com_content&view=article &id=25&Itemid=28

[42] Italian Government, Decreto Ministeriale 270/2004, 2004, http://www.miur.it/Miur/UserFiles/Notizie/2007/DMCdL_magistrale.pdf (last access March, 2012).

[43] E.Di.Ma.S., Emergency and Disaster Management Studies, 2012 http://edimas.net (last access March, 2012).

[44] AssDIMA, Associazione Italiana Disaster Manager, 2012, http:// www.associazioneitalianadisastermanager.it/1/certificazioni_emic_202706 5.html (last access March, 2012).

[45] ISO, International Organization for Standardization, Societal security – Guideline for incident preparedness and operational continuity management – ISO 22399:2007, 2007, http://www.iso.org/iso/catalogue_detail? csnumber=50295 (last access March, 2012).

[46] ISO, International Organization for Standardization, Risk management – Principles and guidelines – ISO 31000:2009, 2009, http://www.iso.org/ iso/catalogue_detail?csnumber=43170 (last access March, 2012).

Fuzzy utility models: possible applications in evacuation conditions in smart cities

M. L. De Maio
Dipartimento di Ingegneria dell'Informazione, delle Infrastrutture e dell'Energia Sostenibile. DIIES, Università degli Studi Mediterranea di Reggio Calabria, Italy

Abstract

In this paper the fuzzy utility models approach is proposed in relation to route choice in a network in evacuation conditions. Fuzzy logic is introduced and the main advantages are presented: the key concept of possibility allows a better representation of human minds. As a consequence, better results may be obtained in relation to users' behaviour representation. A possible application in evacuation conditions in a smart city is described.
Keywords: evacuation, smart city, fuzzy utility models, possibility, random utility models, route choice.

1 Introduction

Flows, travel times and congestion which occur on a transportation network depend on choices made by users. Generally users make their choices in an uncertain environment. In order to obtain a fair simulation of users' choices, several mathematical models where developed. Two main classes of models can be identified: Random Utility Models – RUM [1, 17] and Fuzzy Utility Models – FUM [3, 4].

Many researchers, investigating the issue of choices on a transport system, used fuzzy logic and mathematics [3, 5–7]. The main difference which characterizes RUM and FUM is related to the way of representing uncertainty: in RUM uncertainty is expressed in terms of probability whereas in FUM uncertainty is expressed in terms of possibility [3, 4].

The main aim of this paper is to specify a mathematical model for route choice in evacuation conditions, in a smart city. Two mathematical formulations

 WIT Transactions on Ecology and The Environment, Vol 173, © 2013 WIT Press
www.witpress.com, ISSN 1743-3541 (on-line)
doi:10.2495/SDP130651

will be proposed: one using RUM and another using FUM. If the analyst is able to forecast users' behaviour, using a suitable model, he may design the network and introduce route guidance policy, in order to improve performances on the network. In this paper we do not want to state that FUM is better than RUM: we only aim at showing differences between them, advantages and disadvantages.

Four sections follow this introduction. Section 2 provides a general view about the state of the art on route choice. Section 3 summarizes RUM. Section 4 summarizes possible applications of FUM in a smart city in emergency conditions. Section 5 summarizes FUM and a model specification is proposed. Conclusions and further developments are put in section 6. In this paper all matrices, vectors and scalars related to RUM are characterized by an R as superscript else, if they are related to FUM, they are characterized by an F as superscript.

2 State of the art

In this section we are going to describe some of the works available in literature: the first part of this section is related to fuzzy logic applications and the second part deals with route choice simulation.

Non-RUM models where born after Zadeh proposed his fuzzy logic theory [8, 9]. Dubois and Prade proposed the possibility theory [10].

Fuzzy logic is used in many works about transportation system simulation: Atanu and Kumar [11] proposed an algorithm to solve the shortest path problem; Brito *et al.* [12] dealt with the distribution of frozen food using a fuzzy approach in order to obtain an optimal solution; Chang and Chen [13] deal with route choice using a user-optimal approach; Wang and Liao [14] solve a user equilibrium assignment problem.

Several applications of fuzzy logic in relation to choice dimensions are available in literature: for modal choice [7], route choice [3, 4, 6, 15]. Several researchers consider attributes represented by fuzzy numbers and users' behaviour based on the paradigm of rational user, as in RUM.

In relation to route choice simulation, it is worth underlying that models related to choice dimensions should be specified on three levels [16]: generation level, perception level, choice level.

In literature it is also possible finding approaches which simulate two levels instead of three levels: generation and perception levels are aggregated. In other works perception and choice levels are aggregated [17]. In the end some researchers consider a single level, aggregating generation, perception and choice [18].

Coming back to the three levels approach, we are going to describe simulation of each level. At the first level, alternatives are generated. Generation of alternatives can be carried out using different approaches: mono-set or multi-sets, exhaustive or selective, mono criteria or multi criteria. Alternatives generated compose the choice set or the choice sets. Each alternative which belongs to a choice set is characterized by a specific perception. Hence, at the second level, a perception probability is calculated [17, 19–21]. Perception probability is calculated using RUM or FUM. In the end, each alternative is characterized by a choice probability, calculated at the third level [11, 17, 23–25].

3 RUM

Random utility theory is the most consolidated theory available in literature for transportation systems simulation. According to RUM each decision maker, assigns to each perceived alternative, belonging to the choice set, a perceived utility U^R_k which is a random variable, in order to take into account aspects not certainly known ([17]). U^R_k is characterized by an expected value $E(U^R_k) = V^R_k$, which is specified through some attributes $\mathbf{y}^R_k$ and some parameters $\boldsymbol{\beta}^R$ and θ^R:

$$V^R_k = v\,(\mathbf{y}^R_k;\ \boldsymbol{\beta}^R/\theta^R) = \Sigma_{i=1..N}\,(\beta_i^R/\theta^R)\cdot y_{ik}^R \tag{1}$$

In this paper we are focusing our attention on route choice and therefore we are interesting in the possibility to calculate route choice probability using RUM. In the following we are going to present some specification available in literature for route choice calculation like multinomial logit [11], nested logit [26], cross nested logit and link-nested logit [27], probit [28] and modified multinomial logit such as C-logit [21], DC-logit [21], path size logit [23] and mixed logit [17].

Being I the choice set, if U^R_k is independently and identically distributed (iid) according to a Gumbel random variable characterized by mean equal to V^R_k and variance parameter θ^R, the multinomial logit model is obtained [2]:

$$p^R(k/I) = (\exp\,(V_k^R))/(\Sigma_{i\in I}\,\exp(V_i^R)) \tag{2}$$

The C - logit model specification (Russo *et al.* 2003):

$$p^R(k/I) = (\exp\,(V_k^R + CF_k))/(\Sigma_{i\in I}\,(\exp(V_i^R + CF_i)) \tag{3}$$

In the C-logit model, the introduction of the commonality factor CF_k allows overcoming the independence of irrelevant alternatives (IIA), maintaining a simple mathematical formulation.

The Path Size model [23, 29]:

$$p^R(k/I) = (\exp\,(V_k^R + PS_k))/(\Sigma_{i\in I}\,(\exp(V_i^R + PS_i)) \tag{4}$$

In the Path Size model, as in the C-logit, the correction term Path Size (PS) is introduced in the specification, in order to take into account overlapping of alternatives.

The link nested logit model [27]:

$$p^R(k/I) = \Sigma_l[\alpha_{lk}^{1/d}_l \exp\,(-x_k/\varphi)\cdot(\Sigma_{h\in I(l)}\,\alpha_{lh}^{1/d}_l$$
$$\exp\,(-x_h/\varphi))^{d}_l^{-1}]/\Sigma_{l'}\,(\Sigma_{h\in I(l')}\,\alpha_{lh}^{1/d}_{l'}\cdot \exp(-x_h/\varphi))^{d}_{l'}^{-1} \tag{5}$$

In the link nested logit model, the choice set I is divided in subsets.

Application of the link nested logit model reveals several limits. For example route choice probability depends on the number of links belonging to the considered route.

If random residuals are distributed with a multivariate normal random variable, characterized by zero mean and general variances and covariances, the probit model is obtained [30].

For RUM calibration, the method of Maximum Likelihood is used in many works.

4 Possible application in evacuation conditions in a smart city

In ordinary conditions both applications of RUM and FUM are available. In RUM users' uncertainty is represented by random residuals, whereas in FUM uncertainties are represented by possibility calculation. FUM applications are quite rare; on the contrary RUM use are consolidated.

In emergency conditions, a wide literature is available: travel demand during evacuation was treated in [31]; concerning transport supply, calibration of cost function was carried out in [32]; traffic assignment models in evacuation conditions and DSS for supply-demand interaction were dealt in [33] and [34]; in particular the issues of within-day traffic assignment and signal setting were addressed in [35]; specific attention was paid to path design form emergency vehicles and emergency vehicles routing [36–39]; the ITS may play a key role during an evacuation [40]; moreover, the planning process is dealt in [41, 42] and [43]; the issue of humanitarian logistics, particularly concerning relief vehicles is treated in [44]; moreover, carrying out training activities may improve evacuation planning and implementation [45].

A possible classification of path choice models in emergency conditions is proposed in [46]. Models applied in emergency conditions may be classified in relation to users' classes monoclass or multiclass) and instant of choice (pre-trip, en-route, hybrid). FUM applications in emergency conditions are quite rare. Sun et al. [47] dealt with the selection of the best path in emergency conditions considering four fuzzy factors in order to simulate users' choices. In relation to the same theme Wu et al. [48], proposed a Multi-target fuzzy decision-making mathematic model.

FUM keep some positive aspects of well-known RUM like simple mathematical formulation and easiness of calculation. One of the main differences between RUM and FUM is related to the main output: probability is the main output of RUM, possibility is the main output of FUM. It is worth noting that in situation characterized by lack of knowledge and high level of uncertainty, users will have a confused idea of alternatives and will associate to each of them a low value of possibility/credibility. This means that likely the sum of possibilities/credibilities will not be equal to one. In relation to this aspect, it is worth underlying that in RUM the sum of probabilities of alternatives belonging to the choice set has to be necessarily equal to one, whereas in FUM the sum of possibilities is not equal to one. In emergency situations, characterized by a very high level of uncertainty, confusion and quite completely absence of trustful information, possibilities may represent better than probabilities the way human mind works.

Efficacy of FUM application in evacuation conditions is a key issue to be investigated.

Recently, the definition of smart city spread up all over the world. According to the report "Smart cities – Ranking of European medium-sized cities" [49], smart cities definition is based on the definition of six dimensions:

1. Smart economy (Innovative spirit, Entrepreneurship, Economic image and trademarks, Productivity, Flexibility of labour market, International embeddedness, Ability to transform);
2. Smart mobility (Local accessibility, (Inter-)national accessibility, Availability of ICT-infrastructure, Sustainable, innovative and safe transport systems);
3. Smart environment (Attractivity of natural conditions, Pollution, Environmental protection, Sustainable resource management)
4. Smart people (Level of qualification, Affinity to lifelong learning, Social and ethnic plurality, Flexibility, Creativity, Cosmopolitanism /Openmindedness, Participation in public life);
5. Smart living (Cultural facilities, Health conditions, Individual safety, Housing quality, Education facilities, Touristic attractivity, Social cohesion);
6. Smart governance (Participation in decision-making, Public and social services, Transparent governance, Political strategies and perspectives).

In order to make smarter a city several actions should be introduced. Implementation of Information and Communication Technologies (ICTs) may help at reaching the general goal. For example this may help at providing information to users about the actual condition of the network and also may give the possibility to manage traffic providing specific route guidance to users. Many issues related to the kind of information to be provided and users' compliance to guidance should be investigated. It is worth underlying that only if intelligent systems are based on mathematical models which properly represent users' behaviour efficacy of actions implemented would be realized. The possibility to manage traffic in a smart city may lead to a smart mobility and this could allow rescuing many human lives in evacuation conditions.

5 FUM

Fuzzy model specification is based on the assumption that the generic user behave as a quasi-rational decision maker. Each user associates a utility U^F to each alternative: U^F is a fuzzy number characterized by a membership function μ_U. The membership function μ_U may have values in the [0, 1] range. U^F is characterized by a crispy part called V^F, specified through some attributes $\mathbf{y}^F$ and some parameters $\boldsymbol{\beta}^F$ and θ^F.

$$V^F = \omega\,(\mathbf{y}^F;\,\boldsymbol{\beta}^F\,/\theta^F) = \sum_{i=1..N}\,(\beta_i^F/\theta^F)\cdot y_i^F \qquad (6)$$

Another specification of the crispy part V^F is proposed in [50], where a commonality factor CF was introduced in order to take into account similarity between alternatives: the C-fuzzy model is obtained.

The membership function μ_U numerically coincides with the possibility function [8]. For each alternative it is necessary calculating the possibility that the considered alternative has maximum utility: the possibility is obtained as the possibility of intersection between the perceived utility of the considered alternative and the maximum perceived utility, as expressed by (7).

$$\text{Poss}(k) = \text{Poss}(U^k \geq U^{max}) \tag{7}$$

From possibility it is possible obtaining probability of alternative k. A method to obtain a choice percentage distribution from possibility is proposed by Klir [51]:

$$p^F(k/I) = (q^F)^\gamma / (\textstyle\sum_{i..N} (q_i^F)^\gamma) \tag{8}$$

5.1 Comparison between RUM and FUM

In this section a comparison between RUM and FUM is proposed. At this aim a logit model (superscript L), belonging to the RUM family, and a fuzzy model are considered. First of all, RUM and FUM are characterized by a simple mathematical structure. For this reason, three different steps may be identified. It is worth noting that not all the three steps are available both in RUM and FUM. Anyway the logic process is the same for both FUM and RUM. First of all, the systematic utility has to be specified: at this aim attributes (y^L – RUM; y^F – FUM) and coefficients (β^L – RUM; β^F – FUM), to be calibrated, have to be used. The second step for FUM is the calculation of possibility: when a triangular distribution is chosen for the membership function, the calibrated parameters α_1 and α_2 and the scale parameter θ^F are necessary for possibility calculation. This step is not present in RUM. On the contrary it is necessary in FUM in order to get the last step: the calculation of probability.

Probability is calculated both in RUM and FUM but different inputs are necessary: in RUM probability calculation appears V^L, the variance parameter θ^L; in FUM probability calculation appears the possibility $q(U^F)$ (obtained in the second step) and the scale parameter γ.

5.2   5.2 Proposed FUM Specification

In order to complete the specification of the fuzzy model the membership function distribution has to be chosen. In this paper we are going to choose a triangular distribution: U^F is a fuzzy interval, characterized by a core value (V^F) and two bounds, U_s on the left and U_d on the right (Figure 1). U_s and U_d are assumed to depend on two shape parameters α_1 and α_2. U_s and U_d are expressed as a function of V^F, through the shape parameters.

$$U_s = \alpha_1 V^F \qquad U_d = \alpha_2 V^F \quad \text{if } U_c \geq 0 \tag{9}$$

$$0 < \alpha_1 < 1; \, \alpha_2 > 1 \tag{10}$$

The user perceives several alternatives. Each alternative is represented by a fuzzy interval as the one specified above. Amongst all the perceived alternatives, there is one alternative characterized by the largest perceived utility U^{max} (core value V^{max}). Moreover also the alternative chosen by the user is characterized by a fuzzy interval U^{SC} (core value V^{SC}). In order to calculate the possibility, as explained in section 4, it is necessary to identify an intersection between the triangular fuzzy distribution of the alternative characterized by the maximum utility (U^{max}) and the triangular fuzzy distribution of the chosen alternative (U^{SC}). If no intersections can be found the possibility is equal to zero. On the contrary, if there is an intersection, it is possible calculating it as follows:

$$y = q(U^{max}) = q^F = ((U_C^{max} \cdot \alpha_1) - (U_C^{SC} \cdot \alpha_2)) / ((U_C^{SC} \cdot (1 - \alpha_2))$$
$$- (U_C^{max} \cdot (1 - \alpha_1))) \qquad (12)$$

For more detail about possibility calculation please see [50].

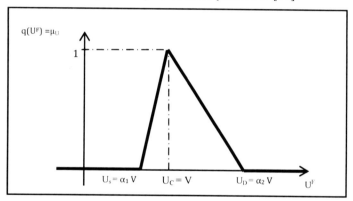

Figure 1:   Graphical representation of the fuzzy number $U^F = (U_s, U_c, U_d)$.

5.3 Application on a test network

The model proposed in section 6 is applied on a test network. Moreover also RUM described in section 3 are applied. In figure 5 the test network used for the application is presented: it is characterized by a single o-d pair, four links and three routes, indicated in Figure 2 as a, b and c.

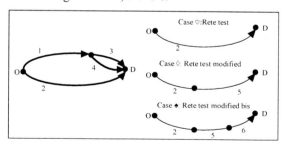

Figure 2:   Test network.

Please find the basic test network in Figure 2 indicated as the test network case ♡. Moreover a modified network is considered: it is obtained splitting link 2 in two parts by a new node. In the modified network all paths consists of two links. Please find the modified network in Figure 2 as case ◊. In addition to this, a modified network bis is represented in Figure 2 and indicated as case ♠: it is obtained, splitting link 2 again by introducing another node. For links costs please see Table 1.

Table 1: Link – route incidence matrix for test network[b].

Link			1	2	3	4	5	6
	a	Case ♡	0	1	0	0		
		Case ◊	0	1	0	0	1	
Route		Case ♠	0	1	0	0	1	1
	b		1	0	1	0		
	c		1	0	0	1		
Link costs			k	10	10-k	10-k+h		

[b]1= link belongs to the path; 0= link does not belong to the path.

In the following we are going to discuss results obtained applying models on the test network, represented in Figure 3.

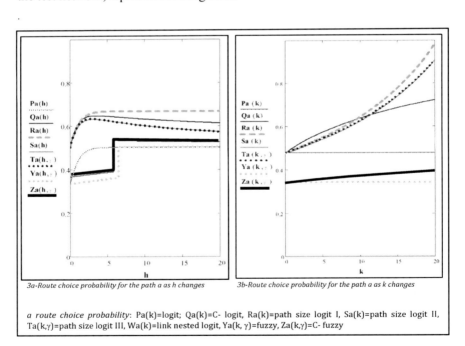

3a-Route choice probability for the path a as h changes   *3b-Route choice probability for the path a as k changes*

a route choice probability: Pa(k)=logit; Qa(k)=C- logit, Ra(k)=path size logit I, Sa(k)=path size logit II, Ta(k,γ)=path size logit III, Wa(k)=link nested logit, Ya(k, γ)=fuzzy, Za(k,γ)=C- fuzzy

Figure 3: Route choice probability for path a.

Figure 3 is composed of two figures. Figure 3a make us clearer the effect of changes in the value of h on route choice probability of path a. On the contrary, figure 3b make us clearer the effect of changes in the value of k on route choice probability of path a.

In figure 3a, we can observe that if h is great, all models applied provide a probability equal to 0.5. The main difference between figure 3a and figure 3b is the jump which characterizes probability of C – Fuzzy in figure 3a. This is because when possibility overcomes a limit (after which it would be negative that is impossible by definition) it is assumed equal to zero. On the contrary in figure 3b there is no jump because the value of k does not influence route cost.

6 Conclusions

In this paper we proposed a specification for a fuzzy model and compared FUM and RUM. An application of the proposed model on a test network is presented. Moreover possible applications in evacuation conditions in a smart city are described in section 4. Considering the application on a test network, FUM are characterized by a simple mathematical formulation and calculation is not difficult. This makes FUM suitable for practical application.

Features of FUM described in this paper and results obtained from the application on a test network, suggest that FUM application may provide good results also in special context, for instance in evacuation conditions. In addition to this, intelligent systems available in a smart city, jointed with specific abilities of FUM to represent fuzziness in users' behaviour, may allow to realize good practices and lead to obtain good performances on the network, also in evacuation conditions. Uncertainty and lack of knowledge grow up in emergency conditions: therefore introducing possibility instead of probability, using FUM instead of RUM in emergency environments applications may lead to better results.

Delving into advantages and limits of the described methodology is necessary and for this reason the proposed model has to be applied in a real network. Calibration of parameters which characterize FUM and RUM has to be carried out.

References

[1] Domencich T. and McFadden D., *Urban Travel Demand: A Behavioural Analysis*. North-Holland, Amsterdam, 1975.
[2] Cascetta E., *Transportation systems engineering: theory and methods*. Kluwer Academic Publisher, Dordrecht, The Netherlands, 2001.
[3] Henn V., What is the meaning of fuzzy costs in fuzzy traffic assignment models? *Transportation Research Part C* 13, pp. 107–119, 2005.
[4] Henn V. and Ottomanelli M., Handling uncertainty in route choice models: From probabilistic to possibilistic approaches, *European Journal of Operational Research*, 175(3), pp. 1526–1538, 2006.

[5] Lotan T., Modelling route choice behaviour in the presence of information using concepts of fuzzy sets theory and approximate reasoning. PhD thesis, Massachusetts Institute of Technology, Boston, MA, 1992.

[6] Russo F., Fuzzy Theory in Transportation Field: Fuzzy Sets for Simulating Path Choice Behaviour. In Morabito F.C. (ed.): *Advanced in Intelligent Systems*, IOS Press, 1997.

[7] Cantarella G.E. and Fedele V., Fuzzy utility theory for analysing discrete choice behaviour. In: *Proceedings of the Fourth International Symposium on Uncertainty Modelling and Analysis*, pp. 148–154, 2003.

[8] Zadeh L., Fuzzy sets. *Information and Control* 8(3), pp. 338–353, 1965.

[9] Zadeh L., Fuzzy sets as basis for a theory of possibility. *Fuzzy Sets and Systems*, pp. 3–28, 1978.

[10] Dubois D. and Prade H., *Possibility theory*. Plenum, New York, 1988.

[11] Atanu S. and Kumar P. T., Solving the Shortest Path Problem with Interval Arcs. *Fuzzy Optimization and Decision Making*, 5(1), pp. 71–89, 2006.

[12] Brito J., Martinez F. J., Moreno J. A. and Verdegay J. L., Fuzzy optimization for distribution of frozen food with imprecise times. *Fuzzy Optimization and Decision Making*, 11(3), pp. 337–349, 2012.

[13] Chang M.S. and Chen H.K., A fuzzy user-optimal route choice problem using a link-based fuzzy variational inequality formulation. *Fuzzy Sets and Systems* 114, pp. 339–345, 2000.

[14] Wang H.F., Liao H.L., User equilibrium in traffic assignment problem with fuzzy N–A incidence matrix. *Fuzzy Sets and Systems*, 107 (3), pp. 245–253, 1999.

[15] Ridwan M., Fuzzy preference based traffic assignment problem. *Transportation Research Part C* 12, pp. 209–233, 2004.

[16] Manski, The structure of random utility models. *Theory and Decision* 8, pp. 229–254, 1977.

[17] Cascetta E., Russo F., Viola F.A. and Vitetta A., A model of route perception in urban road networks. Transportation Research Part B, 36, pp. 577–592, 2002.

[18] Morikawa T., A hybrid probabilistic choice set model with compensatory and non-compensatory rules. In: *Proceedings of the 7th WCTR*, Sydney, Australia, 1996.

[19] Swait J. and Ben-Akiva M., Incorporating Random Constraints in Discrete Models of Choice Set Generation. *Transportation Research B*, 21B(2), pp. 91–102, 1987.

[20] Ben-Akiva M.E. and Boccara B., Discrete choice models with latent choice sets. In: *International Journal of Research in Marketing* 12, pp. 305–329, 1995.

[21] Russo, F. and Vitetta, A., An assignment model with modified Logit, which obviates enumeration and overlapping problems. *Transportation* 30, pp. 177–201, 2003.

[22] Antonisse R.W., Daly A.J. and Ben Akiva M.E., Highway assignment method based on behavioural models of car driver's route choice. *Transportation Research Record* 1220, pp. 1–11, 1985.

[23] Ben-Akiva M. E. and Bierlaire M., Discrete choice methods and their applications to short term travel decisions. In R. Hall (ed.), *Handbook of Transportation Science,* Vol. 23 Kluwer, 1999.

[24] Polimeni A. and Vitetta A. Optimising waiting at nodes in time-dependent networks: cost functions and applications. *Journal of optimization theory and applications,* 156(3), pp. 805–818, 2013.

[25] Russo F. and Vitetta A., Reverse assignment: Calibrating link cost functions and updating demand from traffic counts and time measurements. *Inverse Problems in Science and Engineering* 19(7), pp. 921–950, 2011.

[26] Vovsha P., Cross-nested logit model: an application to mode choice in the Telaviv metropolitan area. In: *Proceedings of the Annual Meeting of the Transportation Research Board,* Washington DC, 1997.

[27] Vovsha P. and Bekhor S., The link-nested logit model of route choice: overcoming the route overlapping problem. *Transportation Research Record* 1645, pp. 133–142, 1998.

[28] Sheffi Y., Hall R. and Daganzo C., On the estimation of the multinomial probit model, *Transportation Research A,* vol. 16 (5-6), pp. 447–456, 1982.

[29] Frejinger E. and Bierlaire M., Capturing correlation with subnetworks in route choice models. *Transportation Research Part B* 41 (3), pp. 363–378, 2007.

[30] Daganzo C. F., Multinomial probit: the theory and its application to demand forecasting. Academic press, New York, 1979.

[31] Russo F. and Chilà G., Safety of users in road evacuation: Demand models. *WIT Transactions on the Built Environment* 96, pp. 773–782, 2007.

[32] Vitetta A., Musolino G. and Marcianò F.A., Safety of users in road evacuation: Calibration of cost functions and simulation. WIT Transactions on the Built Environment 101, pp. 715–725, 2008.

[33] De Maio M.L., Musolino G., Vitetta A, Traffic assignment models in road evacuation. *WIT Transactions on Ecology and the Environment,* 155, pp. 1041–1051, 2011.

[34] Vitetta A., Musolino G., Marcianò F.A., Safety of users in road evacuation: Modelling and DSS for transport supply and supply-demand interaction. *WIT Transactions on Ecology and the Environment,* 120, pp. 475–484, 2009.

[35] Marcianò F.A., Musolino G. and Vitetta A., Within-day traffic assignment and signal setting in road evacuation: A procedure with explicit path enumeration. *WIT Transactions on the Built Environment* 117, pp. 403–414, 2011.

[36] Vitetta A., Quattrone A. and Polimeni A., Safety of users in road evacuation: Design of path choice models for emergency vehicles. *WIT Transactions on the Built Environment* 96, pp. 803–812, 2007.

[37] Vitetta A., Quattrone A. and Polimeni A., Safety of users in road evacuation: Modelling and DSS for paths design of emergency vehicles. WIT Transactions on Ecology and the Environment 120, pp. 485–495, 2009.

[38] Polimeni A. and Vitetta A., Dynamic vehicle routing in road evacuation: Route design experimentation, *WIT Transactions on the Built Environment* 117, pp. 391–402, 2011.

[39] Polimeni A., The role of optimization models for rescue vehicles routes in evacuation. *WIT Transactions on Information and Communication Technologies*, 44, pp. 477–489, 2012.

[40] De Maio M.L., Musolino G., Vitetta A, The role of ITS in evacuation route choice. *WIT Transactions on Information and Communication Technologies*, 44, pp. 503–515, 2012.

[41] Russo F. and Rindone C., Safety of users in road evacuation: Planning internal processes and guidelines. *WIT Transactions on the Built Environment* 96, pp. 825–834, 2007.

[42] Russo F. and Rindone C., Safety of users in road evacuation: Modelling and DSS for LFA in the planning process. *WIT Transactions on Ecology and the Environment,* 120, pp. 453–464, 2009.

[43] Russo F. and Rindone C., Data Envelopment Analysis (DEA) for evacuation planning. *WIT Transactions on Information and Communication Technologies,* 43(PART I), pp. 455–467, 2010.

[44] Russo F. and Trecozzi M.R., Models for humanitarian logistics. *WIT Transactions on Ecology and the Environment* 155, pp. 1079–1089, 2011.

[45] Russo F., Rindone C. and Trecozzi M.R., The role of training in evacuation. *WIT Transactions on Information and Communication Technologies*, 44, pp. 491–502, 2012.

[46] De Maio M. L., The role of path choice and traffic assignment models in evacuation, *WIT Transactions on Information and Communication Technologies,* 44, pp. 465–476, 2012.

[47] Sun X. and Lu J., A method of emergency logistics route choice based on fuzzy theory. Proceedings of ICLEM 2010: *Logistics For Sustained Economic Development: Infrastructure, Information, Integration*, 2010.

[48] Wu Q., Chen T. and Su Y., The Best Path Analysis Based on Multi-target Fuzzy Decision-making. *Computer simulation* 22(12), 106–109, 2005.

[49] Giffinger R., Christian F., Hans K., Robert K., Nataša P.-M., Evert M., Smart cities – Ranking of European medium-sized cities. http://www.smart-cities.eu/. Vienna: Centre of Regional Science, 2007.

[50] Quattrone A. and Vitetta A., Random and fuzzy utility models for road route choice. *Transportation Research Part E: Logistics and Transportation Review,* 47(6), pp. 1126–1139, 2011.

[51] Klir G. J., A principle of uncertainty and information invariance. *International Journal of General Systems* n.2/3, pp. 249–275, 1990.

Designing escape routes for buildings through an aggregate approach

M. Di Gangi
Department of Civil and Environmental Engineering, Informatics and Applied Mathematics, University of Messina, Italy

Abstract

In this paper a method for the definition of effective destination and escape routes by means of the simulation of pedestrian outflow related to the evacuation of a building is described. The generated feasible alternatives are compared in terms of evacuation time by means of an aggregate assignment model. Such a method can be easily implemented in a spreadsheet and can be used to give a first evaluation of evacuation procedures without performing evacuation drills. It can also be used to give a fast response in identifying critical points on the network. To check the capabilities of the proposed procedure, results obtained from simulations are compared with data recorded from experimentation on a test site conducted in a primary school located in an Italian town.
Keywords: evacuation, simulation.

1 Introduction

One of the aspects that in the last years attracted the attention of some experts of the field on transport model consists in the analysis of working modality of a transport system when it is subjected to emergency conditions. Such approach should allow the availability of tools able to conduct simulations of evacuations avoiding expensive drills or to give useful indications to enhance evacuation processes of different extended areas (building, industrial site, town, etc.).

An evacuation can be defined as a general mobilization of people (and/or goods) due to the occurrence of a calamitous event. Its main objective is to reduce the number of people (and/or goods) present in the area where the event strikes [1]. Evacuation drills are mainly performed to practice the people to leave the interested area; these tests can also be used for getting information

WIT Transactions on Ecology and The Environment, Vol 173, © 2013 WIT Press
www.witpress.com, ISSN 1743-3541 (on-line)
doi:10.2495/SDP130661

concerning the behavior of the people in order to build a set of mathematical models able to reproduce the evacuation. These models can constitute a Decision Support System (DSS) to be used for planning emergences [2].

Pedestrian evacuation has been considered in the last years a lead issue from both theoretical and practical point of view. On the one hand details of pedestrian evacuation have been cast into mathematical formulations yielding to various representations of pedestrian interactions. On the other hand theoretical developments have conducted to model emergency evacuation and situations [3–12] using sophisticated simulation methodologies.

Computational complexity of proposed models requires the analysis outflow conditions of networks, and the adoption of dedicated and sophisticated tools. On the other hand there is also, in certain circumstances, a need for simple tools able to quantify, in terms of evacuation time, the effectiveness of an evacuation plan.

Such aggregate approaches, in order to simulate pedestrian movements, consider laws of motion of pedestrian flow using, in general, relationships between speed and density [13–16] or deriving from continuum theory of traffic flows [17, 18].

In this paper a specific methodology (models and procedure) to define effective escape routes by simulating evacuation of buildings is shown. The proposed aggregate approach allows a prompt first attempt evaluation in case of the lack of commercial software or tools suitable to perform advanced and more sophisticated simulations.

The paper is structured as follows: in section 2 it is described the proposed method to define evacuation routes in case of buildings, in section 3 results of an application to a real case represented by a provisional school unit built after L'Aquila earthquake is presented and some remarks are reported in section 4.

2   Methodology

2.1 Definition of evacuation scenarios

Steps followed to define evacuation scenarios are described in the following and their connections are sketched in Fig. 1.

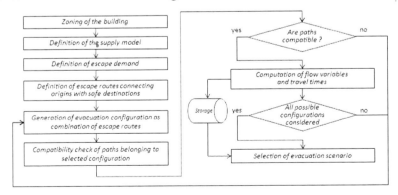

Figure 1:   Scheme of the activities to define evacuation scenarios.

2.1.1 Zoning of the building

Every starting and terminal area is identified within the building (and eventually its surroundings if safe areas are located outside the building) yielding to the definition of origin and destination zones. Every zone is approximated with a single point (zone centroid) representing origin or destination nodes of escape routes, that can be divided in:

- *zone centroids*: these nodes represent the barycentre of each zone (rooms, offices, etc.) comprising the building. They sum up the origins of the trips of all the people who, at emergency time, are within the considered area making up a zone. There is a centroid for each zone in which the building is divided;
- *destination nodes* (centroids): these represent the safe areas towards which people converge in an emergency; they correspond to the destinations of evacuation routes;

2.1.2 Definition of the supply model

In this step geometric characteristics of elements of the building are acquired; then, considering the elements of a building, the classes of components making up the graphs are:

- *network nodes*: these are located at each potential change of direction along a generic evacuation route or at significant variations in geometric and/or functional characteristics of a trunk (i.e. width variations);
- *real arcs*: these represent the connection between two network nodes or a network and a destination node; they coincide with trunks of the pedestrian network and are classified into flat ramps (corridors) and descending or ascending ramps (stairs);
- *connector arcs*: these are used to represent the connection between an area centroid and a network node.

2.1.3 Definition of escape demand

In this step data concerning occupants, defining both their number and their positions, are acquired. Those values are attributed to the correspondent origin nodes representing each considered site (*zone centroid*). Different scenarios should be considered for the analysis of evacuation considering different numbers and distributions of occupants.

2.1.4 Generation of escape routes: path generation

After building the graph of the network representing the elements, in term of components of the escape ways (ramps, corridors, stairs, etc.) of the building, a set of evacuation routes connecting each origin with each defined safe destination is generated. In order to explore a wide range of alternatives, for each origin-destination pair more than one path is taken into consideration. To define these evacuation routes a set of paths is generated considering a K shortest loopless path algorithm considering as arc cost its travel time. One of the possibilities, in order to take into account of the environmental condition of each link within conventional path search algorithms, can be to weight travel time associated to the generic arc of the graph by means of the level of risk associated to the arc [19], assuming that the role of risk can be associated similarly to the one played by saturation level in congested networks. The relationship between the weighted arc cost and the travel time can be written as follows:

$$Tw_i = Tt_i \cdot \{ 1 + \alpha[\ln(1/s_i)]^\beta \} \qquad (1)$$

where:
Tw_i is the weighted cost associated to arc i;
Tt_i is the travel time of arc i;
s_i is a *safety probability* $0 < s_i \leq 1$;
α,β are parameters.

The level of the reliability of an arc (*safety probability*) depends on the nature of the considered event (i.e. an evacuation route using downstairs can be considered safe in case of fire but can be unsafe in case of flood).

2.1.5 Generation of feasible alternatives

The number of alternative is strictly influenced by the value assumed the number K of alternative evacuation routes considered for each origin/destination pair, since the number of potential alternatives is given by the permutation of the K paths on N_{od} origin/destination pairs, that is N_{od}^K (in the hypothesis that for every pair it is possible to identify k different paths; in general if K_i is the number of path for the i-th pair, the number of potential alternatives is given by $\Pi_{i \in od} K_i$).

The scenario is generated by applying a selection rule to the set of potential alternatives. The rule here introduced, in order to define a feasible set, consists in eliminating those combinations where contra flow is potentially allowed; this implies that each element of the network (ramp, corridor, stair, etc) can be covered in one way only.

In order to establish feasibility, given a path k let $l_k(r,s)$ be a generic arc belonging to path k connecting nodes r and s; two paths, h and k, are compatible if, considering each arc $l_h(r,s)$ of path h, it does not exist an arc $l_k(s,r)$ belonging to path k. Such rule is implemented by defining a compatibility incidence matrix $C [n_k \times n_k]$ where the generic element c_{hk} is equal to 1 if paths h and k are compatible, otherwise it is equal to 0.

2.2 Computing flow variables and evacuation time

The proposal of this method arises from the need to have a tool, even though approximate, able to give some indications both on the outflow conditions and on the evacuation times of a building. One of the advantages of this method consists on the possibility to evaluate evacuation times with the only support of a common worksheet application, avoiding the necessity to use specific commercial software.

2.2.1 Main hypotheses

The proposed method of estimating evacuation time is based on the following assumptions:
- all occupants will begin evacuation at the same time and will not hinder each other;
- occupants will evacuate via a previously defined escape route;

- initial walking speed depends on the density of persons, assuming that the flow is only in the direction of the escape route, and that there is no overtaking;
- full availability of escape arrangements is considered, unless otherwise stated;
- people can move unhindered;
- effects of passenger age and mobility impairment, flexibility of arrangements, unavailability of corridors, restricted visibility due to smoke, can be accounted for in specific correction factors.

Proposed method can be summarized through a succession of operations finalized to the evaluation of evacuation time.

2.2.2 Demand-supply interaction model

- *Computation of occupants for each element q_i.* For each element of escape routes, the flow of occupants (vector q) is computed using the arc-path incidence matrix (A) as $q = Ad$, where d is the vector of demand.
- *Computation of the specific flow (q_s).* This value is computed dividing flow q by the effective width w of the considered element except for connectors; for those latter components specific relationships based on density are adopted.
- *Computation of speed.* Once specific flow q_s is known, the following two cases arise:
  - values of q_s do not reach the value q_s^{max} of characteristic maximum specific flow for the considered element; speed v' is computed using specific relationships depending on specific flow;
  - values of q_s overtake the value q_s^{max} of characteristic maximum specific flow for the considered element; in this case queues arise in correspondence of transition points; correspondent speed v'' is given by the limit value indicated by relationships expressing speeds depending on specific flow.

2.2.3 Computation of times

- *Computation of flow time for each element (tf_i).* Those values are computed once evaluated walking speed for each considered element as $tf_i = l_i / v_i$.
- *Computation of queue time for each element (tq_i).* Those values are computed depending on specific flow q_s and the value q_s^{max} of characteristic maximum specific flow for the considered element as $tq_i = (q_s - q_s^{max}) / q_s^{max}$.
- *Computation of travel time for each escape route (T).* Travel times are computed, for the whole set of evacuation routes, considering the arc-path incidence matrix as $T = A^T (t_f + t_q)$.
- *Computation of evacuation time.* After computing travel time for each evacuation route, the higher value T among all the travel times is considered as the evacuation time.

3   Applicative context

3.1   Model calibration

The part of the methodology concerning demand/supply interaction has been calibrated in a real context [20–24] where evacuation drills have been carried out in order to collect data to validate proposed models. In particular two evacuation tests (drills) have been carried out and data were gathered concerning supply and demand. During the drills a monitoring system was arranged, with manual/automatic tools and 12 video cameras, in order to acquire data concerning pedestrian outflow (times, densities) both inside and outside the building until the gathering places were reached.

3.2   Application of the methodology

The application of the methodology was performed to define the evacuation routes on one of the provisional school units (MUSP – Lotto 16) built after L'Aquila earthquake of April 6th 2009. Plans of the two floors of the considered building are sketched in Fig. 1. In the following of this paragraph operations conducted at each step of the proposed procedure in the considered context are explained.

3.2.1   Zoning of the building
Considering each room as a distinct zone, 39 potential origins and 2 destinations outside the building have been identified. For the sake of simplicity dressing rooms have not been considered as origin. Origins are treated as actual if, in the considered scenario, the presence of people attributed to the area they represent is thought. A centroid has been attributed to each zone.

3.2.2   Definition of the supply model
The building has been schematized considering the network of all possible pathways. Corridors were considered in both directions and a specific arc has been considered for each door aperture. The resulting plan, shown in Fig. 2, consists of 170 nodes and 189 arcs (note that arcs related to vertical connections – stairs – are not visible).

3.2.3   Definition of escape demand
In the considered scenario the hypothesis made is that only classrooms and offices are in use, no activities are conducted in laboratories and in the school gym and there is no one in the toilets. So, only 25 of the potential 39 origins are then considered, and occupants of each room correspondent to the origin node have been defined as indicated in Tab. 1.

Following these hypotheses, the total number of occupants to evacuate is of 451 people, 330 located at the first floor and 121 located at the ground floor.

3.2.4   Definition of escape routes
Paths connecting the 25 origins with the 2 assembly point have been generated. In order to explore a wide range of alternatives, for each origin-destination up to

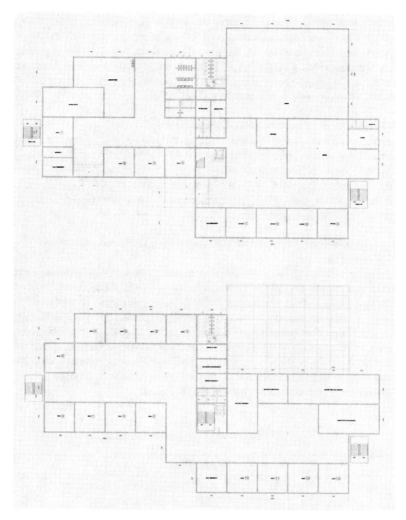

Figure 2:   Plan of the ground and first floors of the provisional school units.

Table 1:   Definition of occupants for each origin node.

Ground floor													
Origin node	1	3	4	5	6	11	12	13	14	15	16		
Occupants	25	5	25	25	25	5	2	2	2	2	3		
First floor													
Origin node	85	86	87	88	89	90	91	92	93	94	95	96	97	98
Occupants	25	25	25	25	25	25	25	25	25	5	25	25	25	25

3 evacuation routes for each O/D pair have been taken into consideration. Free-flow time has been considered as cost of each arc; it is given by arc length divided by its free flow speed, supposed equal to 0.8 m/s for corridors and 0.5 m/s for descending stairs. A k-shortest path algorithm has been used to evaluate escape routes; results consist of 59 generated evacuation routes since, for some O/D pair, only 1 or 2 path are obtainable.

3.2.5 Generation of evacuation configurations

Considering the set of evacuation routes computed above, feasible evacuation scenarios have been built taking account of the selection rule consisting in eliminating those combinations where contra flow is potentially allowed. So, starting from the 306,110,016 possible combinations obtained combining paths for all the O/D pair each other, the application of such selection rule reduces the number of feasible configurations to 22,712.

3.2.6 Computation of flow variables and travel times and selection of scenario

For each one of the feasible configurations, using the aggregate model described before, travel times and flow characteristics are computed in order to define indicators on evacuation conditions. The effective scenario has been identified considering, among all the simulated configurations, the one that minimize evacuation time. The selection of a configuration implies the attribution of the safe area to be reached from evacuees; attribution of destinations (safe area) to each origin (room) is shown in Tab. 2. In Tab. 3 some statistics expressed in terms of evacuation time and total time are shown, whilst indicators obtained for the selected configuration are summarized in Tab. 4.

Table 2:   Definition of safe area for each origin node.

Ground floor													
Origin node	1	3	4	5	6	11	12	13	14	15	16		
Destination (Safe area)	78	78	78	78	78	78	78	78	78	78	78		
First floor													
Origin node	85	86	87	88	89	90	91	92	93	94	95	96	97	98
Destination (Safe area)	78	78	78	78	78	78	78	78	170	78	170	170	170	170

Table 3:   Statistics obtained for the whole set of configurations.

	Min		Max			
	Time [s]	Scenario	Time [s]	Scenario	Mean [s]	Var. [s²]
Evacuation time	445	90	1432	232	744	9275
Total time	153,024	19,963	480,711	232	216,296	7.77E+08

Table 4:   Indicators obtained for optimal configuration.

Indicator	Time [s]	Time [hh:mm:ss]
Evacuation time	445	00:07:25
Total time	154,327	42:52:07
Max queue time	279	00:04:39
Total queue time	93,097	25:51:37

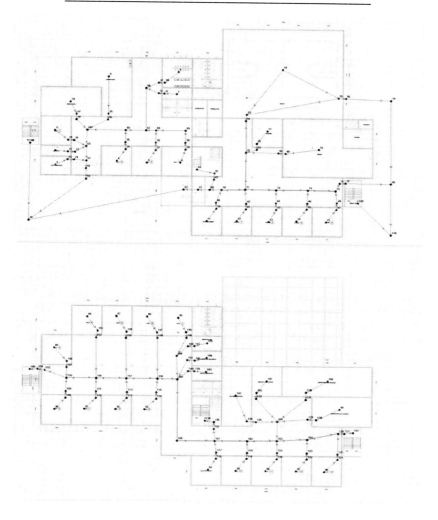

Figure 3:   Plans of the pedestrian network of the provisional school unit.

3.3 Computational issues

Since one of the aim of this work was to build up a simple tools able to quantify, in terms of evacuation time, the effectiveness of an evacuation plan, the whole procedure, except for the zoning and the graph definition, has been implemented in a Microsoft Excel© spreadsheet where the modules of the procedure were coded using the VBA language.

Running times for each step, obtained on an AMD Athlon II, 2 GB RAM with Windows 7 and Office 2007, are shown in Tab. 5.

Table 5:   Running time for each step of the procedure.

Step	Time [s]
Path generation	0.406
Evaluation of path compatibility	3,543
Generation of alternatives	1,328
Evaluation of alternatives	40,387

4 Conclusions and perspectives

The main result of this paper concerns a method for the definition of effective escape routes by means of the simulation of pedestrian outflow related to the evacuation of a building using an aggregate model for the estimation of evacuation time. A comparison between experimental data and simulation results shows how the usage of appropriate simulation models can realistically reproduce user behavior. It was shown that such models could be used as a support both to verify effectiveness of existing evacuation plans without resorting to expensive drills and to draw up evacuation plans and can be used to give a fast response in identifying critical points on the network. The capabilities of the proposed approach have been shown by means of an application on a real case.

Implementation of appropriate cost functions can make the applied methodologies suitable for any building and/or area with homogeneous characteristics in terms of activities. Further investigations on travel time functions under different operative conditions are under development.

Acknowledgements

The author wishes to thank Prof Mauro Dolce and Dr Elvezio Galanti, members of the Italian Civil Protection, for their contribution in the availability of details on the provisional school unit of L'Aquila considered in the application.

References

[1] Russo F., Chilà G., A sequential dynamic choice model to simulate demand in evacuation conditions. *Proc. of Risk analysis VII & Brownfields V*, Brebbia C.A. (ed.), WIT Press, Southampton, 2010, pp. 431–442.

[2] Russo F., Rindone C., Evaluation methods for evacuation planning. *Proc. of Urban Transport XVI, Urban Transport and the Environment in the 21st century*, Brebbia C.A. (ed.), WIT Press, Southampton, 2010, pp. 335–343.

[3] Helbing, D., Farkas, I.J., Molnár, P., Vicsek, T., Simulation of Pedestrian Crowds in Normal and Evacuation Situations. M. Schreckenberg and S. D. Sharma (eds.) *Pedestrian and Evacuation Dynamics*, Springer, 2002, pp. 21–58.

[4] ASERI (Advance Simulation of Evacuation of Real Individuals) A model to simulate evacuation and egress movement based on individual behavoural response, 2004. http://www.ist-net.de [Online].

[5] Parke, J., Gwynne, S., Galea, E.R., and Lawrence, P. Validating the building EXODUS Evacuation Model using Data from an Unannounced Trial Evacuation. In E.R. Galea, Editor, *Proceedings of 2nd International Pedestrian and Evacuation Dynamics Conference*, CMS Press, Greenwich, UK (2003) ISBN 1904521088, pp. 295–306.

[6] Fraser-Mitchell, J. Simulated Evacuations of an Airport Terminal Building, Using the CRISP Model. In *2nd International Symposium in Human Behaviour in Fire* (pp. 89–100). Boston, MA, 2001.

[7] Ketchell, N., Cole, S. S., and Webber, D.M. The EGRESS Code for Human Movement and Behaviour in Emergency Evacuation. In R.A. Smith and J.F. Dickie (Eds.), *Engineering for Crowd Safety* (pp. 361–370). London: Elsevier, 1994.

[8] Fahy, R.F. EXIT89 – An Evacuation Model for High-rise Buildings – Model Description and Example Applications. In *Fire Safety Science – Proceedings of the 4th International Symposium* (pp. 657–668), 1994.

[9] Cappuccio, J. Pathfinder: A Computer-Based Timed Egress Simulation. *Fire Protection Engineering, 8*, 11–12, 2000.

[10] Klupfel, H. and Meyer-König, T. Characteristics of the PedGo Software for Crowd Movement and Egress Simulation. In E.R. Galea, Editor, *Proceedings of 2nd international pedestrian and evacuation dynamics conference*, CMS Press, Greenwich, UK ISBN 1904521088 (pp. 331–340), 2003.

[11] Di Gangi, M., Russo, F. and Vitetta, A., A mesoscopic method for evacuation simulation on passenger ships: models and algorithms. In *Pedestrian and Evacuation Dynamics 2003*, pp. 197–208 CMS Press, London ISBN 1-904521-08-8, 2003.

[12] Oven, V.A., Cakici, N. Modelling the evacuation of a high-rise office building in Istanbul. *Fire Safety Journal* No. 44, 2009, pp. 1–15.

[13] Proulx, G., Evacuation time and movement in apartment buildings, *Fire Safety Journal* Volume 24, Issue 3, 1995, pp. 229–246.

[14] Smith, R.A., Density, velocity and flow relationships for closely packed crowds, *Safety Science* Volume 18, Issue 4, 1995, pp. 321–327.

[15] Fang, Z., Lob, S.M., Luc, J.A. On the relationship between crowd density and movement velocity. *Fire Safety Journal* Volume 38, Issue 3, 2003, pp. 271–283.

[16] Kholshevnikov, V.V., Shields T.J., Boyce, K.E., Samoshin, D.A. Recent developments in pedestrian flow theory and research in Russia Fire Safety Journal No. 43, 2008, pp. 108–118.

[17] Hughes, R.L., A continuum theory for the flow of pedestrians, Transportation Research Part B, Elsevier, No. 36, 2002, pp. 507–535.

[18] Huang, L., Wong, S.C., Zhang, M., Shu, C., Lam, W.H.K. Revisiting Hughes' dynamic continuum model for pedestrian flow and the development of an efficient solution algorithm, *Transportation Research Part B*, Elsevier, No. 43(1), 2009, pp. 127–141.

[19] Di Gangi M., Evaluation of reliable path in risk areas, in *Risk Analysis V.* Southampton, U.K.: WIT Press, 2006, pp. 371–377.

[20] Di Gangi M., Musolino G., Rindone C., Vitetta A., An Italian project for exposure reduction in an urban area: experimentation design and DSS development. *Proceedings of European Transport Conference*. Strasbourg, Sept. 2006, ISBN/ISSN: 1-905701-01-2, 2006.

[21] Di Gangi, M., Approaching the analysis of transport networks in emergency conditions for the design of evacuation plans. In *Risk Analysis IV*,2004, pp. 485–494, WIT Press. ISBN 1-85312-736-1.

[22] Di Gangi M., Planning Evacuation by Means of a Multi-modal Mesoscopic Dynamic Traffic Simulation Model. B. Murgante, G. Borruso, A. Lapucci (Eds.): *Geocomputation and Urban Planning*, SCI 176, 2009, pp. 99–115. Springer-Verlag Berlin Heidelberg ISBN: 978-3-540-89929-7.

[23] Di Gangi M., Velonà P., Multimodal mesoscopic approach in modelling pedestrian evacuation *Transportation Research Record*, vol. 2090, 2009; p. 51–58, ISSN: 0361-1981, doi: 10.3141/2090-06.

[24] Di Gangi, M., Modeling Evacuation of a Transport System: Application of a Multimodal Mesoscopic Dynamic Traffic Assignment Model *Intelligent Transportation Systems, IEEE Transactions on Intel. Transportation Syst.*, vol. 12, Issue 4, 2011, pp. 1157–1166 doi: 10.1109/TITS.2011.2143408.

Author Index

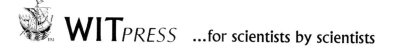

Environmental Impact

Edited by: **C.A. BREBBIA**, *Wessex Institute of Technology, UK and* **T-S. CHON**, *Pusan National University, Korea*

Containing papers from the first International Conference on Environmental Impact and Development organised by the Wessex Institute of Technology, *Environmental Impact* fills the need for inter-disciplinary coverage of the most serious problems that affect sustainable development. The basic premise is that development projects need to consider the most pressing issues related to environmental impacts in order to provide complete solutions.

The current emphasis on sustainable development is a consequence of a general awareness of the various environmental problems that result from our modern society. This has led to the need to assess the impact of economic investments on the environment. Investment assessment and environmental economics need to be discussed in an integrated way, in accordance with the principles of sustainability. We must consider the social and environmental aspects of new investments, as well as possible environmental damage, including the destruction of natural resources and larger releases of waste and pollution into the environment.

The book covers such topics as: Environmental Policies and Planning; Environmental Assessments; Development Issues; Sustainable City; Economic Analysis; Natural Resources Management; Energy and the Environment; Food and the Environment; Ecosystems Health; Brownfields Rehabilitation; Water Resources Management; Soil Contamination; Air and Water Pollution; Toxicity Studies; Environmental Health Risk; Risk Analysis.

WIT Transactions on Ecology and the Environment, Vol 162
ISBN: 978-1-84564-604-2   e-ISBN: 978-1-84564-605-9
Published 2012 / 660pp / £284.00

Lightning Source UK Ltd.
Milton Keynes UK
UKOW03n0736050813

214868UK00001B/73/P